ANNALS OF
THE NEW YORK ACADEMY
OF SCIENCES

Volume 480

EDITORIAL STAFF
Executive Editor
BILL BOLAND
Managing Editor
JUSTINE CULLINAN
Associate Editor
STEFAN MALMOLI

The New York Academy of Sciences
2 East 63rd Street
New York, New York 10021

NEW TECHNIQUES AND IDEAS IN QUANTUM MEASUREMENT THEORY

ANNALS OF THE NEW YORK ACADEMY OF SCIENCES
Volume 480

NEW TECHNIQUES AND IDEAS IN QUANTUM MEASUREMENT THEORY

Edited by Daniel M. Greenberger

The New York Academy of Sciences
New York, New York
1986

Cover: *The cover shows the Poincaré sphere for specifying photon polarizations (see page 357).*

Library of Congress Cataloging-in-Publication Data

New techniques and ideas in quantum measurement theory.

(Annals of the New York Academy of Sciences; v. 480)
Papers presented at a conference entitled New Techniques and Ideas in Quantum Measurement Theory, held by the New York Academy of Sciences, on January 21–24, 1986, in New York City.
Bibliography: p.
Includes index.
1. Quantum theory—Congresses.   2. Physical measurements—Congresses.   I. Greenberger, Daniel M.
II. Series.
Q11.N5 vol. 480   500 s   86-28595
[QC173.96]   [530.1'2]
ISBN 0-89766-355-1
ISBN 0-89766-356-X (pbk.)

SP
Printed in the United States of America
ISBN 0-89766-355-1 (cloth)
ISBN 0-89766-356-X (paper)
ISSN 0077-8923

ANNALS OF THE NEW YORK ACADEMY OF SCIENCES

Volume 480
December 30, 1986

NEW TECHNIQUES AND IDEAS IN QUANTUM MEASUREMENT THEORY[a]

Editor and Conference Chairman
DANIEL M. GREENBERGER

Conference Organizing Committee
OLIVER COSTA DE BEAUREGARD, LLOYD MOTZ, ABNER SHIMONY,
and ANTON ZEILINGER

CONTENTS

[a]The papers in this volume were presented at a conference entitled New Techniques and Ideas in Quantum Measurement Theory, which was held by the New York Academy of Sciences on January 21–24, 1986, in New York City. The conference was respectfully dedicated to Eugene P. Wigner. In addition, the conference was listed as a topical conference by the American Physical Society.

Part XII. Poster Papers

Part XIII. Summary of Conference

Financial assistance was received from:
- THE GEORGE W. CHURCH, JR. FOUNDATION
- THE EXXON EDUCATIONAL FOUNDATION
- MR. CRAWFORD GREENWALT
- THE HAMAMATSU CORPORATION
- THE IBM THOMAS J. WATSON FOUNDATION
- THE RICHARD LOUNSBERY FOUNDATION
- THE NATIONAL SCIENCE FOUNDATION
- THE UNIVERSITY OF NEW MEXICO
- THE REALITY FOUNDATION
- THE ALFRED P. SLOAN FOUNDATION

Dedicated to

EUGENE P. WIGNER

EUGENE P. WIGNER

Preface

DANIEL M. GREENBERGER

Department of Physics
The City College of the City University of New York
New York, New York 10031

Unlike most physics meetings, which are regular affairs held once every year or two, this conference on fundamental problems in quantum theory is to my knowledge the first comprehensive meeting on the subject to be held in the United States in a very long time. (In fact, I am aware of no previous one.) Elsewhere, however, interest in the subject has been growing steadily, both inside and outside of the profession. This is especially true in Europe and Japan, which have seen a number of such conferences during the last few years, and which have set a trend that was briefly accelerated during the recent centennial year of the birth of Niels Bohr.

Up until the time of Bell's theorem in 1964, it was not realized that certain theoretical assumptions about the nature of quantum measurement theory had experimental consequences. However, since then, interest in the area has grown steadily. Yet even the several beautiful experiments that have been done since then, which have pretty well convinced the scientific community that standard quantum theory yields the correct experimental answers, have not silenced the debate over its interpretation. Rather they have more squarely focused the problems involved, and the unqualified success of the predictions of quantum theory have only more sharply delineated the unsatisfactory status of measurement theory.

This situation runs quite counter to the history of science as usually preached. Normally, an accepted theory has run into trouble when its experimental predictions have failed, or when new phenomena cannot be easily incorporated into its conceptual framework and it is increasingly forced to introduce ad hoc hypotheses to explain phenomena that one might expect to follow naturally from a correct theory.

Quantum theory today faces none of these problems. In fact, the opposite is true. It was developed to explain atomic and electromagnetic phenomena, and it yielded a deep understanding of chemistry and the solid state. Yet it has proven itself applicable as a metatheory constraining the detailed laws that govern both nuclear physics and weak interaction physics, where entirely different forces enter. These phenomena are applicable over vastly different energy ranges and distance scales than atomic physics, and so the extent of the success of quantum theory comes rather as an undeserved gift from the gods. Far from breaking down, the range of validity of quantum theory is limited today only by our experimental techniques. (For example, C. Shull has pointed out that, experimentally, neutrons so far show both particle and wave phenomena over the range from 10^{-7} eV to over 10^8 eV, which is over 15 orders of magnitude.)

Thus, today there is no experimental evidence that points to the breakdown of the theory. Instead, there are a large number of physicists who are troubled by the state of the foundations of the theory and its implications for causality and epistemology in general.

However, more important than the theoretical uneasiness that hovers over the theory is the fact that today there are becoming available a whole range of experimental techniques that are applicable to the area and that, at last, make possible the idea of setting meaningful experimental limits to the validity of the theory. They have already led to the verification of some of the more unintuitive features of the theory.

Some of these techniques are neutron and X-ray interferometry, electron interferometry and holography, Josephson tunneling and the SQUID, the quantum Hall effect, squeezed states, quantum demolition, and ultrafast optical and laser techniques. Also certain colateral ideas, such as quantum computing, have come into play as an alternate arena in which to frame the same questions. Thus, it is an exciting time to think about the foundations of quantum theory.

Because of their intrinsic interest, the problems concerning causality, etc., have also spawned a growing popular interest in the subject that has been fed by an increasing number of books on the topic specifically written for laymen. This general interest led to the conference being covered by reporters from the *New York Times, Nature, Science, Mosaic, Science News, Physics Today, Discovery,* and the *New Yorker* (whose reporter's article actually finally appeared in *Science Digest*). This is probably some kind of record for coverage of such an esoteric conference.

The conference started as a suggestion several years ago by E. P. Wigner, who was worried about the space-time framework in which quantum theory is embedded. However, the initial attempts to hold such a conference floundered for a lack of money, and a new start was made by the present organizers, who also broadened the scope of the conference. We are very grateful to E. P. Wigner for allowing us to dedicate the conference to him, as I am sure that all the participants consider themselves in one way or another to be his students. We would also like to thank Gerhard Heise for making available to us a list of participants and the plans for the earlier aborted conference.

We are particularly grateful to the sponsors, who were very generous in supporting this one of a kind event. I would personally like to thank the participants themselves, for the extremely high level of involvement and discussion, that made the conference, for me, one of the most rewarding I have every attended. Thanks are also due to the staff of the New York Academy of Sciences, especially the director, Heinz Pagels, whose interest in the subject made the task easier, Barbara Parker, who made the conference run smoothly, Albert Capozzelli, her assistant, and Kevin Pope, who deftly handled the publicity. We would finally like to thank the editorial department of the New York Academy of Sciences, especially Bill Boland, for editorial guidance, and Stefan Malmoli, for ably editing the proceedings.

Note: In presenting the material, we have not followed the chronological sequence of sessions and papers within sessions. Rather, we have arranged it so as to group papers on similar subjects close together. At the conference itself, this was largely precluded by individual scheduling problems, etc. Therefore, we would like to specifically thank here each of the session chairmen: Asim Barut, John F. Clauser, Leonard Cohen, James T. Cushing, Akira Inomata, Lloyd Motz, Mikio Namiki, Laura Roth, and Cliff Shull. In addition, we are including a few papers by authors who were not able to attend the conference because of other commitments, but who were able to send the papers they would have presented.

E. P. Wigner: An Introduction

A. S. WIGHTMAN

Department of Physics
Princeton University
Princeton, New Jersey 08544

This meeting entitled "New Ideas and Techniques in Quantum Measurement Theory" is dedicated to Eugene P. Wigner, and I have the pleasure of introducing him. It is an occasion to recall a few old Wigner stories to explain to those who might not otherwise know, why those of us who have known him admire his work and are fond of him.

The first time I ever saw Eugene was in the spring of 1946. I was just out of the Navy and was in Princeton looking for housing for the fall term. A seminar was announced: Fritz London was talking on his theory of superconductivity. I attended, and at the end, somewhat diffidently, Eugene started asking questions about the gauge invariance of the theory. The questions were framed apologetically, but they were very persistent. London seemed to take them very seriously. The gauge invariance of the theory of superconductivity was a problem for the following two decades. That was the way it was with Eugene's questions.

To understand how Eugene's questions stood out, you have to know the Princeton context. The main theoretical seminar in Princeton after 1947 was Oppenheimer's, in which a painstaking answer to a simple question was regarded as bad show; Oppenheimer did not suffer fools gladly. Most of the bright young theoreticians adopted his style, so when Eugene would say, "I am sorry to appear so stupid, but what do you mean by crystal momentum?", it was conspicuous.

I recall another occasion on which activities in the question period caused consternation. It gave birth to the so-called W^3 paper (Wick, Wightman, and Wigner on superselection rules). It all began when Yang and Tiomno discovered the Yang-Tiomno phases. They recognized that a spinor field can have a variety of distinct transformation laws under P, T, and C, and that by choosing the laws differently for different fields, one could forbid certain interaction terms between fields. [Part of this story was already known to E. Cartan, who pointed out that while a connected Lie group has a uniquely determined covering group, a Lie group with several connected components may have several nonisomorphic covering groups. Cartan used this to introduce the distinction between spinors of the first and second kind for $SU(2)$.] At a conference in Chicago, E. Fermi expressed enthusiasm for the Yang-Tiomno phases, and posed it as a task for experimental physics to determine which are the phases for the electron field, the proton field, etc. In the question period, Eugene remarked that the distinction between Yang-Tiomno phases could very well be without physical meaning, that is, unmeasurable. He was, in effect, discussing the possibility of a superselection rule. The audience was stunned. Gian Carlo Wick said to Eugene that he absolutely had to write up these remarks, and volunteered to help. Thus was born W^3. How did I get into it? In the preceding year, I had spent some time studying Wigner's theory of invariance in quantum mechanics and had worried together with Eugene about phases. Nothing very good came of it until Wick precipitated W^3. I have always had the theory that Eugene already understood that there might be superselection rules at the time of the writing of his book on group theory and atomic spectra. That book has a lot more in it than group theory and atomic spectra if you read it carefully.

Now, I would like to mention some other Wigner papers of the 1950s, specifically those dealing with the limitations on the quantum theory of measurement imposed by the internal consistency of the theory. This work, and the work of Yanese and Araki that followed it, opened a new chapter in the subject. Curiously enough, these papers did not seem to arouse much interest at the time. Even today, it seems to me there is much left to do before we can have a clear picture of what is really measurable and approximately measurable.

Eugene Wigner was famous as a young man for his ability to squeeze physics out of quantum mechanics using general principles; in a complimentary sense, he was a great technician. In recent years, being more mature, he has become a radical. He tries to convince us, as he did two days ago, that quantum mechanics fails in the macroscopic domain. He proposes to make radical alterations in the Schrödinger equation to account for the traditional collapse of the wave packet. He offers us the conundrum commonly known as the Paradox of Wigner's Friend to torture the philosophically minded among us. Perhaps indiscreetly, I am going to offer you an explanation of this. It is that there is a little known experiment, performed by Wigner himself, that gave such discouraging results that Wigner abandoned quantum mechanics. My account of this experiment is a fabrication contained in the Wigner Archives in Princeton. What I am about to offer you are transcriptions from the tapes of the experiment.

In order to describe the protocol of the experiment, I am going to have to remind you about Schrödinger's cat and Wigner's Friend. Recall that Schrödinger's cat was in a box with a radioactive source whose emissions at some random instant could trigger a mechanical device that in turn would release hydrogen cyanide and kill the cat. According to quantum mechanics, the cat after some time will be in a pure superposition state with probability, α, of being alive and $(1 - \alpha)$ of being dead. Wigner's Friend observes whether the cat is alive or dead, thereby causing the second stage of a quantum mechanical measurement to take place: the superposition gets coupled to Wigner's Friend and collapses to a density matrix. However, Wigner himself describes cat plus Friend as a pure state until he asks his Friend or actually looks himself.

Now what actually happened in the experiment? Wigner, being concerned about the kind of unconscious signaling that has plagued so many experiments in extrasensory perception, made an enclosure for the cat inside a large box for the Friend, and arranged that there was only telephonic communication between the Friend (WF) and Wigner (W), who recorded the conversation on tape.

FROM THE WIGNER ARCHIVE

WF: You know, Eugene, I do not think this Schrödinger was very practical about cats.

W: Why?

WF: Do you have any idea what the smell is like in here?

W: First verify that the radioactive source is in position in the enclosure and then put the cat inside.

WF: There seems to be some kind of a label on the radioactive source. It says, "Free sample from the Atomic Industrial Forum." Things from the Atomic Industrial Forum are sometimes not what they seem.

W: Never mind. Get the cat in there.

WF: Eugene, it seems to me that you have underestimated grossly the subtleties of superpositions of macroscopic quantum states.

W: Why?

WF: It is not so easy to get this cat and myself into a superposition state. OUCH!

W: What is going on?

WF: To think that I should have gotten tetanus shots to participate in a philosophical experiment.

The tape breaks off at this point.

Judge for yourself. Over to you, Eugene.

Response

E. P. WIGNER

Department of Physics
Joseph Henry Laboratories
Princeton University
Princeton, New Jersey 08544

Thank you very much for your very kind introduction. I am truly receiving a very great and very unexpected honor. Let me also tell you that I truly enjoyed your presentations. They induced me to ponder whether one can learn and understand better by reading an article or by hearing it presented at a meeting like ours.

Reading has the advantage that one can stop, reread some parts of what one has read, and recall more easily earlier articles; in other words, reading brings in other thoughts and information.

However, in attending this meeting, I have found that the arguments in favor of learning from a presentation are even more valid. I enjoyed most of the presentations, and, perhaps, even more the subsequent remarks. I not only hope, but believe that most of you feel the same way, and not only liked, but also learned a good deal from most of the presentations and the discussions that followed.

I have perhaps five more minutes and would like to present to you what I call a "crazy idea." This is that we should abandon the idea of sharply defined space-time points and that we should modify the underlying geometry. In prequantum theory, and I believe also in general relativity, a space-time point is specified as the crossing point of two world-lines, and general relativity is based on the postulate that the distance between two very close points is sharply defined. However, in quantum theory, the point of collision is not sharply defined and no space-time point can be defined that way.

Another reason for changing the postulate of sharply definable space-time points is that there is no wave function that could specify it. A delta function of space coordinates is not permissible because it contains negative energy states. However, I must admit that even if we permit a function of finite size, it is, as a rule, not possible to make it invariant under all transformations that leave a point invariant (Lorentz transformations without displacements). Finally, I would like to see the idea of sharply defined space-time points changed because it is the source of the need for renormalization in the present theory. I must admit, on the other hand, that the introduction of a new geometry in space-time of relativistically invariant structures is difficult because the distance, if relativisitically invariant, vanishes for two states that are on the same light cone. Nevertheless, I believe we should overcome this difficulty.

Well, I presented what I called a "crazy idea," but I hope you will forgive me on this occasion.

The Nonrelativistic Nature of the Present Quantum Mechanical Measurement Theory

E. P. WIGNER

Department of Physics
Joseph Henry Laboratories
Princeton University
Princeton, New Jersey 08544

SOME PROBLEMS OF EARLIER THEORIES

I wish to recall first some problems of earlier theories of physics that are similar to the present ones of quantum mechanics. (These will be discussed later.) There was, after each great discovery in physics, some puzzlement and realization of incompleteness in the definition of some of the basic concepts in terms of which the "laws" were formulated. Let me begin with the first great discovery of Copernicus, Kepler, Tycho Brahe, and others, which took place about 450 years ago. Copernicus (1473–1543), afraid of the church's disapproval, said that it is "easier to describe" the motion of the planets by assuming that the sun is at rest, while the planets, including the Earth, are moving. However, even then, it was not clear what "at rest" and what "moving" meant—it was only clear that the description of their relative positions was easier to describe in a coordinate system attached to the sun. Of course, the motion of the planets was communicated to us only by the light they reflected, and the basic properties of light were not described by the physics of that time.

Their description of the planets' motion led to the wonderful theory of Newton. His description of the forces by which the sun attracts the planets was based on Galileo's observation on the laws of free-fall here on the Earth, and on the improved determination of the moon's distance from it, leading to an improved value of the moon's centripetal acceleration. However, the transmittal of the information about the motion of the planets, that is, light, was not part of that time's physics, and the specification of the basic coordinate system in which the postulated laws of motion are valid was left to the distant future—in fact to Einstein's general relativity. Still, the establishment of laws of nature and the separation of initial conditions from them were truly miraculous accomplishments that cannot be forgotten.

The next fundamental discovery, describing a new set of phenomena, was initiated by James C. Maxwell. His laws of nature abandoned the idea of the "action at a distance" of Newton gravitational forces and introduced a field theory. (For the gravitational forces, this was accomplished only much later by Einstein's general relativity theory.) His laws of nature, apparently designed to describe electromagnetic phenomena, also described light as an electromagnetic process (1873). His idea of fields, quantities depending on three space coordinates and one time coordinate, introduced a much more complicated description of nature than that of Newton, whose

1

description of the state of his systems contained only a set of numbers—six times more than were objects contained in the system (three position coordinates and three velocity components for each). The idea of fields was also a wonderful idea, but its union with the idea of discrete objects—particles—led to difficulties (two very important ones, in fact). The existence of particles, in particular of electrons, could not be denied.

The first of these difficulties—much more at the center of interest in the early part of this century than it is now—concerned the energy of the field connected with a pointlike particle. The electric field strength near to an electron is inversely proportional to the square of the distance from the electron, with the energy density then proportional to the inverse fourth power. The total energy of the electric field next to a charged pointlike particle would then be infinite. There were attempts to overcome this difficulty (leading to an infinite mass of the particle) by attributing a finite size thereto, but no such proposal turned out to be simple and attractive. The other difficulty stemmed from the consideration of a thermal equilibrium between particles and the field. It turned out that the heat capacity of the field was infinite so that, in a true equilibrium, the field would deprive the particles of all their kinetic energy. This was evidently totally unreasonable.

It was this second difficulty that the next terribly big step intended to eliminate. Max Planck (1858–1947) in 1900 proposed a new law of nature: that the particles, in particular, the atoms (and molecules), can absorb and emit only definite amounts of light energy, the amount being $h\nu$, with ν giving the frequency of the light absorbed or emitted and h being a new natural constant (Planck's constant). This was, of course, a terribly new idea, but considering the generally realized need for a new idea, it was quite soon favorably considered. It was evident that a new natural constant was needed also for an expression of the thermal equilibrium energy density of the radiation. If we disregard the possible use of the electron's electric charge, e, the earlier natural constants, c and k, cannot produce an expression of the dimension of energy per unit volume as a function of the temperature, T. With h, there is such an expression, which has, naturally, a factor of T^4 (it is $k^4 T^4 / h^3 c^3$ and has a factor 48π).

Even though Planck's ideas originally sounded somewhat unreasonable, they were soon (very soon) generally accepted. Einstein's observation (1905) on the dependence of the maximum energy of the electrons produced by the photoelectric effect on the frequency of the light producing them helped a great deal, as did observations by M. von Laue, W. H. Nernst, and many, many others.

THE DEVELOPMENT OF QUANTUM THEORY

A new breakthrough came with Niels Bohr's explanation of the hydrogen spectrum. He introduced the postulate that the orbits of electrons in atoms obey certain rules; thus, no orbit violating these rules is possible. He formulated the rules for the possible orbits of a single electron, that is, the electron of the hydrogen atom or that of ionized helium, and his rules explained the spectra of these elements with amazing accuracy. Unfortunately, his postulates could not be really applied to systems with more than one electron. However, Bohr also established a wonderful school for young physicists, and many of the later contributions to the development of the physics of atoms and molecules greatly benefited from that school. Unfortunately, no theory for systems with more than one electron could be developed by them. Naturally, therefore, the whole theory was very puzzling: how does the electron jump from one orbit to another? The light emission that results from such a jump takes of the order of 10^{-8} seconds of time, whereas the electron runs around the orbit in about 10^{-16} seconds or a little more.

Even though I was studying for a degree in chemical engineering at the "Technical High School" in Berlin, I attended the physics colloquia at the University. They were very interesting and I learned a lot there. However, what I want to tell you in this connection is that I had a subconscious impression that those in the first row, including Einstein, Planck, von Laue, and some others, were afraid that man is not bright enough to formulate a consistent theory for microscopic (that is, atomic) phenomena, of elementary systems involving small numbers of electrons, protons, atoms, etc. I also believed that many others had the same impression. My impression, though, was changed suddenly after two years (which I spent as a chemical engineer) when I read an article by M. Born and P. Jordan that was based on a 1925 article by Werner Heisenberg. This was then followed (in 1926) by an article of the three of them. In these articles, they abandoned the idea of describing the positions and motions of the electrons in the atom (or molecule) and restricted the problem of microscopic physics to the determination of the energy levels and the probabilities of the possible transitions between these by the emission or absorption of light. The latter process's probability is, of course, proportional to the intensity of light of the proper frequency. This was a wonderful suggestion and, in fact, led to the establishment of a theory that permits the calculation of the quantities just mentioned—absorption and emission probabilities. It was the beginning of quantum mechanics and it showed that the classical description of atomic systems must be greatly modified.

The wonderful Heisenberg-Born-Jordan theory, though, has some weaknesses. The most fundamental of these is that it described only light absorption and emission, and as it turned out later, even these were not described completely. What is even more fundamental, though, is that it did not describe at all collision phenomena, which play a very important role in physics. In fact, in a sense, light absorption is also a collision phenomenon. What it did show, persuasively, was that ordinary physics, based, as far as particles are concerned, on the description of the states of these by giving positions and velocities, must be fundamentally modified. This was a very useful and important observation.

The next fundamental change in our description of basic (that is, microscopic) phenomena was brought about by Schrödinger's introduction of wave mechanics. This is, in a way, a return to the concepts of the earlier theories of physics inasmuch as it postulates the existence of a description of the state of the system and not only probabilities for the various possible observable changes. In fact, it was terribly effective—the quantities that the earlier theory gave only for one-electron systems were now given quite generally. It also described other changes, including the effects of collisions, which was a very important accomplishment. Actually, eventually Heisenberg claimed that the collision matrix (calculable from the wave function) is the most fundamental concept of quantum theory. However, the fact that there is an equation describing the time-dependence of the "wave function" is perhaps an equally valid evidence of its effectiveness.

In the whole discussion so far, relativity theory was not mentioned; it will play an important role in the discussion of the weaknesses of the theory that follows. In addition, the special theory of relativity, though immensely important, did not introduce new concepts; it only changed some basic ones, in particular, the meaning of simultaneity. General relativity, though, did give a new theory of gravitation and a wonderful one of that. It also eliminated, as was mentioned before, the problem of defining the coordinate systems in which the common equations of physics are valid. However, it has, also in this last regard, difficulties when used for microscopic (in particular, for atomic) systems. This last point will be discussed in the next section.

THE PROBLEMS AND DIFFICULTIES OF QUANTUM MECHANICS

The pre-quantum-mechanical laws of physics told us how to calculate the future state of a physical system (which is "isolated," that is, not influenced by any other material or radiation) if its initial state (that is, its state at a definite earlier time) is given. It must be admitted that the processes to determine either its initial or its final states were rarely discussed (as was mentioned in the discussion of the motion of the planets and Newton's law of gravitation). However, it was assumed that this is possible, and indeed it was, with sufficient accuracy, for the physical systems considered, which were macroscopic.

The big change, though, came as a result of the description of the states of microscopic systems by Schrödinger's wave function or a mathematical equivalent of this—a vector in an infinite dimensional space. Because the systems considered are microscopic, their state is influenced by the process of observation. According to the usually propagated theory, the observation, in general, changes the state of the system; its state after the observation is one of the characteristic functions of the "observed quantity." The same holds for the determination of the final state; that is, the equations of quantum mechanics give us only the probabilities for the different possible results of the second observation. One can, therefore, say that quantum mechanics gives us the probabilities of the possible outcomes of the second observation and, of course, the state of the system is then again known. Thus, it becomes the characteristic function of the quantity observed, which corresponds to the characteristic value that the observation gave.

I described the basic idea of the verification of the quantum mechanical laws probably in much more detail than is necessary. However, I wish to give now the weaknesses of this theory, which was, incidentally, most clearly formulated by John von Neumann.

First, just as in classical theory, the method of observation is not generally described. In fact, it has been demonstrated that the variety of quantities (functions of position and momentum) that can be observed by a finite "measuring apparatus" is very limited; the corresponding operator must commute with all additive conserved quantities. These involve electric charge, number of protons plus neutrons, total linear momentum, and total angular momentum in any direction. Most operators, of course, do not commute with all these quantities and they can be measured with high (but finite) accuracy only with large measuring apparatuses. Incidentally, the measuring apparatuses must clearly be large because they show the outcome of the observation to the observer who can perceive only macroscopic pointers or other indicators of the measuring apparatuses.

This brings us to two other problems of the quantum mechanical measurement theory. The first and perhaps most obvious is that because the wave function of the system on which the measurement is undertaken has a finite size in space, it takes some time for the information from its distant parts to reach the apparatus, even if it comes with light velocity. Hence, the information that the apparatus can obtain does not refer to an instantaneous state of the system (the state of which is measured), but, at best, to its state on the negative light cone. Similarly, the change of its state vector, which the observation provides, can influence the state of the system at best on the positive light cone. Because quantum mechanics deals, as a rule, only with microscopic systems, these are not terrible limitations; they are substantial ones, though, if the state of the system is changing fast, which is the rule for systems in the description of which relativity theory plays a significant role. The original theory of measurement, as formulated by von Neumann, disregards this point. This is natural, though, because quantum mechanics was a nonrelativistic theory in the days of his contributions to the measurement problem.

The second and, in my opinion, equally important limitation of quantum theory is the fact that the measurement theory implicitly assumes that the outcome of the measurement (for instance, the position of the indicator of the measuring apparatus) has a definite value. If the linear nature of the quantum mechanical equations were valid, this could not be the case. Therefore, the only thing that the equations permit us to postulate for the measurement results is a state of object plus apparatus, which shows a correlation between the states of both. This is essentially a wave function of the two, which is of the form,

$$\Sigma \, a_\kappa \psi_\kappa \phi_\kappa.$$

In this, the a's are constants, the ψ_κ is the state of the object in which the measured quantity surely has the value κ, and ϕ_κ is a state of the apparatus showing that result. However, the equations of quantum mechanics are deterministic and the outcome of the measurement, which gives *one* of the possible values for κ, would be in contradiction to linearity.

This shows that the process of measurements cannot be described by the equations of quantum mechanics because their existence is in contradiction to its principles. It is important to realize this fact. I originally thought that the limitation of quantum mechanics' validity excludes only living beings. However, an important article of J. C. Bell convinced me that the limitation excludes macroscopic objects because he found evidence for this fact and proposed some superficial modification of the equations of quantum mechanics. (I did also.) This contradicts its linear character for the state vector, but preserves it for the density matrix. However, that equation, though taking care of the problem here discussed, surely does not have universal validity.

Quantum Theory and the Appearance of a Classical World

E. JOOS[a]

Institut für Theoretische Physik
Universität Heidelberg
D-6900 Heidelberg, Federal Republic of Germany

It is a puzzling fact that the most successful theory of this century, namely, quantum theory, until now has been bothered by severe interpretation problems. Every physicist knows how to manage with the symbols of quantum theory—wave functions, operators, probabilities, and so on. On these points, there is complete agreement. If, however, a physicist is urged to explain what these symbols mean, then it seems that there are not even two physicists professing to the very same interpretation of these symbols.

From a practical point of view, quantum mechanics talks about measurement results. However, what is a measurement? Since the analysis given by John von Neumann, we are quite sure that a measurement process cannot be described by a Schrödinger equation. The Copenhagen school strongly insisted that measurement results had to be described in classical terms. This leads to a new problem: What is or when is a classical object?

Is there some way, at least some hint, how to understand classical concepts out of quantum concepts? This is the topic of the following discussion.

WIDESPREAD BELIEF

"Quantum mechanics contains classical mechanics in the form of a certain limiting case."[1] This quotation from the famous textbook series written by Landau and Lifschitz provides a typical claim of nearly all textbook expositions of quantum mechanics. The (approximately) classical motion of a macroscopic mass point is usually founded on the Ehrenfest theorems on mean values and the fact that an initially small wave packet spreads very slowly if the mass of the particle is "large enough." By this formal elaboration of the "correspondence principle," one seemingly has proven that the Schrödinger equation contains Newton's law of motion as a limiting case. Similar arguments are put forward in other situations where objects always behave classically. For example, chiral molecules, such as sugar or alanine, are only observed in states of well-defined spatial orientation, namely, right-handed or left-handed

---

[a]Present Address: Center for Theoretical Physics, The University of Texas at Austin, Austin, Texas 78712.

spatial states. The tunneling probability between these states is extremely small and this is usually considered as a sufficient explanation of the observed facts.

The appearance of classical space-time according to the theory of general relativity and the corresponding absence of quantum effects of gravitation is usually traced back to the small value of the Planck scale, $L_p = (\hbar G/c^3)^{1/2} \simeq 10^{-33}$cm. This argument resembles the nonspreading of wave packets in the limit of infinite mass. This list could easily be continued.

CRITICISM

What is wrong with these commonplace arguments? There are essentially two reasons why the points made above are not conclusive.

The first is the superposition principle of quantum theory. It allows arbitrary superpositions of "macroscopically different" states. Classical states are very exceptional among all possible states. This was, for example, stressed by Einstein in a letter[2] to Born in 1954:

> Ψ_1 and Ψ_2 seien zwei Lösungen derselben Schrödinger-Gleichung. Dann ist $\Psi = \Psi_1 + \Psi_2$ ebenfalls eine Lösung der Schrödinger-Gleichung mit gleichem Anspruch darauf, einen möglichen Realzustand zu beschreiben. Wenn das System ein Makro-System ist, und wenn Ψ_1 und Ψ_2 "eng" sind in Bezug auf die Makro-Koordinaten, so ist dies in der weitaus überwiegenden Zahl der möglichen Fälle für Ψ nicht mehr der Fall. Enge bezüglich der Makro-Koordinaten ist eine Forderung, die nicht nur *unabhängig* ist von den Prinzipien der Quantenmechanik, sondern auch *unvereinbar* mit diesen Prinzipien.[b]

Of course, it would still be true that an observation may produce a classical state, which then would remain approximately classical for dynamical reasons. Einstein comments on this in another letter[3] to Born:

> Dann müßte man sich z. B. sehr wundern, wenn ein Stern oder eine Fliege, die man zum ersten Mal sieht, so etwas wie quasi-lokalisiert erscheinen.[c]

This second criticism provides, at the same time, the starting point of the following ideas. It is a trivial observation that all objects in our world interact more or less. This interaction, however, is by no means negligible for macroscopic quantum objects.[4,5] As a consequence, they cannot even approximately obey a Schrödinger equation by themselves. All derivations of Ehrenfest theorems use Schrödinger dynamics and are therefore invalid for such objects. A more realistic treatment thus should start with a global Schrödinger equation for a macrosystem plus environment.

---

[b]"Let Ψ_1 and Ψ_2 be two solutions of the same Schrödinger equation. Then $\Psi = \Psi_1 + \Psi_2$ also represents a solution of the Schrödinger equation, with equal claim to describing a possible real state. When the system is a macrosystem, and when Ψ_1 and Ψ_2 are 'narrow' in relation to the macro-coordinates, then in by far the greater number of cases, this is no longer true for Ψ. Narrowness in regard to macro-coordinates is a requirement which is not only *independent* of the principles of quantum mechanics, but, moreover, *incompatible* with them."

[c]"For example, one would then be very surprised if a star, or a fly, seen for the first time, appeared even to be quasi-localized."

NEW OUTLOOK

The unavoidable interaction of every macroscopic system with its natural environment now opens a new way to understand classical properties in the framework of quantum theory. Because of the nonlocal properties of quantum states, a system interacting with another one in general has no state by itself, but can only be described by its density matrix, which contains all that can be observed at the considered system by local observers. Every interaction between two systems that are initially in a factorizing state will lead to a quantum correlated state. With respect to the basis in the state space of the considered object in which the interaction Hamiltonian is diagonal, this corresponds to a (more or less complete) measurement of the respective observable.[6] As a consequence, interference terms (nondiagonal elements) in the density matrix of the measured system may be destroyed to a certain extent with respect to the measurement basis. If the interaction with the environment is "strong enough" (to be defined below), then the density matrix is always approximately diagonal in a certain basis that depends not on the initial state, but only on the interaction Hamiltonian. This basis then defines what a "classical property" is, in the sense that there are never interferences (superpositions) of these "classical states" (superselection rule[7]). If these mechanisms are indeed relevant, then it is immediately clear that a "classical property" is not defined by some inherent properties of the object, but is given by the nature of the interaction with the environment.[8]

The general scheme as introduced by von Neumann is the following: If the measured system, ϕ, is initially in an eigenstate state, $|n\rangle$, of the "observable" and the environment (in principle, the rest of the universe) is in a state, $|\Phi_0\rangle$, where

$$|\Psi(0)\rangle = |n\rangle|\Phi_0\rangle, \tag{1}$$

then the environment will "recognize" the quantum number, n, via the interaction,

$$|\Psi(t)\rangle = |n\rangle|\Phi_n(t)\rangle. \tag{2}$$

In the general case, where ϕ is initially in a superposition of different states, $|n\rangle$, one has

$$|\Psi(t)\rangle = \sum_n c_n|n\rangle|\Phi_n(t)\rangle. \tag{3}$$

The local density matrix reads for $t > 0$,

$$\rho_\phi = \mathrm{tr}_\Phi|\Psi(t)\rangle\langle\Psi(t)| = \sum_{n,m} c_m^* c_n|n\rangle\langle m|\langle\Phi_m(t)|\Phi_n(t)\rangle. \tag{4}$$

Thus, nondiagonal elements are multiplied by a factor that is the overlap of the two corresponding "pointer positions." In proper measurements, one has after a certain measuring time, T,

$$\langle\Phi_m(t)|\Phi_n(t)\rangle \simeq \delta_{nm}, \quad t > T; \tag{5}$$

that is, the pointer states are orthogonal for different measurement results. (This, however, does not explain the reduction of the state vector, which is implicitly contained in the density matrix formalism.) In the following, I shall give two examples of how this mechanism works in realistic situations.

APPEARANCE OF PARTICLES

The fact that all macroscopic objects seem to be well localized in ordinary space (and not, for example, in momentum space) cannot be understood by considering these systems alone. Microscopic systems are usually found in energy eigenstates. These are, however, plane waves in the case of a free mass point.

It turns out that scattering processes are of utmost importance.[8] The scattered state (of a photon or a molecule) depends on the position, x, of the scattering center, and thereby the scattered particle, Φ, measures this position. Formally,

$$|x\rangle|\Phi_0\rangle \rightarrow |x\rangle|\Phi_x\rangle = |x\rangle S_x|\Phi_0\rangle, \tag{6}$$

where S_x is the scattering matrix with a scattering center located at x. Here, the last equation is valid for sufficiently large time. On each scattering process, the density matrix, $\rho(x, x', t)$, of the position of the scattering center is multiplied by the overlap of the corresponding scattered states, $|\Phi_x\rangle$ and $|\Phi_{x'}\rangle$:

$$\rho(x, x') \rightarrow \rho(x, x') \langle\Phi_0|S_{x'}^\dagger S_x|\Phi_0\rangle. \tag{7}$$

This factor is, of course, approximately zero if the wavelength of the incoming particle is smaller than $|x - x'|$ (resolution of a microscope):

$$\langle\Phi_0|S_{x'}^\dagger S_x|\Phi_0\rangle \simeq \begin{cases} 0 & \text{if } |x - x'| \gg \lambda \\ 1 - O[(x - x')^2] & \text{if } |x - x'| \ll \lambda. \end{cases} \tag{8}$$

The case of poor resolution in the second line is especially interesting because one would expect no effect from such "incomplete" measurements. Certainly, one scattering process cannot, in this case, resolve the distance of $|x - x'|$ and therefore will not destroy coherence between x and x'. However, if there are a great many of such scattering processes, it turns out[8] that the overall effect is an exponential damping of coherence,

$$\rho(x, x', t) = \rho(x, x', 0) \exp[-\Lambda(x - x')^2 t], \tag{9}$$

with a "localization rate," Λ, given by

$$\Lambda = k^2 \sigma_{\text{eff}} Nv/8\pi^2 V, \tag{10}$$

where k is the wave number of the incident particles, σ_{eff} is a typical cross section, and Nv/V is the incoming flux (for details, see reference 8). This damping of coherence between different positions can be expressed by means of a coherence length, l, where

$$l(t) \simeq (\Lambda t)^{-1/2}. \tag{11}$$

The value of Λ depends on the special situation and can be quite large. For a dust particle with radius 10^{-5}cm, cosmic background radiation gives $\Lambda = 10^{-6}$ cm^{-2} sec^{-1}, thermal radiation of room temperature gives $\Lambda = 10^{12}$ cm^{-2} sec^{-1}, and scattering of air molecules gives $\Lambda = 10^{32}$ cm^{-2} sec^{-1} and $\Lambda = 10^{19}$ cm^{-2} sec^{-1} in the best available laboratory vacuum (10^6 particles/cm^3). This means that any initial coherence over considerable distances will be destroyed "at once" for all objects, except for very small ones.

For a complete dynamical description of the mass point, the internal dynamics has to be added. By itself, it would lead to the well-known spreading of the wave packet, that is, an increase in coherence length. Inclusion of the scattering processes leads to a Boltzmann-type master equation,

$$i\dot{\rho} = [H_{\text{internal}}, \rho] + \left.\frac{\partial\rho}{\partial t}\right|_{\text{scatt}}. \tag{12}$$

An equation of this kind was suggested by Wigner some years ago.[9] For a "free" particle, $H_{\text{internal}} = \text{p}^2/2m$, and the equation of motion for one space dimension reads

$$i\frac{\partial\rho(x, x', t)}{\partial t} = \frac{1}{2m}\left[\frac{\partial^2}{\partial x'^2} - \frac{\partial^2}{\partial x^2}\right]\rho - i\Lambda(x - x')^2\rho. \tag{13}$$

This equation can be solved, for example, in the case of an initial Gaussian wave packet. It turns out that, in all realistic cases, the measured object is well localized and the spreading of the wave packet does not occur. In general, measurement dominates over the internal dynamics, and for large times, the coherence length decreases proportional to $(\Lambda t)^{-1/2}$. (For a thorough analysis, see reference 8). If recoil is taken into account, the limiting coherence length must be the thermal de Broglie wavelength for the object. Therefore, the conclusion is:

All "macroscopic" objects can be assumed to be localized within their thermal de Broglie wavelength.

This is a very small quantity. For example, at room temperature for the dust particle of the above example, its value is about 10^{-14} cm. It turns out that even large molecules are well localized and will show no interference effects over considerable distances. Therefore, a double-slit experiment even with such tiny objects would hardly seem feasible; that is, it would show no interference pattern. The high effective resolution of the scattering processes also leads to a well-defined spatial structure of molecules, except for very small ones like ammonia. The usual pictures drawn in chemistry are therefore justified because the spatial structure of molecules is continuously measured by their surroundings.

APPEARANCE OF SPACE-TIME

I will now try to apply these considerations to quantum gravity: All experimental evidence supports a classical space-time structure down to distances of the order of 10^{-15}cm. In particular, at a macroscopic level, all our (local) experience is described in terms of space and time. General relativity tells us that space-time and gravity are intimately connected dynamical entities. If gravity is subject to quantum laws, then the superposition principle would allow states that are arbitrary superpositions of different field strengths (or different space-times). However, our universe is not empty. Space-time is strongly coupled to matter, which in turn "measures" space-time. The same mechanisms as before also apply here. As a very simple example, consider some volume of lateral size, L, containing a superposition of homogeneous gravitation fields with two different values of acceleration, g:

$$|\Phi\rangle = c_1|g\rangle + c_2|g'\rangle. \tag{14}$$

Every particle traveling through this volume will measure the value of g; that is, its resulting state, $|\chi^{(g)}(\tau)\rangle$, after passing the volume will depend on the particular value of g,

$$|g\rangle|\chi(0)\rangle \rightarrow |g\rangle|\chi^{(g)}(\tau)\rangle \tag{15}$$

(back-reaction on the metric is neglected). Thus, coherence between different values of g will be destroyed. It turns out[10] that nondiagonal elements in the density matrix, $\rho(g, g')$, of the field strength are damped according to

$$\rho(g, g',t) = \rho(g, g', 0) \exp[-\Gamma(g - g')^2 t], \tag{16}$$

where

$$\Gamma = nL^4(\pi m/2kT)^{3/2} \tag{17}$$

for a gas with particle density, n, and temperature, T. For example, air under usual conditions here on earth and $L = 1$ cm yields, for $t = 1$ sec, a remaining relative coherence "length," Δ_g, of $\Delta_g/g \simeq 10^{-6}$. This simple example demonstrates the dynamical mechanism leading to the classical behavior of space-time. A full quantum theoretic treatment would require the use of the Wheeler-DeWitt equation, as was done recently by Hawking and co-workers.[11,12] There the time parameter of quantum mechanics has to be replaced by some intrinsic dynamical variable of the universe. The model of Halliwell and Hawking,[12] for example, exhibits clearly the strong quantum correlations between a timelike dynamical variable, namely, the radius of a closed Friedmann universe, and other gravitational and matter degrees of freedom, represented as higher multipoles, which thereby render this "time" as a classical entity.

DISCRETE VERSUS CONTINUOUS

According to the rules of quantum theory, every subsystem has to be described by a density matrix (for the purpose of calculating probabilities for future local measurements), which in turn may be diagonalized by an ensemble of states.

There is an important difference between discrete or continuous spectra of the considered degrees of freedom. In the first case, the density matrix is diagonalized by the representation being measured by the interaction (neglecting internal dynamics). For optically active molecules, for example, these states would be the right- or left-handed configurations. On the other hand, for a continuous degree of freedom, such as, for example, the translational motion of a small dust particle, the eigenstates are not small wave packets, as one would perhaps expect, but broad wave functions with many nodes. (In the case of a Gaussian density matrix, they are given by oscillator wave functions.)

However, proper measurements seem always to contain a discrete level at some stage. We experience the world around us by discrete visual cells or discrete states of our nervous system. Interaction with the environment destroys any interference between these discrete states and thereby renders our experience as classical.

SUMMARY AND CONJECTURES

The interaction with the environment, which is in principle present for all systems, seems to play a decisive role for an understanding of classical properties in the framework of quantum theory. The destruction of interference with respect to local observations and the resulting nonunitary dynamics for a subsystem of the universe is achieved by the irreversible coupling to the environment, together with the nonlocality properties of quantum theory. This means that initial states may be assumed to factorize or fulfill a Sommerfeld radiation condition, which is in analogy to Boltzmann's Stoβzahlansatz. From this point of view, macroscopic properties are not inherent in certain objects (although, for example, a "large" mass may be important for dynamical stability), but are, in a sense, created by the environment. "Particles"appear localized in space not because there are particles, but because the environment continually measures position. The concept of a particle seems to be derivable from the quantum concept of state, and, at this stage, it therefore seems superfluous to introduce additional concepts like particle trajectories. In this derivation, the dynamical laws are as important as boundary (initial) conditions. Both have the same significance and they should perhaps be treated as a whole in a future theory, as was often stressed by Wheeler. A step in this direction may be the quantum theory of gravity.

Of course, the above considerations do not allow a complete derivation of classical concepts because the use of a local density matrix contains the axiom of measurement, which cannot be derived by any unitary treatment.

In regard to the interpretational problems of quantum theory, one may hope that these superselection rules can be helpful in developing new ideas on what distinguishes measurement processes from "normal" physical processes. One may also conjecture that an ensemble interpretation of the wave function (or of local density matrices) is possible because, for certain objects, quantum coherence is absent (i.e., unobservable for observers who do not "see" the whole universe) in principle (because of the boundary conditions of this universe). Quantum nonlocality, which has been extensively discussed during the last decades, would play no role for the same reason. One would be able to ascribe state vectors to certain subsystems of the universe without running into contradictions. Of course, the central question of quantum theory remains unsolved: Why are there local observers?

ACKNOWLEDGMENTS

I wish to thank W. K. Wootters and H. D. Zeh for critically reading the manuscript.

REFERENCES

1. LANDAU, L. D. & E. M. LIFSCHITZ. 1958. Quantum Mechanics. Pergamon. Elmsford, New York.
2. BORN, M., Ed. 1969. Albert Einstein, Hedwig und Max Born Briefwechsel, pp. 283–284.
3. See reference 2, p. 278.
4. ZEH, H. D. 1970. Found. Phys. **1:** 69–76.
5. BAUMANN, K. 1970. Z. Naturforsch. **25a:** 1954–1956.
6. ZUREK, W. H. 1981. Phys. Rev. **D24:** 1516–1525.
7. ZUREK, W. H. 1982. Phys. Rev. **D26:** 1862–1880.
8. JOOS, E. & H. D. ZEH. 1985. Z. Phys. **B59:** 223–243.
9. WIGNER, E. P. 1983. *In* Quantum Optics, Experimental Gravity and Measurement Theory. P. Meystre & M. O. Scully, Eds. Plenum. New York.
10. JOOS, E. 1986. Phys. Lett. **A116:** 6–8.
11. HAWKING, S. W. 1984. Nucl. Phys. **B239:** 257–276.
12. HALLIWELL, J. J. & S. W. HAWKING. 1985. Phys. Rev. **D31:** 1777–1791.

Relativity and Quantum Mechanics—Conflict or Peaceful Coexistence?

MICHAEL L. G. REDHEAD

Department of History and Philosophy of Science
King's College (KQC)
University of London
London SW3 6LX, England

INTRODUCTION

Nonlocality in quantum mechanics provides a *prima facie* conflict with the foundations of special relativity that is usually taken to forbid causal processes operating outside the light cone, that is, at spacelike separation. In the recent literature,[1] various senses of locality have been distinguished, and the question of which of these is violaṭed by quantum mechanics depends crucially on the interpretation of quantum mechanics adopted. In the case of deterministic hidden-variable interpretations, action-at-a-distance (in the sense of instantaneously affecting the possessed value of some attribute belonging to one member of a pair of spatially separated systems by altering the physical arrangement of an apparatus interacting with the other member) appears to be clearly demonstrable. Here, a direct conflict with special relativity seems difficult to avoid except by appealing to the problematic topic of tachyonic interactions.[1]

On the other hand, in the case of indeterministic or stochastic hidden-variable interpretations, the issues raised are much more subtle. No straightforward derivation of the Bell inequalities is possible along the lines available in the deterministic case. Therefore, an appeal has to be made to two conditions spelled out in detail by Jarrett.[2] The first condition, Jarrett locality (or, as Shimony prefers to call it, parameter independence[3]), is equivalent to requiring that one cannot use quantum mechanical correlations for signaling.[4] The second condition, Jarrett completeness (or, in Shimony's terminology, outcome independence), identifies the hidden-variable description of the source as the common cause for the possessed values of spin-components in the idealized Bohm-Bell experiment. If Jarrett completeness is violated, it is often argued that the spatially separated spin-components must then exhibit a direct stochastic causal link on the grounds that the correlations can only be accounted for on the basis of stochastic links to a common cause or a direct stochastic causal link. The purpose of the present paper is to question this conclusion by exhibiting a "third way," which may arguably be regarded as a mathematical explication of what Shimony has termed passion-at-a-distance.[4]

NECESSARY CONDITIONS FOR STOCHASTIC CAUSALITY

Causal relations exhibit a quality of robustness. Suitably small disturbances of either relatum do not modify or affect the causal relation. This is essentially the basis

14

of the mark method for identifying causal processes.[5-7] The processes propagate small disturbances (marks) in a local event-structure in accordance with the causal law at issue.

We shall now translate this idea in the context of stochastic causal relations by formulating the following necessary condition for stochastic causality:

> Physical magnitudes, a and b, pertaining to two separated systems, A and B, exhibit a stochastic causal connection only if there exists a class of sufficiently small disturbances acting on $B(A)$ such that $b(a)$ screens off $a(b)$ from these disturbances.

Denoting the disturbance acting on B by d and denoting the possible values of a by ϵ_a and of b by ϵ_b, then the first part of this condition can be rendered formally as

$$\exists D(\forall d \epsilon D[\text{Prob}\,(a = \epsilon_a | b = \epsilon_b \,\&\, d) = \text{Prob}\,(a = \epsilon_a | b = \epsilon_b)]). \tag{1}$$

A similar condition can be written down for disturbances acting on A.

Furthermore, we are going to apply this condition to the case of the singlet state, $|\psi\rangle$, of two distinguishable spin-$\frac{1}{2}$ particles denoted by A and B. We let a denote the spin-projection, $\underline{\sigma}_A \cdot \hat{\underline{a}}$ (in units of $\hbar/2$), along the direction of the unit vector, $\hat{\underline{a}}$. Similarly, b denotes $\underline{\sigma}_B \cdot \hat{\underline{b}}$ for some, generally different, direction $\hat{\underline{b}}$. Then, it is well known that $\epsilon_a = \pm 1$ and $\epsilon_b = \pm 1$.

Now, we will consider the possible perturbations of the state, $|\psi\rangle$, by disturbances acting on the particle B. In order to make the problem tractable, we shall restrict the discussion to the coupling of particle B to uniform c-number fields of arbitrary strength, which are switched on for some specified interval of time to provide the perturbation. Let ψ' be a variable ranging over these perturbed states. Then, a necessary condition that a and b exhibit a stochastic causal connection for arbitrary choice of the directions, $\hat{\underline{a}}$ and $\hat{\underline{b}}$, is

$$\exists D \forall a \forall b (\forall |\psi'\rangle \epsilon D \,[\text{Prob}^{|\psi'\rangle}(a = \epsilon_a | b = \epsilon_b) = \text{Prob}^{|\psi\rangle}\,(a = \epsilon_a | b = \epsilon_b)]), \tag{2}$$

where the superscript on "Prob" denotes the quantum mechanical state and where the class, D, is some nonempty set of perturbed states arising from sufficiently weak perturbing fields. However, we shall now show by explicit calculation that the condition in equation 2 is violated. Because equation 2 is a necessary condition for a direct stochastic causal link between a and b, it will follow that no such link exists.

THE NONROBUSTNESS OF THE SINGLET STATE

We denote the spin-projections of $\underline{\sigma}_A$ and $\underline{\sigma}_B$ along the arbitrarily chosen z-axis by σ_{A_z} and σ_{B_z}, respectively. Then, we have

$$|\psi\rangle = \frac{1}{\sqrt{2}}\,(|\sigma_{A_z} = +1\rangle|\sigma_{B_z} = -1\rangle - |\sigma_{A_z} = -1\rangle|_{B_z} = +1\rangle), \tag{3}$$

which is a vector in $\mathcal{H}_A \otimes \mathcal{H}_B$ (the tensor product of the Hilbert space, $\mathcal{H}_A$ and $\mathcal{H}_B$, for the particles, A and B).

Next we need to consider an arbitrary perturbation acting on $\mathcal{H}_B$. It will induce a 2×2 unitary transformation on all vectors belonging to $\mathcal{H}_B$. This transformation is thus an element of $U(2)$, which is the group of two-dimensional unitary transformations. It is also well known that $U(2)$ can be exhibited as the direct product of $U(1)$, the group of one-dimensional unitary transformations, and $SU(2)$, the group of two-dimensional unitary unimodular transformations. Formally, this is

$$U(2) = U(1) \times SU(2). \tag{4}$$

However, we need to note that an element of $U(1)$ merely induces a phase-shift that does not change the physical state (ray) associated with particle B. Thus, it can be ignored in computing all probabilities. The action of an element of $SU(2)$ can always be represented as $e^{i(\sigma_B \cdot \hat{n})\phi/2}$, where the direction of the unit vector, $\hat{n}$, and the magnitude of the angle ϕ range over the three parameters of the group. (Note that $0 \leq \phi < 4\pi$.) In addition, we denote $e^{i(\sigma_B \cdot \hat{n})\phi/2}$ by $u(n, \phi)$. Then the most general perturbed state is given by

$$|\psi'\rangle = \frac{1}{\sqrt{2}} [|\sigma_{A_z} = +1\rangle\, u(n, \phi)|\sigma_{B_z} = -1\rangle - |\sigma_{A_z} = -1\rangle\, u(n, \phi)|\sigma_{B_z} = +1\rangle]. \tag{5}$$

In what follows, we shall consider the particular choice, $\epsilon_a = \epsilon_b = 1$.

We now have the familiar results,

$$\text{Prob}^{|\psi\rangle}(a = 1) = \frac{1}{2}, \tag{6}$$

$$\text{Prob}^{|\psi\rangle}(b = 1) = \frac{1}{2}, \tag{7}$$

$$\text{Prob}^{|\psi\rangle}(a = 1 \,|\, b = 1) = \sin^2 \tfrac{1}{2}\theta_{ab}, \tag{8}$$

where θ_{ab} is the angle between the directions, $\hat{a}$ and $\hat{b}$. Therefore, we are interested in calculating $\text{Prob}^{|\psi'\rangle}(a = 1)$, $\text{Prob}^{|\psi'\rangle}(b = 1)$, and $\text{Prob}^{|\psi'\rangle}(a = 1 \,|\, b = 1)$. The robustness condition for stochastic causality is simply

$$\text{Prob}^{|\psi'\rangle}(a = 1 \,|\, b = 1) = \text{Prob}^{|\psi\rangle}(a = 1 \,|\, b = 1). \tag{9}$$

We shall show that for any given disturbed state, $|\psi'\rangle$, there always exist directions, $\hat{a}$ and $\hat{b}$, for which equation 9 is violated.

To calculate the new probabilities, we proceed to apply the unitary transformation, $u(\hat{n}, -\phi)$ $[=u^{-1}(\hat{n}, \phi)]$, to the space, $\mathcal{H}_B$. This converts $|\psi'\rangle$ back into $|\psi\rangle$, but induces a rotation, $R(\hat{n}, -\phi)$, in the operator, σ_B. $R(\hat{n}, \phi)$ is an element of the three-dimensional rotation groups, $SO(3)$, that corresponds to an (active) clockwise rotation about the direction, $\hat{n}$. The above result is a direct expression of the famous homomorphism that exists between $SU(2)$ and $SO(3)$. [$SU(2)$ is just the simply connected universal covering group of $SO(3)$.] Succinctly,

$$u(\hat{n}, \phi)\sigma_B\, u(\hat{n}, -\phi) = R(\hat{n}, \phi)\sigma_B. \tag{10}$$

On the left of equation 10, u acts on the spinor indices of σ_B, while on the right, R acts on the vector indices. Thus, the effect of our unitary transformation on the operators, a and b, is as follows:

$$a = \sigma_A \cdot \hat{a} \rightarrow a' = a, \tag{11}$$

$$b = \underline{\sigma}_B \cdot \underline{\hat{b}} \rightarrow b' = [u(\hat{n}, - \phi) \, \underline{\sigma}_B u(\hat{n}, \phi)] \cdot \underline{\hat{b}}$$

$$= [R(\hat{n}, -\phi)\underline{\sigma}_B] \cdot \underline{\hat{b}} = \underline{\sigma}_B \cdot [R(\hat{n}, \phi)\underline{\hat{b}}] = \underline{\sigma}_B \cdot \underline{\hat{b}}', \tag{12}$$

where

$$\underline{\hat{b}}' = R(\hat{n}, \phi)\underline{\hat{b}}. \tag{13}$$

Hence, we immediately have the following results:

(i) $\text{Prob}^{|\psi'\rangle}(a = 1) = \text{Prob}^{|\psi\rangle}(a' = 1) = \text{Prob}^{|\psi\rangle}(a = 1) = \frac{1}{2}.$ (14)

This shows that the perturbation acting on particle B cannot be used to send signals to the location of particle A. Notice that the result is quite general because it does not depend on the connections between $u(\hat{n}, \phi)$ and $R(\hat{n}, \phi)$, but only on the existence of the unitary transformation, u. In the appendix to this paper, we shall show how our method of proof of this no-signaling theorem can be given in full generality;

(ii) $\text{Prob}^{|\psi'\rangle}(b = 1) = \text{Prob}^{|\psi\rangle}(b' = 1) = \frac{1}{2}.$ (15)

This is a rather surprising result that is a special property of the example under discussion;

(iii) $\text{Prob}^{|\psi'\rangle}(a = 1 \mid b = 1) = \text{Prob}^{|\psi\rangle}(a' = 1 \mid b' = 1)$

$$= \text{Prob}^{|\psi\rangle}(a = 1 \mid b' = 1) = \sin^2\frac{1}{2}\theta_{ab'}. \tag{16}$$

Based on these results, the robustness condition (given in equation 9) thus reduces to $\sin^2\frac{1}{2}\theta_{ab'} = \sin^2\frac{1}{2}\theta_{ab}$, or

$$\theta_{ab} = \theta_{ab'}, \tag{17}$$

because the angles all lie in the range of 0 to π. Equation 17 can also be given a simple geometrical interpretation (see FIGURE 1). In this figure, ON represents the unit vector, $\hat{n}$, OB represents the unit vector, $\hat{b}$, OB' represents the unit vector, $\hat{b}'$, B and B' lie on a circle with center, O', whose plane is perpendicular to ON, and $\angle$BO'B' = ϕ. Now, $\theta_{ab} = \theta_{ab'}$ is equivalent to $\cos\theta_{ab} = \cos\theta_{ab'}$, or $\hat{a} \cdot \hat{b} = \hat{a} \cdot \hat{b}'$ or $\hat{a} \cdot (\hat{b} - \hat{b}') = 0$. Hence, $\hat{a}$ must line in the plane perpendicular to the line BB'. We call this plane, Π. Π can equally well be characterized as the plane through ON and OC, where OC is the bisector of the angle between $\hat{b}$ and $\hat{b}'$. The plane, Π, is shown shaded in the diagram. Therefore, we have the following:

Theorem: For any given perturbation on particle B that issues in a rotation of $\hat{b}$ to $\hat{b}'$, the conditional probability, $\text{Prob}^{|\psi\rangle}(a = 1 \mid b = 1)$, will be invariant (robust) under the perturbation if and only if the direction, $\hat{a}$, lies in the plane defined by the axis of rotation and the bisector of the directions, $\hat{b}$ and $\hat{b}'$.

Corollaries:

(1) If $\hat{n}$ coincides with $\hat{a}$, $\text{Prob}^{|\psi\rangle}(a = 1 \mid b = 1)$ is robust for all $\hat{b}$;
(2) If $\hat{n}$ coincides with $\hat{b}$, $\text{Prob}^{|\psi\rangle}(a = 1 \mid b = 1)$ is robust for all $\hat{a}$;

(3) For any perturbation (rotation), no matter how small, there always exist directions, $\hat{a}$ and $\hat{b}$, for which $\text{Prob}^{|\psi\rangle}$ ($a = 1 \mid b = 1$) is not robust.

I believe it is this last corollary that demonstrates that a and b cannot be regarded as being related by stochastic causality.

Therefore, the correlations between a and b are a property of the particular quantum mechanical state, namely, the singlet state, in which the particles emerge from the source. This property, it is claimed, explicates Shimony's passion-at-

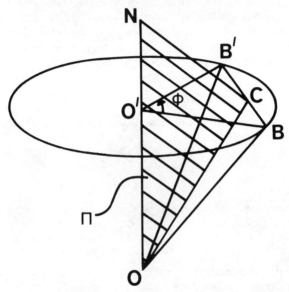

FIGURE 1. Rotation of unit vector $\overrightarrow{OB}$ through angle ϕ about axis $\overrightarrow{ON}$ into new position $\overrightarrow{OB'}$. OC is the bisector of the angle between $\overrightarrow{OB}$ and $\overrightarrow{OB'}$. The plane, NOC, denoted by Π, is shown shaded.

a-distance, and points the way to peaceful coexistence between quantum-mechanical nonlocality and special relativity.

ACKNOWLEDGMENTS

Part of this work was done while the author was a Visiting Fellow at the Center for Philosophy of Science, University of Pittsburgh. I am very grateful for the warm hospitality afforded by Nicholas Rescher and his colleagues. I particularly benefited from discussions about stochastic causality with Paul Humphreys and Wesley Salmon. They are not, however, to be held responsible for any of the views expressed herein.

REFERENCES

1. REDHEAD, M. L. G. 1983. Relativity, causality and the Einstein-Podolsky-Rosen paradox: nonlocality and peaceful coexistence. *In* Space, Time, and Causality. R. Swinburne, Ed.: 151–189. Reidel. Dordrecht.
2. JARRETT, J. 1984. On the physical significance of the locality conditions in the Bell arguments. Nôus **18**: 569–589.
3. SHIMONY, A. 1986. Events and processes in the quantum world. *In* Quantum Concepts of Space and Time. C. Isham & R. Penrose, Eds.: 182–203. Cambridge Univ. Press. London.
4. SHIMONY, A. 1984. Controllable and uncontrollable non-locality. Proceedings of the International Symposium: Foundations of Quantum Mechanics in the Light of New Technology. S. Kamefuchi *et al.,* Eds.: 225–230. Physical Society of Japan. Tokyo.
5. REICHENBACH, H. 1928. Philosophie der Raum-Zeit-Lehre. de Gruyter. Berlin. (1958. English translation. Dover. New York.)
6. REICHENBACH, H. 1956. The Direction of Time. Univ. of California Press. Berkeley and Los Angeles.
7. SALMON, W. 1984. Scientific Explanation and the Causal Structure of the World. Princeton Univ. Press. Princeton, New Jersey.
8. EBERHARD, P. 1978. Bell's theorem and the different concepts of locality. Nuovo Cimento **46B**: 392–419.
9. GHIRARDI, G. C., A. RIMINI & T. WEBER. 1980. A general argument against superluminal transmission through the quantum mechanical measurement process. Lett. Nuovo Cimento **27**: 293–298.
10. PAGE, D. N. 1982. The Einstein-Podolsky-Rosen physical reality is completely described by quantum mechanics. Phys. Lett. **91A**: 57–60.
11. JORDAN, T. F. 1983. Quantum correlations do not transmit signals. Phys. Lett. **94A**: 264.

APPENDIX

The General No-Signaling Theorem

Several previous proofs that quantum-mechanical correlations cannot be used for signaling have been given in the literature.[4,8–10] The following proof combines generality and brevity.

Consider two systems, A and B, with associated Hilbert spaces, $\mathcal{H}_A$ and $\mathcal{H}_B$. Let C be a third system that may interact with system B with an associated Hilbert space, $\mathcal{H}_C$. Denote $\mathcal{H}_B \otimes \mathcal{H}_C$ by $\overline{\mathcal{H}}_B$. Here, a is any observable on $\mathcal{H}_A$, which is extended to $a \otimes I$ on $\mathcal{H}_A \otimes \overline{\mathcal{H}}_B$. Consider any state, $|\psi(t)\rangle$, of the triple system at time, t, and denote

$$\text{Prob} (\lambda) \, \frac{|\psi(t)\rangle}{a(t) \otimes I}$$

as the probability that the time-dependent observable, $a(t) \otimes I$, will yield the measurement result, λ, in the state, $|\psi(t)\rangle$. We shall work in the interaction representation, so in the absence of perturbation, $|\psi(t)\rangle$ is constant, while in all cases, $a(t) \otimes I$ evolves in time according to the unperturbed Hamiltonian.

Now, perturb the system B in any way in the time interval, (t, t'), by the action of a unitary time-evolution operator, $U_B (t, t')$, acting on $\overline{\mathcal{H}}_B$. Then, at time, t', the state of the triple system is

$$|\psi(t')\rangle = [I \otimes U_B(t, t')]|\psi(t)\rangle.$$

We now compute

$$\text{Prob}(\lambda)\frac{|\psi(t')\rangle}{a(t') \otimes I} = \text{Prob}(\lambda)\frac{|\psi(t)\rangle}{a'(t') \otimes I},$$

where

$$a'(t') \otimes I = (I \otimes U_B^{-1})\,[a(t') \otimes I]\,(I \otimes U_B)$$
$$= (I \otimes U_B^{-1})\,[a(t') \otimes U_B]$$
$$= a(t') \otimes (U_B^{-1}U_B) = a(t') \otimes I.$$

Thus,

$$\text{Prob}(\lambda)\frac{|\psi(t')\rangle}{a(t') \otimes I} = \text{Prob}(\lambda)\frac{|\psi(t)\rangle}{a(t') \otimes I}.$$

However, the right-hand side of this equation is the probability of finding the result, λ, by measuring a on A at time, t', in the absence of perturbation. This is so because then the state vector at t' is the same as the state vector at t. In other words, the probability of obtaining the result, λ, by measuring a on A at any time, t', is independent of any possible perturbation of the system B between t and t'.

Quantum Mechanics and Realism at the Macroscopic Level

Is an Experimental Discrimination Feasible?

A. J. LEGGETT

Department of Physics
University of Illinois
Urbana, Illinois 61801

Because the topic of my talk is one on which I have written extensively elsewhere, I shall here give merely a summary of the main points that I believe to be important and refer the reader to existing papers[1-8] for the details of the argument. The following discussion is not intended to be self-contained, and many important caveats and references are omitted; they are supplied in the papers referred to.

The quantum measurement paradox arises because the linear formalism of quantum mechanics, when applied to experimental setups of the "Schrödinger's Cat" type,[1] can describe macroscopic objects (in particular, measuring devices and their immediate environments) by a linear superposition of states with macroscopically different properties, or by a classical probabilistic mixture of such linear superpositions.[1] Consequently, if one takes the same interpretation of the formalism at the macroscopic level as is conventional at the microscopic level, then under certain circumstances, a macroscopic object need not "actually be" in a definite macroscopic state until it is actually observed to be so. This conclusion is clearly in severe conflict with the "realistic" point of view that we would normally take of the macroscopic world in everyday life.

The "orthodox" resolution of the paradox, that is, the one that most working physicists who have thought seriously about the question would probably accept, in effect rests on two claims: claim (1) The extrapolation of quantum mechanics to the macroscopic level (in the sense necessary to generate the paradox) is indeed legitimate and does lead formally to linear superpositions of macroscopically distinct states (or classical mixtures of such superpositions). However, [claim (2)] all experimental predictions of such a description are indistinguishable from those of a "realistic" description, in which the macroscopic object in question is in a definite macroscopic state with a certain probability. Whether or not claim (2), if true, resolves the paradox is a hotly debated issue[2] that I shall not discuss here; in any case, it is clear that if claim (2) is true, then claim (1) is untestable.

What I shall claim here is that modern advances in cryogenics, microfabrication, noise control, and other technologies may well have made claim (2) false and therefore claim (1) testable. In other words, I am claiming that it is probably possible to generate a situation involving a macroscopic object (though not, I stress, one that in the context could be used as a measuring device) with two macroscopically distinct states available to it such that extrapolation of the formalism of quantum mechanics unambiguously predicts that a linear superposition of these states should occur, and, moreover, such that the experimental predictions of such a description differ substantially from those of macroscopic realism. If this is right, the answer to the question posed in my title is "yes."

To begin with, let us pretend that we are totally ignorant of the literature of the last five decades of the quantum theory of measurement. Therefore, we describe our macroscopic system as (a) completely isolated from its environment and (b) character-ized by a single macroscopic variable (such as the position of the center of mass; however, see below). How then would we go about testing the predictions of quantum mechanics *vis-à-vis* those of macroscopic realism? As in the case of Bell's theorem, the most spectacular divergences occur when the Hilbert space of the system in question can be taken as two-dimensional. This suggests that we consider[3] a system moving in a potential that has two degenerate minima (as in the case of the NH_3 molecule) at temperatures low enough so that excitation of the higher levels in each well is negligible. Then (if we believe quantum mechanics) the system, if started in one well, will oscillate coherently backwards and forwards between the two wells at a frequency determined by the amplitude for tunneling through the barrier between them. In most macroscopic systems, the barrier height is itself macroscopic, and the period of this oscillation is astronomically long and hence of no interest to us; however, in certain special systems, in particular, Josephson devices (where the macroscopic variable is the trapped flux), the barrier height can be made very small and the oscillation frequency can be quite substantial (in fact, of the order of MHz). In such systems, the two states in question could correspond to circulating currents that differ by something on the order of a microamp; by most reasonable criteria, they are therefore "macroscopically distinct."(For details, see references 4, 5, 9, and 10.)

Let us define "macroscopic realism" by two postulates: (1) The macroscopic system must at all times (or more accurately, at "nearly all" times[3]) be in one or the other of the two macroscopically distinct states; (2) It is, in principle, possible (e.g., by an "ideal-negative-result" measurement[3]) to determine that the system is in a particular state without affecting its subsequent motion. Define a quantity, $P(t)$, that is assigned the value $+1$ if the system is observed to be in (say) the "right-hand" state, and -1 if it is observed to be in the "left-hand" one; in addition, define the experimentally observed ensemble-averaged correlations $K(t_1, t_2) \equiv \langle P(t_1) P(t_2) \rangle$. Then, by a simple adaptation of Bell's theorem, it can be shown[3] that the form of the experimentally observed quantity, $K(t_1, t_2)$, predicted by quantum mechanics [namely, $K(t_1, t_2) \sim \cos(\Delta[t_2 - t_1])$, where Δ is the tunneling frequency], violates an inequality that must be satisfied by any theory embodying macroscopic realism. An experimental discrimination is therefore indeed possible.

At this point, anyone who has any familiarity with the literature on quantum measurement theory will raise the obvious objection:[6] It is surely totally unrealistic to describe the macroscopic system as isolated from its environment or as characterized by a single macroscopic degree of freedom. The results of a more realistic description will surely be qualitatively completely different. Indeed, it has been a major theme of five decades' worth of literature in this area that the coupling of a macroscopic system to the external world, and/or the coupling of the macroscopic degree of freedom to the internal ones, is guaranteed to destroy any interference between macroscopically distinct states, and hence, in the opinion of many writers in this area, to "solve" the quantum measurement paradox. Why am I then flying in the face of this conventional wisdom?

The fact is that while there are very many papers in the literature that make qualitative and illustrative remarks about the phenomenon of coherence destruction by the environment, there are very few that bother to construct a serious and plausible model of the kind of system that would have to be used in the above experiment, taking into account its interactions with its environment in a realistic way, and that then actually calculate the rate at which the destruction of coherence takes place. In fact, it is only in the last five years or so, to the best of my knowledge, that this has been attempted in any systematic way (for the details, see references 4, 5, and 9).

When one actually gets down to doing it, one finds some surprises. In the first place, much of the system-environment interaction turns out to be adiabatic in nature: most of the degrees of freedom of the environment are associated with frequencies much higher than that of the macroscopic variable and they therefore adapt instantaneously to it, thereby preserving the possibility of observing interference effects (*cf.* references 6 and 7). In fact, it is only those degrees of freedom whose characteristic frequencies are comparable to that of the macrovariable that are "dangerous" (that is, they can destroy the coherence). Secondly, it turns out that the purely quantum mechanical phenomenon of coherence destruction is intimately related to the phenomenon of dissipation, which is, of course, present even in the classical limit. Even more strikingly, in many cases, it turns out that one can relate the rate of coherence destruction to the dissipation observed in a purely classical experiment; with certain rather general assumptions, this relation does not depend on the details of the model. This point is crucial, in the experiment described, because it means that a failure to see coherent oscillations where predicted cannot be ascribed to a wrong choice of microscopic Hamiltonian. In fact, it turns out that with values of the dissipation parameters which may not be unrealistic in practice (*cf.* reference 10), the complete quantum theory of the macrosystem interacting with its environment still does indeed predict coherent oscillations as in the idealized case; while these oscillations are indeed damped, the damping is weak enough that the quantum mechanical predictions for the real-life situation are still incompatible with the predictions of macroscopic realism. Thus, the well-known considerations of the quantum measurement literature need not in fact destroy the possibility of an experimental test.

Existing experiments have adequately verified that quantum mechanics does indeed adequately describe the motion of a macroscopic variable as regards the barrier penetration process itself and also as regards the quantization of classical motion within a metastable well (see references 5 and 11 for details). The stage is thus set for a crucial test of quantum mechanics versus macroscopic realism.[10] If the experiment can be done, one can envisage at least three possible outcomes: (1) New sources of dissipation are discovered in the relevant frequency region which ensure that the predictions of a quantum mechanical treatment after all agree with those of realism. This would be rather disappointing, but there would at least have been plenty of technical spin-off; (2) The experiment confirms the quantum mechanical predictions. This would make the quantum measurement paradox several orders of magnitude sharper (and incidentally would refute some possible "resolutions" of it; *cf.* reference 8); (3) The experiment finds results in conflict with the quantum mechanical predictions. This would be the most exciting outcome of all: after all the (many) experimental and theoretical loopholes had been plugged, we would then have to take seriously the possibility[2,8] that the physics of complex macroscopic objects cannot be deduced in all respects from that of their constituents—a conclusion that would clearly run totally counter to the "reductionist" wisdom of the science of the last two hundred years, but might in the end have a liberating effect that outruns our present imagination.

REFERENCES

1. LEGGETT, A. J. 1984. Contemp. Phys. **25:** 583.
2. LEGGETT, A. J. 1986. *In* Quantum Theory and Beyond. B. J. Hiley & F. D. Peat, Eds. Routledge & Kegan Paul. London.
3. LEGGETT, A. J. & ANUPAM GARG. 1985. Phys. Rev. Lett. **54:** 857 and 2724.
4. LEGGETT, A. J. 1984. *In* Percolation, Localization, and Superconductivity. A. M. Goldman & S. Wolf, Eds. Plenum. New York. (NATO ASI Series, ser. B: Phys., vol. 109.)
5. LEGGETT, A. J. 1986. *In* Directions in Condensed Matter Physics. World Scientific. Singapore.
6. LEGGETT, A. J. 1980. Prog. Theor. Phys. Suppl. **69:** 80.
7. LEGGETT, A. J. 1984. *In* Proc. Int. Symposium on the Foundations of Quantum Mechanics in the Light of New Technology. S. Kamefuchi *et al.,* Eds. Physical Society of Japan. Tokyo.
8. LEGGETT, A. J. 1985. *In* Proc. Niels Bohr Centennial Symposium, Copenhagen (October 1985).
9. CHAKRAVARTY, S. 1986. These proceedings.
10. TESCHE, C. D. 1986. These proceedings.
11. WASHBURN, S. & R. A. WEBB. 1986. These proceedings.

Quantum Mechanics on a Macroscopic Scale[a]

SUDIP CHAKRAVARTY

Department of Physics
State University of New York at Stony Brook
Stony Brook, New York 11794

INTRODUCTION

The present paper is not intended to be a complete review; rather, its purpose is to give the reader a flavor of the interesting questions that have been asked in the field. In recent years, the subject of Macroscopic Quantum Tunneling (MQT) in superconducting systems and related problems has grown immensely.[1] In a short space, it is not possible to give an historically accurate account, and I shall refrain from doing so. I shall also try to keep the technical details to a bare minimum; the interested reader is encouraged to peruse through the literature cited at the end.

The important issue from the point of view of the present conference is what we can learn about quantum measurement theory in the light of rapidly developing technology. As we discuss this problem, it will become evident that we are beginning to uncover some novel aspects of the theory of superconductivity and, in particular, of the theory of the Josephson effect.

QUANTUM MECHANICS ON A MACROSCOPIC SCALE

That quantum mechanics can lead to observable consequences in the properties of a macroscopic system is well known. It is so ingrained in our minds that it leads to some misunderstanding when it comes to the subject of MQT and related problems. In this section, I shall try to clarify precisely what we mean by quantum mechanics on a macroscopic scale. In this respect, my discussion is going to be very similar to that of A. J. Leggett.[2]

The specific heat of an insulating solid deviates markedly from the classical value at low temperatures, that is, at temperatures below the so-called Debye temperature. Thus, the Debye temperature, like the Fermi temperature of a metal, differentiates the regime where classical mechanics is adequate from the low-temperature regime where quantum statistics must be used. The observed specific heat of a macroscopic sample is, therefore, a result of the quantum mechanical behavior of the normal modes of a solid. Does this mean that we have to invoke the superposition principle involving 10^{23} particles? The answer is no. It is only necessary to invoke quantum mechanics for a

[a]This work was supported by a grant from the National Science Foundation (NSF-DMR-83-01510).

normal mode and the rest follows. This is one level at which quantum mechanics affects the macroscopic behavior of a solid.

Let us now proceed to more "subtle" effects involving quantum mechanics on a macroscopic scale. We shall see that, subtle though they may be, they do not involve the superposition principle at a level of more than a few particles. Once we have discussed these examples, it will become clear as to why the recent activity in the present area is so interesting: it involves the superposition principle at the level of 10^{23} particles.

The following examples will be from superconductivity.[3] The BCS N-particle wave function for a superconductor is

$$\Psi(r_1, r_2, \ldots, r_N) = A\chi(r_1, r_2)\chi(r_3, r_4) \cdots \chi(r_{N-1}, r_N), \tag{1}$$

where the spin indices have been suppressed, A is the antisymmetrization operator, and χ, loosely speaking, is the wave function of a Cooper pair. Note that χ's are the same for all pairs, which reflects the Bose condensed nature of the ground state. Because of the condensation in the ground state, what normally for a single particle would be the probability current becomes the physically measurable current. The argument has been beautifully given by Feynman.[4]

Consider single particle quantum mechanics. The square of the wave function of the particle represents the probability density, not the physical density. When we measure at a point, we either find the particle or not. We never find a fraction of the particle. However, suppose we have N identical Bose particles that are condensed into the same state, and also suppose that they are so weakly interacting that one can ignore their interactions (the argument goes through equally well in the presence of interactions, but a much heavier machinery is needed to explain it). The probability to find any one of these particles at a given point is still proportional to the square of the wave function. However, in the thermodynamic limit, if we look in a small volume element (that is, small in comparison to macroscopic scales, but large in comparison to microscopic scales), we will find a number also proportional to the square of the same wave function. Thus, because these particles are indistinguishable bosons, the probability density can also be interpreted as the physical density. Clearly, the same arguments hold for the current.

Let us now return to the problem of superconductor and write

$$\chi(\vec{r}_1, \vec{r}_2) = \chi(\vec{R}, \vec{r}) = |\chi(\vec{R})|\, e^{i\theta(\vec{R})}, \tag{2}$$

where R is the center of mass coordinate and r is the relative coordinate. The relative coordinate, r, is of no importance in the present discussion and we shall suppress it. The velocity is then given by

$$\vec{v}_s(\vec{R}) = (\hbar/2m)\{\vec{\nabla}\theta(R) - 2e\vec{A}(\vec{R})/\hbar\}, \tag{3}$$

where $\vec{A}(\vec{R})$ is the vector potential. The gradient of the phase of a quantum mechanical wave function thus appears in the definition of a physical current (not probability current). This equation then straightforwardly leads to the Aharonov-Bohm effect on a macroscopic scale, as was experimentally demonstrated.[5] Note that nowhere are we testing the superposition principle at a level higher than two particles.

Let us now consider the Josephson effect.[6] Here, we have two bulk superconductors connected by a weak link that can be an oxide layer, a layer of a normal metal, a constriction, etc. Here, the Cooper pair wave function can be in a linear superposition of an amplitude for being on the left and an amplitude for being on the right. An argument similar to that given above leads to an expression for the physical current (Josephson supercurrent) given by

$$I_J = I_C \sin \Delta\theta, \qquad (4)$$

where $\Delta\theta$ is the phase difference and I_C is the critical current, which is the maximum supercurrent that the junction can sustain. The astute reader would immediately recognize that this implies that the total energy of the system contains a part that depends on the phase difference between the Cooper pair wave functions belonging to the two sides of the superconductors. That this must be so can be made plausible from the following considerations.[7] The two superconductors connected by a superconducting bridge must by definition have a well-defined condensate wave function (an appropriate average of relevant quantum field operators). Therefore, if there was no stiffness associated with the phase difference (that is, if the phases of the wave functions of the two sides could fluctuate independently), this would not be true, and hence the validity of the above statement. The Josephson coupling energy is given by

$$U(\Delta\theta) = -\frac{I_C\phi_0}{2\pi}\cos\Delta\theta, \qquad (5)$$

where $\phi_0 = h/2e$ is the superconducting flux quantum. If the junction is biased by an external current, I_{ext}, then one must add a term, $-I_{ext}\phi_0\Delta\theta/2\pi$, as required by current conservation. The total potential is commonly known as the washboard potential.

The usual theory of the Josephson effect treats $\Delta\theta$ as a c-number. At the same time, it also recognizes that any transfer of Cooper pairs across the junction charges it up like a capacitor; hence, there should be a charging energy,

$$\frac{1}{2}CV^2 \equiv \frac{C}{2}\left(\frac{\hbar}{2e}\right)^2(\Delta\dot\theta)^2, \qquad (6)$$

where C is the capacitance of the junction. Here, we have used the Josephson relation,

$$\Delta\dot\theta = \frac{2eV}{\hbar}, \qquad (7)$$

where V is the voltage. Furthermore, the dissipation across the junction is dealt with phenomenologically by noticing that the normal dissipative current (as opposed to the Josephson supercurrent) is given by V/R, where R is the resistance of the junction. The complete dynamics is then described by the so-called resistively shunted junction (RSJ) equation that has been singularly successful in describing various devices based on Josephson junctions. The equation is given by

$$C\left(\frac{\hbar}{2e}\right)^2\Delta\ddot\theta + \left(\frac{\hbar}{2e}\right)\frac{1}{R}\Delta\dot\theta = \left(-\frac{\partial}{\partial\Delta\theta}\right)\left(-\frac{I_C\phi_0}{2\pi}\cos\Delta\theta - \frac{I_{ext}}{2\pi}\phi_0\Delta\theta\right) \qquad (8)$$

For further discussion, let us also introduce a device called an rf-SQUID (radio frequency superconducting quantum interference device).[3,6] It is simply a supercon-

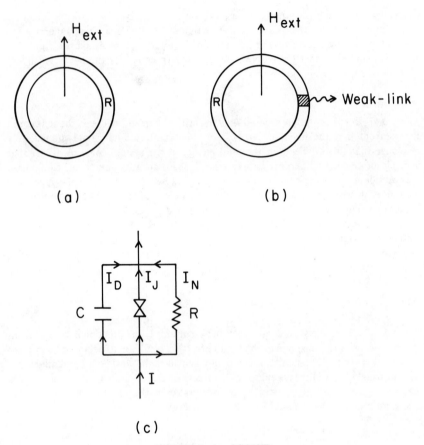

FIGURE 1. An rf-SQUID.

ducting ring, as shown in FIGURE 1a, interrupted by a Josephson junction, as shown in FIGURE 1b. The dynamics of the total flux, ϕ, through the ring (i.e., the flux due to the external magnetic field, H_{ext}, and the induced flux, $\phi_{ind} = LI$, where L is the self-inductance of the ring and I is the current flowing through the ring) is given, as before, by the RSJ equation:

$$C\ddot{\phi} + \frac{1}{R}\dot{\phi} = -\frac{\partial}{\partial\phi}U(\phi). \tag{9}$$

In FIGURE 1c, the current paths through the junction are shown. The displacement current is $I_D = -C\ddot{\phi}$, the normal current is $I_N = -\dot{\phi}/R$, and the Josephson supercurrent is $I_J = I_C \sin(2\pi\phi/\phi_0)$. The potential energy, $U(\phi)$, is now given by

$$U(\phi) = \frac{(\phi - \phi_{ext})^2}{2L} - \frac{I_C\phi_0}{2\pi}\cos\left(\frac{2\pi\phi}{\phi_0}\right). \tag{10}$$

Equation 9 mimics the behavior of a pseudoparticle of coordinate, ϕ, that obeys a damped Newtonian equation of motion. As shown in FIGURES 2a–c, one can adjust the external magnetic field to trap the particle in one of the metastable wells. $U(\phi)$ exhibits more than one metastable well if $2\pi LI_C/\phi_0 > 1$. In fact, by adjusting ϕ_{ext}, one can render the well unstable, and thus the particle will roll down the hill as shown in FIGURE 2c. This periodic trapping and retrapping of flux is the whole basis of operation of an rf-SQUID.

A similar discussion can be carried out for the current biased Josephson junction (see the article by Washburn and Webb in the present volume). In the discussion, so far, we have neglected all fluctuations of the variables, $\Delta\theta$ and ϕ, and have treated these variables as c-numbers. Given a fixed external bias, there is no way for the particle to overcome the barrier as shown in FIGURES 3a and 3b. We are now going to examine the nature of the fluctuations and their implications.

The variables, $\Delta\theta$ and ϕ, are collective coordinates of the system. They characterize the states of 10^{23} particles. That they are physically good collective variables is evidenced by the fact that the above equations are sufficient to describe the normal operations of all devices based on the Josephson effect. The important point to note is that a change in the flux state of a SQUID or the phase difference across a current biased Josephson junction amounts to changes of the states of a macroscopic number of

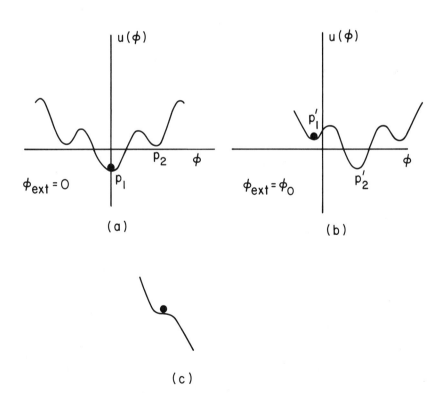

FIGURE 2. The potential energy, $U(\phi)$.

particles. Now, if we can demonstrate that the superposition principle applies to these collective coordinates, we will have also demonstrated that the superposition principle of quantum mechanics applies to distinct macroscopic states. This is very different from the examples discussed above where we had to invoke the superposition principle only at the level of a few particles. We can therefore ask the question:[2] Is it possible to verify experimentally that the state of a complex macroscopic system is a linear superposition of two distinct macroscopic states?

Normally, it would be difficult to ask such questions. This is because the energy scales involved are humongous for macroscopic systems. One of the beauties of the Josephson effect is that the tiniest of tiny energy scales can lead to observable macroscopic consequences. The energy barriers shown in FIGURES 3a and 3b can be as small as 20 K ($I_C \phi_0/2\pi$). This is tiny even by the standards of atomic physics, which

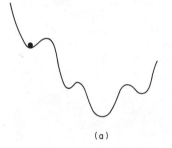

(a)

FIGURE 3. Decay from a metastable well.

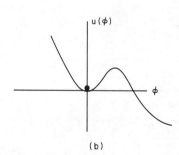

(b)

involve energy scales of the order of 10 eV ($\sim 10^5$ K). This is the reason why it is possible to explore the question about the superposition of macroscopic states using devices involving the Josephson effect.

One now would like to understand the nature of these collective coordinates. In the usual discussion of the Josephson effect, the variables, $\Delta\theta$ and ϕ, are treated as c-numbers, as discussed earlier. However, strictly speaking, they are quantum dynamical variables. Although this was noticed a long time ago,[8,9] not much attention was paid to this fact. The reason is that usually the capacitance, which is equivalent to the "mass" of the pseudoparticle mentioned earlier, is so large that quantum fluctuations of the collective coordinates are negligible. However, the present-day technology allows us to fabricate junctions with capacitance as small as 5×10^{-15} F. For such small capacitance junctions, it is no longer possible to treat $\Delta\theta$ and ϕ as c-numbers. For a careful discussion of the quantization, see the papers by Ambegaokar *et al.*[10] and Leggett.[11] Here, we merely note that the essence of the quantization is that one can write, using $\Delta N \Delta \theta \geq 1$, the charging energy as

$$\frac{Q^2}{2C} \equiv \frac{(2e)^2}{2C} (\Delta N)^2 = -\frac{2e^2}{C} \frac{\partial^2}{\partial(\Delta\theta)^2}. \tag{11}$$

For the case of an rf-SQUID, the consideration of the fluctuations of the electromagnetic field leads to the fact that the collective coordinate, ϕ, should be quantized.[12]

One must, however, not forget the fact that these collective coordinates couple strongly to the dissipative degrees of freedom of the environment, and it is imperative that we include them in any realistic discussions. This has been carried out in great detail[13] and a number of predictions have been made,[14] of which some have already received experimental verification. Except for one experiment on quantization of energy levels,[15] all others[16] have been attempts to observe decay out of a metastable well as shown in FIGURE 3b (see the papers by Washburn and Webb, and Hanggi in the present volume). There is no doubt whatsoever that our basic ideas about the quantum dynamics of the collective coordinates, $\Delta\theta$ and ϕ, are correct.

The encouraging experimental situation involving decay out of a metastable well leads us to envisage the possibility of observing quantum coherence,[17] which is a laboratory version of Schrödinger's cat (see the articles by Leggett and Tesche in the present volume). If we return for the moment to equation 10, we note that when $\phi_{ext} = \frac{1}{2}\phi_0$ and $2\pi L I_C/\phi_0 > 1$, $U(\phi)$ consists of a double well in the flux space, as shown in FIGURE 4 ($\tilde{\phi} = \phi - \frac{1}{2}\phi_0$). If there was no dissipation to worry about, one would conclude that the quantum mechanical ground state would be a linear superposition of states centered at the left well and the right well. One must recognize that the state centered at the left well corresponds to a clockwise rotation of the supercurrent and that at the right well to a counterclockwise rotation. The quantum mechanical transition between the wells requires reorganization of the macroscopic number of Cooper pairs. We shall discuss this problem in more detail later.

DISSIPATION

In problems involving quantum mechanics of macroscopic systems, it is important to understand the role of dissipation. As mentioned earlier, we expect the relevant collective coordinates to be strongly coupled to the dissipative degrees of freedom of the environment. From a calculational point of view, one needs to develop a Hamiltonian that includes the environment and its coupling to the system. This is generally a difficult task. Fortunately, considerable progress has been made in recent years.

First, it is recognized that dissipation can simply be described as an energy transfer from the system to the environment. The environment consists of infinitely many degrees of freedom with a continuum of energy levels. Thus, once the energy is transferred out, it cannot return to the system on a physical time scale. An appropriate formalism was described by Feynman and Vernon.[18] Because environment degrees of freedom are not of primary interest (only their effect in perturbing the system is of interest), these degrees of freedom are integrated out, thus leaving us with a clear-cut problem involving the system variable only. In the path integral formulation, one thus arrives at an effective nonlocal action. The nonlocality arises due to the interaction with the environment. The expectation value of any operator that depends on the system variable alone can equally well be calculated with the help of the effective action. More accurately, such an expectation value is to be interpreted as the expectation value of the operator acting on the system and, simultaneously, the unit operator acting on the environment.

In superconducting systems, dissipation has been taken into account by starting from a microscopic Hamiltonian where BCS quasiparticles act as the reservoir degrees of freedom.[19] However, often the environment is too complicated to be accounted for in this way. Caldeira and Leggett[13] have argued that in such cases it may be useful to take a more general approach. They have stressed that if the situation is such that any one degree of freedom is weakly perturbed, the environment can be considered as a collection of harmonic oscillators. The remaining task is to fix the parameters such that one recovers the phenomenological RSJ equation in the classical limit. In other words, by knowing experimentally the parameters that enter equations 8 and 9, one can predict what the quantum dynamics of the system are going to be. It is difficult to do justice to their work in such short a space and the reader is urged to consult their paper. One point needs special attention, though. We should explore how general the idea of a harmonic oscillator heat bath is. This question has been partially investigated in some recent papers.[20,21] The point of view taken by Chang and Chakravarty[21] has been to assert, following Landau, that the weakly excited states of a macroscopic system can be described in terms of quasiparticles that need not of course be necessarily bosons. Thus, the case of a fermionic heat bath was given some attention. The curious feature that was discovered was that with respect to dissipation, in many aspects, but not all, the bosonic heat bath with Ohmic dissipation (see the dissipative terms in equation 8 or 9) behaves in a way very similar to the fermionic heat bath. However, an important parameter as discussed in this paper assumes a different range of values depending on the heat bath. A possible mechanism to explore the nature of the heat bath would be to perform the experiment suggested by Chakravarty and Kivelson.[22]

A LABORATORY VERSION OF SCHRÖDINGER'S CAT

Let us now return to the double well problem that is shown in FIGURE 4 and mentioned in the second section of this paper. If the flux variable were a c-number, the ground state would be twofold degenerate, corresponding to two different senses of the rotation of the supercurrent. However, considering the flux as a quantum mechanical variable and ignoring dissipation for the moment, it is easy to see that the ground state is unique and nondegenerate. If we initiate the system in one of the wells, the probability will slosh back and forth between the two wells with a frequency proportional to the tunnel splitting. Thus, the supercurrent will change the sense of rotation periodically. This, if observed, would be spectacular. For realistic estimates of the feasibility of this experiment, see the paper by Tesche in this volume. Once again, the crucial question one must investigate is the role of dissipation.

The problem of a double well coupled to a Ohmic heat bath was discussed by the present author[23] and Bray and Moore.[24] The conclusion arrived at was rather striking. It was found that for dissipation larger than a critical value, the symmetry in the ground state between the left and the right wells was spontaneously broken; that is, the ground state was twofold degenerate as in the classical case. This spontaneous symmetry breaking is a characteristic of the Ohmic heat bath. One might ask if the result then is somewhat pathological or not. To the extent that the phenomenological resistively shunted junction equation is valid, it is certainly not so. Moreover, it is only necessary that the dissipation is linear at the relevant frequency scale, that is, at the frequency scale characteristic of the tunnel splitting. In the non-Ohmic case, one expects the environment to quench the coherence, but not efficiently enough to cause a breakdown of symmetry. Later, the dynamics of the same problem was studied by Chakravarty and Leggett.[25] The case of the biased double well has also been recently studied.[26] The literature on this topic has grown immensely, some of which is discussed in a recent paper.[27]

I want to end this section by noting that as far as the quantum coherence in a SQUID is concerned, we have by now a reasonably accurate set of predictions that can

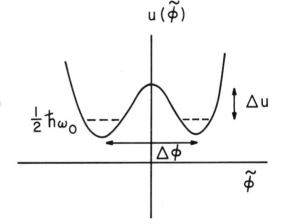

FIGURE 4. Symmetric double well in a SQUID.

be tested. In particular, for a region of the parameter space, the coherent oscillations should persist. This is as far as we can get to the laboratory version of the Schrödinger's cat.

From the point of view of the Josephson effect, we have learned something novel: the supercurrent carrying state can be stabilized in the presence of dissipation. This is a new concept of the theory of superconductivity. Were it not for dissipation, the quantum fluctuations of the flux and the phase variables would have wiped out the Josephson effect. The decay of supercurrent has been a fascinating topic for a long time.[28] The present ideas have added a new dimension to it. In a recent experiment,[29] it has been found that in granular superconductors where the grains are coupled by the Josephson mechanism, the onset of global superconductivity depends critically on dissipation. The theoretical explanation[30] involves ideas similar to the ones discussed here. It is my belief that further research on the role of dissipation on the onset of superconductivity is likely to produce many surprises.

CONCLUSION

In this paper, I have tried to give a survey of the interesting issues in the subject of macroscopic quantum tunneling and the related problems in superconducting systems. There is one aspect, though, that I would have loved to touch upon, but I do not have the space to discuss: namely, the connection between spontaneous symmetry breaking and quantum measurement theory.[31]

REFERENCES

1. LEGGETT, A. J. 1984. Macroscopic quantum tunneling and related effects in Josephson systems. *In* Percolation, Localization, and Superconductivity. NATO ASI series B, vol. 109. A. M. Goldman & S. Wolf, Eds.: 1–41. Plenum. New York; AMBEGAOKAR, V. 1984. Quantum dynamics of superconductors and tunneling between superconductors. *In* Percolation, Localization, and Superconductivity. NATO ASI series B, vol. 109. A. M. Goldman & S. Wolf, Eds.: 43–63 Plenum. New York; CHAKRAVARTY, S. 1984. Physica **126B:** 385–391; CHAKRAVARTY, S. 1986. *In* Fundamental Questions in Quantum Mechanics. Gordon & Breach. In press.
2. LEGGETT, A. J. 1980. Prog. Theor. Phys. **69**(suppl.): 80–100.
3. TINKHAM, M. 1975. Introduction to Superconductivity. McGraw–Hill. New York.
4. FEYNMAN, R. P. *et al.* 1965. The Feyman Lectures in Physics. Vol. III, pp. 21–6. Addison–Wesley. Reading, Massachusetts.
5. JACKLEVIC, R. C. *et al.* 1964. Phys. Rev. Lett. **12:** 159–160.
6. BARONE, A. & G. PATERNO. 1982. Physics and Applications of the Josephson Effect. Wiley. New York. See also reference 3.
7. ANDERSON, P. W. 1984. Basic Notions of Condensed Matter Physics, pp. 229–248. Benjamin/Cumming. Menlo Park, California.
8. ANDERSON, P. W. 1964. *In* Lectures on Field Theory and the Many-Body Problem. Vol. 2. E. R. Caianiello, Ed.: 113–135. Academic Press. New York.
9. SCALAPINO, D. J. 1969. *In* Tunneling Phenomenon in Solids. E. Burstein & S. Lundqvist, Eds.: 477–518. Plenum. New York.
10. AMBEGAOKAR, V., U. ECKERN & G. SCHON. 1982. Phys. Rev. Lett. **48:** 1745–1748; ECKERN, U., G. SCHON & V. AMBEGAOKAR. 1984. Phys. Rev. **B32:** 6419–6431.
11. See LEGGETT, A. J. in references 1 and 2.
12. CHAKRAVARTY, S. 1984. Physica **126B:** 385–391.
13. CALDEIRA, A. O. & A. J. LEGGETT. 1983. Ann. Phys. N.Y. **149:** 374–456; 1984(E). Ann. Phys. N.Y. **153:** 445.
14. CHANG, L. D. & S. CHAKRAVARTY. 1984. Phys. Rev. **B29:** 130–137; 1984(E). Phys. Rev. **30:** 1566; GRABERT, H., P. OLSCHOWSKI & U. WEISS. 1985. Phys. Rev. **B32:** 3348–3351; LARKIN, A. I. & YU. N. OVCHINIKOV. 1983. Pis'ma Zh. Eksp. Teor. Fiz. **37:** 322–325. (Sov. Phys. JETP Lett. 1983. **37:** 382–385.); GRABERT, H., U. WEISS & P. HANGGI. 1984. Phys. Rev. Lett. **53:** 1787–1790; GRABERT, H. & U. WEISS. 1984. Phys. Rev. Lett. **53:** 1787–1790; WAXMAN, D. & A. J. LEGGETT. 1985. Phys. Rev. **B32:** 4450–4468; see also reference 13 for the first important calculation.
15. MARTINIS, J. M., M. H. DEVORET & J. CLARKE. 1985. Phys. Rev. Lett. **55:** 1543–1546. A theoretical analysis is given by BIALEK, W., S. CHAKRAVARTY & S. KIVELSON. 1985. Preprint no. NSF-ITP-85-114. Univ. of California Santa Barbara. Santa Barbara, California.
16. VOSS, R. F. & R. A. WEBB. 1981. Phys. Rev. Lett. **47:** 265–268; JACKEL, L. D. *et al.* 1981. Phys. Rev. Lett. **47:** 697–700; WASHBURN, S. *et al.* 1985. Phys. Rev. Lett. **54:** 2712–2715; SCHWARTZ, D. B. *et al.* 1985. Phys. Rev. Lett. **55:** 1547–1550; DEVORET, M. H. *et al.* 1985. Phys. Rev. Lett. **55:** 1908–1911.
17. DEN BOER, W. & R. DE BRUYN OUBOTER. 1980. Physica. **98B:** 185–187. The measurement issue is clearly spelled out in LEGGETT, A. J. & A. K. GARG. 1985. Phys. Rev. Lett. **54:** 857–860.

18. FEYNMAN, R. P. & F. L. VERNON, JR. 1963. Ann. Phys. N.Y. **24:** 118–173.
19. See reference 10.
20. GUINEA, F. 1984. Phys. Rev. Lett. **53:** 1268–1271.
21. CHANG, L-D. & S. CHAKRAVARTY. 1985. Phys. Rev. **B31:** 154–164.
22. CHAKRAVARTY, S. & S. KIVELSON. 1983. Phys. Rev. Lett. **50:** 1811–1814; **51:** 1109(E); 1985. Phys. Rev. **B32:** 76–87.
23. CHAKRAVARTY, S. 1982. Phys. Rev. Lett. **49:** 681–684.
24. BRAY, A. J. & M. A. MOORE. 1982. Phys. Rev. Lett. **49:** 1545–1549.
25. CHAKRAVARTY, S. & A. J. LEGGETT. 1984. Phys. Rev. Lett. **52:** 5–8.
26. FISHER, M. P. & A. T. DORSEY. 1985. Phys. Rev. Lett. **54:** 1609–1612; GRABERT, H. & U. WEISS. 1985. Phys. Rev. Lett. **54:** 1605–1608.
27. LEGGETT, A. J. et al. Rev. Mod. Phys. To be published.
28. LANGER, J. S. & V. AMBEGAOKAR. 1967. Phys. Rev. **164:** 498–510.
29. ORR, B. G. et al. 1986. Phys. Rev. Lett. **56:** 378–381.
30. CHAKRAVARTY, S. et al. 1986. Phys. Lett. **56:** 2303–2306.
31. ZIMANYI, G. T. & K. VLADAR. 1986. Symmetry breaking and measurement theory. Preprint. Institut für Festkörperforschung der Kernforschungsanlage Jülich, Jülich, Federal Republic of Germany.

Schrödinger's Cat: A Realization in Superconducting Devices

C. D. TESCHE

IBM Research Laboratory
Yorktown Heights, New York 10598

INTRODUCTION

The purpose of this paper is to describe in some detail a feasible experiment that would test for macroscopic quantum coherence effects in a single junction SQUID. Following Tony Leggett's original suggestion that superconducting devices (and in particular, rf SQUIDs) might be appropriate systems for the observation of macroscopic quantum effects, considerable theoretical analysis of the behavior of these devices in the quantum limit has been performed.[1-8] In addition, several experiments have demonstrated macroscopic quantum behavior in superconducting devices that are natural prerequisites for the observation of macroscopic quantum coherence effects.[9-14] Although these experiments require careful isolation from environmental noise, the direct observation of coherent macroscopic behavior requires an even greater degree of isolation from dissipative elements (both within the SQUID and in the environment) than has been necessary in the previous experiments. As a result, it is essential to analyze not only the behavior of the rf SQUID as a dissipative two-state system, but also to analyze the action of the measurement apparatus and environment on the coherent system.

The following problems must be solved. First, we must determine device parameters for the rf SQUID that are realizable given present fabrication capabilities. Next, the effects of dissipation in the environment must be modeled and appropriate shielding must be designed. Finally, a measurement strategy must be developed such that the noise inherent in the amplification chain does not destroy the coherent oscillations of the macroscopic SQUID before the measurement occurs. The detailed analyses that have been conducted up to this time give the prospective experimentalist guidance for the resolution of the first problem. However, the second and third problems have yet to be discussed for a superconducting system. Because the isolation and measurement of a macroscopic quantum system has been the subject of intense discussion for many years, it is extremely important to continue the analysis of the experiment through the measurement stage. In order to do this, we need a well-defined, experimentally realizable system. This is of interest not only as a precursor to an actual experiment, but also because the superconducting circuit elements that are involved can be modeled using fairly simple elements. As a result, this system can be used as an object for discussion of more abstract concepts in the theory of measurement in quantum mechanics. A brief description of this measurement strategy has been presented elsewhere.[15]

36

THE RF SQUID

A widely used model for the rf SQUID is shown in FIGURE 1a. The rf SQUID consists of a loop of superconducting material interrupted by a single Josephson tunnel barrier. The SQUID loop of inductance, L, supports a macroscopic circulating current, J, whose magnitude is determined by the external flux, ϕ_x, which links the loop. The net flux, $\phi = \phi_x + LJ$, is a macroscopic variable that plays the role of the tunneling coordinate. The junction is usually described by a lumped circuit element (RSJ) model, in which the junction with critical current, I_0, is shunted by an external ohmic resistance, R, and capacitance, C.[16] The classical equation of motion for the macroscopic flux (in the absence of fluctuations) is then

$$C\ddot{\phi} + (1/R)\dot{\phi} = - \partial U/ \partial\phi ,$$

where ϕ_0 is the flux quantum. The potential, U, is given as a function of the net flux, ϕ,

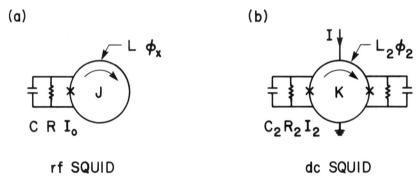

(a)

rf SQUID

(b)

dc SQUID

FIGURE 1. The RSJ model for (a) the rf SQUID and (b) the dc SQUID.

as[17]

$$U = (\phi - \phi_x)^2/2L - (I_0\phi_0/2\pi) \cos (2\pi\phi/\phi_0) . \tag{2}$$

For $1 < \beta = 2\pi LI_0/\phi_0 \lesssim 5\pi/2$ and applied flux, $\phi_x \approx \phi_0/2$, there are two wells separated by a barrier height, ΔU, as shown in FIGURE 2. The distance between the minima is $\Delta\phi$. For a symmetric potential, the orientation of the current, J, is either clockwise or counterclockwise around the loop. The frequency of small oscillations in the well is ω_0. The quality factor for the SQUID in the classical limit, $Q_j = \omega_0 RC$, determines the rate at which transient currents decay in the loop. The behavior of current biased junctions is determined by the junction hysteresis parameter, $\beta_c = 2\pi I_0 R^2 C/\phi_0$. In a SQUID with screening parameter $\beta \gtrsim 1$, $\beta_c \approx Q_j^2$.

For a double well potential at finite temperature, Johnson noise in the shunt resistance will cause the net flux in the loop to thermally activate between the two minima at a rate that depends exponentially on the barrier height.[18] At sufficiently low temperatures, the behavior of the system becomes dominated by quantum mechanical effects. In particular, the SQUID can be described as a dissipative two-state system provided that several constraints are met.[1,3] First, the wave packet describing the flux must be sufficiently localized in the well so that a semiclassical approximation for the system can be used, namely, $\lambda = (8CI_0\phi_0^3/\pi^3\hbar^2)^{1/2} \gg 1$. The SQUID parameters must be chosen such that there is a pair of states well below the barrier, $\hbar\omega_0 \ll \Delta U$. Finally, the occupation of all other states at the operating temperature, T, must be negligible: $\hbar\omega_0 \ll k_B T$. The behavior of the system is then described by a probability, $P(t) = P_L(t) - P_R(t)$. Chakravarty and Leggett have demonstrated that weakly dissipative systems at $T = 0$ undergo damped oscillations at a frequency on the order of the renormalized tunneling frequency, with a small power-law background contribution.[4]

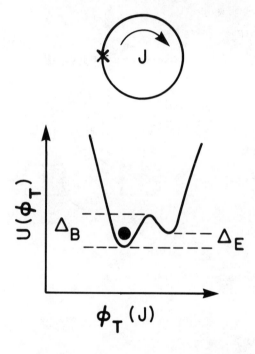

FIGURE 2. The potential energy, U, as a function of the net flux, ϕ_T, for the rf SQUID.

In the limit, $\alpha = (\Delta\phi)^2/2\pi\hbar R \ll 1$, the oscillatory part of $P(t)$ is given by

$$P_0(t) = A(\alpha) \cos (\pi\alpha\Delta t/2) \exp [-\sin (\pi\alpha\Delta t/2)], \quad (3)$$

where the tunneling angular frequency is

$$\Delta = 2\sqrt{3} \, \omega_0(S_0/2\pi\hbar)^{1/2} \exp (-S_0/\hbar) \quad (4)$$

and the action is

$$S_0/\hbar = (16/3)\Delta U/\hbar\omega_0 . \quad (5)$$

The transition into the thermal activation regime occurs at a temperature, $T^* = \hbar\Delta/\pi k_B \alpha$.[19,20] Recently, Grabert and Weiss have determined an expression for $P(t)$ as a function of temperature in the coherent oscillation regime for both a symmetric and slightly biased potential that agrees with the results of Chakravarty and Leggett in the limit, $T = 0$:[5]

$$P_0(t) = A \exp(-\Gamma_c t) \cos(\Delta_c t - \phi_c)/\cos(\phi c),$$

$$a = 1 + \tfrac{1}{2}\,\zeta(3)\alpha^3(T^*/T)^2,$$

$$\Delta_c = \pi\alpha k_B(T^{*2} - T^2)^{1/2}/\hbar, \qquad\qquad (6)$$

$$\Gamma_c = \pi\alpha k_B T/\hbar,$$

$$\varphi_c = \arcsin(T/T^*).$$

This expression can be used to estimate the stability of the dc flux bias, which must be maintained for the duration of the experiment.

In addition, there must be a constraint on the amount of external broadband flux noise. Although a calculation of photoinduced macroscopic quantum tunneling in SQUIDs under the influence of a sinusoidal applied field has been performed, an analysis of the effects of broadband noise is not yet available.[20] The following approximation is used: Johnson noise in the junction shunt resistance at high temperatures is characterized by a broadband voltage noise spectral density, $S_v = 4k_B TR$. This noise source is included directly in the lumped circuit element equations as a broadband flux noise with spectral density, $S_\phi = S_v(L/R)^2$. Thus, broadband flux noise generated by external sources inductively coupled to the SQUID loop can also be characterized by an effective temperature, $4k_B T_e = S_\phi R/L^2$. However, external noise generated by highly nonlinear sources such as a magnetometer coupled to the rf SQUID must be modeled in more detail because complex nonlinear interactions can occur. In addition, readout circuitry that is sufficiently tightly coupled to the SQUID can alter the flux bias point of the SQUID. In the absence of detailed calculation in the quantum regime, we shall require that the effective temperature be much less than the ambient temperature.

With these constraints in mind, a search of the rf SQUID parameter space was made.[15] The most difficult condition to be met is the constraint on the temperature. In order to directly observe coherent oscillations, an oscillation frequency of a few tens of megahertz and an operating temperature on the order of ten millikelvin are desirable. As a result, the junction must be extremely underdamped: $\alpha < 0.01$ and $R > 0.1$ MΩ. A word of caution is necessary at this point. At the present time, there is some uncertainty about the relationship of the parameter, "R," in the theoretical models to the fairly complex IV characteristics observed in actual junctions. Because high resistance is necessary, it is most likely that the intrinsic resistance of the junction (rather than any external ohmic shunt) must be used. For high quality niobium-lead alloy edge junctions, the subgap resistance can be on the order of 50 times greater than the resistance above the gap.[21] Furthermore, the behavior of high resistance current biased junctions can be dominated by that of the external bias lines and associated filters, rather than that of the intrinsic junction resistance.[13] As a result, values for "R" determined in other experiments may not be at all characteristic of those observed in the coherence experiment. The value of "R" must be determined for the particular junction used in the rf SQUID when it is operated in a shielded environment with the readout circuitry in place. In this case, inductively coupled lossy elements, rather than bias lead filters, are the potential problem. As we shall show later, it is possible to reduce the inductive coupling of the SQUID to the external world and thus eliminate some potential difficulties. For the purpose of this discussion, we shall assume that the resistance, "R," scales inversely with the junction critical current. We also assume that the magnitude of "R" is determined by a conservative estimate for the subgap resistance in a high quality Nb-lead alloy edge junction ($I_0R \sim 20$nA MΩ), with the caution that this assumption must be verified experimentally.

The constraint on the junction resistance forces the junction critical current below 100 nA. Fabrication uncertainties impose a variation of about 10% on the junction critical current. Because the coherent oscillation frequency is exponential in I_0, an attempt was made to reduce the dependence on the variations in I_0. The results are shown in FIGURE 3. Nominal values of $I_0 = 48$ nA, $L = 10$ nH, $C = 0.2$ pH, and $R = 0.42$ MΩ yield a coherent oscillation frequency of 18.5 MHz at $T^* = 77$ mK. The frequency of small oscillations within the well is 3.2 GHz. The SQUID loop quality factor $Q_j = 1.7 \times 10^3$. As a result, transients in the circulating current around the loop decay with a time constant that is long compared to the period of the coherent oscillations. Thus, great care must be exercised in generating the initial state of the rf SQUID.

The operating temperature must be well below T^* in order to observe several periods of oscillation. The coherent oscillation pattern for $P(t)$ is shown in FIGURE 4 as

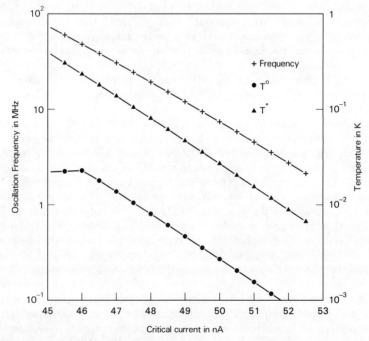

FIGURE 3. The coherent oscillation frequency, the maximum crossover temperature, T^*, and the operating temperature, T^0, as a function of the rf SQUID critical current for SQUID parameters, $L = 10$ nH, $C = 0.2$ pH, and IR = 20 MΩ.

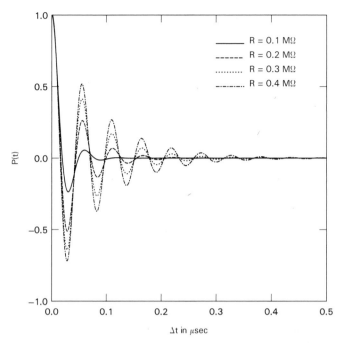

FIGURE 4. The probability, $P(t)$, as a function of elapsed time for an rf SQUID with $I_0 = 48$ nA, $L = 10$ nH, $C = 0.2$ pH, and $T^0 = 7.7$ mK for various values of the shunt resistance, R.

a function of the junction resistance, R, for $T^0 = 7.7$ mK. Provided that values of "R" on this order can be obtained, SQUIDs with device parameters sufficiently close to the nominal values can be fabricated by presently available thin-film technology with reasonable yield.[22]

THE ENVIRONMENT

In contrast to the macroscopic quantum tunneling experiments performed on current biased junctions, the dominant source of perturbations from the environment in the rf SQUID results from variations in the flux through the SQUID loop. The dependence of the oscillation pattern on the dc flux bias shift, $\Delta\phi_x$, is shown in FIGURE 5. As can be seen from the figure, a flux stability of greater than $10^{-4}\phi_0$ is required. This constrains the external magnetic field as follows: A 10-nH thin-film SQUID with a loop in the form of a square has an effective area of 0.025 square cm, which implies a field stability of much less than 0.1 pT. The tolerable broadband flux noise for the rf SQUID parameters given above must be much less than $0.01\text{fT}/\sqrt{H_z}$. These constraints can be significantly relaxed if the SQUID loop is deformed into a series of coplanar counterwound loops. The effective area of the loop is then reduced by the degree to which the individual coil areas can be balanced. This reduces the area over which the external field stability must be maintained by at least four orders of

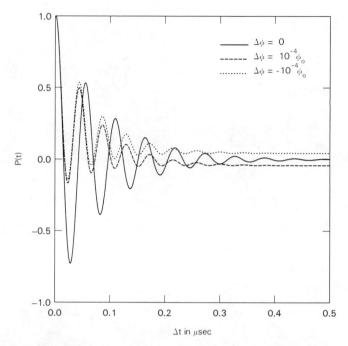

FIGURE 5. The probability, $P(t)$, as a function of elapsed time for an rf SQUID with $I_0 = 48$ nA, $R = 0.42$ MΩ, $L = 10$ nH, $C = 0.2$ pH, and $T^0 = 7.7$ mK for various values of the flux bias shift, $\Delta\phi$.

magnitude. In addition, a SQUID with a twisted coil configuration is strongly decoupled from the radiation field. The required flux stability of the isolated device can now be assured using carefully designed bulk superconducting shields. Perturbations such as blackbody radiation or changes in the state of distant massive bodies are negligible. Furthermore, undesirable inductive coupling to dissipative elements has been strongly reduced because the effective interaction length of the twisted coil SQUID is determined by the size of the small loop elements rather than the total area of the SQUID. Planar self-shielding structures of this kind have recently been used with excellent results in the design of large area monopole detectors.[23]

DC SQUID MAGNETOMETERS

The final requirement is to design a measurement apparatus that does not destroy the free oscillation of the rf SQUID before the measurement of the circulating current around the SQUID loop is initiated. The state of the rf SQUID can be determined by measuring the magnetic field generated by the screening current with a magnetometer. The most sensitive magnetometers now available are high resolution dc SQUIDs. The isolated dc SQUID consists of a superconducting loop of inductance, L_2, interrupted by two Josephson tunnel junctions (FIGURE 1b). The average voltage developed across the junctions is a function of both the net flux threading the SQUID loop and of the dc bias current, I. For bias currents below some threshold value, the behavior of the device is similar to that of the rf SQUID. The system variables are the quantum mechanical phase drops across the two junctions. We shall use the average of the two phases, δ_{dc}, and the circulating current, J_{dc}, which is determined by the difference of the two phases, as the variables for the dc SQUID. These variables develop in time like the coordinates of a particle moving in a two-dimensional potential with dissipation.[24] The potential surface resembles that of the surface of a glacial valley threaded along the floor by a chain of small pools or wells (FIGURE 6). The average slope of the valley floor is determined by the bias current, I. The slope increases with increasing bias current. The location and structure of the wells is determined by the applied flux. The pattern of wells repeats if the flux increases by ϕ_0 or if the average phase is increased by 2π.

Below threshold, the device parameters can be chosen such that the particle thermally activates between two adjacent potential wells. Brownian motion within the wells generates broadband noise in the circulating current and average phase.[24] At low temperatures, zero point motion and quantum tunneling effects become significant. The voltage developed across the junctions is proportional to the time derivative of the average phase. Thus, the time-averaged voltage for a particle trapped in a single well is zero. Brief voltage pulses are generated during transitions from one well to the next. At

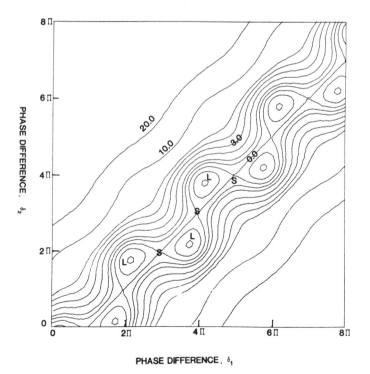

FIGURE 6. An example of a typical potential-energy contour map for a dc SQUID biased below threshold.

the threshold bias current, the slope of the valley floor has increased to the point that the particle now propagates freely down the valley floor. The output voltage and circulating current become periodic functions of time with average values that are functions of the applied flux and broadband noise components determined by Johnson noise or "quantum noise" effects. In this mode, the SQUID operates as a flux to voltage transducer that can be incorporated into a magnetometer or linear amplifier circuit.[25]

The conventional dc SQUID magnetometer can be turned on and off at the output by changing the bias current above and below threshold. The flux resolution above threshold is determined by the flux to voltage transfer function, $\partial V/\partial \phi$, and by the intrinsic broadband voltage noise at the output, S_v. The rms voltage noise is determined by the measurement bandwidth, B. The equivalent rms flux noise referred to the input is $\phi_{rms}^2 = 2LS_E B$, where the output energy factor is $S_E = S_v/2L(\partial V/\partial \phi)^2$.

The dc SQUID magnetometer is coupled to the source through a mutual inductance, $M^2 = \alpha_0^2 LL_2$. In many applications, the only important role that the mutual inductance plays is to couple the signal to the SQUID. In those cases, tight coupling is advantageous. However, in this case, the back action of the dc SQUID on the rf SQUID must be taken into consideration. The back action results from the coupling of the screening current in the dc SQUID to the rf SQUID loop through the mutual inductance. This constrains the strength of the coupling. The minimum strength of the coupling is determined as follows: The flux difference between the two states of circulating current, J, in the rf SQUID must be distinguishable in a time that is short compared to the period of the coherent oscillations. Thus, the equivalent dc SQUID flux noise at the input must be smaller than the flux change in the signal flux, $2 MJ$, for a bandwidth, $B \gg \Delta/2\pi$. This constrains the coupling constant to

$$\alpha_0^2 \gg S_E[\Delta/I_0\phi_0\gamma] , \tag{7}$$

where the term in the brackets is determined by the rf SQUID coherent oscillation frequency, Δ, and the junction critical current, I_0, and where γ is a numerical factor on the order of unity. This constraint is easily satisfied provided that a high resolution dc SQUID with an energy factor approaching $\hbar$ is used.

The maximum strength of the coupling is determined by the noise in the circulating current around the dc SQUID loop. At high temperatures, the dc SQUID output voltage and circulating current noise spectral densities, S_v and S_J, respectively, are determined by the Johnson noise in the junction shunt resistances.[25] At low temperatures, quantum effects become important.[26] Because the dc SQUID can be incorporated into a linear amplifier circuit, it is possible to derive an expression for the optimal noise temperature of the device as a function of both the voltage noise at the output and the current noise at the input. Quantum constraints on the optimal noise temperature of an arbitrary phase-preserving linear amplifier imply that $(S_E S_{E'})^{1/2} > \hbar$, where $S_{E'} = LS_J/2$ is the equivalent input energy noise factor determined by the noise in the circulating current.[27]

The effect of broadband flux noise on the rf SQUID in the classical limit is modeled as an equivalent Johnson noise source with effective temperature, T_e. If we assume that the nonlinear interaction between the two SQUIDs can be ignored, the effective noise temperature must satisfy $T_e \ll T^0$. This places a constraint on the strength of the coupling,

$$\alpha_0^2 \ll \left(\frac{1}{S_{E'}}\right)\left[\frac{\hbar^2 \Delta}{Q I_0 \phi_0 \zeta}\right], \tag{8}$$

where the first term is the effective input energy noise figure for the dc SQUID. The term in the brackets is determined by the rf SQUID parameters and ζ is a numerical factor on the order of unity.

From equations 7 and 8, we see that it is not possible in practice to detect coherent oscillations in the rf SQUID with a quantum limited dc SQUID without destroying the coherent state. In particular, the amplification of the rf SQUID signal by the dc SQUID is increased by increasing the coupling. If the amplification is sufficient to permit a determination of the state of the rf SQUID in the measurement period, then the coherent state is destroyed by the back action of the amplifier over that measurement interval. This effect makes it impossible to perform repeated measurements on an rf SQUID in a coherent state, but it does not necessarily preclude the possibility of observing coherent behavior in a system that has been initiated by some other means. The real problem with a dc SQUID detection scheme is that it is impossible to turn off the back action of the SQUID during the time before the measurement is initiated. Coherent oscillations are observed only if the rf SQUID is permitted to develop freely during some period of time, independent of the action of the measurement system. Thus, it must be possible to turn off the back action of the dc SQUID during this time. Physically removing the measurement system is impractical. Turning off the bias current to the dc SQUID will eliminate the possiblity of detecting the state of the rf SQUID because the average output voltage will fall to zero. However, as we have seen in the beginning of this section, the state of the dc SQUID at subthreshold bias current is described by that of a particle trapped in a two-dimensional well. Although the net velocity (and thus the net voltage) is zero, the particle undergoes Brownian motion within the well. As a result, the current noise spectral density is not zero. In fact, for a conventional dc SQUID with screening factor near unity, the current noise in the well is relatively unchanged over that of a device biased in the voltage state.[24] In the quantum limit, the behavior of the combined dc and rf SQUID system is more appropriately described as the tunneling of a particle in a three-dimensional potential. The destruction of the coherent state is then a result of the coupling to the dissipative elements in the dc SQUID, which has a typical junction shunt resistance of less than a few tens of ohms.

THRESHOLD SQUID MEASUREMENT SYSTEM

Although the dc SQUID cannot be used directly as the first stage of a measurement system for the rf SQUID in the coherent state, it is an appropriate first element in a linear amplifier chain. There are two reasons for this: First, because nearly quantum limited devices can be fabricated conveniently on chip with the rf SQUID. Second, the conventional dc SQUID has a very low reverse transfer function. Thus, noise generated by sources following the dc SQUID appear at the input to the dc SQUID as noise currents of negligible amplitude. As a result, if the inductive coupling to the input of the dc SQUID is reduced below that determined by the constraint on the back action noise of the dc SQUID itself, then in most cases no further noise sources in the amplifier chain need be considered. Let us suppose that the coupling to the dc SQUID has been chosen such that the dc SQUID back action on the rf SQUID is negligible. The problem now is to devise a method for decreasing the measurement bandwidth because the signal-to-noise ratio at the output of a weakly coupled SQUID can only be improved by increasing the length of time over which the dc SQUID signal is averaged. This implies that a method must be devised for slowing down the coherent oscillations abruptly at the moment when the measurement interval begins. This can be accomplished by coupling the rf SQUID to an intermediate superconducting structure that is equipped with a switch. When the intermediate structure is "off," the coherent oscillations of the rf SQUID should proceed as before. When the switch is "on," the combined system should undergo a transition into one of a pair of very stable states that can be distinguished by the dc SQUID magnetometer. There are several possibilities. One approach is to alter the parameters of the rf SQUID. This technique, although relatively straightforward, has the disadvantage of compromising the isolation of the rf SQUID from the environment. Another approach is to interpose another two-state system whose properties can be varied externally between the rf and dc SQUIDs. We shall discuss this possibility in some detail.

An appropriate two-state system that can be coupled inductively to both the rf and dc SQUID is a dc SQUID threshold magnetometer. This is just a current biased dc SQUID operated below threshold. The external flux bias is chosen such that there are two distinct states available to the system. The effect of the rf SQUID screening current on the dc SQUID potential energy is sketched in FIGURE 7. The dc SQUID potential is indicated in one dimension only. The behavior of the combined system can be described by the motion of a particle moving in a three-dimensional potential with dissipation. However, for the purpose of this discussion, we shall approximate the

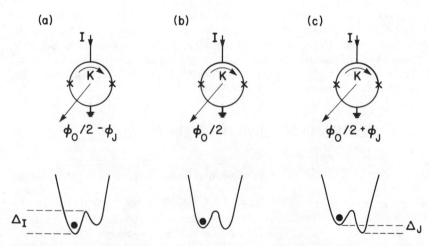

FIGURE 7. Sketch of the effect on the dc SQUID potential of the rf SQUID screening current, J. In this figure, the dc SQUID is in the "off" state. The barrier height is large.

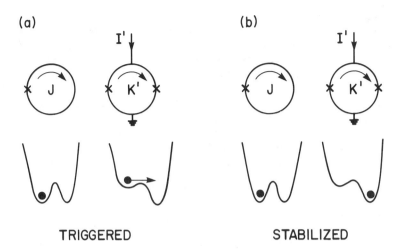

FIGURE 8. Sketch of the effect on the dc SQUID potential for a dc SQUID in the "on" configuration. In (a), the dc SQUID is in an initial state that becomes unstable. In (b), the dc SQUID is in an initial state that is stabilized. In both figures, only the final state of the dc SQUID is drawn.

motion of the system by the interplay between the two one-dimensional potentials shown in the figure. The relative depth of the dc SQUID potential wells, ΔJ, depends on the orientation of the circulating current in the rf SQUID as shown. The bias flux generated by the rf SQUID is $\pm\phi_J$. The external flux and current bias points and operating temperature are chosen such that the threshold magnetometer does not undergo a transition between the two states for either value of incremental flux bias generated by the rf SQUID. This is the state of the threshold magnetometer when the switch is "off."

The state of the threshold magnetometer when the switch is "on" is shown in FIGURE 8. The bias current to the dc SQUID has been increased to I'. The barrier has been reduced to the point that the perturbing flux generated by the rf SQUID is sufficient to cause a transition in the dc SQUID, provided that the dc SQUID has been initiated into a state that is destabilized by the rf SQUID flux (FIGURE 8a). The dc SQUID screening current after the increase in the bias current is K'. In FIGURE 8b, the initial state of the dc SQUID was chosen such that the rf SQUID flux bias stabilizes the state of the dc SQUID. No transition in the dc threshold SQUID occurs. Thus, the state of the rf SQUID can be made to be reflected in the presence or absence of a switching event in the dc SQUID. Although it is possible to use a single threshold SQUID as a pointer to indicate the state of the rf SQUID, the stability of the system is improved by using two threshold magnetometers biased in opposition. This addition to the measurement scheme was suggested by A. Peres. This scheme has the additional property of providing redundancy in the measurement because one and only one of the dc SQUIDs should be triggered.

The back action of the threshold magnetometer on the rf SQUID is sketched in FIGURE 9. The threshold SQUID circulating currrent, K, shifts the flux bias point of the rf SQUID. A dc offset can be compensated by altering the flux bias point of the rf

SQUID. Broadband noise generated by motion within the potential well of the threshold SQUID is characterized by an effective temperature as before. The coupling to the threshold SQUID is adjusted such that the effect of the threshold SQUID broadband noise is negligible. Because the threshold SQUID does not act as a linear amplifier, a decrease in the coupling need not be compensated for by an increase in the measurement bandwidth, which was the case with the conventional dc SQUID magnetometer. Thus, in FIGURE 9a, the back action of the threshold SQUID in the "off" state can be made negligible. In FIGURE 9b, we see that the switching of the threshold SQUID circulating current acts so as to enhance the stability of the rf SQUID. In this configuration, the threshold SQUID is "on." The coherent oscillations in the rf SQUID are effectively frozen due to the large splitting between the wells $(\Delta_{K'})$.

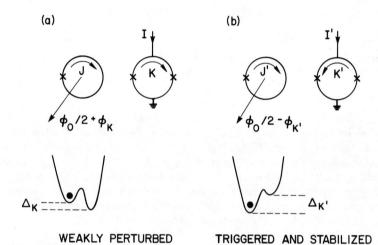

FIGURE 9. Sketch of the effect on the rf SQUID potential of the dc SQUID screening current. In (a), the initial state of the threshold dc SQUID weakly perturbs the rf SQUID potential. The rf SQUID remains in the left-hand well. In (b), the dc SQUID has been triggered. The final dc SQUID current now acts so as to stabilize the rf SQUID in the left-hand well.

A fairly detailed analysis of the interaction between the rf and threshold SQUID can be undertaken based on the results available from the thermal activation model for the dc SQUID provided that the system is approximated as a one-dimensional system interacting with a two-dimensional system through the intermediary of the linked flux. However, the system actually behaves as a unit that should be described in terms of a single three-dimensional potential energy. The external switch alters the form of this potential from one in which the dominant motion is coherent oscillation along the rf SQUID coordinate to one in which the new well structure does not permit coherent oscillations over the time scale of the experiment. A careful analysis of this behavior would require expressions for coherent behavior in a multidimensional potential, including the effects of a change in form of the potential. The time scale of this change is fast compared to the coherent oscillation period and to the characteristic period of oscillation in the well, but it is slow compared to the decay time of current transients in the loop.

CONCLUSIONS

A description of an experimental strategy to test for macroscopic quantum coherence effects in rf SQUIDs has been discussed. Isolation from dissipative elements within the SQUID requires the use of a high quality junction. Isolation from dissipative elements in the environment is a consequence of the proposed planar, self-shielding geometry, and of the use of conventional superconducting shields. Isolation from the dissipative elements in a linear amplifier chain used to display the state of the rf SQUID to the experimentalist may be achieved by the interposition of a two-state system that can be switched off and on externally. The two-state system freezes the coherent oscillations of the rf SQUID, amplifies the signal, and isolates the rf SQUID from broadband noise in the amplifier chain.

ACKNOWLEDGMENTS

It is a pleasure to acknowledge many stimulating discussions with A. J. Leggett, who has made numerous valuable suggestions regarding this work. In addition, I would like to thank S. Chakravarty, A. Peres, H. Grabert, W. Gallagher, M. Fisher, and D. Fisher for a series of most useful and informative conversations.

REFERENCES

1. LEGGETT, A. J. 1980. Prog. Theor. Phys. **69**(suppl): 80; LEGGETT, A. J. Percolation, Localization, and Superconductivity, vol. 109. A. M. Goldman & S. Wolf, Eds. Plenum. New York.
2. KURKIJÄRVI, J. 1980. In SQUID-80. H. D. Hahlbohm & H. Lübbig, Eds.: 247. de Gruyter. Berlin.
3. CALDEIRA, A. O. & A. J. LEGGETT. 1981. Phys. Rev. Lett. **46**: 211; 1983. Ann. Phys. **149**: 374.
4. CHAKRAVARTY, S. & A. J. LEGGETT. 1984. Phys. Rev. Lett. **52**: 5.
5. GRABERT, H. & U. WEISS. 1984. Phys. Rev. Lett. **53**: 1787.
6. LEGGETT, A. J., S. CHAKRAVARTY, A. T. DORSEY, M. P. A. FISHER, A. GARG & W. ZWERGER. 1985. Preprint.
7. LARKIN, A. I. & YU. N. OVCHINNIKOV. 1984. Zh. Eksp. Theor. Fiz. **86**: 719. (JETP **59**: 420.)
8. GRABERT, H., U. WEISS & P. HANGGI. 1984. Phys. Rev. Lett. **52**: 2193.
9. DEN BOER, W. R. & R. DE BRUYN OUBOTER. 1983. Physica **98B**: 185; BOL, D. W., R. VAN WEELDEREN & R. DE BRUYN OUBOTER. 1983. Physica **122B**: 1.
10. JACKEL, L. D., J. P. GORDON, E. L. HU, R. E. HOWARD, L. A. FETTER, D. M. TENNANT, R. W. EPWORTH & J. KURKIJÄRVI. 1981. Phys. Rev. Lett. **47**: 697.
11. VOSS, R. F. & R. A. WEBB. 1981. Phys. Rev. Lett. **47**: 265.
12. SCHWARTZ, D. B., B. SEN, C. N. ARCHIE, A. K. JAIN & J. E. LUKENS. 1985. Phys. Rev. Lett. **55**: 1547.
13. DEVORET, M. H., J. M. MARTINIS & J. CLARKE. 1985. Phys. Rev. Lett. **55**: 1908.
14. WASHBURN, S., R. A. WEBB, R. F. VOSS & S. M. FARIS. 1985. Phys. Rev. Lett. **54**: 2696.
15. TESCHE, C. D. 1985. Proceedings of the Third International Conference on Superconducting Quantum Devices (IC SQUID). Berlin.

16. STUART, W. C. 1968. Appl. Phys. Lett. **12:** 277; MCCUMBER, D. E. 1968. J. Appl. Phys. **39:** 3113.
17. KURKIJÄRVI, J. 1972. Phys. Rev. **B6:** 832.
18. KRAMERS, H. A. 1940. Physica **7:** 284.
19. GARG, A. 1985. Preprint; LEGGETT, A. J. Private communication.
20. CHAKRAVARTY, S. & S. KIVELSON. 1983. Phys. Rev. Lett. **50:** 1811.
21. GALLAGHER, W. J., S. I. RAIDER & R. E. DRAKE. 1983. IEEE Trans. Magn. MAG-19 **3:** 807.
22. GALLAGHER, W. J., S. I. RAIDER, A. KLEINSASSER & W. STASIAK. Private communication.
23. TESCHE, C. D., C. C. CHI, C. C. TSUEI & P. CHAUDHARI. 1983. Appl. Phys. Lett. **43:** 384.
24. TESCHE, C. D. 1979. J. Low Temp. Phys. **44:** 119.
25. TESCHE, C. D. & J. CLARKE. 1977. J. Low Temp. Phys. **29:** 301.
26. KOCH, R. H., D. J. VAN HARLINGEN & J. CLARKE. 1981. Appl. Phys. Lett. **38:** 723.
27. TESCHE, C. D. 1982. Appl. Phys. Lett. **41:** 490.

Macroscopic Quantum Tunneling at Finite Temperatures[a]

PETER HANGGI

Department of Physics
Polytechnic Institute of New York
Brooklyn, New York 11201

INTRODUCTION

There are a great variety of phenomena in physical, chemical, and biological sciences that are caused by transitions between locally stable states. In the absence of thermal and quantal fluctuations, no such transitions would occur; that is, the states would remain stable. Over the last few years, the common theme underlying the description of escape processes has been based on Brownian motion theory. In adapting this theme, the motion of the principal degrees of freedom is treated explicitly, while the interactions with the other degrees of freedom, including those of the environment (heat baths) coupled to the system of interest, are represented by frictional forces and random noise. The noise represents the key input, thus allowing the system to get away from preferred states of local stability. At high temperatures, thermal activation is the dominant process wherein a particle hops over the intervening potential barrier. This process has been studied in its various complexities in great detail over the last two decades.[1,2] When the temperature is lowered, thermally activated hopping processes become rarer and the effect of quantum tunneling becomes increasingly important.

Mainly inspired by ideas of Anthony Leggett,[3,4] there has been renewed interest in the quantum dynamics of a system where dissipation is important. In particular, there is the problem of low temperature tunneling and coherence of macroscopic quantum variables. These processes are necessarily also subject to dissipative forces. Ideal experimental systems where the predicted phenomena might be observable are the decay of the zero-voltage state in a current biased Josephson junction, or the fluxoid quantum transitions in a single junction superconducting quantum interference device (SQUID) ring. In the first case, the macroscopic quantum variable is given by the phase difference across the junction, while in the latter case, the appropriate macroscopic variable is the magnetic flux trapped through the ring. Encouraged by a set of recent experiments[5-7] that are in qualitative agreement with theory, this field has seen many rapid new developments.[2,8,9] Caldeira and Leggett[3] have shown that the tunneling probability at zero temperature is strongly affected by the dissipation that results in a strong suppression of the decay rate. Furthermore, at finite temperatures, Grabert, Weiss, and Hanggi[10] found a drastic change of the temperature dependence of the tunneling probability in the presence of dissipation. Apart from the phenomenon of macroscopic quantum tunneling, other macroscopic quantum effects have recently

[a]This research was supported by the Joint Service Electronics Program, Contract Nos. F49620-85-C-0078 and F49620-82-C-0084.

been predicted. In particular, they are:

(i) the phenomenon of coherent oscillations in a symmetric[8,9,11] or in a weakly asymmetric double well[12,13] in the presence of Ohmic-like dissipation;

(ii) macroscopic energy quantization;[14]

(iii) Bloch oscillations in Josephson junctions that are driven by a weak external current.[15]

The decay of a metastable quantum state is usually referred to as "macroscopic quantum tunneling" (MQT), whereas the phenomenon of damped, coherent oscillations of a macroscopic quantum variable between two almost degenerate, distinct macroscopic states is known as "macroscopic quantum coherence"(MQC).[11] Interestingly enough, the very recent, appealing experiments by Washburn et al.[16,17] on MQT in the regime of moderate Ohmic-like friction, and by Schwartz et al.[18] in the strongly overdamped friction regime, have confirmed quantitatively many of the predicted universal temperature effects[2,9,10] of Ohmic-like dissipation. As of yet, MQC experiments[7,19] have not been carried out.

In the following, we restrict the discussion to dissipative MQT only, elaborating on the historic background, the method, the results, and a discussion of the regime of validity.

HISTORIC BACKGROUND AND STATEMENT OF THE PROBLEM

The quantum description of metastable and unstable states has been a subject of many investigations since the early days of quantum mechanics. As is well known, the description of such states gives rise to several conceptual problems that arise from the difficulty of finding a satisfactory characterization of these states. There are several methods available in the literature[20] that characterize the decay of a metastable state at zero temperature. Some of the more familiar ones are:

(a) The axiomatic S-matrix theory,[20,21] wherein one associates decay rates in a one-to-one correspondence with poles of the S-matrix close to the real axis on the unphysical sheet of the energy Riemann surface, provided that the S-matrix can be analytically continued there.

(b) A time-dependent wave function approach, whereby one considers the outgoing scattering wave near a resonance energy.[20,22] In this case, there occurs a typical time delay, $t_D = 2/\Gamma$, in the arrival of the scattered wave of the order of the inverse decay rate, Γ, with respect to the case in which no resonance occurs.

(c) A dynamical semigroup approach for the evolution of the density operator.[23]

The approaches in (a) and (b) are not readily extended to finite temperatures and to situations where the interactions with the environment become important. For the following, we should also remind ourselves that a pure exponential decay at all times can only occur if a rescattering from the decay products (backscattering) were to be absent. However, the rescattering phenomenon cannot be forbidden unless one chooses a Hamiltonian that is not bounded from below. Khalfin[24] has pointed out, by use of a fundamental theorem of Paley and Wiener,[25] that the quantum nondecay probability,

$P(t)$, cannot be purely exponential for very large times if the minimum of the energy spectrum of the Hamiltonian is bounded from below at $E_{min} \neq -\infty$. Moreover, the quantum nondecay probability then also possesses a vanishing derivative at the origin of time evolution; that is, $P(t)$ is also not of exponential form for very short times. Throughout the rest of the paper, therefore, we will focus our attention only on the decay law at intermediate times for which the decay law has approximately exponential form. In practice, this intermediate time regime is very large;[20] it usually extends over a time scale at which 99% of the reduction in $P(t)$ has occurred already.

Over the last two decades, probably the most developed theory to describe dissipative quantum mechanics[26] at finite temperatures has been the semigroup approach.[23] This type of method has been very popular in describing damping phenomena in nonlinear optics[27-29] and in spin relaxation theory.[29] However, these dissipative semigroup methods treat the coupling to the environment perturbatively. This restricts the treatment only to the weak damping regime, where the largest damping coefficient, γ, typically obeys[29]

$$\gamma \ll \omega_0, \quad \hbar\gamma \ll kT. \tag{1}$$

Here, ω_0 is the smallest frequency typical for reversible motion. In a tunneling system, ω_0 may differ from zero just by the tunnel splitting. Thus, the first inequality is violated already for very weak damping. Furthermore, macroscopic tunneling phenomena occur at extreme low temperatures; that is, the second inequality is then also violated for an appreciable amount of dissipation. Hence, for tunneling systems, a more accurate description of dissipation is needed.

THE FUNCTIONAL INTEGRAL APPROACH

As is well known, tunneling problems are advantageously treated in terms of complex-time path integrals.[2,3,9] A detailed description of all aspects of this method is certainly beyond the scope of this article. Here, therefore, I will confine myself to a brief outline only, wherein I will present the main ingredients of the method. First, let us consider the partition function,

$$Z = \text{tr} \exp(-\beta H), \quad \beta = 1/(kT). \tag{2}$$

Following Feynman,[30] this quantity can be expressed (without having to refer to any dubious analytic continuation tricks) in the form of a (Euclidian) functional path integral,

$$Z = \int \mathcal{D}q(\tau) \exp\{-(S_E[q(\tau)]/\hbar)\}. \tag{3}$$

The integral in equation 3 runs over all paths that are periodic with period $\theta = \hbar\beta$. Each path is weighted by the Euclidian action, S_E. For our applications, we also must account for the dissipation being induced by the coupling of the tunneling coordinate to the heat bath. In doing so, we start out from the functional integral expression in full phase-space of particle plus environment. Furthermore, we assume that the environmental degrees of freedom couple bilinearly to the tunneling coordinate. If we present the environmental degrees (bath modes) by a set of harmonic oscillator modes, one succeeds in integrating out the bath modes exactly.[3,30] This procedure leaves one with an effective action that models the influence of dissipation by a nonlocal term. For Ohmic dissipation,

$$\ddot{q} = -\frac{1}{M}\frac{\partial V}{\partial q} - \gamma\dot{q}, \tag{4}$$

so the result obtained for the effective (Euclidian) action is[9,10]

$$S_E[q] = \int_{-\theta/2}^{\theta/2} d\tau[\tfrac{1}{2}M\dot{q}^2 + V(q)] + \tfrac{1}{2}\int_{-\theta/2}^{\theta/2} d\tau \int_{-\theta/2}^{\theta/2} d\tau'\, k(\tau - \tau')q(\tau)q(\tau'). \tag{5}$$

The first term describes the reversible motion of the particle in the absence of an environmental coupling. The second nonlocal term, given here in the form used by Grabert *et al.*,[10] describes the influence of dissipation. For the Ohmic dissipation in equation 4, it has the explicit form,[9,10]

$$k(\tau) = \frac{M}{\theta}\sum_{n=-\infty}^{n=+\infty}|\nu_n|\,\gamma\exp(i\nu_n\tau), \quad \theta = \hbar\beta, \tag{6a}$$

with

$$\int_{-\theta/2}^{\theta/2} k(\tau)\,d\tau = 0, \tag{6b}$$

and $\nu_n = n2\pi/\theta$ being the Matsubara frequency. In addition, the dissipative, nonlocal part can alternatively be recast in the form used by Bray and Moore,[11]

$$-\tfrac{1}{4}\int_{-\theta/2}^{\theta/2} d\tau \int_{-\theta/2}^{\theta/2} d\tau'\, k(\tau - \tau')\,[q(\tau) - q(\tau')]^2, \tag{6c}$$

which reveals explicitly the translational invariance of the dissipative part of the effective action.

Instead of the presented Euclidian (imaginary-time) formulation, a real-time formulation, being necessary for the problem of MQC, can also be used. This objective is advantageously treated by use of Feynman-Vernon theory.[31,32] Let $P_o(q)$ be the probability density of the tunneling particle in configuration space, q, at initial time, $t = 0$. Then, the probability, $P_t(q)$, at time, t, may be recast in the form of a double path integral,[12,32]

$$P_t(q) = \int \mathcal{D}q \int \mathcal{D}q' \exp\{i(S_o[q] - S_o[q'])/\hbar\} \cdot \exp(i\phi[q,q']/\hbar) \cdot P_o(q_o), \tag{7a}$$

where the integral is over all paths of $q(s), q'(s)$, and $0 \le s \le t$, with $q(0) = q'(0) = q_o$; $q(t) = q'(t) = q$, and q_o being integrated over. S_o denotes the unperturbed (Minkowskian) action,

$$S_o[q] = \int_0^t ds\,\{1/2\,M\dot{q}^2(s) - V[q(s)]\}. \tag{7b}$$

For Ohmic dissipation, the influence functional, $\phi[q,q']$, is given by[12,32]

$$\phi[q,q'] = \int_0^t ds \int_0^s ds'\,[\dot{q}(s) - \dot{q}'(s)]$$

$$\cdot [Q(s - s')\,\dot{q}(s') - Q^*(s - s')\,\dot{q}'(s')], \tag{7c}$$

where

$$Q(s) = \frac{M\gamma}{\pi} \ln \{(\hbar\beta\,\omega_0/\pi) \sinh (s\pi/\hbar\beta)\} + 1/2\,iM\gamma, \tag{7d}$$

and $\omega_0^2 = V''(q_{\min})/M$ denotes the angular frequency at the well bottom. Both the Euclidian-time formulation (equations 3 and 5) and the real-time representation (equation 7) are suitable starting points to discuss tunneling phenomena in the presence of dissipative interactions.

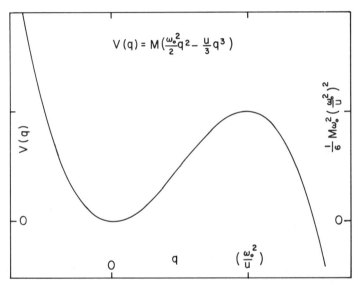

FIGURE 1. The metastable potential field, $V(q) = M\,[\tfrac{1}{2}\omega_0^2 q^2 - \tfrac{1}{3}uq^3]$, used in the text. The top of the barrier is located at $q_b = \omega_0^2/u$.

THE TUNNELING RATE

Now we are prepared enough to discuss the MQT decay in a metastable potential field, $V(q)$, of the form depicted in FIGURE 1. Initially, the particle is located near $q = 0$. The free energy, F, of the particle is then given by (see equation 3)

$$F = - kT \ln Z = - kT \ln \{\int \mathcal{D}q \exp (-S_E[q]/\hbar)\}, \tag{8}$$

with S_E given as in equations 5 and 6. The state near $q = 0$ is metastable if its lifetime, $\tau_0 = \Gamma^{-1}$, is long compared to all other characteristic time scales that describe the relaxation towards the locally stable state at $q = 0$. Keeping this situation in mind, it turns out that the functional integral in equation 8 is not real, but possesses an exponentially small imaginary part that is proportional to the decay rate, Γ. This fact should, of course, not come as too big of a surprise. After all, we are attempting to compute a decay rate that is not part of the spectrum of a Hamiltonian that is bounded from below. This same difficulty has already been seen in Langer's picture modeling classical nucleation.[33] For the problem of quantum decay at zero temperature and vanishing dissipation, Callan and Coleman[34] beautifully popularized Langer's technique. They explained that the free energy can still be defined if one uses an analytic continuation from a stable to an unstable situation. An evaluation of the integral in equation 8 can be obtained by summing the contributions of the paths that make the Euclidian action (equation 5) stationary or almost stationary. As is evident from equation 5, the Euclidian action is stationary for those paths that are solutions of the classical equation of motion in an inverted potential, $V(q) \rightarrow - V(q)$; that is,

$$M\ddot{q}_B = \frac{\partial V}{\partial q_B} + \int_{-\theta/2}^{\theta/2} d\tau' \, k(\tau - \tau') q_B(\tau') \tag{9}$$

with $q_B(\tau)$ obeying the periodic boundary condition of

$$q_B(\tau = -\tfrac{1}{2}\theta) = q_B(\tau = \tfrac{1}{2}\theta). \tag{10}$$

Because of equation 6b, we also observe that equation 9 possesses two trivial solutions: $q_1(\tau) = 0$, where the particle just sits on top of the inverted potential, $-V(q)$, and $q_2(\tau) \equiv q_b = \omega_0^2/u$ (see FIGURE 1), where the particle is located at the minimum of the well of $-V(q)$. Equation 9 possesses a nontrivial solution at sufficiently low temperatures, T, below a certain crossover temperature, T_o:[10,35,36]

$$T_o = (\hbar/2\pi k) \, [(\omega_b^2 + \tfrac{1}{4}\gamma^2)^{1/2} - \tfrac{1}{2}\gamma], \quad \omega_b^2 = -V''(q_b)/M. \tag{11}$$

At temperatures, $T < T_o$, the solution, $q_B(\tau)$ (see equation 9), describes an oscillating motion in the classically forbidden regime. Coleman has coined the name "bounce" for this particular tunneling trajectory. In FIGURE 2, we depict this bounce solution for the potential field in FIGURE 1 at various temperatures. Below $T < T_o$, the trivial solution, $q_2(\tau) = q_b$, can be disregarded. FIGURE 3 shows the "entrance" and the "exit" points of the bounce solution. The difference in energy between these two reference points may then be identified with the energy loss in quantum tunneling.[37] At zero temperature, this energy loss is always negative, and it has the characteristic feature that it saturates for increasing strength of dissipation.[37] At finite temperatures, however, the particle may lose or gain energy in tunneling across the potential barrier.[38]

The detailed analysis shows that the solutions of $q_B(\tau)$, $T < T_o$ (or $q = q_b$ for $T > T_o$), are not minima of the action S_E, but represent a saddle-point solution. This simply means that there is one fluctuation mode in function space with respect to which the bounce is a maximum of the action. This characteristic fluctuation mode thus has a negative eigenvalue. This obviously plagues the evaluation of the partition function. What is needed here is an analytical continuation, mentioned above, where the integral of the unstable (negative eigenvalue) mode is distorted in the complex plane so that it passes through the saddle point and then into the complex plane.[33,34] If we observe that the canonical operator, $\exp(-\beta H)$, is the evolution operator for imaginary times, $\tau = -i\hbar\beta$, we find that with a decay rate of Γ, that is,

$$\tau H \rightarrow \tau(H - \tfrac{1}{2}i\hbar\Gamma), \tag{12}$$

the exponentially small complex part of the free energy obeys the relation,[2,9,35–39]

$$\Gamma = -(2/\hbar) \, \text{Im} \, F. \tag{13}$$

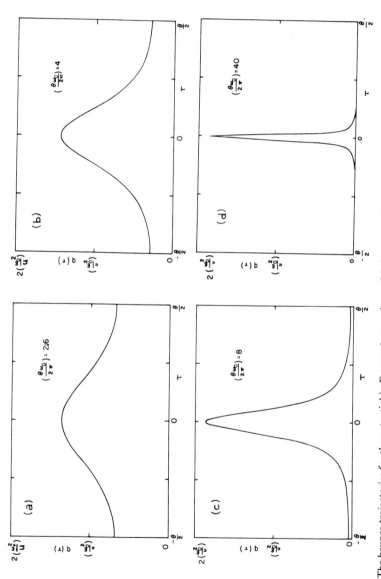

FIGURE 2. The bounce trajectories for the potential in FIGURE 1 at moderate friction strength, $\gamma/\omega_0 = 2$, for a sequence of decreasing temperatures, $\theta = \hbar\beta$.

For temperatures above T_o, a detailed evaluation of equations 8 and 13 then gives

$$\Gamma = (kT_o/\hbar) \left\{ \frac{\mathrm{Det}(\delta^2 S_E/\delta q^2) q(\tau) = 0}{|\mathrm{Det}(\delta^2 S_E/\delta q^2) q(\tau) = q_b|} \right\}^{1/2} \exp(-\beta E_b), \quad T > T_o, \quad (14)$$

where E_b denotes the barrier height. For strict Ohmic dissipation (see equation 4), this explicitly yields[35,36,40,41]

$$\Gamma = (kT_o/\hbar) \frac{\omega_0}{\omega_b} \left(\prod_{n=1}^{\infty} \frac{n^2\nu^2 + \omega_0^2 + n\nu\gamma}{n^2\nu^2 - \omega_b^2 + n\nu\gamma} \right) \exp(-\beta E_b), \quad (15)$$

where $\nu = 2\pi/\theta$, $\omega_0^2 = V''(q = 0)/M$, and $\omega_b^2 = -V''(q_b)/M$. The above result can also

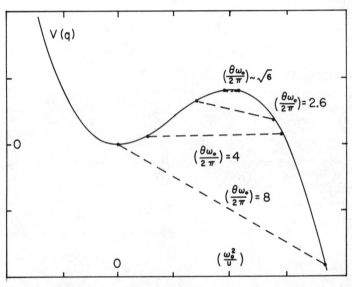

FIGURE 3. The variation of the extrema of the bounce trajectories as the temperature is decreased. At the crossover temperature, T_o, the bounce remains at the top of the potential barrier at $q_B(\tau) = q_b$.[38]

be generalized to the case of memory friction, $\gamma(t)$;[40] that is,

$$\ddot{q} = -\frac{1}{M}\frac{\partial V}{\partial q} - \int_0^t \gamma(t - s)\, \dot{q}(s)\, ds. \quad (16)$$

Then, in equation 15, we only have to substitute γ by $\hat{\gamma}(n\nu)$, where $\hat{\gamma}(z)$ denotes the Laplace transform of the memory friction, $\gamma(t)$. For memory damping (equation 16), the crossover temperature, T_o, will also be memory-renormalized to give[40]

$$T_o = \hbar\mu/(2\pi k) \quad (17)$$

with μ being the largest positive root of

$$\mu^2 + \mu\hat{\gamma}(\mu) = \omega_b^2. \tag{18}$$

Combining equations 16 and 17 with equation 15, we can recast the result for the decay rate in the form of

$$\Gamma = \left\{(\mu/\omega_b)\frac{\omega_0}{2\pi}\exp(-\beta E_b)\right\}Q, \quad T > T_o. \tag{19}$$

The term in the braces just equals the classical, dissipation, and memory renormalized thermal activation rate.[42] The factor Q accounts for the quantum effects at $T > T_o$, namely,

$$Q = \prod_{n=1}^{\infty}\frac{n^2\nu^2 + \omega_0^2 + n\nu\,\hat{\gamma}(n\nu)}{n^2\nu^2 - \omega_b^2 + n\nu\,\hat{\gamma}(n\nu)} \geq 1, \tag{20}$$

and approaches unity for $T \gg T_o$. This quantum correction can be quite large, even at temperatures of the order of a few T_o. Thus, these deviations from the classical hopping rate are essential in a precise analysis of parameters in MQT experiments.[16–18,43] There exists, then, a very useful, simple working approximation to the quantum enhancement factor Q, which reads[40]

$$Q \simeq \exp\left[\frac{\hbar^2}{24}\frac{(\omega_0^2 + \omega_b^2)}{(kT)^2} + O(T^{-4})\right]. \tag{21}$$

This approximation is most accurate for weak-to-moderate zero-frequency friction, denoted by γ_0, where

$$\gamma_0 \equiv \hat{\gamma}(z = 0) \simeq O(\omega_b). \tag{22}$$

It also becomes even more accurate for a dissipative mechanism with a large memory friction relaxation time.[40] The effect of quantum tunneling thus results essentially in a T-dependent renormalization of the barrier (Arrhenius) factor towards smaller values. In FIGURE 4, we depict this quantum correction Q (see equation 20) together with the working approximation in equation 21. It should also be noted here that the approximation of the order T^{-2} does not depend on the detailed dissipative mechanism. In contrast, the crossover temperature, T_o, depends via equation 18 on the amount and form of dissipation: For fixed zero-frequency dissipation, γ_0, the crossover temperature is monotonically increasing towards its undamped value, $\mu = \omega_b$, with increasing memory friction relaxation time.[40]

At temperatures below T_o, though, the relevant contribution to the decay rate is made up by the bounce. This bounce trajectory, however, is not uniquely defined in the sense that a translation, $q_B(\tau) \rightarrow q_B(\tau + b)$, also generates a solution that leaves the Euclidian action invariant. This invariance of the action S_E (equation 5) is revealed by an eigenmode, $y_1(\tau) \propto \dot{q}_B(\tau)$, with zero eigenvalue, $\lambda_1 = 0$. This means that an infinitesimal translation ϵ in $q_B(\tau)$ does not change the action: The variation of

$$y(\tau) = q_B(\tau + \epsilon) - q_B(\tau) = \dot{q}_B(\tau)\epsilon$$

gives $\delta S_E = 0$. The best medicine to take in order to avoid the difficulties generated by

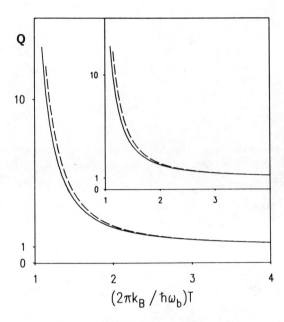

FIGURE 4. The approximation (dashed line) of equation 21 for the quantum correction factor Q compared with the exact expression of equation 20 (solid line) for a memory damping $\gamma(t) = \kappa\omega_b J_1(\kappa\omega_b t/r)/t$, with $\omega_b = \omega_0$, $\kappa = 0.5$, and $r = 0.25$. The inset shows the same for an exponential memory damping $\gamma(t) = \kappa\omega_b/\tau_c \exp(-t/\tau_c)$, with $\omega_b = \omega_0$, $\kappa = 0.5$, and $\omega_b \cdot \tau_c = 0.5$.[40]

this zero-mode is to perform a change of coordinates and to integrate directly over the translation variable b,[34] rather than over the zero-mode $y_1(\tau)$. Following the recipe of Faddeev and Popov[44] (gauge fixing condition; see also references 35 and 38), one finds that this procedure induces a zero-mode normalization factor, A, where

$$A = \left\{ \frac{M}{2\pi\hbar} \int_{-\theta/2}^{\theta/2} \dot{q}_B^2(\tau)\, d\tau \right\}^{1/2}. \tag{23}$$

Thus, the final result for the decay rate at $T < T_o$ is given by[2,9,10,35,38]

$$\Gamma = A \left\{ \frac{\mathrm{Det}\,(\delta^2 S_E/\delta q^2)q(\tau) = 0}{|\mathrm{Det}'(\delta^2 S_E/\delta q^2)q(\tau) = q_B(\tau)|} \right\}^{1/2} \exp\left[-S_B(\theta,\hat{\gamma})/\hbar\right], \quad T < T_o. \tag{24}$$

Here, $S_B(\theta,\hat{\gamma})$ is the bounce action, $S_B(\theta,\hat{\gamma}) = S_E[q_B(\tau)]$, and the prime indicates that the eigenvalue zero is to be omitted. At temperature, $T = T_o$, the bounce action, $S_B/\hbar$, matches smoothly with the Arrhenius factor, E_b/kT_o.[10,38] An *analytical evaluation* of equation 24 is possible only for the cubic potential shown in FIGURE 1 at weak[3,38,39] and very strong Ohmic damping[3,35,38] (see equation 4), and at one particular moderate friction value.[38] In practice, one must therefore resort to a numerical evaluation (see reference 45 for $T = 0$ and reference 46 for $0 \leq T \leq T_o$).

Just as in the case of $T > T_o$, where the prefactor is increasing with increasing memory relaxation time,[40] and with γ_0 held fixed, we find that the decay rate is exponentially enhanced with increasing memory friction relaxation time (decrease of S_B for fixed dissipation strength, γ_0, and fixed dimensionless temperature, θ/θ_o).[47]

The low temperature behavior of equation 24, however, exhibits a universal behavior. Grabert, Weiss, and Hanggi[10] have shown that the temperature enhancement follows a characteristic power law,[10]

$$S_B(T,\hat{\gamma}) = S_B(T = 0,\hat{\gamma}) - \frac{\pi}{6}\gamma_o M q_o^2 (kT\tau_B/\hbar)^2, \tag{25a}$$

where in terms of the tunneling distance, q_o, with $V(q = 0) = 0 = V(q_0)$, the bounce length, τ_B, is defined by

$$q_o \tau_B = \int_{-\infty}^{\infty} q_B(T = 0,\hat{\gamma};\tau)\,d\tau. \tag{25b}$$

The law, $\ln[\Gamma/\Gamma(T = 0)] \propto T^2$, holds for all systems with Ohmic-like damping, namely, where $\hat{\gamma}(z = 0) = \gamma_0 > 0$. The factor of proportionality depends via equation 25b on potential form and dissipation strength only. For example, for a weakly asymmetric double well potential with bias $\hbar\sigma$, $\sigma < 0$ (see FIGURE 5), the bounce length, τ_B, is estimated to be[37]

$$\tau_B = M\gamma_o q_o^2/(\pi\hbar|\sigma|) \equiv 2\,\alpha_c/|\sigma|. \tag{26}$$

In this case, the zero-temperature incoherent tunneling rate, Γ_o, is a nonanalytic function of the bias. It explicitly reads[37]

$$\Gamma_o = \frac{\pi}{2}\frac{\Delta^2}{\omega_o}\frac{1}{\Gamma(2\alpha_c)}\left\{\frac{|\sigma|}{\omega_o}\right\}^{2\alpha_c - 1}, \qquad \alpha_c > \tfrac{1}{2}, \tag{27a}$$

where Δ^2 denotes the friction renormalized tunneling matrix element. From equation 25a, we then find for the low temperature enhancement,

$$\ln[\Gamma(T)/\Gamma_o] = \frac{4\,\pi^2\omega_0^2}{3|\sigma|^2}\alpha_c^3\left(\frac{kT}{\hbar\omega_o}\right)^2. \tag{27b}$$

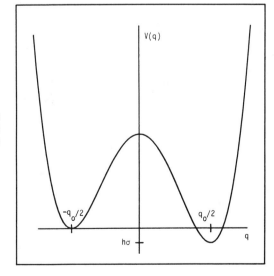

FIGURE 5. A slightly asymmetric double well in which incoherent Ohmic tunneling occurs with a rate given by equations 27 and 28.

For moderate-to-large friction, α_c, this result coincides with the leading low temperature behavior of a more elaborate treatment:[12,13]

$$\Gamma(T) = \frac{1}{2}\frac{\Delta^2}{\omega_o}\left(\frac{\hbar\beta\,\omega_0}{2\pi}\right)^{1-2\alpha_c}\cosh\left(\hbar\beta\sigma/2\right)\frac{|\Gamma\left(\alpha_c + i\hbar\beta\sigma/2\pi\right)|^2}{\Gamma(2\alpha_c)}. \tag{28}$$

The detailed behavior of the rate close to crossover, $T \simeq T_o$, is again more complicated because of the occurrence of a second quasi zero-mode.[36] As can be seen in FIGURE 2, the bounce solution, $q_B(\tau)$, approaches the trivial solution, $q_B(\tau) = q_b$, more closely as $T \uparrow T_o$. Thus, any linear combination of the two solutions is an almost stationary solution of the Euclidian action. Each one of these two quasi-stationary solutions separately induces a quasi zero-mode (an exact zero-mode and a quasi zero-mode[36,38]). This problem is best dealt with by treating the two dangerous modes in the effective action, S_E, up to cubic and quartic order.[35,36,38] Moreover, Grabert and Weiss[36] have shown that near $T \simeq T_o$, there exists a frequency scale Λ and a temperature scale x_o (which depend on the particular system under consideration) such that in the region of $|T - T_o| \lesssim x_o$, the rate exhibits a universal scaling behavior; that is,[9,36]

$$\Gamma/\Lambda = \text{Erfc}\,(\chi)\exp{(\chi^2)}, \quad \chi = (T - T_o)/x_o, \tag{29}$$

where Erfc (χ) is the integral, $2\pi^{-1/2}\int_{-\infty}^{\chi} dt \exp{(-t^2)}$.

DISCUSSION

In this final section, we comment on the regime of validity of the dissipative MQT rates derived in equation 19 for $T > T_o$ and in equation 24 for $T < T_o$. As mentioned previously, the rate expression for temperatures above crossover (see equation 19) approaches the classical activation rate,[1,2,42] which is valid for moderate-to-large friction strength; that is,[2]

$$\hat{\gamma}(\mu) \gtrsim \omega_b, \quad T > T_o. \tag{30}$$

For high barrier factors, $\beta E_b \gg 1$, the regime of friction values for which the thermal equilibrium population is maintained in the initial well (yielding the formula for the decay rate in equation 14) extends to even lower friction where the Kramers theory[1,2,42] approaches the result of standard transition-state-theory;[2] that is, the regime extends to weak-to-moderate-to-large friction, obeying

$$\hat{\gamma}(\mu) \gtrsim kT\omega_b/E_b, \quad T > T_o. \tag{31}$$

In other words, with a high potential barrier, the time scale for escape is so large that the thermalization in the initial well then occurs even for weak damping (equation 31); that is, it occurs on such a sufficiently slow time scale that deviations from the thermal equilibrium distribution inside the well can safely be neglected. For even weaker damping, however, deviations from thermal equilibrium start to play a role. For such small friction values, that is, for[2,48]

$$\int_0^\infty \gamma(t)\cos\left(\omega_o t/2\pi\right)dt < kT/J(E_b) \simeq kT\omega_b/E_b \tag{32}$$

with $J(E_b)$ denoting the classical (Minkowskian) action at energy E_b^-, the rate dominating mechanism is energy diffusion.[2] For extreme weak friction, $\hat{\gamma}(\mu) \ll kT\omega_b/E_b$, the classical activation rate vanishes proportional to the dissipation strength.[1,2,48,49] Clearly, the rate never vanishes completely in practice; it is bounded from below by the tunneling rate at low temperatures. The quantum corrections for $T > T_o$ for weak-to-moderate-to-large friction, as specified by equations 30 and 31, are given by the factor Q in equations 20 and 21. For extreme weak damping (equation 32), there occur above crossover, $T > T_o$, (apart from the ever-present quantum correction in equations 20 and 21) additional small quantum corrections[b] to the weak damping classical hopping rate that are of the type discussed recently by Melnikov[50] and Larkin and Ovchinnikov.[51] For this small regime of very weak friction, the precise form of these corrections (which originate from the quantum effects on the high temperature deviations from the thermal equilibrium population inside the well) are not known as of the present time; it is only known that the corrections derived in references 50 and 51 do not approach the correct classical limiting weak friction results obtained recently by Risken and Voigtlaender.[52]

For temperatures below crossover, $T < T_o$, the quantum tunneling rate is so sufficiently small that for all practical purposes, weak friction does not have any impact on deviations from the thermal equilibrium population inside the well. This can be readily understood if we note that the golden-rule calculation for the activation rate to the first few excited energy levels is proportional to the dissipation strength, $\hat{\gamma}(\mu)$, whereas the time scale for decay is set by the inverse of the low temperature tunneling rate, Γ. Using as a guide the undamped, zero-temperature rate in equation 24 (which always exponentially overestimates the zero-temperature dissipative decay rate in that equation), we can expect that deviations from equation 24 occur possibly only for exponentially small friction values; that is, for

$$\hat{\gamma}(\mu)/\omega_0 \lesssim \Gamma(\hat{\gamma} = 0)/\omega_0$$
$$= [216\, E_b/(\hbar\omega_0\pi)]^{1/2} \exp\{-[36E_b/(5\hbar\omega_b)]\} \lesssim 10^{-6}, \quad T < T_o. \quad (33)$$

For such exponentially small friction, the tunneling rate, Γ, and the activation rate into an excited state start to compete with each other; that is, the decay rate then no longer possesses a well-defined meaning. In conclusion, unless one starts out with an externally imposed initial preparation far from thermal equilibrium, the low temperature tunneling rate in equation 24 is valid for the whole damping regime.

ACKNOWLEDGMENTS

The author would like to thank Hermann Grabert, Gert Ingold, and Ulrich Weiss (University of Stuttgart), and Evgenii Freidkin and Peter Riseborough (Polytechnic Institute of New York) for an enjoyable collaboration in tunneling problems.

---

[b]It can be shown that these do not exceed the classical, next higher-order correction in order of magnitude because they are proportional to $\gamma_0^{3/2}$.[2]

REFERENCES

1. KRAMERS, H. A. 1940. Physica 7: 284–304.
2. HANGGI, P. 1986. Escape from a metastable state. J. Stat. Phys. 42: 105–148.
3. CALDEIRA, A. O. & A. J. LEGGETT. 1983. Ann. Phys. (N.Y.) 149: 374–456; 1984. Ann. Phys. (N.Y.) 153: 445 (Erratum).
4. LEGGETT, A. J. 1984. Phys. Rev. B30: 1208–1218; Prog. Theor. Phys. Suppl. 80: 10–18.
5. VOSS, R. F. & R. A. WEBB. 1981. Phys. Rev. Lett. 47: 265–268.
6. JACKEL, L. D., J. P. GORDON, E. L. HU, R. E. HOWARD, L. A. FETTER, D. H. TENNANT, R. W. EPWORTH & J. KURKIJARVI. 1981. Phys. Rev. Lett. 47: 697–700.
7. DE BRUYN OUBOTER, R. 1984. Physica 126B: 423–430.
8. CHAKRAVARTY, S. 1984. Physica 126B: 385–391.
9. GRABERT, H. 1985. In SQUID 85—Superconducting Quantum Interference Devices. H. D. Hahlbohm & H. Lubbig, Eds. de Gruyter. Berlin.
10. GRABERT, H., U. WEISS & P. HANGGI. 1984. Phys. Rev. Lett. 52: 2193–2196; 1984. Z. Phys. B56: 171–183.
11. CHAKRAVARTY, S. 1982. Phys. Rev. Lett. 49: 681–684; BRAY, A. J. & M. A. MOORE. 1982. Phys. Rev. Lett. 49: 1545–1549; CHAKRAVARTY, S. & A. J. LEGGETT. 1984. Phys. Rev. Lett. 52: 5–8; STRATT, R. M. 1984. Phys. Rev. Lett. 53: 1305–1308; 1985. Phys. Rev. Lett. 55: 1443–1445; CARMELI, B. & D. CHANDLER. 1985. J. Chem. Phys. 82: 3400–3404; WEISS, U. & H. GRABERT. In SQUID 85—Superconducting Quantum Interference Devices. H. D. Hahlbohm & H. Lubbig, Eds. de Gruyter. Berlin.
12. GRABERT, H. & U. WEISS. 1985. Phys. Rev. Lett. 54: 1605–1608.
13. FISHER, M. P. A. & A. T. DORSEY. 1985. Phys. Rev. Lett. 54: 1609–1612.
14. MARTINIS, J. M., M. H. DEVORET & J. CLARKE. 1985. Phys. Rev. Lett. 55: 1543–1546.
15. WIDOM, A., G. MEGALOUDIS, T. D. CLARK, H. PRANCE & R. J. PRANCE. 1982. J. Phys. A15: 3877–3879; LIKHAREV, K. K. & A. B. ZORIN. 1985. J. Low Temp. Phys. 59: 347–361; GUINEA, F. & G. SCHÖN. 1985. Preprint. KFA Jülich, Federal Republic of Germany.
16. WASHBURN, S., R. A. WEBB, R. F. VOSS & S. M. FARIS. 1985. Phys. Rev. Lett. 54: 2712–2715.
17. WASHBURN, S. & R. A. WEBB. 1986. Effects of dissipation and temperature on macroscopic quantum tunneling in Josephson junctions. Ann. N.Y. Acad. Sci. 480: 66–77.
18. SCHWARTZ, D. B., B. SEN, C. N. ARCHIE & J. E. LUKENS. 1985. Phys. Rev. Lett. 55: 1547–1550.
19. TESCHE, C. 1986. Schrödinger's cat—a realization in superconducting devices. Ann. N.Y. Acad. Sci. 480: 36–50.
20. FONDA, L., G. C. GHIRARDI & A. RIMINI. 1978. Rep. Prog. Phys. 41: 589–631.
21. BOHR, A. & B. MOTTELSON. 1969. Nuclear Structure, vol. I, pp. 438–447. Benjamin. New York.
22. FUDA, M. G. 1984. Am. J. Phys. 52: 838–842.
23. SINHA, K. 1972. Helv. Phys. Acta 45: 619–628; GORINI, V., A. KOSSAKOWSKI & E. C. G. SUDARSHAN. 1976. J. Math. Phys. 17: 821–825; ALICKI, R. 1977. Rep. Math. Phys. 1: 1–6.
24. KHALFIN, L. A. 1957. Zh. Eksp. Teor. Fiz. 33: 1371–1382. (1958. Sov. Phys. JETP 6: 1053–1063.)
25. PAYLEY, R. & N. WIENER. 1934. Fourier Transforms in the Complex Domain, theorem XII, p. 18. Am. Math. Soc. Providence, Rhode Island.
26. DEKKER, H. 1981. Phys. Rep. 80C: 1–112.
27. HAAKE, F. 1973. Springer Tracts Mod. Phys. 66: 98–168.
28. HAKEN, H. 1975. Rev. Mod. Phys. 47: 67–121.
29. GRABERT, H. 1982. Springer Tracts Mod. Phys. 95: 1–164; 1985. In Quantum Probability and Applications. L. Accardi & W. von Waldenfels, Eds. Springer-Verlag. Berlin; TALKNER, P. 1986. Ann. Phys. (N.Y.) 167: 390–436.
30. FEYNMAN, R. P. 1972. Statistical Mechanics, chapt. 3, pp. 72–95. Benjamin. New York.
31. FEYNMAN, R. P. & F. L. VERNON. 1963. Ann. Phys. (N.Y.) 24: 118–173.
32. SCHMID, A. 1982. J. Low Temp. Phys. 49: 609–626; CALDEIRA, A. O. & A. J. LEGGETT.

1983. Physica **121A**: 587–616; AMBEGAOKAR, V. 1984. *In* Percolation, Localization, and Superconductivity, NATO Adv. Stud. Inst., vol. 109. A. M. Goldman & S. A. Wolf, Eds. Plenum. New York.

33. LANGER, J. S. 1967. Ann. Phys. (N.Y.) **41**: 108–157; see also BÜTTIKER, M. & R. LANDAUER. 1982. *In* Nonlinear Phenomena at Phase Transitions and Instabilities. T. Riste, Ed.: 111–143. Plenum. New York.
34. CALLAN, C. G. & S. COLEMAN. 1977. Phys. Rev. **D16**: 1762–1768; see also SCHMID, A. 1986. Ann. Phys. (N.Y.) In press.
35. LARKIN, A. I. & YU. N. OVCHINNIKOV. 1984. Zh. Eksp. Teor. Fiz. **86**: 719–726. (1984. Sov. Phys. JETP **59**: 420–424.)
36. GRABERT, H. & U. WEISS. 1984. Phys. Rev. Lett. **53**: 1787–1790.
37. WEISS, U., P. S. RISEBOROUGH, P. HANGGI & H. GRABERT. 1984. Phys. Lett. **104A**: 10–13; 1984. Phys. Lett. **104A**: 492 (Erratum).
38. RISEBOROUGH, P. S., P. HANGGI & E. FREIDKIN. 1985. Phys. Rev. **A32**: 489–499.
39. AFFLECK, I. 1981. Phys. Rev. Lett. **46**: 388–391.
40. HANGGI, P., H. GRABERT, G. L. INGOLD & U. WEISS. 1985. Phys. Rev. Lett. **55**: 761–764.
41. WOLYNES, P. G. 1981. Phys. Rev. Lett. **47**: 968–971.
42. GROTE, R. F. & J. T. HYNES. 1980. J. Chem. Phys. **73**: 2715–2732; HANGGI, P. & F. MOJTABAI. 1982. Phys. Rev. **A26**: 1168–1170 (Rapid Communication section).
43. GRABERT, H., P. OLSCHOWSKI & U. WEISS. 1986. Phys. Rev. Lett. **56** (Comment). In press.
44. FADDEEV, L. & V. POPOV. 1967. Phys. Lett. **25B**: 29–30.
45. CHANG, L. D. & S. CHAKRAVARTY. 1984. Phys. Rev. **B29**: 130–137; 1984. Phys. Rev. **B30**: 1566 (Erratum).
46. GRABERT, H., P. OLSCHOWSKI & U. WEISS. 1985. Phys. Rev. **B32**: 3348–3351 (Rapid Communication section).
47. FREIDKIN, E., P. S. RISEBOROUGH & P. HANGGI. 1986. Phys. Rev. **B34**: no. 3 (August).
48. HANGGI, P. & U. WEISS. 1984. Phys. Rev. **A29**: 2265–2267.
49. BÜTTIKER, M., E. P. HARIS & R. LANDAUER. 1983. Phys. Rev. **B28**: 1268–1275; 1984. Phys. Rev. **B30**: 1551–1553.
50. MELNIKOV, V. I. 1984. Zh. Eksp. Teor. Fiz. **87**: 663–673. (1984. Sov. Phys. JETP **60**: 380–385.)
51. LARKIN, A. I. & YU. N. OVCHINNIKOV. 1985. J. Stat. Phys. **41**: 425–443.
52. RISKEN, H. & K. VOIGTLAENDER. 1985. J. Stat. Phys. **41**: 825–863.

Effects of Dissipation and Temperature on Macroscopic Quantum Tunneling in Josephson Junctions

SEAN WASHBURN AND RICHARD A. WEBB

IBM Thomas J. Watson Research Center
Yorktown Heights, New York 10598

In 1978, Leggett[1] pointed out that the direct measurement of the lifetime of a macroscopic quantum state was feasible and worthwhile. The large number of degrees of freedom both internal (within the objects considered) and in the coupling to the environment (there are no realizable isolated macroscopic objects) mixes the quantum mechanical states of the macroscopic body so that, in most cases, quantum mechanical behavior is averaged out. The question arose of whether (and under what conditions) the same quantum mechanical behavior would appear at the macroscopic levels as is familiar in the microscopic world. The answer, according to a series of papers,[2] is that the quantum mechanical principles (e.g., superposition) do survive in systems with sufficient internal correlation of the kind called "disconnectivity." The most thoroughly studied system of this type is the superconducting tunnel junction or Josephson junction.[3]

In the case of the Josephson junction, as the Cooper pair tunnels through the barrier, the wave function changes its phase by an amount that is equal to the time integral of the voltage across the barrier. The quantum mechanical wave function is linked directly to the macroscopic (experimentally accessible) voltage. Measuring the current-voltage characteristics of the junction will then sample the quantum mechanical behavior of the Cooper pair wave functions.[4]

The standard phenomenological model of the Josephson junction is the following equation of motion for the phase difference, ϕ, across the junction:[3]

$$C\left(\frac{\Phi_0}{2\pi}\right)^2 \frac{d^2\phi}{dt^2} + \frac{1}{R}\left(\frac{\Phi_0}{2\pi}\right)^2 \frac{d\phi}{dt} + I_0 \sin\phi = I. \qquad (1)$$

C is the junction capacitance; R is the resistive impedance of the junction (usually it is approximated by the resistance of the junction in the normal or voltage state); I_0 is the maximum supercurrent that the junction will support; $\Phi_0 = h/2e$ is the flux quantum; and I is the bias current being driven through the junction. The parameter, ϕ, is usually taken to be the average value of the quantum mechanical dynamical variable, which is the phase difference.

This model is formally equivalent to the classical equation of motion, $m\ddot{\phi} + \eta\dot{\phi} + \partial U/\partial\phi = 0$, which describes a particle of mass, $m = C(\Phi_0/2\pi)^2$, located at position ϕ in a one-dimensional potential,

$$U(\phi) = -\left(\frac{I_0\Phi_0}{2\pi}\right)(x\phi + \cos\phi), \quad x = I/I_0, \qquad (2)$$

66

under the influence of a friction coefficient, $\eta = (\Phi_0/2\pi)^2/R$. The potential is a series of wells on a sloping background (see FIGURE 1a), and the two macroscopically distinguishable states are analogous to the "phase-marker" particle being trapped in a well (zero-voltage state) or sliding down the cascade of wells (voltage state). The particle caught in the well oscillates (zero-point energy) at the plasma frequency, $\omega_0 = \omega_J(1 - x^2)^{1/4}$, where $\omega_J = \sqrt{2\pi I_0/C\Phi_0}$. In the microscopic case, a particle in the well might either activate over the barrier (if there is sufficient thermal energy available) or tunnel quantum mechanically through the barrier (see FIGURE 1a). The rate of thermal activation (TA) is given by an Arrhenius formula,[5]

$$\Gamma = A_T e^{-(U_0/kT)}, \tag{3}$$

where A_T is approximately $\omega_0/2\pi$ times the rate of escape attempts, and $U_0 \simeq (\Phi_0 I_0/3\pi)[2(1 - x)]^{3/2}$ is the height of the barrier. On the other hand, at zero temperature, the escape of the phase-marker must proceed via quantum tunneling. The rate of tunneling is

$$\Gamma = A_Q e^{-B_Q}. \tag{4}$$

If there is no friction, a simple WKB calculation yields $B_Q = B_{WKB} = 36U_0/5\hbar\omega_0$, and one expects that $A_Q \sim \omega_0/2\pi$. In the presence of dissipation, B_Q is the path integral average over the possible trajectories through the barrier:[6]

$$B_Q = \frac{1}{\hbar}\left[\int_0^t d\tau \left\{\frac{1}{2}C\left(\frac{\Phi_0}{2\pi}\right)^2 \dot\phi(\tau)^2 + U[\phi(\tau)]\right\}\right.$$
$$\left. + \frac{\eta}{4\pi}\int_{-\infty}^{+\infty} d\tau \int_0^t d\tau' \frac{[\phi(\tau) - \phi(\tau')]^2}{(\tau - \tau')^2}\right]. \tag{4a}$$

The first term reduces to the WKB probability of escaping through the barrier and the second term is the correction due to energy dissipated while the particle is inside the barrier. For low dissipation, $B_Q \simeq B_{WKB}(1 + 1.74\alpha)$, where $\alpha = \eta/2M\omega_0 = 1/(2RC\omega_0)$ is the dimensionless dissipation of the system. The question posed by Leggett and answered by the early experiments[7-9] was whether or not a macroscopic variable (the phase difference, ϕ, across the Josephson junction) could exhibit the same tunneling. The answer was that indeed it could tunnel, and the observed tunneling rate[8] was just that predicted by the theory that accounted properly for the dissipation of energy into the environmental degrees of freedom as the "particle" passed through the barrier.[6]

In the absence of dissipation, thermal activation and quantum tunneling are essentially independent processes, and the escape rate is simply the faster of the two. The case of a macroscopic object coupled to a thermal bath is more complicated.[6,10] The exchange of energy with the environment through dissipation affects both quantum tunneling[11,12] and thermal activation.[5,13,14] Since the early experiments, there have been more accurate calculations of the effects of dissipation on the zero-temperature tunneling rate,[15] and there have been calculations that predicted the effect of small, finite temperature on quantum tunneling in the presence of dissipation.[16-18] Finally, very recently, the functions, $A(\alpha,T)$ and $B(\alpha,T)$, have been solved accurately for the parameter space, $\langle\alpha,T\rangle$.[19-21] It is this new set of predictions that we have attempted to test with the experiments described here.[22]

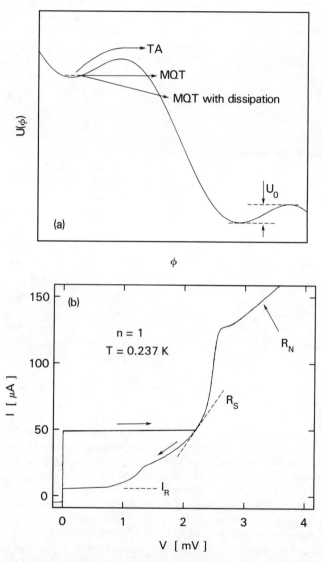

FIGURE 1. (1a) A schematic picture of the escape mechanisms available to the phase-marker particle in the potential of equation 2. The escape paths depicted represent thermal activation (TA) and macroscopic quantum tunneling (MQT) with and without the effect of dissipation. (1b) A typical current-voltage characteristic of a junction used in the experiment. The hysteretic behavior of the junction is illustrated by the arrows. The resistances at the switch to the voltage state and above the gap are indicated by the tangent R_S and R_N. The current, I_R, at which the junction returns to the zero-voltage state is also marked.

The devices used in these experiments are Nb-Nb$_2$O$_5$-Nb edge junctions,[23] which have an intrinsic capacitance (junction capacitance[24] plus parasitic capacitances) of $C_0 \simeq 0.02$ pf. In addition to the intrinsic capacitance, a different shunting capacitor, $0 \le C_n \le 12$ pf, was added to each junction lithographically. All of the junctions and their shunting capacitors were formed in the same lithographic process, which ensured uniformity in the junction characteristics. All of the critical currents were within 6% of $I_0 = 54\mu A$, and the I-V characteristics were virtually identical except for the amount of hysteresis that is directly attributed to the different shunting capacitors. A list of measured junction parameters is given in TABLE 1.

The junctions were cooled by direct contact with the dilute solution of a ^{3}He-^{4}He dilution refrigerator. The electrical leads were thermally sunk at the same temperature, and a series of filters (both at low temperature and at room temperature) isolated the devices from external noise. For each junction studied, starting in the zero-voltage state at $I = 0$, the bias current was increased slowly until the junction switched to the voltage state (see FIGURE 1b): the phase ϕ escaped from the well into the continuum. The switching current was measured repeatedly ($\simeq 10^5$ times) so that a histogram of the switching currents could be constructed. The histogram represents the probability,

TABLE 1. Junction Parameters

n	C	R_N	$I_0(T = 0)^a$	α
1	0.03 pf	23Ω	52.2 μA	0.64
2	0.05	24	54.5	0.47
3	0.15	24	57.3	0.26
4	0.67	24	(53)	0.13
5	2.9	22	(56)	0.066
6	12	24	(52)	0.031

^{a}The critical currents, I_0, that are enclosed in parentheses were measured from the I-V characteristic and not from fitting to the MQT theory.

$P(I)$, of ϕ tunneling at that particular value of bias current.[25] This process was repeated at different temperatures for each of the junctions. Some representative data for junction 3 are displayed in FIGURE 2. At high temperature, $P(x)$ is rather broad; then, as the temperature decreases, the distribution shifts toward $x = 1$ and becomes narrower. If quantum tunneling did not occur, then this process would continue until $T = 0$, where the distribution would be a delta function at $x = 1$. (At $T = 0$, thermal activation cannot occur. The state is bound until the well disappears at $I = I_0$.) What actually happens is that at some temperature, $T \simeq T_0$, $P(x)$ nearly ceases to shift and to become narrower as the temperature decreases; macroscopic quantum tunneling "short-circuits" the thermal activation rate.

In FIGURE 3, the rms width of $P(x)$ is plotted as a function of temperature for four devices. At higher temperatures, the widths, Δx, follow the thermal activation curve.[5] Below some temperature, the widths cease to be temperature dependent, and the smaller the capacitance of the junction, the larger the limiting width of the distribution. The dashed lines are the zero-temperature distribution widths predicted[15] using the lithographically defined capacitance and the resistance determined from the I-V curves. The agreement between the theory and the experiment is excellent. The

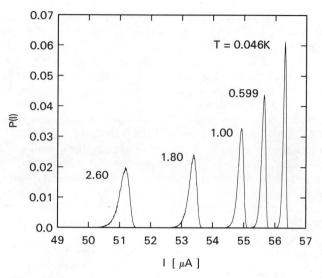

FIGURE 2. Representative probability distributions, $P(I)$, for junction 3 at several temperatures.

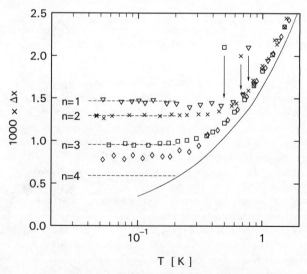

FIGURE 3. The width, Δx, of the probability distributions for junctions 1, 2, 3, and 4. (The data for junctions 5 and 6 are equivalent to those of junction 4.) The arrows mark the values of T_0 appropriate to junctions 1, 2, and 3. The dashed lines indicate the values of Δx predicted by the zero-temperature theory[15] and the solid line illustrates the thermal activation prediction.[5]

crossover temperatures, T_0, at which thermal activation ceases to dominate the escape rate, are marked by the arrows for junctions 1, 2, and 3. This parameter is calculated from the formula,[17]

$$T_0 = \frac{\hbar \omega_0}{2\pi k_B} [\sqrt{1 + \alpha^2} - \alpha]. \tag{5}$$

The predicted values of T_0 fall just above the "break" in the $\Delta x(T)$ curves; this is in agreement with predictions.[19] The dissipation was calculated using the resistance, R, of the junction measured in the linear portion of the I-V curve at voltages larger than the superconducting gap, $2\Delta/e$. This value, $R = R_N$, is the conventional choice, and in this experiment, it predicts much of the behavior of the junction, including, as we have just shown, the crossover from thermal activation to macroscopic quantum tunneling and the absolute width of the probability distribution for the escape from the well.

Junction 4 is not described very well by the theoretical curve, and further increasing the size of the capacitor (junctions 5 and 6) did not change the escape-rate data. The only effect of larger capacitors was to increase the amount of hysteresis. The current, I_R, at which the junctions returned to the zero-voltage state decreased monotonically as the capacitor size increased up to $C_n = 12$ pf. The physics of this "recapture" of the phase-marker particle occurs on a relatively slow time scale, namely, the rate (~ 10 Hz) at which the bias current in the junction is ramped up and down while accumulating the switch-point histogram. This frequency is 11 orders of magnitude lower than the intrinsic plasma frequency of the bare junction; that is, it is in the low-frequency limit and the entire patterned area of the capacitor contributes to the circuit. The anomaly in the escape-rate data is attributed to the breakdown[26] of the lumped circuit (RSJ) model of the junction. For a capacitor of large area, the junction, which tends to operate at the plasma frequency set by the intrinsic capacitance of the junction, is unable to sample all of the large lithographic capacitor at a rate that is fast compared to the intrinsic plasma frequency. The problem is analogous to that of a resonant circuit connected to a long transmission line: above some characteristic frequency (or beyond some length), increasing the length of the transmission line no longer affects the resonance frequency. In our case, only a fraction (which is determined by the intrinsic frequency of the bare edge junction) of the area is "seen" by the junction. This is a fundamental limit set by the speed of light in all experiments of this kind; to be relevant to the dissipation in the junction, the external element must be very close to the junction. We note that aside from posing lithographic difficulties, this is an advantage to the experimentalist. If the junction were to consider everything connected to it as part of its circuit impedance, then the value of η would include effects from everything in the measurement circuit (including power generators). This self-enforced isolation of the junction is partly responsible for our ability to measure these quantum effects.

The distribution, $P(x)$, can be decomposed to give the escape rate, Γ, at which the phase activates or tunnels into the continuum. This is given by the formula,[25]

$$\Gamma(x) = \frac{(dx/dt) P(x)}{1 - \int_0^x P(z)dz}. \tag{6}$$

The results for two of our junctions are presented in FIGURE 4. The data have been

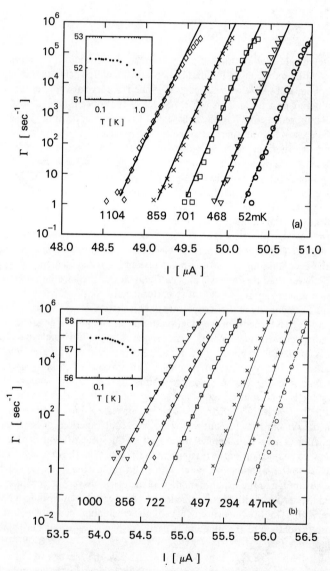

FIGURE 4. The tunneling rates at several temperatures for (a) junction 1 and (b) junction 3. The solid lines are fits to the full theory[19] and the dashed lines are fits to the zero-temperature theory.[15] The insets illustrate the temperature dependence of the fitted critical current, I_0.

fitted using the calculated capacitance, $C = C_0 + C_n + \delta C$, and the resistance, R_N, with I_0 as a free parameter. The small correction, $\delta C = 0.006$ pf, is a correction to the capacitance due to quasi-particle tunneling.[27] The dashed lines indicate the zero-temperature rates,[15] and the solid lines are for the finite temperature theory.[19] The fitted I_0 are displayed in the insets of the figure. Any attempt to fit the rates at all of the temperatures with a single value of critical current fails. The observed temperature dependence is far larger than that predicted for the BCS critical current in the Nb; for the moment it remains unexplained. Because the theory works so well in describing the behavior junction, we conclude that the observed changes in I_0 are real and not an artifact of the analysis. We speculate that it may be related to temperature dependences in the junction impedances, which may appear in the Werthamer theory

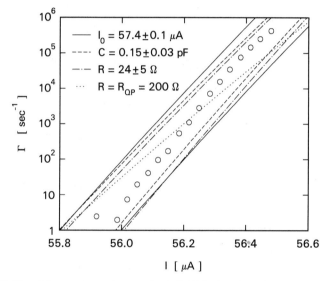

FIGURE 5. Plot of the experimental rate at $T = 0.079$ K for junction 3. The various lines indicate the effect on fit quality of 20% variations in R and C, and of a 0.2% variation in I_0. The dotted line is the best fit obtainable from the resistance, $R = R_{QP} = 200\Omega$.

of the Josephson junction.[28] For all of our junctions, at temperatures, $T \lesssim 0.2$ K, the value of I_0 was constant to within the uncertainty in our data, which yields an uncertainty in I_0 of ± 0.02 μA.

These two graphs together with FIGURE 3 provided a quantitative confirmation of the theory of MQT at $T \to 0$ for the dissipation range, $0.2 \le \alpha \le 0.7$, covered by these devices. They were the first such experimental verification of the theory in the interesting region of $\alpha \simeq 1$ and the first for such a wide range of dissipation.[22]

In FIGURE 5, we illustrate the effects on the fit quality of variations in the junction parameters. It is clear that small adjustments of I_0 could accommodate variations of 20% in R or C. We wish to make the point that much larger changes in these dissipation parameters would give a theoretical fit with the wrong slope, $d(\ln\Gamma)/dI$. In particular, for underdamped RSJ junctions near the return to the voltage state, the I-V characteristic is described by[29]

$$\frac{I - I_R}{I_R} = \left(A\frac{V_0}{V} + B\right)e^{-V_0/V}, \quad V_0 = \frac{\Phi_0\omega_0^2}{\sqrt{(RC)^{-2} + \omega_0^2}}. \tag{7}$$

Fitting this equation to the return to the voltage state yields $R \simeq 200\Omega$. It is at least plausible that this resistance value, R_{QP}, might represent the dissipation "felt" by the phase-marker particle when it is trapped in the well or tunneling through the barrier. Unfortunately for this point of view, the dotted line in FIGURE 5 is the best theoretical fit possible with this value of the resistance. It has the wrong slope, $d(\ln\Gamma)/dI$, and is clearly inferior to the fits that assume $R = R_N$. Those who have developed the theory of MQT in non-RSJ devices[30] have not provided a method for extracting the friction, η, from the I-V characteristic. Until such a prescription is put forth, we rely on the existing RSJ model, which yields $\eta = (\Phi_0/2\pi)^2/R_N$. As an aside, we remark that the data permit the choice of $R = R_S = dV/dI$ at $I = I_0$ (see FIGURE 1b); however, because it is not clear whether this phenomenological "resistance" represents the friction in the junction, we pursue it no further.

As the temperature was increased slightly from the $T = 0$ limit, Grabert, Weiss, and Hanggi[17] predicted that the MQT rate would be enhanced according to

$$\ln\left\{\frac{\Gamma(T)}{\Gamma(0)}\right\} = s(\alpha)T^2, \tag{8}$$

where[12]

$$s(\alpha) \simeq \frac{2}{\pi}\left(\frac{18k_B}{\hbar\omega_0}\right)^2\frac{U_0}{\hbar\omega_0}\frac{\alpha}{\left[\sqrt{\alpha^2 + 9/\pi^2} - \alpha\right]^2}. \tag{9}$$

This T^2 enhancement of the MQT rate may be contrasted with simple thermal activation, which falls off exponentially as the temperature decreases (and is negligible in this temperature range). In order to demonstrate this enhancement in our data, we display the rate, $\Gamma(x)$, at $x = 0.97$ as a function of temperature in FIGURE 6. As illustrated by the solid lines, the data are indeed linear in T^2. We emphasize that the temperature range covered, $0 \leq T \leq 0.15$ K, is the region where I_0 has become temperature-independent; thus, the observed increases in Γ cannot be an artifact of changes in I_0, which happen only at higher temperatures. The dashed lines illustrate the slopes, $s(\alpha)$, calculated with $\alpha = 1/(2\omega_0 C R_N)$. Although the predicted trend to larger slope at larger capacitance is born out, the predicted slopes are all smaller than the experimental slopes by about a factor of two ($n = 1$) to four ($n = 3$).

The question of which value of R to choose resurfaces here; the slopes predicted by the theory are smaller than those observed in the experiment. As demonstrated above, R_N correctly describes the $T = 0$ macroscopic quantum tunneling rate. There is, however, no *a priori* reason to expect R_N to represent the dissipation below the gap ($eV < 2\Delta$) for our devices that are not externally shunted. In principle, the dissipation below the gap will be dominated by the quasiparticle (single electron) current through the tunnel junction. Although the T^2 dependence is universal for any form of the friction, $\eta(\omega)$, that is regular near $\omega = 0$ (so that η approaches a constant as $\omega \to 0$), the value of the slope, $s(\alpha)$, depends on the details of the dissipation. Strictly speaking, the value of η that enters the calculation is neither the dissipation inside the well nor R_N. The theory calculates the dissipation over the course of the particle's traversal through the barrier. The time scale for this traversal is given by a WKB-like argument[31] to be $\simeq \omega_0^{-1}$. If the RSJ model (frequency independent resistance) describes the system, then R_N is certainly the appropriate choice of resistance. The I-V characteristics of our junctions, however, are not described very well by the RSJ theory; the characteristics are more nearly those of unshunted tunnel junctions. It is a little curious that the resistance, R_N, that agreed with the theoretical tunneling rate does not also yield the correct slope, $s(\alpha)$, in the analysis of FIGURE 6. The discrepancy has not been resolved at this time. We note that choosing the resistance obtained from the hysteretic return,

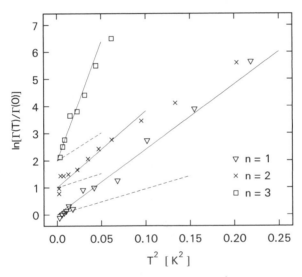

FIGURE 6. The experimental rate at $x = 0.97$ as a function T^2 for junctions 1, 2, and 3. The dashed lines represent the theoretical slopes (equation 9) and the solid lines guide the eye.

$R_{QP} \simeq 200\Omega$, causes an even worse discrepancy with the theoretical $s(\alpha)$, and that choosing the "resistance" at the switch point, $R_S = 19\Omega$, improves it slightly.

In conclusion, we remark that the experiments described here have confirmed the MQT theory at $T \to 0$ in the dissipation range of $0.26 < \alpha < 0.64$. Also, the effects of a small, finite temperature on dissipative quantum tunneling have been observed. Since the first report of these results,[22] other experiments on Josephson junctions employing different experimental techniques have corroborated our findings over a wider range of dissipation. For large dissipation, $\alpha = 5$, both the MQT ($T \to 0$) predictions and the T^2 enhancement of MQT were observed.[32] For small dissipation, $\alpha = 1/60$, the $T = 0$ theory was confirmed and no T^2 enhancement was reported.[33] (The absence of thermal enhancement of MQT at very low dissipation is consistent with theory.)

ACKNOWLEDGMENTS

Throughout the analysis of these experiments, we have benefited repeatedly from conversations with Markus Büttiker, Sudip Chakravarty, Hermann Grabert, Peter Hanggi, Joe Imry, Tony Leggett, and Peter Riseborough. We are grateful to our experimental collaborators, Sadeg Faris and Richard Voss. We also thank Robert Drake for making the junctions.

REFERENCES

1. LEGGETT, A. J. 1978. J. Phys. (Paris) Colloq. **39**(C6): 1264–1269.
2. LEGGETT, A. J. 1980. Prog. Theor. Phys. **69**(suppl.): 80–100; 1983. Proc. Int. Symp. Foundations of Quantum Mechanics, pp. 74–82; 1984. Macroscopic quantum tunneling and related effects in Josephson systems. *In* Percolation, Localization, and Superconductivity, NATO ASI Series B, vol. 109. A.M. Goldman & S. Wolf, Eds.: 1–41. Plenum. New York; 1984. Contemp. Phys. **25**: 583–598; 1986. Quantum mechanics and realism at the macroscopic level. Ann. N.Y. Acad. Sci. **480**: 21–24.
3. BARONE, A. & G. PATERNO. 1982. Physics and Applications of the Josephson Effect. Wiley. New York.
4. LIKHAREV, K. K. 1983. Sov. Phys. Usp. **26**: 87–95.
5. BÜTTIKER, M., E. P. HARRIS & R. LANDAUER. 1983. Phys. Rev. **B28**: 1268–1275, and references cited therein.
6. CALDEIRA, A. O. & A. J. LEGGETT. 1983. Ann. Phys. **149**: 374–456; 1984(E). Ann. Phys. **153**: 445.
7. DEN BOER, W. & R. DE BRUYN OUBOTER. 1980. Physica **98B**: 185–187; PRANCE, R. J. *et al.* 1981. Nature **289**: 543–549.
8. VOSS, R. F. & R. A. WEBB. 1981. Phys. Rev. Lett. **47**: 265–268.
9. JACKEL, L. D. *et al.* 1981. Phys. Rev. Lett. **47**: 697–700.
10. CHAKRAVARTY, S. 1986. Quantum mechanics on a macroscopic scale. Ann. N.Y. Acad. Sci. **480**: 25–35.
11. HANGGI, P. 1986. J. Stat. Phys. **42**: 105–140; 1986. Macroscopic quantum tunneling at finite temperatures. Ann. N.Y. Acad. Sci. **480**: 51–65.
12. GRABERT, H. 1985. Macroscopic quantum tunneling and quantum coherence in Josephson systems. *In* Proceedings of SQUID-85.
13. MELNIKOV, V. I. 1984. JETP **60**: 380–385.
14. HANGGI, P., H. GRABERT, G-L. INGOLD & U. WEISS. 1985. Phys. Rev. Lett. **55**: 761–764.
15. CHANG, L-D. & S. CHAKRAVARTY; 1984. Phys. Rev. **B29**: 130–137; 1984(E). Phys. Rev. **30**: 1566.
16. LARKIN, A. I. & YU. N. OVCHINNIKOV. 1984. J. Stat. Phys. **59**: 425–443, and references cited therein.
17. GRABERT, H., U. WEISS & P. HANGGI. 1984. Phys. Rev. Lett. **52**: 2193–2196; GRABERT, H. & U. WEISS. 1984. Z. Phys. **B56**: 171–183.
18. ZWERGER, W. 1985. Phys. Rev. **A31**: 1745–1753.
19. GRABERT, H., P. OLSCHOWSKI & U. WEISS. 1985. Phys. Rev. **B32**: 3348–3350.
20. RISEBOROUGH, P. S., P. HANGGI & E. FREIDKIN. 1985. Phys. Rev. **B32**: 489–499.
21. WAXMAN, D. & A. J. LEGGETT. 1985. Phys. Rev. **B32**: 4450–4468.
22. WASHBURN, S., R. A. WEBB, R. F. VOSS & S. M. FARIS. 1985. Phys. Rev. Lett. **54**: 2712–2715.
23. BROOM, R. F., A. OOSENBRUG & W. WALTER. 1980. Appl. Phys. Lett. **37**: 237–239.
24. MAGERLEIN, J. H. 1981. IEEE Trans. Magn. **MAG-17**: 286–289.
25. FULTON, T. A. & L. N. DUNKELBERGER. 1976. Phys. Rev. **B9**: 4760–4768.
26. CHAKRAVARTY, S. & A. SCHMID. 1986. Phys. Rev. **B33**: 2000–2002.
27. LARKIN, A. I. & YU. N. OVCHINNIKOV. 1983. Phys. Rev. **B28**: 6281–6285.
28. BRUNK, G., H. LÜBBIG & CH. ZURBRÜGG. 1984. Proc. LT-17: 219–220; 1985. Intrinsic

tunnel junction properties and Kramers's macroscopic escape problem. *In* Proceedings of SQUID-85.

29. LEGGETT, A. J. Private communication.
30. LEGGETT, A. J. 1984. Phys. Rev. **B30:** 1208–1218; ECKERN, U., G. SCHÖN & V. AMBEGAOKAR. 1984. Phys. Rev. **B32:** 6419–6431.
31. BÜTTIKER, M. & R. LANDAUER. 1985. Traversal time for tunneling. *In* Festkörperprobleme. Advances in Solid State Physics, vol. XXV. P. Grosse, Ed.: 711–717. Vieweg. Braunschweig.
32. SCHWARTZ, D. B., B. SEN, C. N. ARCHIE & J. E. LUKENS. 1985. Phys. Rev. Lett. **55:** 1547–1550; GRABERT, H., P. OLSCHOWSKI & U. WEISS. 1986. Phys. Rev. Lett. **56.** To appear.
33. DEVORET, M. H., J. M. MARTINIS & J. CLARKE. 1985. Phys. Rev. Lett. **55:** 1908–1911.

Quantum Mechanics of Macroscopic Systems and the Measurement Process

MIKIO NAMIKI

Department of Physics
Waseda University
Tokyo 160, Japan

INTRODUCTION

The problem of measurement in quantum mechanics has always been one of the most fundamental and controversial topics since its birth. The central question is whether the reduction of wave packet (RWP) by measurement of an observable can be described by quantum mechanics itself. In trying to answer this question among many theories of measurement, we know the von Neumann–Wigner theory[1,2] gives a negative answer to the question, while the ergodic amplification theory[3] gives an affirmative answer. We also know of the remarkable debates between them.[4] The many-worlds interpretation,[5] though, is famous for a quite different approach to the problem. Several years ago, S. Machida and myself[6,7] proposed a new theory of measurement to explicitly give RWP, in which the macroscopic nature of apparatus systems is to be represented quantum-mechanically in terms of density matrix on a continuous direct sum of many Hilbert spaces. This may be called the many-Hilbert-spaces interpretation. In this paper, we present a brief survey of the Machida-Namiki theory and its recent developments.

MEASUREMENT PROBLEMS

First of all, we have to set up the final goal of the theory of measurement, that is, the mathematical expression of RWP. Consider a measurement of an observable, F, in a quantum-mechanical object system, Q, in a superposed state described by $\psi^Q = \Sigma_i c_i u_i$, or equivalently, by the density matrix,

$$\rho^Q = |\psi^Q\rangle\langle\psi^Q| = \sum_i |c_i|^2 \xi^Q(u_i) + \sum_{i \neq j} c_i c_j^* |u_i\rangle\langle u_j|, \tag{1}$$

where u_i is the i-th eigenstate of F and $\xi^Q = |u_i\rangle\langle u_i|$. For the complete description of RWP, it is inevitable to bring apparatus states into the mathematical expression;[8] that is,

$$\Xi^{tot} = \rho^Q \times \sigma^A \rightarrow \overline{\Xi}^{tot} = \sum_i |c_i|^2 \xi^Q(u_i) \times \sigma_F^A(i), \tag{2}$$

where Ξ^{tot} and σ^A stand for the initial state density matrices of the total system and of apparatus system, A, respectively, $\overline{\Xi}^{tot}$ stands for the final state density matrix of the total system, and $\sigma_{F(i)}^A$ stands for the final state density matrix of system A representing the observation of the i-th eigenvalue of F. Therefore, to derive equation 2, the theory of measurement has to apply quantum mechanics to the total system composed of object system, Q, and apparatus system, A, with interactions. Needless to say, the essential question is whether the phase correlations among u_i's in ψ^Q or ρ^Q can be erased out through the measurement process.

The ergodic amplification theory[3] attempted to give the answer "yes" by identifying RWP with thermal irreversible processes (such as discharge phenomena in counters). One of the basic ideas is to erase the phase correlations by destroying the unitarity of time evolution in the thermal irreversible processes. However, Wigner categorically refuses to destroy the unitarity, and he criticizes[4] the ergodic amplification theory on the basis of the Wigner theorem and the negative-result-measurement paradox. The Wigner theorem[2,9] states that the total system can never reach RWP via unitary time evolution starting from an initial state in which system Q is in a superposed state and system A is in a mixed state. The ergodic amplification theory also fails in the negative-result-measurement paradox,[10] as will be seen shortly.

According to the von Neumann–Wigner theory, the measurement process should be written as

$$\Psi \equiv \psi^Q \times \Phi^A = \sum_i c_i u_i \times \Phi^A \rightarrow \sum_i c_i u_i \times \Phi_i \equiv \tilde{\Psi} \,, \tag{3}$$

where Φ^A is the initial state of the apparatus system and Φ_i stands for the i-th eigenstate of an appropriate observable (of system A) designed to have the one-to-one correspondence to u_i. Equation 3 was derived by strict application of the superposition principle to the measurement process, but it never gives RWP because $\tilde{\Psi}$ is still in a pure state, while the right-hand side of equation 2 is in a mixed state. This was generalized to the above Wigner theorem later. Their theory, though, can never give RWP as a physical process, and thus it eventually leads us to the introduction of the "abstract ego" or "consciousness," as is well known.

However, we should point out here that Wigner's theorem was proved by assuming system A to be in a mixed state in one Hilbert space. We shall see later that one Hilbert space is not enough to describe macroscopic systems and then RWP.

The above discussions tell us that the target of our theory of measurement is to break through the Wigner theorem and to explicitly derive RWP (equation 2), even in the case of the negative-result measurement. Therefore, we need to consider the negative-result-measurement paradox for the case of the Stern-Gerlach experiment, which is a simple and typical quantum-mechanical measurement to be divided into two steps—spectral decomposition and detection. In the first step, a stationary beam of particles (with spin one-half, for example) in a superposed state is spatially decomposed by a magnetic field in upward and downward directions in such a way that

$$\psi_0^Q = (c_a u_a + c_b u_b)\phi \rightarrow \psi^Q = c_a u_a \phi_a + c_b u_b \phi_b \,, \tag{4}$$

where c_a and c_b are constants, u_a and u_b represent up-spin and down-spin eigenfunctions, respectively, and ϕ, ϕ_a, and ϕ_b stand for position wave functions. In the standard experiment, ϕ_a and ϕ_b are, respectively, wave packets going to different detectors, say counters D_a and D_b (see FIGURE 1a). Each detection by D_a or D_b means that the particle has up-spin or down-spin, respectively, and that the measurement has been completed. Therefore, one may consider it as if the very measurement, that is, RWP, could be

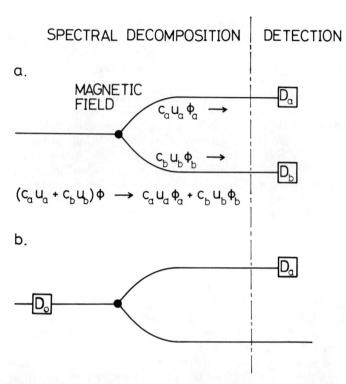

FIGURE 1. Schematic illustrations of the Stern-Gerlach experiment: (a) standard experiment; (b) negative-result measurement.

brought about by the "firing" in counters. However, this idea will fail in the case of negative-result measurement.

The case of negative-result measurement is brought about by removing D_b and locating another counter, say D_0, in the front of the magnetic field (see FIGURE 1b). An anticoincidence experiment of D_0 and D_a gives us the so-called negative-result measurement, which tells us that the particle went downward and hence had down-spin. This means that the down-spin measurement is completed, and consequently, RWP takes place without resort to the "real firing" of D_a. In this case, the "no firing" of D_a never means that the particle wave function did not interact with detector D_a. Both the "firing" and the "no firing" are only a sort of displays to show results of the measurement, that is, of RWP, made by interaction of the wave function with D_a. Note that the firing of D_0 is connected only to the formation of the wave packet, ϕ, in the right-hand side of equation 4, irrelevant to the spin-measurement.

The negative-result-measurement paradox teaches us that RWP is to be distinguished from thermal irreversible processes such as "real firing" in counters. Machida and I[6,7] have further remarked (based on a gedanken-experiment by the perfect-mirror model and on more realistic ones) that any energy supply or amplification is not essential for RWP. Consequently, we do not agree with the ergodic amplification theory.

Nevertheless, the above objection does not necessarily imply an agreement with the von Neumann–Wigner theory. Here, we have to remark on a misleading opinion mentioned in some important papers of the latter theory.[2,4] Some authors have considered the process in equation 4 to be a measuring process by formally identifying it with equation 3. They then concluded that the particle position itself plays a role in the apparatus system and that RWP never occurs in the Stern-Gerlach experiment. However, the process in equation 4 is merely a spectral decomposition and does not contain any detection. However, we note that there should exist no measurement without detection.

The many-worlds-interpretation theory can also hardly expect us to agree with it because the theory considered the measurement process to be completed by the spectral-decomposition step and thus ignored the detection step.

It is repeatedly noted that every quantum-mechanical measurement is completed by detection and that RWP takes place at the detection step.

SIMPLE MODELS AND BASIC IDEAS FOR MEASUREMENT PROCESSES

In order to examine the essential role of the detection step to make RWP (even in the case of the negative-result measurement), let us first consider a very simple model. RWP in this case is realized by erasing the coherence between two components of the objective wave function—one being modified by detector and the other not being modified at all. Suppose that we are doing a negative-result measurement as illustrated in FIGURE 2. There the object wave function, ψ, is spatially decomposed by an appropriate instrument into two parts, ψ_a and ψ_b, for spectral decomposition, where only ψ_a is guided to a detector. The detector generates a signal to us and changes ψ_a to ψ'_a, while ψ_b is kept unmodified. Afterward, ψ'_a and ψ_b are both gathered into a single channel to examine the presence of coherence. We can use the interference term, $2\mathrm{Re}(\psi_b^* \psi'_a)$, of $|\psi'_a + \psi_b|^2$ inside the channel as a measure of the coherence. In other words, RWP takes place or the coherence still remains, all depending on whether the interference term vanishes or not.

One of the simplest models for a detector may be a one-dimensional lattice composed of N pointlike scatterers, with spacing a, which gives $\psi'_a = 1/\sqrt{2}$ $\exp(-i\bar{k}Na) \exp(ikx)$ for $\psi_a = \psi_b = 1/\sqrt{2} \exp(ikx)$, with $\bar{k}$ being a sort of effective

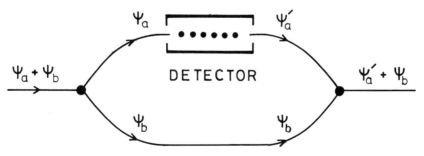

FIGURE 2. Schematic illustration of a simple model for the negative-result measurement.

momentum. The phase-shift proportional to the size parameter, $l \equiv Na$, is common in a wide class of collisions with targets having finite size (as will be discussed shortly). The above measure of the coherence becomes $2\mathrm{Re}(\psi_b^* \psi_a') = \cos(\overline{k}Na)$. Here, we have imagined as if each scatterer in the lattice were rigidly frozen at each lattice site, thus keeping an equal spacing, a. In real cases, however, scatterers must distribute at random within a certain allowance and must have thermal oscillations. For such fluctuations of each scatterer, we may substitute a Gaussian distribution of a around $\overline{a}$ with width, δa, which yields

$$\cos(\overline{k}N\overline{a}) \exp[-N(\overline{k}\delta a)^2/2] \tag{5}$$

for the average of the above measure (note that $\delta a < \overline{a}$). This will vanish if N goes to infinity. Therefore, we have derived RWP at the infinite N limit. In this sense, we can assert that RWP takes place as a sort of phase transition.

However, one may remark that the infinite N limit keeping $\overline{a}$ finite is not realistic and that we have to take fluctuations of N into account in the above arguments. Naturally, a theoretical formulation of the phase transition requires one to perform a scale transformation from microscopic to macroscopic scales; this is accomplished by taking the limits, $N \to \infty$ and $a \to 0$, while keeping $l = Na$ finite, and by averaging over l. Consequently, the above measure can be replaced with

$$I(\overline{k}, \Delta L) \equiv \left| \int dl\, W(l) \exp(-i\overline{k}l) \right|. \tag{6}$$

Here, $W(l)$ is a weight function of l-distribution around L with width, ΔL (for example, $W(l) = (1/\Delta L\sqrt{2\pi}) \exp[-(l - L)^2/2\Delta L^2]$). The scale transformation implies that l is the size parameter of the detector on the microscopic scale, while L is its size on the macroscopic scale. The Gaussian weight gives us

$$I(\overline{k}, \Delta L) = \exp[-(\overline{k}\Delta L)^2/2]. \tag{7}$$

Therefore, we understand that RWP takes place or the coherence still remains, depending on

$$\overline{k}\Delta L \gg 1 \text{ or } \overline{k}\Delta L \lesssim 1. \tag{8}$$

Needless to say, a nice detector must be a macroscopic system (with $N \gg 1$) subject to $\overline{k}\Delta L \gg 1$. It is important to examine the condition in detail by an estimation of $\overline{k}$ and ΔL. ($\Delta L = \delta a \sqrt{N}$ in the above simple model, and also see discussions in the next section or reference 11.)

In the above arguments, one of the most important points is the phase-shift proportional to the size parameter of the detector. Generally speaking, the object system does not always interact with the whole detector, but only with its local system (which is microscopically very large, yet macroscopically very small). The "genuine" detector is nothing other than the local system, which is still macroscopic and subject to $\overline{k}\Delta L \gg 1$, because one collision of the object with such a local system is enough to make RWP. The above size parameter is, of course, of the local system and finite on a microscopic scale. The theory of nuclear reactions[12] teaches us that the S-matrix for collisions of a particle with a finite-size system is decomposed as follows:

$$S = e^{i\delta}(1 + iK)/(1 - iK)e^{i\delta}, \tag{9}$$

with δ being diagonal and K being off-diagonal in the channel representation. Here, the finite-size effect appears in diagonal elements of δ equal to $-\bar{k}l/2$, where l stands for the linear size of the compound system in the relevant channel and $\bar{k}$ stands for a sort of effective momentum. Indeed, we have obtained $\delta = -\bar{k}l/2$ and $\bar{k} = k$ both in the perfect-mirror model[6] and in the Dirac-comb model,[7,13] with the detector size, l, and the incident particle momentum, $\hbar k$.

Another solvable model, namely, a one-dimensional emulsion model given by previous papers,[7,11] is very interesting from the view of scale transformation mentioned above. In this model, we suppose that an extremely relativistic particle interacts with a one-dimensional emulsion having AgBr molecules at N sites with equal spacing, a. Assuming each molecule to have only two eigenstates of the "spin" matrix, $\sigma_3 = \begin{vmatrix} 1 & 0 \\ 0 & -1 \end{vmatrix}$, corresponding to states before and after separation of Ag, we can exactly represent the elementary interaction processes in terms of the S-matrix : $S = \exp[-i\bar{k}l\Sigma_1^N]$, where $l = Na, \bar{k} = \bar{V}/ch$ [with $\bar{V} = a^{-1}\int V(x)\,dx$], and

$$\Sigma_1^N = N^{-1}\sum_{n=1}^{N}\sigma_1^{(n)}. \tag{10}$$

Here, we have considered $V(x)\sigma_1^{(n)}$ to be the interaction Hamiltonian of system Q and the n-th molecule, in which the "spin" matrix, $\sigma_1 = \begin{vmatrix} 0 & 1 \\ 1 & 0 \end{vmatrix}$ (or $\sigma_2 = \begin{vmatrix} 0 & -i \\ i & 0 \end{vmatrix}$), expresses separation of Ag. In this S-matrix, we have obtained again the phase-shift proportional to the size parameter, l. In this case, however, the phase-shift has the first component of the matrix-valued averaged "spin," Σ_i^N ($i = 1, 2, 3$), subject to the commutation relations,

$$[\Sigma_i^N, \Sigma_j^N] = 2iN^{-1}\epsilon_{ijk}\Sigma_k^N, \tag{11}$$

with ϵ_{ijk} being the totally antisymmetric tensor with $\epsilon_{123} = 1$. The right-hand side of equation 11 vanishes and then every component commutes with each other as $N \to \infty$. This means that the averaged "spin" becomes a classical observable at the infinite N limit. Because $\sigma_1^{(n)}$ represents the separation of Ag at the n-th site, Σ_1^N must have its classical value equal to the ratio of the number of separated Ag's to N at the infinite N limit (that is, the separation probability, say w, for one AgBr molecule). In the diagonal representation of $\Pi_n\sigma_3^{(n)}$, however, Σ_1^N always has vanishing expectation values, but never tends to w as $N \to \infty$. This fact tells us that it is necessary to replace the original representation (before taking the limit $N \to \infty$) with a unitary-inequivalent representation so as to give w if we want to go to the classical description. In the new representation, we have $S = \exp[-i\bar{k}lw]$, where we can use $w = \sin^2(\bar{V}a/ch)$ given by quantum mechanics for the separation probability of one molecule.

The situation is to be compared on an equal footing with the well-known symmetry-breaking problems, such as the Higgs mechanisms in modern field theory or the phase transitions in critical phenomena. The above replacement of the discrete variable, N, with the continuous one, l, and the averaging procedure over l can be regarded as scale transformations to make RWP visible to us as a critical phenomenon. The averaging procedure requires us to introduce a continuous sum of Hilbert spaces.

REDUCTION OF WAVE PACKET BY MEASUREMENT

We summarize the discussions given in previous sections as follows: (i) A quantum-mechanical measurement is generally divided into two steps, namely, spectral decomposition and detection. RWP takes place in the detection step, even though the spectral decomposition is practically just as important; (ii) RWP is to be distinguished from thermal irreversible processes, such as discharge phenomena in counters, which work only for displays of results of RWP; (iii) RWP is produced through interactions of the object system with a local system of the apparatus system subject to $\bar{k}\Delta L \gg 1$. The local system is macroscopically very small (but still keeps the macroscopic nature) and has a finite size (on a microscopic scale) to give the phase-shift proportional to it.

The macroscopic nature is formulated as follows: Due to the uncertainty principle, we cannot have a macroscopic system with a huge number of freedoms prepared so as to be in a stationary state with a definite energy and particle number. This is true even if the system were isolated and even if we spent the longest time available to us for preparation. A usual apparatus, especially its local system, is an open system so that its energy and particle number are much more indefinite. The density matrix to describe such a system is given by $\rho^A = \Sigma_N W_N \rho_N^A$, where W_N is a normalized weight around N_0 with width, ΔN, and ρ_N^A is a density matrix for an N-particle system: $\rho_N^A = \Sigma_n |\Phi_n^N > w_n < \Phi_n^N|$, with Φ_n^N being the n-th energy eigenstate of the N-particle system and w_n being the Boltzmann factor. According to discussions in the previous section, we have to introduce the scale transformation from discrete N to continuous l ($= \lim Na$). From this, we are immediately led to

$$\sigma^A = \int dl \, W(l)\rho^A(l) \equiv \mathcal{W} \cdot \rho^A(l) \tag{12}$$

from the above ρ^A, where $W(l)$ is a continuous positive function distributing around L with width, ΔL, under the normalization condition of $\int dl \, W(l) = 1$. $\rho^A(l)$ is the density matrix of a local system with a sharp size, l. Note that $\rho^A(l)$ is no longer diagonal in the number representation, and note that we are now using another representation, namely, a unitary-inequivalent one, instead of the number representation. Hereafter, we will use the above symbol, $\mathcal{W}$, for the averaging procedure.

The use of equation 12 for the density matrix to describe a macroscopic system with a huge number of freedoms can also be justified from the mathematical point of view.[14] Mathematically, observables can be represented in a large Hilbert space given by the following direct sum of small Hilbert spaces:

$$\mathcal{H} = \mathcal{H}_1 + \mathcal{H}_2 + \cdots + \int d\mu(\zeta)\mathcal{H}(\zeta), \tag{13}$$

where $\mu(\zeta)$ is a smooth function of a continuous parameter, ζ, and where it holds that $\lim_{N\to\infty} \mathcal{H}_N \subset \int d\mu(\zeta) \, \mathcal{H}(\zeta)$. Because we can identify N with the particle number and put $\zeta = l$, we know that σ^A is a density matrix belonging to the continuous superselection rule space, $\int d\mu(\zeta) \, \mathcal{H}(\zeta)$. Mathematics also tells us that the continuous sum has the "center" composed of commutable quantities, that is, classical observables. In the previous section, we indeed have seen the averaged "spin" as an example of a quantum observable that falls into the "center" at the infinite N limit. Thus, a local system of the measuring apparatus is to be described by the density matrix (equation 12) belonging to a continuous direct sum of many Hilbert spaces, but not to any single Hilbert space, which is contrary to the Wigner theorem.

We are now coming to the place to derive RWP in an explicit form. Within the above theoretical framework, the physical process in the detection step can be written down in terms of the total density matrix, Ξ_t^{tot}, as follows:

$$\Xi_t^{tot} \xrightarrow[t \to \infty]{} \overline{\Xi}^{tot} \equiv \mathcal{W} \cdot e^{-iH_0t/\hbar} S \rho_I^Q \times \rho_I^A S^\dagger e^{iH_0t/\hbar}, \tag{14}$$

where we have used the asymptotic relation, $e^{-iHt/\hbar} \xrightarrow[t \to \infty]{} e^{-iH_0t/\hbar}S$, with S being the S-matrix. H and H_0 are the total and free Hamiltonians of the total system, respectively. ρ_I^Q and ρ_I^A are, respectively, the initial state density matrices of the object system and a local system of the apparatus immediately before the detection step. Our task is to show that equation 14 surely means RWP.

In the Stern-Gerlach experiment, we have $\rho^Q = |\psi^Q\rangle\langle\psi^Q|$, that is,

$$\rho_I^Q = |c_a|^2|a\rangle\langle a| + |c_b|^2|b\rangle\langle b| + c_a c_b^*|a\rangle\langle b| + c_b^* c_b|b\rangle\langle a|, \tag{15}$$

correspondingly to ψ^Q (equation 4), where $|a\rangle = u_a\phi_a$ and $|b\rangle = u_b\phi_b$. First, let us consider the standard case (FIGURE 1a), in which we have to use $\rho_I^A = \rho_I^{D_a} \times \rho_I^{D_b}$ and $\mathcal{W} = \mathcal{W}_a\mathcal{W}_b$, which correspond to the presence of two detectors, D_a and D_b. Consequently, the right-hand side of equation 14 becomes

$$\overline{\Xi}_t^{tot} = |c_a|^2\overline{\Xi}_t^{aa} + |c_b|^2\overline{\Xi}_t^{bb} + c_a c_b^*\overline{\Xi}_t^{ab} + c_a^* c_b \overline{\Xi}_t^{ba}, \tag{16}$$

where

$$\overline{\Xi}_t^{aa} = \mathcal{W}_a\mathcal{W}_b \cdot e^{-iH_0t/\hbar}S[|a\rangle\langle a| \times \rho_I^{D_a} \times \rho_I^{D_b}]S^\dagger e^{iH_0t/\hbar}, \tag{17a}$$

$$\overline{\Xi}_t^{ab} = \mathcal{W}_a\mathcal{W}_b \cdot e^{-iH_0t/\hbar}S[|a\rangle\langle b| \times \rho_I^{D_a} \times \rho_I^{D_b}]S^\dagger e^{iH_0t/\hbar}, \tag{17b}$$

and so on. The S-matrix brings in interactions only between couples, $(D_a, |a\rangle$ or $\langle a|)$ and $(D_b, |b\rangle$ or $\langle b|)$, thereby producing the phase factors, $\exp(\pm i\bar{k}_a l_a)$ and $\exp(\pm i\bar{k}_b l_b)$, as was discussed in the previous section. Therefore, the averaging procedures in equations 17a and 17b give the following integrals:

$$[\int dl_a W(l_a) \exp(-i\bar{k}_a l_a) \exp(i\bar{k}_a l_a) \cdots][\int dl_b W(l_b) \cdots], \tag{18a}$$

$$[\int dl_a W(l_a) \exp(-i\bar{k}_a l_a) \cdots][\int dl_b W(l_b) \exp(i\bar{k}_b l_b) \cdots]. \tag{18b}$$

The phase factors in equation 18a cancel each other out in the l_a-integral, while those in equation 18b are separately kept in the different integrals of the Riemann-Lebesgue type similar to equation 6. Hence, the cross-correlation terms, $\overline{\Xi}_t^{ab}$ and $\overline{\Xi}_t^{ba}$, vanish under the condition,

$$\bar{k}_a\Delta L_a \gg 1, \qquad \bar{k}_b\Delta L_b \gg 1, \tag{19}$$

but the auto-correlation terms, $\overline{\Xi}_t^{aa}$ and $\overline{\Xi}_t^{bb}$, remain nonvanishing. Finally, we obtain

$$\Xi_t^{tot} \xrightarrow[t \to \infty]{} \overline{\Xi}^{tot} = |c_a|^2\xi_F^Q(a) \times \sigma_F^{D_a} \times \sigma_I^{D_b} + |c_b|^2\xi_F^Q(b) \times \sigma_I^{D_a} \times \sigma_F^{D_b}, \tag{20}$$

which clearly means RWP. Here, the density matrices with subscript F represent the final states of Q, D_a, and D_b, respectively.

In order to obtain the total density matrix in the case of the negative-result measurement (FIGURE 1b), we have only to remove $\rho_I^{D_b}$ and $\mathcal{W}_b$ in equations 17a and 17b, and then remove the l_b-integral in equations 18a and 18b. Still, we have the

l_a-integrals of the Riemann-Lebesgue type in the cross-correlation terms, which also vanish under the condition in equation 19. Consequently, we obtain the asymptotic behavior,

$$\Xi_t^{\text{tot}} \xrightarrow[t \to \infty]{} \Xi^{\text{tot}} = |c_a|^2 \xi_F^Q(a) \times \sigma_F^{D_a} + |c_b|^2 \xi_I^Q(b) \times \sigma_I^{D_a}, \tag{21}$$

which is nothing other than RWP in this case. Note that the Riemann-Lebesgue integrals to give RWP (equations 20 and 21) come from just the same origin as in the simple model in the previous section.

Here, we should mention the relationship between our theory and the Wigner theorem. If we remove the averaging procedure or, equivalently, if we put $W(l) = \delta(l - L)$, then we can never obtain RWP because the Riemann-Lebesgue lemma does not work. This means that our theory has just returned back to the Wigner theorem because $W(l) = \delta(l - L)$ gives a density matrix on one Hilbert space. Therefore, our theory is not inconsistent with the theorem, and it seems that we can go over its barrier by making use of the continuous superselection rule space.

Even in the case keeping the averaging procedure, we cannot have RWP if $\bar{k}\Delta L \lesssim 1$ (see equations 8 and 19) because the Riemann-Lebesgue lemma also does not work. Of course, such macroscopic systems are not adequate to measurement, even though some of them may be interesting for macroscopic quantum effects. One of the nice examples has been presented by recent experiments on neutron interference,[15] which I have discussed elsewhere.[16] The Al–phase shifter in the experiments gives $\bar{k} = \lambda nb$, where λ, n, and b are, respectively, the neutron wavelength, the Al-nucleus density, and the scattering length of low energy n-Al collisions: $D_\lambda \equiv 2\pi/\bar{k} \simeq 0.01$ cm for their experimental values. In the case in which an oscillating magnetic field (with amplitude, B, and period, T) is imposed on one path of neutron, the neutron suffers only a quasi-static effect because $T \simeq l/v$ (l being the coil size and v being the neutron velocity) under their experimental conditions. Thus, we have $\bar{k} \simeq \mu [B^2 + B_0^2]^{1/2}/vh$, with μ being the neutron magnetic moment. Note that the whole equipment is put in a static magnetic field, B_0. Experimental values give $D_\lambda \equiv 2\pi/\bar{k} \simeq 10$ cm. In both cases, therefore, we know $D_\lambda \gg \Delta L$ or $\bar{k}\Delta L \ll 1$ for the numerical values of ΔL estimated below, so RWP should not take place by the Al–phase shifter and/or the oscillating magnetic field. Hence, we can understand the reason why the interference phenomena are observed despite of spin-flipping.

As for estimation of ΔL, we may use the formula, $\Delta L = \delta a \sqrt{N}$, given by the simple model in the previous section. First, it would be natural to put $N \simeq (10^{24})^{1/3} \simeq 10^8$, based on the Avogadro number, for the order of the lattice-sites number of the one-dimensional chain. If we further substitute a string (with mass density, μ', and sound velocity, v') for the one-dimensional chain,[17] then we can get $\delta a = \sqrt{(\bar{a}k_B T)}/\mu'v'^2)$ for thermal fluctuations of one lattice point. For $\bar{a} \simeq 10^{-8}$ cm, $k_B T \simeq 10^{-14}$ erg, $\mu' \simeq 1$ g/cm, and $v' \simeq 10^5$ cm/s, we have $\delta a \simeq 10^{-16}$ cm and hence $\Delta L \simeq 10^{-12}$ cm. This very small value comes mainly from the vanishing size of each lattice point. To take its finite size into account, it is better to put $\delta a \simeq \bar{a} \simeq 10^{-8}$ cm, which yields $\Delta L \simeq 10^{-4}$ cm. We can use this value as a measure of ΔL. Another estimation based on fluctuations on N also gives the same order of magnitude to ΔL (see reference 11).

CONCLUDING REMARKS

In the previous two sections, we have explicitly derived RWP based on (i) the macroscopic nature of a local system of the measuring apparatus (to be represented by equation 12) within the framework of a continuous direct sum of many Hilbert spaces, and (ii) the phase-shift proportional to the finite size of the local system. Both produce the Riemann-Lebesgue integrals of the form of equation 6 or equation 18b in the cross-correlation terms, which vanish under the condition of equation 19, that is, $\overline{k}\Delta L \gg 1$.

The integral, $I(\overline{k}, \Delta L)$, given by equation 6, or its value, $\exp[-(\overline{k}\Delta L)^2/2]$, offers us a criterion that allows us to judge whether the measurement is perfect or not. Indeed, $I(\overline{k}, \Delta L)$, supplemented by another factor originating in $(1 + iK)/(1 - iK)$ of the S-matrix, represents a sort of theoretical detection efficiency of the apparatus. Rigorously speaking, most of the practical measurements are imperfect because $I(\overline{k}, \Delta L)$ does not exactly vanish. Nevertheless, we can reach a perfect measurement by repetition of imperfect measurements, that is, by successive collisions of system Q with many local systems for which we expect $I^\nu \xrightarrow[\nu \to \infty]{} 0$. This is a sort of continual observation problem.

It would be interesting to make a numerical simulation of the measurement process, that is, of RWP, by exactly solving the Schrödinger equation, for example, for collisions of an object particle with a detector having N scatterers.[18]

ACKNOWLEDGMENTS

The author is very much indebted to S. Machida for many discussions and collaborations.

NOTES AND REFERENCES

1. VON NEUMANN, J. 1932. Mathematische Grundlagen der Quanten-mechanik. Springer-Verlag. Berlin.
2. WIGNER, E. P. 1963. Am. J. Phys. **31:** 6–15.
3. DANERI, A., A. LOINGER & G. M. PROSPERI. 1962. Nucl. Phys. **33:** 297–319.
4. JAUCH, J. M., E. P. WIGNER & M. M. YANASE. 1967. Nuovo Cimento **48B:** 144–151.
5. EVERRET, H., III. 1957. Rev. Mod. Phys. **29:** 454–462; DE WITT, B. S. & N. GRAHAM, Eds. 1973. The Many-Worlds Interpretation of Quantum Mechanics. Princeton Univ. Press. Princeton, New Jersey.
6. MACHIDA, S. & M. NAMIKI. 1980. Prog. Theor. Phys. **63:** 1457–1473, 1833–1847.
7. MACHIDA, S. & M. NAMIKI. 1984. Proc. of the International Symposium on Foundations of Quantum Mechanics—In the Light of New Technology (ISQM). S. Kamefuchi et al., Eds.: 127–135, 136–139. Phys. Soc. Japan. Tokyo; MACHIDA, S. & M. NAMIKI. 1986. Fundamental Questions in Quantum Mechanics. L. M. Roth & A. Inomata, Eds. Gordon & Breach. New York; NAMIKI, M. 1986. Proc. of the International Conference on Microphysical Reality and Quantum Formalism (Fundamental Theories of Physics). A. van der Merwe & G. Tarozzi, Eds. To be published. Reidel. Dordrecht.
8. Otherwise, we meet a contradiction pointed out by S. Watanabe. See references 6 and 7.
9. See reference 2 and FINE, A. 1970. Phys. Rev. **D2:** 2783–2787; SHIMONY, A. 1974. Phys. Rev. **D9:** 2321–2323.

10. RENNINGER, M. 1960. Z. Phys. **158:** 417–421.
11. NAMIKI, M. 1985. Quantum Mechanics of Macroscopic Systems and Measurement Problems (in Japanese). Frontiers of Physics 10. Y. Ohtsuki, Ed: 139–219. Kyoritsu. Tokyo.
12. For example, see McVoy, K. M. 1969. Ann. Phys. **54:** 552–565.
13. KIANG, D. 1974. Am. J. Phys. **42:** 785–787.
14. ARAKI, H. 1980. Prog. Theor. Phys. **64:** 719–730.
15. For example, see RAUCH, H. 1984. Proc. of ISQM. S. Kamefuchi et al., Eds: 277–288. Phys. Soc. Japan. Tokyo.
16. NAMIKI, M., Y. OTAKE & H. SOSHI. 1986. Prog. Theor. Phys. To be published.
17. NAKAJIMA, S. 1983. Comment on Namiki's talk at ISQM.
18. NAMIKI, M., Y. MURAYAMA, H. NAKAZATO & I. OHBA. In preparation.

Reduction of the Wave Packet and Environment-Induced Superselection

W. H. ZUREK[a]

Theoretical Astrophysics
Los Alamos National Laboratory
Los Alamos, New Mexico 87545

INTRODUCTION

"No elementary phenomenon is a phenomenon until it is a registered (observed) phenomenon"—John Archibald Wheeler.

The purpose of quantum theory of measurement is to render present discussions about the interpretation of quantum mechanics unnecessary. This goal can be achieved only by establishing an unambiguous correspondence between the "physical reality" (as we, observers, perceive it) and the formalism of the theory. In the opinion of this author, such a desirable state of affairs has not yet been reached.

The first aim of this paper is to examine some of the interpretations of quantum theory, and to show how they ultimately fail in their task. Having done that, we shall recall key points raised by the model in which the apparent reduction of the wave packet is induced by the interaction with the environment. We shall argue that while this model does not provide a mechanism for truly irreversible "collapses" of the wave packet, it succeeds in making them irreversible in practice. Moreover, it singles out a preferred basis, elements of which correspond to "classical" states. In a more generic situation, they may be regarded as "eigenstates of classical observables." This discussion will focus on present shortcomings of environment-induced superselection rather than on its achievements. The purpose of such a critical analysis is to accelerate further development of this model.

We shall conclude that environment-induced superselection constitutes a useful addition to the Copenhagen (as well as to the "Many-Worlds") Interpretations. It should be regarded as a clue pointing at a still more satisfactory resolution of the measurement problem.

QUANTUM THEORY AND ITS INTERPRETATIONS

"When I hear of Schrödinger's cat, I reach for my gun"—S. W. Hawking.

The difficulties inherent in the interpretation of quantum theory are presumably well appreciated by the potential readers of this paper. We shall, therefore, be rather

[a]W. H. Zurek is a J. Robert Oppenheimer Fellow in theoretical astrophysics.

brief in restating them. More comprehensive descriptions can be found in references 1–6. Popular expositions are also available.[7]

In essence, the problem arises from the conflict between the formalism of quantum theory and our everyday experiences (see, for example, celebrated paradoxes of Schrödinger's cat[8] and Wigner's friend[9]). Objects described by quantum mechanics evolve according to the Schrödinger's equation:

$$i\partial|\psi\rangle/\partial t = H|\psi\rangle. \tag{1}$$

In the conventional use of this equation (e.g., in scattering theory), the initial state of the wave function is known. Given a Hamiltonian, H, and sufficient mathematical skill, one can predict the wave function, $|\psi\rangle$, at an arbitrary later time, t:

$$|\psi(t)\rangle = \exp(-iHt)|\psi(0)\rangle. \tag{2}$$

The conceptual difficulty comes about because the wave function usually emerging from such a calculation is a coherent superposition of various experimentally distinguishable outcomes (e.g., different tracks of the particle in the bubble chamber).

Formally, if we denote the collection of the states corresponding to distinct outcomes by $\{|o_i\rangle\}$, the wave function, $|\psi(t)\rangle$, is given by

$$|\psi(t)\rangle = \Sigma_i c_i|o_i\rangle. \tag{3}$$

Here, $c_i = \langle o_i|\psi(t)\rangle$. An accepted, although once controversial part of the interpretation of quantum mechanics states that the probability of a given outcome, $|o_i\rangle$, is

$$p_i = |c_i|^2 = |\langle o_i|\psi(t)\rangle|^2. \tag{4}$$

It is interesting to note that Born has suggested this interpretation in a "note added in proof."[10] (In the original text, he was arguing for $p_i = c_i$.)

The difficult and still controversial part of the interpretation has to do with the mechanism through which a certain $|o_i\rangle$—a single, definite outcome—is chosen in a particular run of the experiment from all the other possibilities present in the superposition (equation 4). There are several interpretations that suggest a definite "model" for this process. Below, we shall briefly describe three of them.

Copenhagen Interpretation (CI)

According to this school of thought, definite outcomes of measurements emerge as a result of the interaction between a quantum system and a classical measuring apparatus. The key point of CI was stated perhaps most clearly and succinctly by John Archibald Wheeler[11,12] in a sentence that serves as the motto to the introduction of this paper. The difficulty with the interpretation is "settled" by appealing to devices that are classical, and consequently, outside of the realm of quantum mechanics. This may sound like an unfair trick—taking the problem outside of the range where it is clearly defined—but we shall see a similar scheme applied by other interpretations. The advantage of CI is to use this trick openly. In a sense, CI is not really an interpretation, but, rather, a phenomenological description of what we believe really happens. We believe that for one reason or another, classical objects do not appear in superpositions.

Therefore, we appeal to this "classical property" and use it to solve the quantum measurement problem.

The deficiency of CI lies in its failure to provide criteria that would allow one to classify objects as either classical or quantum. CI in its original formulation does not address the question, "how can an object whose constituents are all quantum (atoms) behave classically?" There is no prescription within CI to help one mark the borderline between quantum and classical.

Appeal to Consciousness

Von Neumann[1] and Wigner[9] have suggested a possibility that the collapse of the state vector does not happen at all in the realm of the physical universe. An outcome of the measurement (according to this viewpoint) becomes definite only when "the conscious observer" becomes aware of it. Hence, only during the contact of the wave function with the "consciousness" does the wave function collapse to a definite $|o_i\rangle$.

The trick of appealing for the help from outside of the quantum theory is used here again. Classical objects of CI were at least still in the domain of physics. "Consciousness" must be outside of the physical universe. For if it was describable by physics, it should follow equation 1, and, therefore, one could not appeal to it to cause "collapse" of the wave function.

The failure of this point of view to gain a wider following in the physics community is quite understandable: It does not address the issue of "quantum reality" with tools physicists can handle. On the other hand, it does focus attention on an important point: The relation between the physical universe and the conscious mind. While it is perhaps often useful for us to ignore this issue in everyday work, it is also important to keep in mind that this is an open issue,[13-15] and that science—"hard", experimental science— might be able to address it (see, for example, reference 16 for an intriguing forerunner of possible experiments relevant to this question).

Many-Worlds Interpretation (MWI)

If it is so difficult to propose a physical mechanism for the reduction of the wave packet, then, perhaps, one could get rid of the difficulty altogether and make do without a collapse. This line of thought goes back to Everett,[17] and was explored by many others (see reference 18 for a collection of papers advocating this point of view). At the first sight, it is quite attractive. It claims to achieve a consistent interpretation of quantum theory without a "collapse." According to the proponents of MWI, interactions that force the wave function to split into a multitude of components (see equation 4) force the whole universe to split into different universes. A single specific measurement outcome is realized in each of these alternative universes.

The advantage of this point of view is it allows one to calculate (with well-defined tools of quantum theory) in situations where other interpretations would have forced one to conclude that the calculation is poorly defined because it would not be clear what is quantum and what is classical (and, therefore, one would have to "give up"). The disadvantage is that after the calculation is finished, it is quite difficult to interpret the meaning of the outcome. The best example of such a situation is perhaps afforded by the recent work on the "wave function of the universe" (see, for example, references 19 and 20, and references therein).

The picture of the universe splitting into distinct branches is appealing to some and disturbing to others. I would like to stress that, in a sense, MWI fails to address the key issue of the measurement problem. It is easy to maintain that the wave function evolves forever according to equation 1, and that collapse never really occurs. It is much more difficult to explain why, in spite of this single, global wave function, we perceive only its apparently collapsed "branches." In other words, a question that is unaddressed and, indeed, obscured by MWI is the very central question of the interpretation of quantum theory: How does the unambiguous correspondence between the theory and our individual perceptions come about? The Many-Worlds Interpretation avoids this issue by tacitly assuming that the "consciousness" will perceive the wave function of the universe "branch by branch." In other words, properties of consciousness are being in the end blamed for what appears to have happened in the course of a measurement.

Extensions and Alternatives

The views described above have been investigated by many since their inception. We will not have time to comment on all of the extensions. There is, however, a train of thought dating all the way to Bohr and von Neumann that devotes special attention to the irreversible nature of the collapse. In particular, Daneri, Loinger, and Prosperi,[21] as well as George, Prigogine, and Rosenfeld,[22] have invoked irreversibility to explain reduction of the wave packet. Since then, such a view has been attacked and defended. This author agrees with the analysis of Zeh,[23] who concludes that the problems of measurement and irreversibility are intimately related. If one could solve the problem of irreversibility, then one would also have a mechanism for the reduction of the wave packet. At present, we do not have a convincing solution for either one of them.

There are several alternative points of view of the measurement problem. Except for one, we will leave them unexplored in this paper. Penrose argues that quantum gravity must allow for fundamentally irreversible processes.[24,25] This conjecture is based on the analysis of the gravitational collapse and the subsequent evaporation of black holes. Penrose contends that black holes, in an isolated system, form mostly by collapse and disappear mostly by evaporation. Hence, gravity must be irreversible. Penrose suggests that this irreversibility can also be used to collapse a wave packet when the object described by it is sufficiently macroscopic to significantly alter the metric of the space-time. It should be noted at the outset that most of the researchers disagree with Penrose's analysis of black hole formation and evaporation (see, for example, references 26 and 27). Therefore, his ansatz that the entropy associated with the metric of the space-time is different and more fundamental than the statistical entropy of, say, photon gas cannot be really justified. Indeed, black hole entropy can be regarded as the statistical entropy of the thin "atmosphere" composed of quanta such as photons, gravitons, etc., hovering above its horizon.[28] I bring up Penrose's viewpoint not only because it is truly different, and, as such, deserves attention. I do it also for a self-serving reason: Gravitational field is, obviously, an "ultimate environment" from which there is no isolation. It is, therefore, important to point out that it may play a role in the environment-induced superselection, which is the subject we are about to discuss.

ENVIRONMENT-INDUCED SUPERSELECTION

"*Esse est percipi*" (to be is to be perceived)—Bishop George Berkeley.

The aim of this program is to show that when a quantum system is in contact with other quantum systems (which are summarily described as "an environment"), reduction of the wave packet occurs for all practical purposes directly as a consequence of quantum evolution (see equation 1). The interaction of a quantum system with its environment results in correlations. In a sense, the environment measures (perceives) the system, and in doing so, allows the state of the system to acquire a "classical reality." (Hence, the motto of this section.) The combined system-environment state vector evolves from the direct product state,

$$|\Phi(t_1)\rangle = |\psi(t_i)\rangle \times |\phi_E\rangle, \tag{5}$$

into a correlated state,

$$|\Phi(t_2)\rangle = \Sigma_i c_i |o_i\rangle \times |\epsilon_i\rangle. \tag{6}$$

Here, $|\epsilon_i\rangle$ are distinct (orthogonal) states of the environment. The knowledge of the correlations, and, more generally, of the state of the environment is usually not accessible to the observer. Therefore, he must use the density matrix,

$$\rho_S = \text{tr}_\epsilon |\Phi\rangle\langle\Phi| \simeq \Sigma_i |c_i|^2 |o_i\rangle\langle o_i|, \tag{7}$$

to describe the system. Here, tr_ϵ signifies the trace over the environmental degrees of freedom. Basis $|o_i\rangle$, which appears on the diagonal of ρ_S, is called (in recognition of its role in the measurements process) the "pointer basis."[29] In idealized situations where there is a set of basis states that diagonalizes both the self-Hamiltonian, H_S, of the system, as well as the system-environment interaction Hamiltonian, H_{SE}, the choice of the pointer basis is easy: Projection operators constructed of its elements must commute with the total Hamiltonian,

$$[H_S + H_{SE}, |o_i\rangle\langle o_i|] = 0. \tag{8}$$

In physically realistic situations, this idealized assumption will be satisfied only rarely.[30,31] In more complicated circumstances, the preferred basis will emerge as a result of interaction between the system and the environment, but a simple prescription given by equation 8 may not be sufficient. For instance, when parts of H_S that do not satisfy equation 8 are small compared to H_{SE}, the approximate pointer basis can still be obtained from the requirement that the commutation relation (equation 8) be approximately satisfied.[32-34] There are also situations (e.g., an harmonic oscillator interacting weakly with its environment) when preferred states can turn out to be some other set of states (for instance, "coherent states" for harmonic oscillators).[35,36] One would expect in such cases that the preferred states are these that are least perturbed by the combined action of H_S and H_{SE}.[30-32,34]

It would take more space than is available here to go into the details of environment-induced superselection. We shall not venture to provide such a summary in this paper. Fortunately, both overviews of the general idea and specific calculations of well-defined examples are available inside of this volume and elsewhere.[29–39] It is more useful at this stage of the development of the model of environment-induced superselection to focus on the unsolved problems. The list given below is admittedly rather incomplete. Its purpose is not to discourage, but rather to point out which issues offer (in the opinion of this author) the greatest hope for a significant progress.

Can One Trust Master Equations?

The standard technique used to describe a system interacting with its environment is to obtain a (Markoffian) master equation that describes the reduced density matrix, ρ_S. Master equations were thoroughly tested only for a rather restricted class of problems: They were extensively used to describe the evolution of diagonal elements of the density matrix in some preferred basis on relatively long relaxation time scales. For the issues raised by the proposal of environment-induced superselection, the off-diagonal parts of the density matrix are crucial. By applying master equations, one can calculate that these off-diagonal elements disappear on times very much shorter than the relaxation time scale.[33,35,38,40,41] This conclusion is almost certainly qualitatively right; that is, if the master equation predicts a very short time scale for the decay of correlations, then a more careful analysis invariably confirms this prediction.[32,36,42–44] However, the applicability of such equations on very short time scales and, consequently, the validity of their quantitative predictions should not be taken for granted. Indeed, on very short time scales, evolution is likely to be non-Markoffian. Consequently, the actual evolution may differ substantially from the one obtained by the use of master equations.[36,43,44]

A related concern has to do with the way in which the environment is discarded right from the start in a master equation description of the evolution. This results in a conceptually misleading picture in which the environment is providing nothing more than "dissipation." It is important to keep in mind that the role of the environment in the environment-induced superselection is to "monitor" the system. In this sense, the effect of the system on the environment is as important as the effect of the environment on the system. Fortunately, a number of recent calculations go far beyond the master equation treatment, and, in doing so, allow one to better appreciate the true role of the environment.[30–32,36,42–44] Still, much remains to be done in this area.

How Can One Make a "Relativistic" Environment?

This is a very specific deficiency of the current models of the system-environment interaction: In all of them, the environment is treated as a collection of stationary systems (e.g., harmonic oscillators). Hence, both these treatments that make use of master equations, as well as more ambitious attempts using more faithful representations of the environment, predict that only stationary systems can avoid dissipation. This conclusion implies the existence of an "ether" and is clearly incorrect for such environments as the one provided by the electromagnetic vacuum at $T = 0$: An electron or an atom can move through it at a constant velocity without any damping.

It is quite easy to suggest a remedy to this situation, but it is rather difficult to implement it. A quantum field provides an environment that is relativistically invariant. The difficulty arises when one attempts to repeat the calculations using the system-field coupling that is also invariant. The resulting problem is very difficult mathematically. Nevertheless, this issue must be addressed more fully before one will have complete confidence in the calculations predicting the rapid decay of coherence in interference experiments conducted in a photon heat bath.[40,43,45]

Environment-Induced Superselection for Fields

If a single quantum system can be "measured" by its environment, the same could presumably happen with the field. This problem of environment-induced superselection for fields is especially urgent in the context of inflationary models of the early universe. The choice between the alternative universes that are all present in the global wave function is ambiguous. It is possible that some of the degrees of freedom of the universe can act as an environment that diagonalizes the effective density matrix of the others. It should be stressed that there is a substantial, perhaps crucial difference between this conceivable application of environment-induced superselection and the other examples: Now the whole system—the universe—is closed and isolated (at least when $\Omega > 1$), and there is no outside environment.

SUMMARY AND CONCLUSIONS

"Planck's discovery of the quantum in 1900 drove a crack in the armor that still covers the deep and secret principle of existence. In the exploitation of that opening we are at the beginning"—John Archibald Wheeler.

The aim of the previous section was to indicate the extent to which environment-induced superselection allows one to address issues raised by the apparent conflict between quantum formalism and everyday experiences. In particular, we have argued that it supplies one with: (1) a preferred set of basis states, and (2) a cause of an apparent reduction of the state vector. From the viewpoint of the Copenhagen Interpretation, one receives a well-defined (although still relatively unexplored) model for the transition from quantum to classical: Quantum systems are isolated from their environments, while classical systems are continuously monitored through their interaction with their surroundings. Indeed, in this sense, environment-induced superselection can be regarded as a missing element of CI. It defines what is quantum and what is classical. This gain, namely, the definition of the border between quantum and classical, comes at a rather substantial price: The collapse of the wave function is now only "apparent."

The increase of entropy in the course of the measurement is due to a transfer of information from systems to correlations between them. For all practical purposes, this process can be regarded as irreversible. However, in principle, all the evolutions follow equation 1 and are, therefore, dynamically reversible. Consequently, in the opinion of this author, coupling to the environment does not settle all of the problems of quantum measurement.

It should be noted that this assessment of how much (or how little) can be accomplished by an appeal to environment-induced superselection is not shared by everybody. In particular, Wigner suggested that interaction with the environment may force more than just an apparent collapse of the wave packet.[39] The view I have advocated in this paper is rather more conservative. Environment-induced superselection is, of course, quite compatible with the Many-Worlds Interpretation of quantum mechanics. Indeed, it can supply MWI with a prescription of how to define the branches into which the universe is splitting. Such a prescription was absent in the original proposals. Both of these lines of thought (Wigner's arguments and MWI) would lead one to believe that the problem of measurement is truly solved and that there is nothing more to learn from it. Apart from all the other objections one could raise, this last conclusion is, in my opinion, the best argument against this kind of an "easy" solution. Such a comment may seem paradoxical. After all, a really good resolution of the problem should settle it completely, and if this can be done easily, so much the better. This is certainly true. It is, however, difficult to imagine that the ultimate solution of the measurement problem could provide us with so meager an additional "payoff" in the form of a deeper understanding of what is the role of information in the process of measurement, and of how do we, as "observers," fit into the scheme. For all these reasons, I agree with the motto of this section. Environment-induced superselection appears to me to be a hint about how to proceed rather than the means to settle the issue quickly.

REFERENCES

1. von Neumann, J. 1955. Mathematical Foundations of Quantum Mechanics. Princeton Univ. Press. Princeton, New Jersey.
2. London, F. & E. Bauer. 1939. La Théorie de l'Observation en Mécanique Quantique. Hermann et Cie. Paris. (English translation in reference 6.)
3. Wigner, E. P. 1963. Am. J. Phys. 31: 6; see also Wigner, E. P. 1983. In Quantum Theory and Measurement. Princeton Univ. Press. Princeton, New Jersey.
4. d'Espagnat, B. 1971. Conceptual Foundations of Quantum Mechanics. W. A. Benjamin. Menlo Park, California.
5. Jammer, M. 1974. The Philosophy of Quantum Mechanics. Wiley. New York.
6. Wheeler, J. A. & W. H. Zurek. 1983. Quantum Theory and Measurement. Princeton Univ. Press. Princeton, New Jersey.
7. Herbert, N. 1985. Quantum Reality. Anchor Press/Doubleday. Garden City, New York.
8. Schrödinger, E. 1935. Naturwissenschaften 23: 807–812, 823–828, 844–849. (English translation by: Trimmer, J. D. 1980. Proc. Am. Philos. Soc. 124: 323. Reprinted in reference 6.)
9. Wigner, E. P. 1962. In The Scientist Speculates. I. J. Good, Ed. Reprinted in reference 6.
10. Born, M. 1926. Z. Phys. 37: 863. (English translation in reference 6.)
11. Wheeler, J. A. 1983. Law without law. In Quantum Theory and Measurement. Princeton Univ. Press. Princeton, New Jersey.
12. Wheeler, J. A. 1977. In Foundational Problems in the Special Sciences. R. E. Butts & K. J. Hintikka, Eds. Reidel. Dordrecht.
13. Dyson, F. J. 1979. Disturbing the Universe. Harper & Row. New York.
14. Wheeler, J. A. 1986. In Frontiers of Nonequilibrium Statistical Physics. G. T. Moore & M. O. Scully, Eds. Plenum. New York.

15. PERES, A. & W. H. ZUREK. 1982. Am. J. Phys. **50:** 807.
16. ECLLES, J. C. 1986. Do mental events cause neural events analogously to the probability fields of quantum mechanics? Proc. R. Soc. London **22:** 411–428.
17. EVERETT, H. 1957. Rev. Mod. Phys. **29:** 454.
18. DEWITT, B. S. & N. GRAHAM, Eds. 1973. The Many-Worlds Interpretation of Quantum Mechanics. Princeton Univ. Press. Princeton, New Jersey.
19. HARTLE, J. B. & S. W. HAWKING. 1983. Phys. Rev. **D28:** 2960.
20. TIPLER, F. J. 1986. Phys. Rep. **137**(4): 231.
21. DANERI, A., A. LOINGER & G. M. PROSPERI. 1962. Nucl. Phys. **33:** 297.
22. GEORGE, C., I. PRIGOGINE & L. ROSENFELD. 1972. Mat. Fyz. Medd. Vidensk. Selsk. **38:** 1.
23. ZEH, H. D. 1970. *In* Foundations of Quantum Mechanics. B. d'Espagnat, Ed. Academic Press. New York.
24. PENROSE, R. 1982. Some remarks on gravity and quantum mechanics. *In* Quantum Structure of Space and Time. M. J. Duff & C. J. Isham, Eds. Cambridge Univ. Press. Cambridge.
25. PENROSE, R. 1985. Gravity and state-vector reduction. *In* Quantum Discussions. R. Penrose & C. Isham, Eds. Oxford Univ. Press. Oxford.
26. PAGE, D. N. 1980. Phys. Rev. Lett. **44:** 301.
27. HAWKING, S. W. 1976. Phys. Rev. **D13:** 191.
28. ZUREK, W. H. & K. S. THORNE. 1985. Phys. Rev. Lett. **54:** 2171.
29. ZUREK, W. H. 1981. Phys. Rev. **D24:** 1516.
30. ZUREK, W. H. 1982. Phys. Rev. **D26:** 1862.
31. ZUREK, W. H. 1983. Information transfer in quantum measurements. *In* Quantum Optics, Experimental Gravity, and Measurement Theory. P. Meystre & M. O. Scully, Eds. Plenum. New York.
32. HAAKE, F. & D. F. WALLS. 1986. Overdamping and quasi quantum non-demolition measurements. University of Waikato preprint (Hamilton, New Zealand).
33. ZUREK, W. H. 1986. Wavepacket reduction: how long does it take? *In* Frontiers of Nonequilibrium Statistical Physics. G. T. Moore & M. O. Scully, Eds. Plenum. New York.
34. PAGE, D. N. 1986. Information basis of states for quantum measurements. *In* Fundamental Questions in Quantum Mechanics. L. M. Roth & A. Inomata, Eds. Gordon & Breach. New York.
35. WALLS, D. F., M. J. COLLETT & G. J. MILBURN. 1985. Phys. Rev. **D32:** 3208.
36. UNRUH, W. G. & W. H. ZUREK. 1986. Reduction of the wavepacket in quantum Brownian motion. Los Alamos preprint. In preparation.
37. JOOS, E. 1986. This volume.
38. JOOS, E. & H. D. ZEH, 1985. Z. Phys. **59:** 223.
39. WIGNER, E. P. 1983. *In* Quantum Optics, Experimental Gravity, and Measurement Theory. P. Meystre & M. O. Scully, Eds. Plenum. New York.
40. SAVAGE, C. M. & D. F. WALLS. 1985. Phys. Rev. **A32:** 2316.
41. MILBURN, G. J. & C. A. HOLMES. 1986. Phys. Rev. Lett. **56:** 2251.
42. HAAKE, F. & R. REIBOLD. 1982. Phys. Rev. **A32:** 2462.
43. CALDEIRA, A. O. & A. J. LEGGETT. 1985. Phys. Rev. **A31:** 1058.
44. HAKIM, V. & V. AMBEGAOKAR. 1985. Phys. Rev. **A32:** 423.
45. SAVAGE, C. M. & D. F. WALLS. 1985. Phys. Rev. **A32:** 3487.

A New Light on Single Photon Interferences

P. GRANGIER, G. ROGER, AND A. ASPECT[a]

Institut d'Optique Théorique et Appliquée
F 91406 Orsay Cédex, France

NONCLASSICAL PROPERTIES OF LIGHT

Introduction

During the past fifteen years, nonclassical effects in the statistical properties of light have been extensively studied from a theoretical point of view,[1] and some have been experimentally demonstrated.[2-7,19] All are related to second-order coherence properties via measurements of intensity correlation functions or of statistical moments. However, there has still been no test of the conceptually very simple situation dealing with single photon states of the light impinging on a beam-splitter. In this case, quantum mechanics predicts a perfect anticorrelation for photodetections on both sides of the beam-splitter, while any description involving classical fields would predict some amount of coincidences. The first purpose of this paper is to report on an experiment close to this ideal situation because we have found a coincidence rate, on both sides of a beam-splitter, five times smaller than the classical lower limit.

When it comes to single photon states of the light, it is tempting to revisit the famous historical "single photon interference experiments."[8] One then finds that, in spite of their denomination,[9] none has been performed with single photon states of the light. As a matter of fact, all have been carried out with chaotic light for which it is well known that quantum second-order coherence properties cannot be distinguished from classical ones, even with a strongly attenuated beam.[10] This is why we have carried out an interference experiment with the same apparatus as used in the first experiment, that is, with light for which we have demonstrated a property characteristic of single photon states. This single photon interference experiment will be described in the last part of this paper.

We shall first summarize briefly the principle of intensity correlation experiments in which striking differences between semiclassical and quantum treatments of light may appear. Then, we shall introduce a simple "anticorrelation" criterion for a nonclassical behavior of light. Eventually, we shall describe the observation of that anticorrelation effect and the single photon interference experiment.

[a]Also with College de France, Laboratoire de Spectroscopie Hertzienne de l'ENS, 24 rue Lhomond, F 75231 Paris Cédex 05, France.

Intensity Correlation Experiments

The correlation of two optical intensities was first measured by Hanbury-Brown and Twiss.[10] This experiment, sketched in FIGURE 1, typifies all subsequent intensity correlation measurements. A stationary beam of light is split by a half-silvered mirror, and the intensities in each portion are measured by photomultipliers. In the counting regime, one measures the single rates, N_T and N_R, and the coincidence rate, $N_C(\tau)$, when a delay, τ, is introduced in one channel. A coincidence window, W, must be defined for coincidence counting. If W is much smaller than the coherence time, τ_c, of the impinging light, and the detecting area, S, is much smaller than the coherence area,

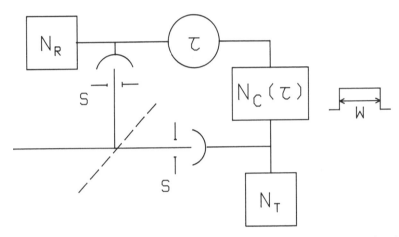

FIGURE 1. Intensity correlation experiment in the counting mode. A delay, τ, is introduced in one channel, N_R and N_T are single counting rates, and $N_C(\tau)$ is the coincidence counting rate. S is the detection area and W is the coincidence window.

σ_c, the measurements yield directly the degree of second-order coherence of the light:

$$g^{(2)}(\tau) = \frac{N_C(\tau)W}{N_T W \cdot N_R W}.$$

Ranges of possible values for $g^{(2)}(\tau)$ are very different according to theoretical descriptions of the light beam. In a classical-wave description, $g^{(2)}(\tau)$ is simply the normalized autocorrelation function of the light intensity (independent of t for a stationary light beam):

$$g^{(2)}_{Class}(\tau) = \frac{\overline{I(t)\,I(t+\tau)}}{[\overline{I(t)}]^2}. \tag{1}$$

In this case, we obtain from simple Cauchy-Schwarz inequalities, the following limits on values of $g^{(2)}_{Class}(\tau)$:

$$g^{(2)}_{Class}(0) \geq 1, \quad g^{(2)}_{Class}(0) \geq g^{(2)}_{Class}(\tau). \tag{2}$$

On the other hand, a quantum formalism predicts

$$g^{(2)}_{QM}(\tau) = \frac{\langle E^-(t) \, E^-(t + \tau) \, E^+(t + \tau) \, E^+(t) \rangle}{(\langle E^-(t) \, E^+(t) \rangle)^2}. \tag{3}$$

Due to the operator character of $E^+(t)$, the inequalities in equation 2 do not hold any longer. A situation where $g^{(2)}_{QM}(0) < g^{(2)}_{QM}(\tau)$ is called "antibunching," and was first observed by Kimble, Dagenais, and Mandel.[4] Other nonclassical behaviors of light already observed are sub-Poissonian photon statistics,[5,7] quantum cross-correlation effects in atomic cascades,[3] and squeezed states.[19] Experimental violations of Bell's inequalities are also purely quantum effects, although in a somewhat different sense.[11]

Triggered Detection Scheme and Anticorrelation Effect

In the following, we shall consider a modification of the experimental scheme of FIGURE 1 in which the coincidence gates, w, are open at arbitrary times, t_n. More precisely, the two photomultipliers, PM_t and PM_r, are enabled only for times, t_n to $t_n + w$; the gate rate (number of gates per second) is denoted by N_1. When the gate is open, a single count may be registered by PM_t or PM_r (singles rates, N_t and N_r), or a coincidence may happen (coincidence rate, N_c).

The measurements of N_1, N_t, N_r, and N_c yield the probabilities for singles counts during w,

$$p_t = \frac{N_t}{N_1} \quad \text{and} \quad p_r = \frac{N_r}{N_1}, \tag{4a}$$

and the probability for a coincidence,

$$p_c = \frac{N_c}{N_1}. \tag{4b}$$

We shall consider first a classical-wave description of this experiment that involves the intensity, $I(t)$, impinging on the beam-splitter. We define the time-averaged intensity for the nth gate, open at time, t_n, as

$$i_n = \frac{1}{w} \int_{t_n}^{t_n + w} I(t) \, dt.$$

The semiclassical model of photodetection[9] thus yields

$$p_t = \alpha_t w \langle i_n \rangle, \quad p_r = \alpha_r w \langle i_n \rangle, \tag{5a}$$

$$p_c = \alpha_t \alpha_r w^2 \langle i_n^2 \rangle, \tag{5b}$$

where α_t and α_r are global detection efficiencies, and the brackets indicate averages defined over the ensemble of gates:

$$\langle i_n \rangle = \frac{1}{N_1 T} \sum_{n=1}^{N_1 T} i_n , \qquad \langle i_n^2 \rangle = \frac{1}{N_1 T} \sum_{n=1}^{N_1 T} i_n^2$$

(T is the total duration of the experiment).

The standard Cauchy-Schwarz inequality,

$$\langle i_n^2 \rangle \geq \langle i_n \rangle^2 ,$$

holds for our average. Therefore, a classical description of this "triggered experiment" would yield counting rates obeying the inequality,

$$p_c \geq p_r p_t , \tag{6a}$$

or equivalently,

$$\alpha \geq 1 \text{ with } \alpha = \frac{p_c}{p_r p_t} = \frac{N_c N_1}{N_r N_t} . \tag{6b}$$

These inequalities clearly mean that the classical coincidence probability, p_c, is always greater than the "accidental coincidence" probability, which is equal to $p_r p_t$. The violation of the inequalities in equations 6a and 6b thus gives an "anticorrelation" criterion for characterizing a nonclassical behavior.

On the other hand, a quantum description of light allows $p_c = 0$, while p_r and p_t are different from zero if single photon states of the light are involved. In the following, we are going to describe an experiment in which the condition, $p_c << p_r p_t$, is achieved. Such an experiment is contradictory with any classical-wave model and demands a quantum description.

OBSERVATION OF THE ANTICORRELATION EFFECT

Principle of the Experiment

Our experimental scheme uses a two-photon radiative cascade described elsewhere[11] that emits pairs of photons with different frequencies, ν_1 and ν_2. The time intervals between the detections of ν_1 and ν_2 are distributed according to an exponential law corresponding to the decay of the intermediate state of the cascade with a lifetime, $\tau_s = 4.7$ ns.

In the present experiment (FIGURE 2), the detection of ν_1 acts as a trigger for a gate generator, thus enabling two photomultipliers in view of ν_2 for a duration of $w \simeq 2\tau_s$. These two photomultipliers, on both sides of the beam-splitter labeled BS, feed singles and coincidence counters. As previously stated, we denote N_1 as the rate of gates, N_t and N_r as the single rates for PM_t and PM_r, and N_c as the coincidence rate.

During a gate, the probability for the detection of a photon, ν_2, coming from the same atom that emitted ν_1 is much bigger than the probability of detecting a photon, ν_2, emitted by any other atom in the source. We are then in a situation close to an ideal

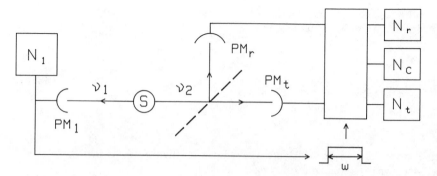

FIGURE 2. Triggered experiment. The detection of the first photon of the cascade produces a gate, w, during which the photomultipliers, PM_t and PM_r, are active. The probabilities of detection during the gate are $p_t = N_t/N_1$ and $p_r = N_r/N_1$ for singles, and $p_c = N_c/N_1$ for coincidences.

single photon state emission, and we can expect the characteristic behavior of such a state, namely, an anticorrelation between detections occurring on both sides of the beam-splitter.

Quantum Mechanical Calculations

The actual values of the counting rates for our experiment are obtained by a straightforward quantum mechanical calculation. Denoting N as the rate of excitation of the cascade, and ϵ_1, ϵ_t, and ϵ_r as the detection efficiencies (including collection solid angle, optics transmission, and detector efficiency), we obtain:

$$N_1 = \epsilon_1 N \tag{7a}$$

$$N_t = N_1 \epsilon_t [f(w) + Nw] \tag{7b}$$

$$N_r = N_1 \epsilon_r [f(w) + Nw] \tag{7b'}$$

$$N_c = N_1 \epsilon_t \epsilon_r [2f(w)Nw + (Nw)^2]. \tag{7c}$$

The quantity, $f(w)$, very close to the value of one in our experiment, is the product of the factor, $1 - \exp(-w/\tau_s)$ (which is the overlap between the gate and the exponential decay in the cascade), multiplied by a factor slightly greater than unity, related to the angular correlation between ν_1 and ν_2.[12]

The comparison of equations 7b, 7b', and 7c clearly shows the anticorrelation: there is a "missing term," $[f(w)]^2$ in N_c, related to the fact that a single photon can only be detected once. The quantum mechanical prediction for α is thus

$$\alpha_{QM} = \frac{2f(w)Nw + (Nw)^2}{[f(w) + Nw]^2}, \tag{8}$$

which is smaller than one. The corresponding effect will be strong if Nw can be chosen much smaller than $f(w)$: thus, the experiment is designed in order to satisfy this requirement.

Experimental Realization and Results

The excitation of the atoms is achieved by a two-photon process using two single-line lasers at different frequencies.[11] Several feedback loops control the laser frequencies and intensities in order to obtain a short- and long-term stability of the excitation rate, N, within a few percent. The gate, w, is realized by using two time-to-amplitude converters followed by threshold circuits. These "single-channel analyzers" are fed by shaped pulses from PM_1 on the START input, and from PM_t or PM_r on the STOP input. The gates corresponding to N_t and N_r can thus be adjusted and superimposed within 0.1 ns. A third time-to-amplitude converter measures the elapsed times between the various detections and allows a permanent control of the gating system.

The value of w is chosen for a maximum violation of the semiclassical inequality, $\alpha \geq 1$, by maximizing the quantity, $(1 - \alpha)/\sigma_\alpha$, where σ_α is the standard deviation on the measurement of α due to the counting process. This criterion yields $w \simeq 9$ ns.

In FIGURE 3, the theoretical and experimental values of α are plotted as a function of Nw (see equation 8), or, equivalently, as a function of the rate of gates, $N_1 = \epsilon_1 N$. A maximum violation of more than 13 standard deviations is obtained for $\alpha = 0.18 \pm 0.06$. The total counting time was $T \simeq 5$ hours, with $N_1 \simeq 8800$ s^{-1} (including the dark rate, 300 s^{-1}) and $N_r \simeq N_t \simeq 5$ s^{-1} (dark rate, 0.02 s^{-1}). In that case, the number of expected coincidences from the classical theory would be $N_c^{class} T \geq 50$, while we found $N_c^{exp} T = 9$. Hence, the light emitted after each "triggering" pulse has been shown to exhibit a specifically quantum anticorrelation behavior.[13]

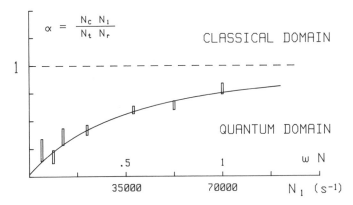

FIGURE 3. Anticorrelation parameter, α, as a function of wN (number of cascades emitted during the gate) and of N_1 (trigger rate). The indicated error bars are $\pm$ one standard deviation. The full-line curve is the theoretical prediction from equation 8. The inequality, $\alpha \geq 1$, characterizes the classical domain.

SINGLE PHOTON INTERFERENCES

Description of the Experiment

By building a Mach-Zehnder interferometer around the beam-splitter BS1 (FIG-URE 4), an actual "single-photon" interference experiment can be designed. According to quantum mechanics, the probabilities, p_{MZ1} and p_{MZ2}, for a detection during the gate in either output of the interferometer are oppositely modulated as a function of the path difference, δ, with a visibility unity.

In the actual experiment, the optical system is designed in order to accept the large optical spread of the beam from the source[11] (beam diameter of 40 mm for a total divergence of 25 mrd) without destroying the visibility of the fringes. This was achieved by observing the fringes in the focal planes of two lenses in view of the outputs, MZ1 and MZ2, and working at a path difference around zero.

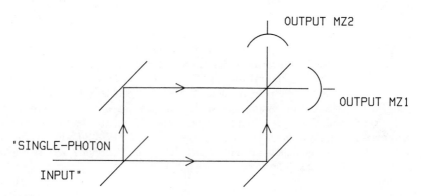

FIGURE 4. Mach-Zehnder interferometer. The detection probabilities in outputs MZ1 and MZ2 are oppositely modulated as a function of the path difference between the arms of the interferometer.

The two beam-splitters, BS1 and BS2, are actually two multidielectric coatings on a single 60×120 mm silica plate. The planarities of this plate and of the mirrors are close to $\lambda/50$; the orientations are controlled by mechanical stages at about the same precision. The counting rates on both outputs of the interferometer are measured as a function of the path difference, δ; δ is variated using a piezodriven mechanical system that insures a parallel translation of the mirrors at the required precision. The optical path in each arm of the interferometer is about 0.25 m.

The interferometer was first checked using light from the actual source, but without any gating system. We found a fringe visibility,[14] $V = 98.7\% \pm 0.5\%$, easily reproducible from day-to-day within the error limit. In the actual gated experiment, δ was variated around $\delta = 0$ over 256 steps of $\lambda/50$ each, with a counting time of 1 s per step. These sweeps over five fringes were stored separately into a computer, and then compiled to improve signal-to-noise ratio. A single sweep and the compiled result for $\alpha = 0.18$ are shown in FIGURE 5. Several methods of data analysis consistently yielded $V > 98\%$ for any value of α (FIGURE 6).

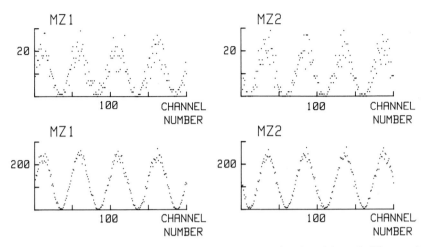

FIGURE 5. Number of counts in outputs MZ1 and MZ2 as a function of the path difference, δ (one channel corresponds to a $\lambda/50$ variation of δ): (a) 1 s counting time per channel; (b) 15 s counting time per channel [compilation of 15 elementary sweeps like in part (a)].

Discussion

Two triggered experiments have thus been performed using the same source and the same triggering scheme for the detectors. They illustrate the wave-particle duality of light. Indeed, if we want to use classical concepts or pictures to interpret these experiments, we must use a particle picture for the first one ("the photons are not split on a beam-splitter") because we violate an inequality holding for any classical-wave model. On the contrary, we are compelled to use a wave picture ("the electromagnetic field is coherently split on a beam-splitter") to interpret the second (interference) experiment. Of course, the two complementary descriptions correspond to mutually

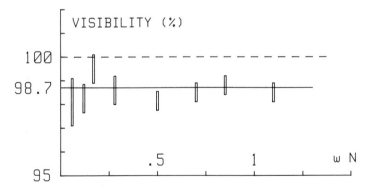

FIGURE 6. Visibility of the fringes in the single photon regime as a function of wN (compare with FIGURE 3). A correction (smaller than 0.3%) has been made for dark counts for the PMTs. Estimations of error bars are conservative.

exclusive experimental setups,[15] just as Bohr taught us in early "gedanken-experiments" about wave-particle dualism.

From the point of view of quantum optics, we will rather emphasize that we have demonstrated a situation with some properties of a "single photon state." An ideal source of such states would involve the collection of the light at frequency v_2 in a 4π solid angle, and a shutter triggered by the photons v_1. One could then carry out many experiments related to nonclassical properties of light—for instance, production of sub-Poisson light.[16]

Although such a scheme can be considered, it would be extremely hard to work out for practical reasons. Nevertheless, there exists a similar scheme that seems more promising: it consists of pairs of photons emitted in parametric splitting.[2,17,18] Due to the phase-matching condition, the angular correlation between photons v_1 and v_2 is very strong, and it becomes possible to produce single photon states in a single spatial mode.

NOTES AND REFERENCES

1. For a review, see: LOUDON, R. 1980. Rep. Prog. Phys. **43:** 913.
2. BURNHAM, D. C. & D. L. WEINBERG. 1970. Phys. Rev. Lett. **25:** 84; FRIBERG, S., C. K. HONG & L. MANDEL. 1985. Phys. Rev. Lett. **54:** 2011.
3. CLAUSER, J. F. 1974. Phys. Rev. **D9:** 853.
4. KIMBLE, H. J., M. DAGENAIS & L. MANDEL. 1977. Phys. Rev. Lett. **39:** 691.
5. SHORT, R. & L. MANDEL. 1983. Phys. Rev. Lett. **51:** 384.
6. CRESSER, J. D., J. HAGER, G. LEUCHS, M. RATEIKE & H. WALTHER. 1982. Topics in Current Physics, vol. 27. R. Bonifacio, Ed.: 21–59. Springer-Verlag. Berlin/New York.
7. TEICH, M. C. & B. E. A. SALEH. 1985. J. Opt. Soc. Am. **B2:** 275.
8. For a review, see: PIPKIN, F. M., 1978. Adv. At. Mol. Phys. **14:** 281.
9. Usually, the single photon character is stated by showing that the amount of energy flowing during a certain characteristic time (coherence-time, or time of flight between source and detector) is small compared to hv. The necessity of the concept of photon is thus postulated probably on the basis that the detection process appears discrete. However, it is well known that this argument is not fully conclusive because all the characteristics of the photoelectric effect can be assigned to the fact that the "atomic detector is controlled by the laws of quantum mechanics" (see reference 1, or: LAMB, W. E. & M. O. SCULLY. 1969. *In* Polarisation, Matière et Rayonnement. Société Française de Physique, Ed. Presses Univ. France. Paris).
10. LOUDON, R. 1983. The Quantum Theory of Light, 2nd Edition, p. 222. Oxford Univ. Press (Clarendon). London/New York.
11. ASPECT, A., P. GRANGIER & G. ROGER. 1981. Phys. Rev. Lett. **47:** 460.
12. FRY, E. S. 1973. Phys. Rev. **A8:** 1219.
13. A counter experiment has been performed using a pulsed photodiode; the rate, N_1, of exciting electrical pulses, and the probabilities, $p_t = N_t/N_1$ and $p_r = N_r/N_1$, can be adjusted to the same values as in the actual experiment. However, because the light pulse from the diode can be described classically, the expected number of coincidences obeys the inequalities of equation 7. This point has been verified experimentally in detail.
14. The fringe visibility is defined by $V = (N_{MZ1}^{Max} - N_{MZ1}^{Min})/(N_{MZ1}^{Max} + N_{MZ1}^{Min})$, where N_{MZ1}^{Max} and N_{MZ1}^{Min} are the maximum and minimum counting rates, respectively, on output MZ1 when δ is variated (dark rates of the PMTs are subtracted for this calculation).
15. The discussion (and possibly the experiment) can be refined by considering a "quantum non-demolition measurement" of the passage cf photons in one arm of the interferometer (IMOTO, N., H. A. HAUS & Y. YAMAMOTO. 1985. Phys. Rev. **A32:** 2287, and references therein). Such a device would entail phase fluctuations destroying the interference pattern.

16.　SALEH, B. E. A. & M. C. TEICH. 1985. Opt. Commun. **52:** 429. Instead of the "deletion" scheme proposed in that paper, one could also use a feedback loop, activated by v_1, and reacting on the cascade rate, in order to quiet the Poisson fluctuations in the number of cascades excited in a certain time. See also reference 18.

17.　HONG, C. K. & L. MANDEL. 1986. Phys. Rev. Lett. **56:** 58.

18.　JAKEMAN, E. & J. G. WALKER. 1985. Opt. Commun. **52:** 429.

19.　SLUSHER, R. E., L. W. HOLLBERG, B. YURKE, J. C. MERTZ & J. F. VALLEY. 1985. Phys. Rev. Lett. **55:** 2409.

Realizations of "Delayed-Choice" Experiments

T. HELLMUTH, ARTHUR G. ZAJONC,[a]
AND H. WALTHER

Sektion Physik
Universität München
and
Max-Planck-Institut für Quantenoptik
8046 Garching bei München, Federal Republic of Germany

INTRODUCTION

According to Bohr, Einstein very early drew attention to a rather striking instance of wave-particle duality:[1]

> If a semi-reflecting mirror is placed in the way of a photon, leaving two possibilities for its direction of propagation, the photon may either be recorded on one, and only one, of two photographic plates situated at great distances in the two directions in question, or else we may, by replacing the plates by mirrors, observe effects exhibiting an interference between the two reflected wave-trains. In any attempt of a pictorial representation of the behavior of the photon we would, thus, meet with the difficulty: to be obliged to say, on the one hand, that the photon always chooses *one* of the two ways and, on the other hand, that it behaves as if it had passed *both* ways.

Bohr viewed this thought-experiment as an excellent demonstration of the impossibility of subdividing quantum phenomena, and also as an example showing that "all unambiguous use of space-time concepts in the description of atomic phenomena is confined to the recording of observations" on measuring instruments. As Bohr repeatedly emphasized, in all such experiments, the *whole* experimental arrangement must be considered.

In 1978, J. A. Wheeler[2] sharpened the example by reformulating the experiment along lines indicated by von Weizsäcker in 1931.[3] FIGURE 1 is a schematic diagram of Wheeler's delayed-choice thought-experiment.[4] A pulsed electromagnetic wave (1) is split into two beams (2a and 2b) by the beam-splitter marked BS1. Two mirrors (M) bring the beams together at the upper right. A detector is placed in each of the two beams. Two arrangements are possible. In the first, no final beam-splitter (BS2) is introduced, and the counters indicate which route the photon has traveled. In the alternate arrangement, a beam-splitter is introduced at the point of intersection. When the path lengths in the two arms of the interferometer are correctly adjusted, no signal appears in the upper counter due to destructive interference, while constructive interference produces a beam incident on D2 with the original intensity of beam 1. The latter experiment is, as Wheeler put it, "evidence that the arriving photon came by

[a]On leave from Physics Department, Amherst College, Amherst, Massachusetts 01002.

both routes. In the new 'delayed-choice' version of the experiment, one decides whether to put in the half-silvered mirror or take it out at the very last minute. Thus one decides whether the photon 'shall have come by one route, or by both routes' after it has 'already done its travel'."[4]

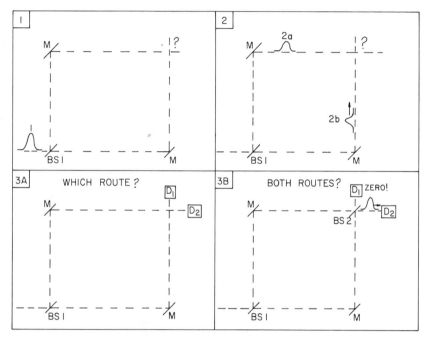

FIGURE 1. Schematic diagram of J. A. Wheeler's delayed-choice experiment. Three times are shown in the evolution of the system. In (1), the pulse of electromagnetic radiation arrives at beam-splitter one (BS1). In (2), the pulse is shown divided (following Wheeler[4]) and reflected off of mirrors labeled M. Up until this time, no choice has been made whether to insert the second beam-splitter (BS2). Without the beam-splitter (3A), the detectors, D_1 and D_2, ascertain which route was traveled by the light quantum. With the beam-splitter in, this information is irreversibly lost and the two detectors show an interference signature; no counts in D_1, all counts in D_2. This implies the quantum of light has traveled both paths. I emphasize that the insertion of BS2, or the lack of it, occurs only after the light pulse has passed BS1.

MACH-ZEHNDER EXPERIMENT

Following a suggestion of Alley,[5] we have realized Wheeler's thought-experiment using the techniques available in quantum optics. FIGURE 2 shows a schematic of the experimental apparatus. A mode-locked, krypton-ion laser provides 150 psec pulses of 647 nm radiation at a repetition rate of 80 MHz. The pulses of light pass through an optical attenuator (10^{-9}), and then through an acousto-optic modulator that reduces the repetition rate to 10 kHz. In addition, the modulator has a measured attenuation of 1.6×10^{-2}. This implies that the 300 milliwatts average power of the initial beam is reduced to 6×10^{-16} watts or 0.4 eV/pulse. The average number of photons per pulse

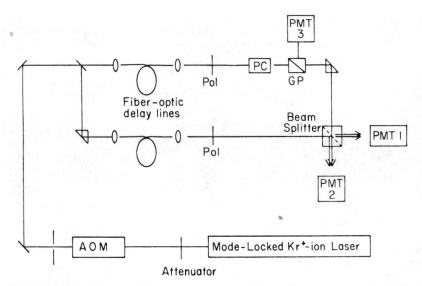

FIGURE 2. Schematic diagram of the experimental apparatus (delayed-choice interferometer). AOM is the acousto-optic modulator. PC is the Pockels cell.

is, therefore, less than 0.2. Photon statistics are given by the Poisson distribution as was confirmed by direct measurement of the correlation function. Thus, one can say that with these light levels, 95% of the pulses have one photon or less (80% have zero, 15% have one).

The incident pulse passes through the first beam-splitter, and the two resulting beams are then directed and focused into two separate single-mode optical fibers that are five meters in length. The transit time is approximately 24 nsec. In one arm of the interferometer, a Pockels cell (PC) is placed. When the appropriate half-wave voltage is applied (3.6kV), a phase-shift of one-half wave is introduced between the two orthogonal polarization components of the incident light. The polarization is thereby rotated by 90 degrees. The Pockels cell is followed by a Glan, polarizing prism (GP), which reflects light polarized in the plane of the figure and transmits the orthogonal polarization. The switching time of the Pockels cell is measured to be 4–5 nsec. The two beams are recombined in the final beam-splitter cube before going to the cooled photomultipliers 1 and 2.

The most important comparison is between the "normal" and the "delayed-choice" modes of operation. In the normal mode, the optical switch is "opened" five nsec before the light pulse reaches the first beam-splitter. Thus, the entire experimental arrangement is in a fixed, Mach-Zehnder configuration before the photon arrives at the first beam-splitter. In the delayed-choice mode, the optical switch is normally closed (reflection to PMT3), and it is only opened five nsec after the pulse passes through the first beam-splitter. In this mode, the photon is well inside the fiber-optic delay lines when the experimental arrangement is reconfigured into a Mach-Zehnder interferometer.

The 40-MHz driver for the mode-locker is used as the master clock. Suitable electronics are employed to provide accurate synchronization and timing for the Pockels cell and detector gates in order to insure clear discrimination between the normal and delayed-choice modes of operation. Further details of the experimental arrangement are available elsewhere.[6]

Data taken for the two modes are presented in FIGURES 3 and 4. The data are identical to within the accuracy of our experiment. Delaying one's choice of experiment has no effect on the outcome of the interference, as one expects.

QUANTUM-BEAT EXPERIMENT

A temporal analog of the interferometer experiment can be performed using the phenomenon of quantum beats.[7] Such an experiment has been successfully completed by two of the authors (T.H. and H.W.). In this experiment, a broadband, laser pulse excites an atom to a coherent superposition of excited-state sublevels. In this case, the

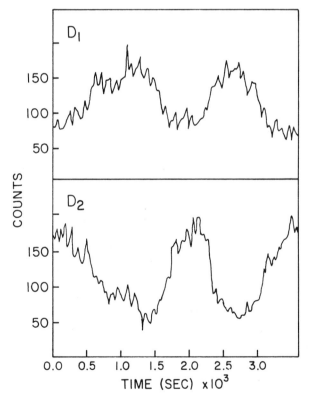

FIGURE 3. BS2 inserted five nsec before the pulse arrives at BS1. Top trace shows signal of D_1 as the relative phase drifts with time (abscissa). Bottom trace shows signal of D_2. The ordinate is intensity (200 counts/channel at peak). The anticorrelation of the top and bottom traces is clear evidence for interference.

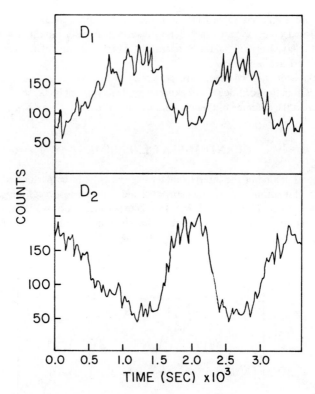

FIGURE 4. Identical to FIGURE 3, but now BS2 is inserted five nsec after the light pulse passes BS1.

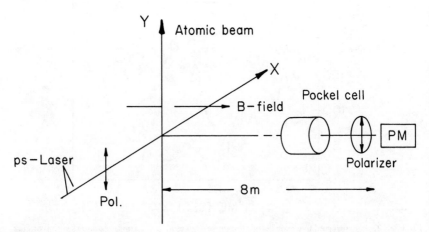

FIGURE 5. Schematic diagram of the crossed atomic and laser beam apparatus. The pulse propagation direction, Ba atomic beam, and magnetic field are mutually orthogonal.

sublevels are two Zeeman components of a Ba P-state split by a weak magnetic field. The $m = +1$ and $m = -1$ sublevels are excited by a linearly polarized pulse of 553 nm radiation, 1.5 ps in duration. The reradiated emission from the barium atom must travel eight meters through $f-1$ optics to the photodetector. Interference is expected because the scattering occurs from two indistinguishable intermediate states ($m = +1$ and $m = -1$ sublevels). If the two scattering channels become distinguishable, for example, by polarization analysis of the decay radiation, then the interference disappears.

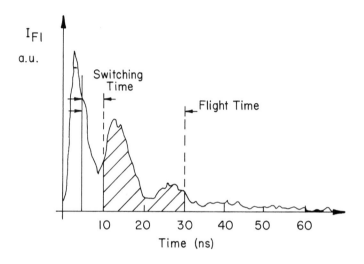

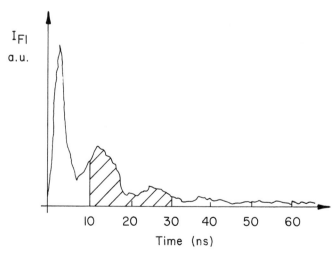

FIGURE 6. "Delayed-choice" (top) and "normal" (bottom) quantum beats. "Flight time" is the time during which the photon is in transit from excitation region to detector. Switching time for the Pockels cell is five nsec.

The choice of whether to analyze the polarization of the decay radiation or not can be delayed until long after the "photon" has been emitted from the barium atom. In a way similar to the previous experiment, the choice of analysis is provided by a Pockels cell placed in front of the photomultiplier. Thus, in a manner entirely analogous to the interferometer, we seem to be able to determine whether the photon has scattered by one path (no interference) or by both paths (interference) long after the photon has scattered from the atom. A schematic of the apparatus is shown in FIGURE 5.

A normal quantum-beat signal consists of an exponentially decaying intensity that is modulated sinusoidally at a frequency equal to the difference frequency between the two excited sublevels. I emphasize that in such "single-atom" quantum beats, the interference occurs between decay channels of single atoms, and not as interference between emission of different atoms.[7] The beat signal is built up from many single-photon detections. One has, therefore, a clean instance of single-photon, delayed-choice interference in this quantum-beat experiment.

FIGURE 6 shows results on the delayed-choice quantum-beat experiment. Once again, no difference is noted between delayed-choice and normal runs. A more detailed treatment including discussion in terms of QED is forthcoming for both experiments.

REFERENCES

1. BOHR, N. 1949. Discussions with Einstein on epistemological problems in atomic physics. *In* Albert Einstein: Philosopher-Scientist. P. A. Schilpp, Ed.: 200–241. The Library of Living Philosophers. Evanston, Illinois.
2. WHEELER, J. A. 1978. *In* Mathematical Foundations of Quantum Theory. J. A. Wheeler & W. H. Zurek, Eds.: 183. Princeton Univ. Press. Princeton, New Jersey.
3. VON WEIZSÄCKER, C. F. 1931. Z. Phys. **70:** 114.
4. WHEELER, J. A. 1983. *In* Quantum Theory and Measurement. J. A. Wheeler & W. H. Zurek, Eds.: 183. Princeton Univ. Press. Princeton, New Jersey.
5. ALLEY, C. O. 1983. *In* Proc. of the Int. Symp: Foundations of Quantum Mechanics. Physical Society of Japan. Kyoto.
6. HELLMUTH, T. 1985. Interferenzexperimente zum Quantenmechanischen Messprozess: Eine Nachwahlversion des Youngschen Doppelspalt-Versuchs. Dissertation. Ludwig-Maximilians-Universität, München; HELLMUTH, T., A. G. ZAJONC & H. WALTHER. To be published.
7. HAROCHE, S. 1976. Quantum beats and time-resolved fluorescence spectroscopy. *In* High-Resolution Laser Spectroscopy. K. Shimoda, Ed. Springer-Verlag. New York.

EPRB and the Wigner Distribution for Spin-½ Particles[a]

MARLAN O. SCULLY[b,c] AND LEON COHEN[b,d]

[b]*Center for Advanced Studies
and Department of Physics and Astronomy
University of New Mexico
Albuquerque, New Mexico 87131*

[c]*Max-Planck Institut für Quantenoptik
D-8046 Garching bei München, Federal Republic of Germany*

[d]*Department of Physics
Hunter College of the City University of New York
New York, New York 10021*

In recent work, we have applied Wigner-type quasi-probability distribution theory to the problem of spin-½ systems.[1-3] We here relate those results to the Einstein-Podolsky-Rosen-Bohm (EPRB) problem. The EPRB "experiment" may be summarized or epitomized by asking: What is the probability for simultaneous passage of both spin partners through Stern-Gerlach apparatuses (SGA) at angles, $+\theta_\alpha$ and $-\theta_\beta$, respectively? If the state of the spin singlet is denoted by $|\psi\rangle$, then this is clearly given by

$$P^{(2)}(+\theta_\alpha, -\theta_\beta) = |\langle+\theta_\alpha|\langle-\theta_\beta|\psi\rangle|^2$$

$$= \langle\psi|+\theta_\alpha\rangle|-\theta_\beta\rangle\langle+\theta_\alpha|\langle-\theta_\beta|\psi\rangle = \langle\psi|\pi(+\theta_\alpha)\pi(-\theta_\beta)|\psi\rangle, \quad (1)$$

where

$$\pi(\pm\theta_i) = |\pm\theta_i\rangle\langle\pm\theta_i| = \tfrac{1}{2}[1 \pm \sigma(\theta_i)]; \qquad i = \alpha, \beta. \quad (2)$$

Because $\pi(\theta_\alpha)$ and $\pi(\theta_\beta)$ commute, we may choose to write equation 1 in the symmetric form,

$$P^{(2)}(+\theta_\alpha, -\theta_\beta) = \langle\psi|\tfrac{1}{2}[\pi(+\theta_\alpha)\pi(-\theta_\beta) + \pi(-\theta_\beta)\pi(+\theta_\alpha)]|\psi\rangle. \quad (3)$$

Taking $|\psi\rangle$ to be in an antisymmetic "S" state, equation 3 yields the usual result:

$$P^{(2)}(+\theta_\alpha, -\theta_\beta) = \tfrac{1}{4}[1 - \cos(\theta_\alpha - \theta_\beta)]. \quad (4)$$

Next we ask, what do we get if we naively extend equation 3 to one-particle physics? To answer this, we calculate

$$P^{(1)}(+\theta_1, -\theta_2) = \langle\psi|\tfrac{1}{2}[\pi(+\theta_1)\pi(-\theta_2) + \pi(+\theta_2)\pi(-\theta_1)]|\psi\rangle, \quad (5)$$

[a]This work was supported by the AFOSR and the ONR.

115

where "1" and "2" signify two arbitrary spin directions for the single particle. After a little algebra, equation 5 reduces to

$$P_{+-}(+\theta_1, -\theta_2) = \frac{1}{4}[1 + \langle \sigma_1 \rangle - \langle \sigma_2 \rangle - \cos(\theta_1 - \theta_2)], \tag{6}$$

and likewise we find

$$P_{-+}(-\theta_1, +\theta_2) = \frac{1}{4}[1 - \langle \sigma_1 \rangle + \langle \sigma_2 \rangle - \cos(\theta_1 - \theta_2)], \tag{7}$$

where the state information appears only in $\langle \sigma_1 \rangle$ and $\langle \sigma_2 \rangle$.

Now, we see that if we take the average of equations 6 and 7, we find the usual EPRB result,

$$\frac{1}{2}(P_{+-} + P_{-+}) = \frac{1}{4}[1 - \cos(\theta_1 - \theta_2)]. \tag{8}$$

Thus, we see that the incoherent average of the single-particle "joint passage" expression (equation 8) equals the EPRB simultaneous passage probability (equation 4).

However, what is the physical and/or mathematical meaning of $P^{(1)}(\pm\theta_1, \mp\theta_2)$ as given by equations 6 and 7? We give two answers to this question as follows:

(A) Wigner joint count probability for spin $\frac{1}{2}$:
     As discussed in detail elsewhere,[1] we define

$$P^{(1)}(s_1, s_2) = \frac{1}{4\pi^2} \int\int e^{-i\xi s_1 - i\tau s_2} M(\xi, \tau)\, d\xi d\tau, \tag{9a}$$

where the characteristic function is

$$M(\xi, \tau) = \frac{1}{2}\langle e^{i\xi\sigma_1} e^{i\tau\sigma_2} + e^{i\tau\sigma_2} e^{i\xi\sigma_1} \rangle. \tag{9b}$$

Evaluating equation 9b and inserting it into equation 9a as in reference 1, we find

$$
\begin{aligned}
P^{(1)}(s_1, s_2) = {} & P_{++}(+\theta_1, +\theta_2)\delta(s_1 - 1)\delta(s_2 - 1) \\
& + P_{+-}(+\theta_1, +\theta_2)\delta(s_1 - 1)\delta(s_2 + 1) \\
& + P_{-+}(+\theta_1, +\theta_2)\delta(s_1 + 1)\delta(s_2 - 1) \\
& + P_{--}(+\theta_1, +\theta_2)\delta(s_1 + 1)\delta(s_2 + 1),
\end{aligned}
\tag{10}
$$

where

$$P_{++} = \frac{1}{4}(1 + \langle \sigma_1 \rangle + \langle \sigma_2 \rangle + \cos\delta), \tag{11a}$$

$$P_{+-} = \frac{1}{4}(1 + \langle \sigma_1 \rangle - \langle \sigma_2 \rangle - \cos\delta), \tag{11b}$$

$$P_{-+} = \frac{1}{4}(1 - \langle \sigma_1 \rangle + \langle \sigma_2 \rangle - \cos\delta), \tag{11c}$$

$$P_{--} = \frac{1}{4}(1 - \langle \sigma_1 \rangle - \langle \sigma_2 \rangle + \cos\delta), \tag{11d}$$

and where δ is the angle formed by directions 1 and 2. We note that equations

10–11 may be written in the compact form,

$$P^{(1)}(s_1, s_2) = \tfrac{1}{4}(1 + s_1\langle\sigma_1\rangle + s_2\langle\sigma_2\rangle + s_1 s_2 \cos \delta), \qquad s_1, s_2 = \pm 1. \quad (12)$$

Thus, we see that $P^{(1)}_{+-}$ and $P^{(1)}_{-+}$ of equations 5 and 6 are just the joint probability distributions of equations 11b and 11c.

(B) "Physical" interpretation for $P^{(1)}(\pm\theta_1, \mp\theta_2)$:

If we consider the state resulting from passing our particles (initially described by $|\psi\rangle$) through an SGA tipped at angle θ_1, and if we accept only those on the $(+)$ path, this is given by

$$|+\theta_1\rangle\langle+\theta_1|\psi\rangle; \quad (13a)$$

likewise, for the particles emerging on the $(-)$ path of an SGA tipped at θ_2, this is given by

$$|-\theta_2\rangle\langle-\theta_2|\psi\rangle. \quad (13b)$$

The overlap between equations 13a and 13b is

$$\langle\psi|-\theta_2\rangle\langle-\theta_2|+\theta_1\rangle\langle+\theta_1|\psi\rangle = \langle\psi|\pi(-\theta_2)\pi(+\theta_1)|\psi\rangle. \quad (14)$$

Hence, we see that, physically, the (symmetrized) overlap matrix element (equation 14) is the same as equation 4.

In conclusion, we see that the two-particle simultaneous passage probability, $P^{(2)}(\theta_1, \theta_2)$, of equation 4 is reproduced by the incoherent average of the single-particle joint quasi-distribution,

$$P^{(2)}(\theta_1, \theta_2) = \tfrac{1}{2}[P^{(1)}_{+-}(+\theta_1, -\theta_2) + P^{(1)}_{-+}(-\theta_1, \theta_2)]. \quad (15)$$

The importance of coherent and incoherent mixtures in the EPRB problem has been stressed elsewhere.[4]

NOTES AND REFERENCES

1. COHEN, L. & M. SCULLY. 1986. John A. Wheeler Festschrift. Found. Phys. **16**: 295. See also: SCULLY, M. 1983. Phys. Rev. **D28**: 2477.
2. We note that O'CONNELL, R. & E. WIGNER (1984. Phys. Rev. **139**: 21617) have studied the application of the Wigner distribution to many particle physics in which spin and statistics are important. That interesting problem is different in scope and direction from the present work. Also see: MARGENAU, H. & R. N. HILL. 1961. Prog. Theor. Phys. **26**: 722.
3. Related studies have been reported by: WOOTTERS, W. & D. MERMIN. 1986. This conference.
4. CANTRELL, C. D. & M. O. SCULLY. 1978. Phys. Rep. **43**: 499; SCULLY, M. O., R. SHEA & J. D. McCULLEN. 1978. Phys. Rep. **43**: 485.

Frontier of Femtosecond and Picosecond Optical Measuring Techniques[a]

R. R. ALFANO

Institute for Ultrafast Spectroscopy and Lasers
Photonic Application Laboratory
Physics and Electrical Engineering Departments
The City College of New York
New York, New York 10031

INTRODUCTION

Over the past two decades, we have seen dramatic advances in the generation of ultrafast laser pulses.[1-12] It is now commonplace to produce picosecond (10^{-12} sec) pulses. New developments have extended this technology into the femtosecond (10^{-15} sec) time region. Soon pulses consisting of 1 cycle will be produced (i.e., 2 fs at 600 nm). These ultrafast pulses permit novel investigations to study phenomena in many fields. The design of sophisticated techniques based on these laser pulses has given rise to instruments with extremely high temporal resolution. Ultrafast laser technology offers the possibility of studying and discovering key processes unresolved in the past. A new era of time-resolved spectroscopy has emerged, with pulses so fast that one can now study the nonequilibrium states of matter and test quantum and light models.

Today, ultrafast laser technology is one of the most active areas of science because it can be used in a diverse number of fields: solid-state physics, biology, and chemistry. TABLE 1 lists the primary relaxation times in condensed matter. This report highlights my presentation on the fs and ps optical measuring techniques available today.

MEASURING TECHNIQUES

It has been over twenty years since picosecond laser pulses were first produced in glass lasers (DeMaria and co-workers) by mode locking.[6] During this time, the solid-state laser has become the workhorse. However, it is slowly being replaced by dye and Yag lasers. A new type of light source on the horizon was discovered in 1970 by Alfano and Shapiro—the ultrafast supercontinuum laser that spans from UV to IR. TABLE 2 lists the currently available ultrafast laser sources.[1-5]

Currently available electronic equipment does not have the time response required to directly measure events that take place in picoseconds or femtoseconds. The fastest oscilloscope, for example, equipped with a sampling head has a resolution of 100 psec. Indirect methods, however, are available for time measurements. The constant speed

[a]The research at IUSL is supported by AFOSR, ONR, ARO, NASA, NSF, NIH, and Hamamatsu Photonic Management Corporation.

118

TABLE 1. Primary Relaxation Time Scales in Physics, Chemistry, and Biology

	Time (sec)	
Photosynthesis	10^{-8}	Acoustic phonon
	10^{-9}	Excitons, Vision
Semiconductors		Spin, Magnon
Dyes	10^{-10}	Rotational
nonradiative		Polaritons
singlet-triplet	10^{-11}	
Charge transfer complex		Energy and temperature relaxation of carriers
Photodissociation	10^{-12}	Vibrational, optical phonon
Photoionization		Momentum relaxation of carriers
Solvent caging, H-bonding	10^{-13}	Electron-scattering times electron-hole plasma
Electron-proton transfer	10^{-14}	Vision, libration, hemoglobin

of light traveling over a known distance provides the basis for the time-measuring mechanism on a picosecond and femtosecond time scale. It takes light 10 fs to travel 3μ in the air. A length of 3μ can be easily and accurately measured with a stepping motor.

Two-Photon Fluorescence and Second Harmonic Methods

The two methods that will be described and that are most often used for pulse width measurements are two-photon fluorescence (TPF) and second harmonic generation (SHG) spatial width.

The TPF method was described first by Giordmaine, Rentzepis, and Shapiro.[8] In this method, a beam is split into two beams and directed into a cell that contains a dye that does not absorb at the laser wavelength. The dye molecules, however, may absorb two photons simultaneously and be raised to an excited state. Then, fluorescence takes place in the normal way. The cross section for two-photon absorption is small, so TPF is not ordinarily observed. The probability of a two-photon transition is proportional to the square of the incident light intensity. The size of the TPF is related to the pulse

TABLE 2. Ultrafast Lasers Available

Oscillator	Wavelength (nm)	Pulse Duration
Ruby	694.3	30 ps
Yag	1,064	30 ps
Silicate glass	1,060	8 ps
Phosphate glass	1,054	6 ps
Dye	tunable (syn or flashlamp)	5–10 ps
Dye	610 (passive)	100 fs
Dye + Pulse compression	tunable	300 fs
Dye + Pulse compression	620	27–90 fs
Dye + 4 Prisms	625	27 fs
Dye + SPM[a]	continuum	80 fs
Dye + SPM[a] + Pulse compression	620	8 fs

[a]SPM = self-phase modulation (supercontinuum laser source).

width through the autocorrelation function, $G^{(2)}(\tau)$:

$$I_{2f} = C[1 + 2G^{(2)}(\tau)],$$

where

$$G^{(2)}(\tau) = \int_0^{t_o} I(t)I(t + \tau)dt \bigg/ \int_0^{t_o} I^2(t)dt.$$

From the autocorrelation function and the pulse shape, the pulse duration can be estimated. The rapidly varying interference times average out using a course stepping motor of 2μ steps. TABLE 3 gives the real values of the pulse width for three different pulse shapes. Typical dye solutions used are Rh6G in methanol for 1060 nm, and coumarin in methanol or BBOT in chlorohexane for 530 nm.

The first measurements of picosecond duration were made using second harmonic generation. In the SHG method, two pulses enter the nonlinear crystal of KDP in either a collinear or noncollinear geometry. One beam is time-delayed using a stepping motor with accuracy of $\frac{1}{2}\mu$. The correlated signal, $G^2(t)$, at harmonic frequency, 2ω, is

TABLE 3. Relation between Pulse Shape and Pulse Duration and Autocorrelation Durations[a]

Pulse	$\gamma = \Delta t_G/\Delta t$	$\Delta t \Delta f$
$\exp(-4ln2t^2/\Delta t)$	1.44	0.441
$\mathrm{sech}^2\lvert(1.76t)/\Delta t\rvert$	1.55	0.315
$\exp\lvert-1n2t/\Delta t\rvert$	2	0.11

[a]Δt_G and Δt are (FWHM) of the pulse width as measured by TPF or SHG and the true pulse width, respectively; γ is the form factor.

highly directional and is measured as a function of time delay. TABLE 3 relates the pulse duration to correlation durations.

The time resolution of the SHG and TPF methods is electronic in origin; however, experimental problems limit these methods to about 5 to 10 fs time resolution.

The Streak Camera

The technique most widely used for luminescence measurements in the picosecond range incorporates a streak camera. Photoelectrons emitted by light striking the photocathode are deflected by an applied voltage ramp that causes the electrons to be transversely streaked across a phosphorescent screen. Photoelectrons released at different times from the photocathode strike the phosphorescent screen at different positions, thus causing a track with a spatial intensity profile directly proportional to the incident temporal intensity profile of the fluorescence. The phosphorescent track may be analyzed by sampling by a video system. The ultrashort pulse from the laser is divided by a beam-splitter. Part of the beam is sent to a photodiode that triggers the streak. The other pulse excites the sample. The pump pulse has to be delayed for a few nanoseconds before the streak camera is ready. To produce that long delay, the pump pulse travels through a white cell. Before the pump strikes the sample, a wedge reflects part of the beam directly into the slit of the streak camera. This prepulse is used for the calibration of the zero time. The fluorescence from the sample is collected and passes through filters to eliminate the excitation pulse. It is then focused onto the slit of the streak camera. A modification of this arrangement allows one to measure the temporal profiles of the fluorescence at both polarizations simultaneously.

The temporal resolution of the streak camera has four components: the range of initial kinetic energies of the electrons emitted from the photocathode; the width of the slit; the scanning velocity; and various edge effects, such as electric-field fringing, optical diffraction, and space-charge effects (Alcock).[11] The temporal resolution of the streak camera is about 1 psec with a jitter of 50 psec. Recent improvements in tube design have reduced the time resolution to 200 fs.

The Optical Kerr Gate

The optical Kerr gate (Duguay and Hansen,[7] and Shimizu and Stoicheff[12]) consists basically of a Kerr active liquid, such as CS_2, situated between two polarizers. Under the intense electric field associated with the laser pulse ($\sim 10^5$ V/cm), the molecules of the Kerr active liquid experience an induced birefringence. The light passing through the liquid becomes generally elliptically polarized and passes partially through the second polarizer. Light can only pass through the gate while it coincides with the intense laser pulse that opens the gate. Thus, the intense laser pulse can be used to carve out successive portions of the temporal profile of the emitted luminescence, $I_L(t)$, to yield the decay time, τ_D.

The resolution of the optical Kerr gate depends on the duration of the gate pulse and the reorientation time of the molecules of the active medium. For CS_2, one of the fastest Kerr-active media available, the reorientation time is 2 ps. The pulse duration of the glass laser (6–10 psec) has in the past been the limiting factor of the resolution of the Kerr gate. The subpicosecond dye laser requires even faster Kerr-active media (polymers, i.e., PDA) based on the electronic distortion rather than the induced orientation of the molecules. Such a gate can have a resolution of 10^{-14} sec.

The theory of the operation of the Kerr gate shows how its time resolution is limited by both the pulse width, T_G, and the lifetime of the birefringence, T_B, of Kerr-active media (T_B is usually limited to over 2 psec by the slow reorientation time of molecules in the liquid). When the lifetime, T_B, of the birefringence (~ 2 psec for CS_2) is much shorter than the pulse duration, T_G (~ 6 psec for solid-state lasers), the birefringence, $\Delta n(t)$, is given by

$$\Delta n(t) = \Delta n_\parallel - \Delta n_\perp = \frac{1}{2} n_2 E_G^2(t) = \frac{1}{2} n_2 I_G(t),$$

where the nonlinear coefficient, n_2, of the index of refraction is about 2×10^{-11} esu for CS_2. The corresponding phase retardation, $\Delta\phi(t)$, in a cell of length, z, is given by

$$\Delta\phi(t) = \omega_L \Delta n(t)(z/c),$$

where ω_L is the frequency of the luminescence and c is the speed of light. These equations apply only when the duration of the pulse, T_G, is much longer than the relaxation time of the Kerr medium, T_B. When this condition is not fulfilled, the more general expression must be used:

$$\Delta n(t) = \frac{1}{2}\frac{n_2}{T_B}\int_{-\infty}^{t} I_G(t')\exp\left[\frac{t-t'}{T_B}\right]dt'.$$

The phase retardation causes the linear polarization of the luminescence to become elliptically polarized and to pass through the second polarizer. The intensity of the transmitted signal with phase retardation, $\Delta\phi$, is proportional to $\sin^2(\Delta\phi/2)$, that is,

$$I_s(\tau, t) \propto I_L(t)\sin^2\left[\frac{1}{2}\Delta\phi(t-\tau)\right],$$

which gives the instantaneous signal. The response, however, of the photomultiplier is much slower than the duration of the laser pulses. The detection system records the total energy transmitted:

$$I_s(\tau) \propto \int_{-\infty}^{\infty} I_s(t, \tau)dt = \int_{-\infty}^{\infty} I_L(t)\sin^2\left[\frac{1}{2}\Delta\phi(t-\tau)\right]dt.$$

When the induced retardation is small, $\sin\Delta\phi \approx \Delta\phi$; I_s is simplified as follows for $T_G > T_B$:

$$I_s(\tau) \propto \int_{-\infty}^{\infty} I_L(t)I_G^2(t-\tau)\,dt.$$

The ultimate time resolution in the fs regime depends on finding a material with a large and electronic fast n_2.

The Parametric Upconversion Gate

The process of parametric upconversion has been used as a mechanism in ultrafast optical shutters (Mahr, Topp).[9] In this technique, the luminescence, $I_L(t)$, from the sample is collected, collimated, and combined with part of the excitation pulse in a noncentrosymmetric crystal (such as ATP, $LiIO_3$, or KDP). The angle of the crystal is set to phase-match the frequency of the gating pulse with a selected frequency of the luminescence. A signal whose frequency is the sum of the laser and luminescence frequencies is generated in the crystal and detected by a photomultiplier. The laser beam is divided by a beam-splitter. One of the beams is directed to a delay prism and reflected back. The other is modulated by a mechanical chopper and excites the sample. The luminescence from the sample is collected and combined with the original laser pulse from the delay prism inside the crystal. When the crystal is tuned to satisfy the matching condition, the sum wave is generated. The signal frequency is separated by a monochromator and detected by a photomultiplier. The lock-in amplifier discriminates whatever background remains. Varying the delay of the gate pulse, we can obtain the temporal profile of the luminescence without the background luminescence. Because upconversion involves virtual electronic transitions, this gate has a response time equal to the pulse width of the pumping laser. To achieve a high efficiency of conversion, the gate has to be tuned to satisfy the phase-matching conditions of

$$\omega_s = \omega_L + \omega_G$$

and

$$\overline{k}_s = \overline{k}_L + \overline{k}_G.$$

The intensity of the generated signal is given by the convolution function of I_L and I_G:

$$I_s(\tau)\alpha \int_{-\infty}^{\infty} I_G(t - T)I_L(t)\ dt.$$

The time resolution is an electronic response of $\sim 10^{-14}$ sec.

Pump and Probe Gate

In this technique, an intense pulse excites a sample. A weaker probe pulse derived from the initial pulse is reflected along a different and variable optical delay path in order to examine a parameter of the system such as light absorption or Raman scattering as a function of delay time after excitation. Probe pulses can be obtained from harmonic generation, stimulated Raman scattering, and self-phase modulation. The latter greatly expands the bandwidth to the so-called "ultrafast supercontinuum" (Alfano, see next section).[1-5]

The timing mechanism is the speed of light itself. It takes light 3.3 psec to travel 1 mm in the air. If the path length of the pump pulse is decreased by 1 mm, by moving the delay prism, the pump pulse will arrive at the sample site at 6.6 psec (twice the change in the path length) before the probe pulse. Using a stepping motor, delays on the order of 10 fs are possible. The kinetics of any absorption changes can be followed point by point by moving the delay prism across the time domain of interest, usually about 300 psec. The probe beam (supercontinuum) is generated by focusing the 1060-nm pulse into a CCl_4 cell (Alfano and Shapiro).[1-5] At the sample site, the probe beam is divided into two pulses of approximately equal intensity, designated $I^e(t)$ and $I^r(t)$. $I^e(t)$ is transmitted through the same area of the sample that is excited by the 530-nm pulse. The intensity of the transmitted probe beam depends, of course, on the changes initiated by the exciting pulse. $I^r(t)$ is the reference beam and is transmitted through a different part of the sample.

The change in optical density (OD) for a given delay time is obtained as

$$\Delta OD(t) = -\log\{[I^e(t)/I^r(t)](I_o^r/I_o^e)\},$$

where the ratio, I_o^r/I_o^e, is the normalization factor for the two beams before the sample. The pump and probe method can have a resolution on the order of pulse duration ~ 10 fs.

Supercontinuum Source (SPM)

A most important nonlinear process with application in absorption spectroscopy and pulse compression into the fs regime is self-phase modulation (SPM) (Alfano and Shapiro).[1-5] SPM can be described by a simple model as follows: an intense optical pulse traveling through a medium can distort the atomic configuration of the material, thus resulting in a change in the refractive index. The electric field of the laser beam in the time domain after traveling a distance, z, in the material is given by

$$E(t) = 1/2 E_o(t) \exp\{- i(\omega_L t - n(t)z\omega_L/c)\} + c.c.,$$

where $E_o(t)$ is the envelope of the pulse, ω_L is the laser angular frequency, and n is the total index of refraction. For a medium having inversion symmetry, the first nonlinear coefficient is $X^{(3)}$ and the index of refraction, n, becomes intensity-dependent:

$$n = n_o + n_2 E^2.$$

The intensity-dependent term in the index of refraction modulates the spectral intensity given by the Fourier transform. It does so by modulating the instantaneous phase. This leads to a broadening of the pulse both on Stokes and anti-Stokes sides. The pulse becomes positively chirped (red in front and blue in the rear of the pulse). The broadening $\Delta\omega$ is given by

$$\Delta\omega = - \frac{\omega_L z}{c} \frac{\delta(n_2 E^2)}{\delta t} \sim \frac{\omega_L n_2 E_o^2 z}{\tau_p} .$$

The pulse modifies its own spectra through a change in phase and envelope. These

TABLE 4. Supercontinuum Generation in Liquids, Glasses, and Semiconductors

Material	Pumping Pulse (nm)	Broadening Useful Continuum (nm)
CCl_4	1,060	440–900
	530	400–900
BK-7	530	400–800
Water	620	300–1,500
GaAs	9,300	3,000–15,000

processes are SPM and self-steepening, respectively. The broadening in liquids and solids is over several thousand wave numbers. TABLE 4 lists typical materials used in SPM. The duration of the broadened emission is comparable to the laser pulse. SPM is the key process behind femtosecond pulse generation by compression.

Pulse Compression

When an intense pulse propagates in a condensed medium, its shape and frequency change due to group velocity dispersion and induced nonlinearity polarization (n_2). The frequency sweep (chirp) is caused by SPM. In most cases, n_2 is positive, causing a positive chirp; that is, it causes a necessary frequency with time that leads to the red part in the leading edge and the blue part in the trailing edge. It is possible to eliminate the linear part of chirp and achieve pulse shortening using a medium with negative $\delta^2 n/\delta\lambda^2$ curvature of dispersion or with a pair of gratings. The degree of compression can be varied by changing the distance between gratings. The central portion of SPM pulse (linear chirp) can be compressed with smaller secondary pulses positioned in the wings. Using long optical fibers, the combination of linear dispersion and n_2 cause the pulse to become rectangular in shape with a chirp. Therefore, the entire pulse can be compressed using a grating pair. Pulse compression from 30 fs down to 8 fs has been achieved by Shank and co-workers using this technique.[10] The key processes in the production of short fs pulses are SPM and a grating pair.

FUTURE DIRECTIONS

The future research trends in ultrafast technology will be in the following areas:

Light Sources:
 —to produce the ultimate shortest light pulse—1 cycle (for 600 nm → 2 fs);
 —to generate a femtosecond pulse with high powers up to 10^{12} watts;
 —to extend the spectral region covering 100 Å to 1 mm;
 —to produce UV and X-ray picosecond lasers;
 —to produce a high-power supercontinuum source.

Detection Techniques:
 —to develop a streak camera with femtosecond time resolution;
 —to develop a neutron and gamma ray picosecond streak camera;
 —to develop optoelectronics with femtosecond resolution;
 —to build an excite and probe device with femtosecond resolution with high sensitivity (1 photon) and spatial resolution (1μ).

Interaction with Matter:
 —to measure the momentum and energy relaxation in semiconductors and microstructures;
 —to investigate ballistic propagation;
 —to induce chemical relaxation and new chemicals;
 —to study effects of laser-induced shock waves in condensed matter;
 —to study precursor propagation;
 —to study damageless propagation;
 —to investigate coherent excitation and coherence of light;
 —to investigate memory effects in matter;
 —to study transparency in matter;
 —to investigate primary steps in biological and medical media;
 —to investigate the nonequilibrium state of matter;
 —and now to test models of quantum theory, relativity, and light.

The field of ultrafast technology in science and engineering is just at its beginning.

REFERENCES

1. ALFANO, R. R. 1984. Semiconductors Probed by Ultrafast Lasers Spectroscopy (Vol. I and II). Academic Press. New York.
2. ALFANO, R. R. 1982. Biological Events Probed by Ultrafast Laser Spectroscopy. Academic Press. New York.

3. SHAPIRO, S. L. 1977. Ultrafast Light Pulses. Topics in Applied Physics 18. Springer-Verlag. New York.
4. ALFANO, R. R. & S. L. SHAPIRO. 1975. Ultrashort phenomena. Phys. Today **28:** 30.
5. ALFANO, R. R. & S. L. SHAPIRO. 1973. Ultrafast phenomena in liquids and solids. Sci. Am. **228:** 42.
6. DeMARIA, A. J., D. STETSER & W. GLENN. 1967. Science **156:** 1557.
7. DUGUAY, M. & J. HANSEN. 1969. Appl. Phys. Lett. **15:** 192.
8. GIORDMAINE, J., P. RENTZEPIS, S. L. SHAPIRO & K. WECHT. 1967. Appl. Phys. Lett. **11:** 216.
9. MAHR, H. & M. HIRSCH. 1975. Opt. Commun. **13:** 96.
10. SHANK, C. V. 1984. Science **219:** 1027.
11. SHELEV, Y., M. RICHARDSON & J. ALCOCK. 1971. Appl. Phys. Lett. **18:** 354.
12. SHIMIZU, F. & W. STOICHEFF. 1966. IEEE J. Quantum Electron **5:** 544.

An Experimental Test of Locality Using a Single-Photon Interferometer[a]

J. D. FRANSON

Applied Physics Laboratory
The Johns Hopkins University
Laurel, Maryland 20707

The question of what happens when a single photon passes through a double-slit diffraction apparatus or an interferometer has been discussed since the earliest days of the quantum theory. Numerous interferometer experiments[1] have given results consistent with the principle of wave-particle duality, including the recent delayed-choice experiments.[2,3] During this same time period, the nonlocal nature of the quantum measurement process has also been under investigation, culminating in the impressive series of experiments by Aspect and his collaborators.[4] There has been little discussion, however, of the fundamental relationship between wave-particle duality and nonlocality.

It has been previously pointed out[1] that, under the assumption that the electromagnetic field is quantized, local realism predicts that a single-photon light source will give no interference effects if there is sufficient separation between two optical paths of equal length through an interferometer. Interferometer experiments are thus as capable of distinguishing between the quantum theory and local realism as are experiments based upon Bell's theorem.[5] This argument will be briefly reviewed here, with emphasis on the necessity of the space-like separation of events and the use of suitable single-photon light sources in experiments of this kind.

When the requirements for a single-photon light source are discussed within the context of the recent delayed-choice experiments,[2,3] it will be seen that the results of those experiments are consistent with various semiclassical field theories in which the electromagnetic field is not quantized. As a result, the existing delayed-choice experiments are capable of demonstrating only the wavelike aspects of light, and are not capable of testing the principles of wave-particle duality or local realism.

An atomic-beam light source and a 45-meter interferometer have been constructed for the purpose of distinguishing between the quantum theory and local realism. The experiment has not been completed, so a brief description of the apparatus is all that can be provided here. The apparatus is also capable of testing the assumption that the electromagnetic field is quantized, in the sense that the light emitted by a single atomic transition can be detected only once, under conditions in which the potential detection events are space-like separated. The present experiment is thus truly capable of testing both the wave and particle aspects of light. The experiment can be viewed as a test of that class[6] of local realistic theories that are not ruled out by the experiment[4] of Aspect *et al.*

[a]This work was supported by the APL Development Fund and by a Stuart S. Janney Fellowship.

127

WAVE-PARTICLE DUALITY AND NONLOCALITY

Perhaps the simplest way to begin a discussion of these issues is by considering a delayed-choice interferometer similar to that used in several recent experiments.[2,3] A single photon is assumed to be incident upon a beam-splitter which divides the probability amplitude equally among two widely separated paths, A and B. After traveling some distance, the two paths converge upon a second beam-splitter, which is assumed to give constructive interference for recombined beam C and destructive interference for recombined beam D. High-speed switches effectively allow the insertion of photon detectors into paths A and B at locations x_A and x_B, respectively, after the photon has already passed through the first beam-splitter. This allows a "delayed choice" as to whether to measure the interference effect or to determine which path the photon traversed.[7]

Now suppose that a detector has just been inserted into path A at x_A, but no detector has been inserted into path B. Suppose further that the detector at x_A succeeds in absorbing the photon and in registering a count. According to the quantum theory, the probability amplitude associated with the photon must now be set to zero instantaneously at all locations, including x_B, regardless of the distance between x_A and x_B. This is necessary in order to prevent the possibility of a second absorption event if a detector were subsequently inserted at x_B, for example. The standard quantum-theoretical interpretation of this situation is well known and needs no further comment here. It should be noted, however, that the instantaneous collapse of the wave function that occurs in this example is totally analogous to the instantaneous, nonlocal changes in the wave function that occur as a result of the measurement process in experiments based on Bell's theorem.[5]

Local theories do not allow such instantaneous changes in the wave function at a distance. To be more specific, the possibility of detecting a photon at x_B must be independent of whether or not a detector was inserted at x_A in a local, realistic theory if the detection of the photon at x_A or x_B would have been space-like separated events. In a local, realistic theory, the only way to prevent the possibility of a second detection event at x_B would be to have maintained zero field at x_B regardless of whether or not a detector was inserted at x_A.

Now there is good evidence[8] that the electromagnetic field is quantized, so let us assume, for the time being, that the field associated with a single photon is, indeed, zero after the detection or absorption of the photon. This is a crucial assumption, however, and will be examined in more detail later. Based on that assumption, the field associated with a single photon in a local theory must be localized at all times within a volume of radius equal to the speed of light multiplied by the maximum time required to absorb the photon. It follows immediately that the photon would have to chose either path A or path B, and could not propagate along both paths simultaneously, if the separation of the two paths was sufficiently large. No interference effects could then occur. Although this argument seems straightforward, a more detailed discussion can be found elsewhere.[1]

The first assumption inherent in this argument is that at least two points, x_A and x_B, are sufficiently distant that the potential absorption of the photon at x_A or x_B would be space-like separated events. If this condition is not satisfied, then it would be possible to construct local, relativistic field theories in which the absorption of electromagnetic energy at x_A could reduce the field at x_B. (Although such "communication" between two detectors may seem unlikely, it should be kept in mind that Maxwell's equations, for example, allow similar effects.) Whether or not the potential absorption events at x_A and x_B are space-like separated thus depends on the maximum time required to absorb a photon. Although the quantum theory allows the instantaneous absorption of photons, this need not be the case for local theories in general. In particular, let us consider only local theories that are invariant under time-reversal. In that case, the time required to absorb a photon would have to be comparable to the time required to emit one. It is also apparent that various local field theories (e.g., Maxwell's equations) may require a time interval comparable to the lifetime of an excited atomic state in order to emit a photon. It follows from this that local theories, in general, may require that the dimensions of the interferometer be much larger than a distance on the order of the natural coherence length due to radiation alone if a decrease in the interference effects is to be expected.

A comment should probably be made at this point with regard to theories similar to de Broglie's "pilot-wave" theory.[9] Such theories are not invariant under time-reversal, and it can be argued that they are not consistent with local realism.[1] In any event, such theories do not satisfy the assumptions stated above, and the present experiment cannot distinguish such theories from the quantum theory.

SINGLE-PHOTON LIGHT SOURCES

Perhaps the most frequent criticism of the above argument is that short pulses of light can obviously be generated using pulsed lasers, and that the intensity of such pulses can be reduced to arbitrarily low values using filters. One might then expect that the dimensions of the interferometer need only be larger than the length of such pulses in order to test local realism or wave-particle duality. This reasoning is not correct; the difficulty has to do with the question of what constitutes a single-photon light source. It will now be argued that such a pulsed-laser light source can be well described by classical field theory and is thus incapable of demonstrating any effects dependent upon field quantization. The question of what constitutes a suitable single-photon light source is crucial not only to this experiment, but to the interpretation of the recent delayed-choice experiments.

Let P_A by the probability of obtaining a pulse from the detector at x_A within time interval Δt, given that a photon has been emitted during the corresponding time interval. Let P_B be the probability of obtaining a pulse from the detector at x_B in the same time interval. Also, let P_{AB} be the probability of obtaining two pulses in Δt (one from each detector), which is proportional to the coincidence counting rate. If only one photon is emitted at a time, then P_{AB} would be zero. No light source is perfect, but it should at least be required that

$$P_{AB} \ll P_A P_B. \tag{1}$$

Equation 1 expresses the fact that the detection of the photon in one arm of the interferometer will greatly reduce the probability of detecting the photon in the other arm of the interferometer. This condition is precisely what requires the collapse of the wave function in the argument presented above, and it represents the fact that the electromagnetic field has been assumed to be quantized.

Most light sources do not satisfy equation 1, but instead are described by the condition that

$$P_{AB} \doteq P_A P_B. \tag{2}$$

Laser light satisfies equation 2 exactly, for example, due to its adherence to Poisson statistics, whereas incoherent light sources may require an additional factor of two on the right-hand side of the equation due to photon-bunching effects. For a light source described by equation 2, the detection of a photon in one arm of the interferometer has no bearing on the probability of detecting a photon in the other arm of the interferometer. As a result of this, no significant collapse or reduction of the wave function is required or expected, and the argument described above is no longer applicable.

A light source described by equation 2 can be thought of as a multiphoton light source, regardless of its intensity. For example, if laser light is reduced to a low intensity by the insertion of filters, then the wave function still describes a large (and indefinite) number of photons, each of which has only a small probability amplitude to be in the region of the detector. The detection and absorption of a photon in one arm of the interferometer thus has negligible effect on the probability of a second detection event in the other arm of the interferometer. Any high-intensity light source that has simply been attenuated by the insertion of filters (or in some other way) will have this property.

A light source described by equation 2 can also be thought of as a classical light source, in the sense that such a light source is incapable of demonstrating any effects due to field quantization. For example, laser light can be represented extremely well by a classical or semiclassical field. Any interferometer experiment utilizing such a light source might therefore be expected to give results consistent with Maxwell's equations. To be more specific, consider the delayed-choice experiments[2,3] performed using a pulsed laser attenuated with filters. The results of those experiments are consistent with a semiclassical field theory in which a real, classical wave propagates simultaneously down both arms of the interferometer. If the choice is made to measure the interference effects, then the classical waves will surely produce that. On the other hand, if the choice is made to insert detectors in both arms of the interferometer, then most of the time a pulse will be observed in only one of the detectors, but not both. However, that is also consistent with real, classical wave pulses propagating in each arm, each of which has only a very small probability of producing a detection event. A light source described by equation 2 will always give results that are subject to such an interpretation. Such experiments simply do not show that "the photon" is located in one path or the other; they cannot even demonstrate the existence of photons, in the sense that the field itself is quantized.

In contrast, a light source described by equation 1 cannot be described classically, and can be thought of as intrinsically quantum-mechanical in nature. If a photon from such a light source is absorbed in one arm of the interferometer, then it can truly be said that the field must now be zero in the other arm, and that the situation is not subject to a semiclassical interpretation. In what follows, a single-photon light source will be taken to be one that satisfies equation 1. As a practical matter, this will require that the light source contain, at most, one excited atom at any given time that is capable of producing a detection event. This condition is considered to be of sufficient importance that the present experiment will test whether or not equation 1 is actually satisfied for the conditions of this experiment.

EXPERIMENT IN PROGRESS

Most of the discussion up to this point was intended to develop the fact that large interferometers and truly single-photon light sources are required in order to test these issues. The present experiment is unique in that no earlier interferometer experiment has satisfied both of these requirements.[1] In fact, most earlier experiments satisfied neither of these requirements. Although the discussion here has been limited to photon interference effects, similar comments can be made with regard to neutron interferometer experiments.

A 25-meter interferometer had previously been constructed by the author and K. A. Potocki, but the results from that apparatus were not considered conclusive.[10] The main limitations in the earlier apparatus were related to the quality of the interferometer plates and the stability of the low-intensity light source. A new Jamin interferometer with a maximum length of 45 m has now been constructed. Custom-made optics of the highest available quality were used to eliminate any concern over the quality of the interference pattern. All the optics are positioned using a total of 22 motorized micrometers equipped with optical encoders. This allows a computer to automatically align the interferometer and collect the data.

Perhaps the main advantage of the new interferometer is the ability of the computer to automatically lock onto the white-light fringes using a high-intensity light source. As a result, the difference in path lengths is known at all times to within a small fraction of a wavelength, and is constantly maintained at a negligible value (less than three wavelengths). The phase of the interferometer has an intrinsic drift (due to thermal stress in the laboratory) of roughly one fringe per hour. The actual phase of the interferometer is measured using a high-intensity white-light source once a minute while the data are being taken. The argument will be that the interferometer must be working properly if the interference pattern from a diffuse white-light bulb can be observed continuously.

A light source that satisfies equation 1 is difficult to achieve in a long-distance experiment. The large distances require a reasonably well-collimated beam, which in turn requires that the light pass through a small pinhole in the collimator. In order to achieve reasonable detection efficiencies, the dimenions of the light source should thus be comparable to the diameter of the pinhole. An atomic-beam light source with an effective diameter of 25 μm has been constructed for this purpose. The new light source has just recently been completed, and new data should be available in the near future.

As mentioned earlier, the apparatus is also capable of determining whether or not equation 1 is satisfied for the conditions of this experiment. In his classic experiment, Clauser[8] showed for the first time that the electromagnetic field itself is quantized (in the sense that equation 1 is satisfied for an appropriate light source). It is desirable, however, to repeat those measurements here to ensure that the light source in use in this experiment is adequate. In addition, there may be some interest in testing the field quantization assumption under conditions in which the potential detection events are space-like separated. This is necessary to rule out any form of "communication" between the two detectors that may allow equation 1 to be satisfied as a result of the quantization of the atoms in the detectors rather than the quantization of the field itself. Once again, such "communication" between the detectors may seem unlikely, but it should be kept in mind that Maxwell's equations, for example, allow similar effects.

In order to perform this test, a set of reflecting prisms will be inserted into only one arm of the interferometer so as to increase its length by 160 feet compared to the other arm. If equation 1 is not satisfied, then an anomalous number of coincidence events should be observed in which two detector pulses are obtained at a delay time of approximately 160 nsec, with each pulse arising from a semiclassical wave propagating in each arm of the interferometer. The experimentally demonstrated detection efficiencies and accidental rates are adequate for this purpose.

SUMMARY

Single-photon interferometer experiments are just as capable of distinguishing between the quantum theory and local realism as are experiments based on Bell's theorem. Such experiments require large interferometers and truly single-photon light sources, which are difficult to realize experimentally, and the present experiment is the first to meet these requirements. This experiment is intended to test that class[6] of local, realistic theories that are not ruled out by the experiment of Aspect et al.,[4] as well as to investigate wave-particle duality under these extreme conditions.

REFERENCES

1. FRANSON, J. D. 1982. Phys. Rev. **D26:** 787–800.
2. ALLEY, C. O. 1983. Proceedings of the International Symposium on Foundations of Quantum Theory. S. Kamefuchi, Ed. Physical Society of Japan. Tokyo.
3. HELLMUTH, T., H. WALTHER & A. ZAJONC. 1985. Preprint. Max Planck Institut für Quantum Optik.
4. ASPECT, A., J. DALIBARD & G. ROGER. 1982. Phys. Rev. Lett. **49:** 1804–1807.
5. BELL, J. S. 1964. Physics **1:** 195–200.
6. FRANSON, J. D. 1985. Phys. Rev. **D31:** 2529–2532.
7. WHEELER, J. A. 1978. Mathematical Foundations of Quantum Theory. Academic Press. New York.
8. CLAUSER, J. F. 1974. Phys. Rev. **D9:** 853–860.
9. DE BROGLIE, L. 1960. Non-Linear Wave Mechanics. Elsevier. Amsterdam.
10. FRANSON, J. D. & K. A. POTOCKI. 1984. Johns Hopkins APL Tech. Dig. **5:** 305–308.

Polarized Neutron Interferometry[a]

G. BADUREK,[b] H. RAUCH, AND D. TUPPINGER

Atominstitut der Österreichischen Universitäten
A-1020 Wien, Austria

INTRODUCTION

Perfect crystal interferometry challenged a variety of new test measurements of quantum mechanics and the results helped to stimulate new discussions about its interpretation. This technique was developed in 1974 by Rauch, Treimer, and Bonse[1] by using a monolithically designed perfect silicon crystal to produce widely separated coherent beams of thermal neutrons ($\lambda \sim 1.8$ Å, $E \sim 0.025$ eV). The neutrons are dynamically Bragg-diffracted at the first crystal plate, then they are reflected at the middle plate, and finally they are superposed at the third plate of such an interferometer. FIGURE 1 shows the standard and the skew symmetrically cut versions of such an interferometer system.

The whole system represents a macroscopic quantum device where the wave functions of the beams can be calculated by solving the Schrödinger equation for a strictly periodical potential representing the perfect crystal (e.g., see references 2 and 3). The wave functions of the beams behind the interferometer are superposed wave functions from beam paths *I* and *II*, respectively:

$$I_0 \propto |\psi_0^I + \psi_0^{II}|^2,$$

$$I_0 + I_H = \text{const.} \tag{1}$$

From symmetry considerations, it can be deduced that for ideal geometry, the following important relation holds:

$$\psi_0^I = \psi_0^{II}. \tag{2}$$

The coherent beams in between the crystal plates can be influenced individually by nuclear, magnetic, and gravitational interactions that cause typical interference patterns in the outgoing beams. These interactions can be described for the forward direction by an index of refraction formalism that, for the nuclear interaction case, reads as

$$n = \sqrt{1 - \frac{\overline{V}}{E}} \simeq 1 - \lambda^2 \frac{Nb_c}{2\pi}. \tag{3}$$

[a]This work was supported by Fonds zur Förderung der Wissenschaftlichen Forschung (Project S 4201).
[b]Present address: Institut für Festkörperforschung KFA, Jülich, Federal Republic of Germany.

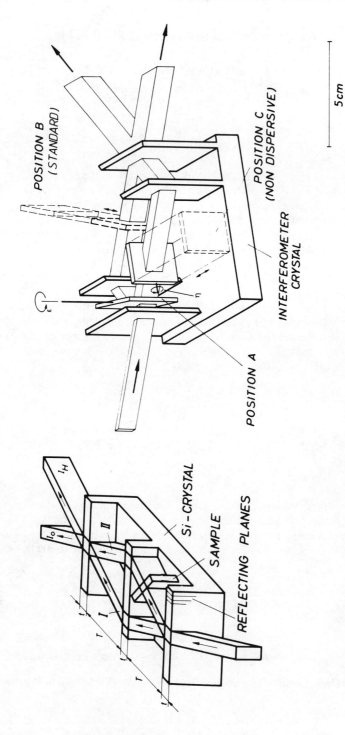

FIGURE 1. Sketch of a standard and of a skew symmetrically cut perfect crystal interferometer, including the indication of various measuring methods.

This changes the phase of the wave function as in optics:

$$\psi_0^{II} \rightarrow e^{-i(1-n)kD}\psi_0^{II} = e^{-iNb_c\lambda D}\psi_0^{II} = e^{i\chi}\psi_0^{II}, \tag{4}$$

which results in a complete beam modulation,

$$I_0 \propto |\psi_0^I + \psi_0^{II}|^2 \propto (1 + \cos Nb_c\lambda D) = 1 + \cos \chi. \tag{5}$$

Here, b_c denotes the coherent scattering length, N denotes the particle density, D denotes the thickness of the phase-shifter, and λ is the wavelength of the neutrons (which is related to their velocity, v, by the well-known de Broglie relation, $mv = h/\lambda$). More details about experiments that have already been performed and about the general capabilities of perfect crystal interferometry can be found in the proceedings of a related workshop, in various review articles, and in contributions to the present conference.[4–7]

All of the observed interference phenomena can easily be interpreted in the frame of the wave picture of nature, but it should be emphasized that the neutron also has well-defined particle properties—such are its mass, $m = 1.6749543(86) \times 10^{-27}$ kg, its spin, $\frac{1}{2}\hbar$, its associated magnetic moment, $\mu = -1.91304308(54) \mu_K$, its effective mass radius of about 0.7 fm, and its internal structure consisting of one "up" and two "down" quarks. Thus, neutrons are a proper tool for testing quantum mechanics with massive particles. The wave-particle dualism becomes obvious and many gedanken-experiments of quantum theory become feasible. All of the experiments performed until now belong to the region of self-interference, where, at a certain time interval, only one neutron is inside the interferometer, if at all. The next one is usually not yet born and is still contained in the uranium nucleus of the reactor fuel. Neutron interferometry also has recently been discussed in terms of quantum potentials where particle trajectories exist in the sense of the the de Broglie–Bohm interpretation of quantum mechanics.[8] In this contribution, we focus our interests on the magnetic interactions and on the experimental aspects of the related investigations.

4π-SYMMETRY OF SPINOR WAVE FUNCTIONS

Shortly after the development of perfect crystal neutron interferometry, the 4π-symmetry of spinors was verified using this technique. It was verified independently by Rauch *et al.*[9] and by Werner *et al.*[10] They followed the theoretical work of Aharonov and Susskind[11] and of Bernstein,[12] who showed that the intrinsic 4π-symmetry of a spinor wave function can be observed in an interference experiment. The related feasibility investigation for the neutron case originated from Eder and Zeilinger,[13] who wrote the propagation of the wave function within a magnetic field, B, as

$$\psi_0^I \rightarrow e^{-iHt/\hbar}\psi_0^I = e^{-i(\vec{\mu}\cdot\vec{B})t/\hbar}\psi_0^I = e^{-i(\vec{\sigma}\cdot\vec{\alpha})/2}\psi_0^I, \tag{6}$$

where $\vec{\sigma}$ is the Pauli spin matrix and $\alpha = (2\mu/\hbar)\int B dt \simeq (2\mu/\hbar v)\int B ds$ is the Larmor precession angle. For unpolarized neutrons, this leads to an interference pattern according to

$$I_0 \propto |\psi_0^I(\alpha) + \psi_0^{II}(0)|^2 \propto \left(1 + \cos\frac{\alpha}{2}\right). \tag{7}$$

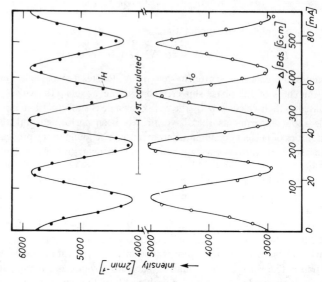

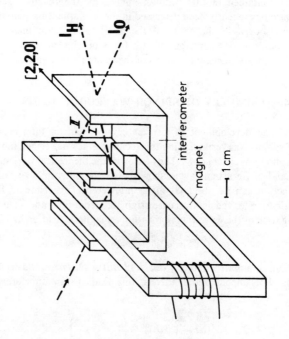

FIGURE 2. Experimental arrangement and results of the 4π-symmetry experiment. (Based on Rauch et al.[9])

FIGURE 2 shows the outcome of one of the first related measurements demonstrating the visibilization of the 4π-periodicity and the intrinsic feature of this phenomenon. A more precise value for the periodicity factor has been obtained in a later experiment by using μ-metal sheets for a better definition of the field integral, $\int Bds$ [$\alpha_0 = 715.87(38)$ deg].[14] These results have been widely debated in the literature, and the reader is referred to these articles.[15–19] In addition, characteristic beat effects concerning the intensity and the polarization of the outgoing beams have been found to exist when nuclear and magnetic phase-shifts are applied simultaneously (as has been demonstrated by Badurek *et al.*[20])

SPIN-SUPERPOSITION EXPERIMENT

The use of magnetic prism deflection in between the perfect crystal monochromator and the nondispersively arranged interferometer crystal has made polarized neutron interferometry feasible at the joint Dortmund-Grenoble-Vienna interferometer setup, S18, at the high flux reactor at Grenoble.[21] Thus, it has been possible to verify the quantum mechanical spin-superposition law on a macroscopic scale according to a proposal of E. P. Wigner from 1963.[22]

A polarized incident neutron beam is split coherently and the spin in one of the two beams is inverted either by a static dc-flipper (FIGURE 3) or by a Rabi-type resonance flipper (FIGURE 4). Both systems are standard in polarized neutron physics (e.g., see reference 23), and flipping efficiencies on the order of 99% can easily be achieved. In the first case, the spin is Larmor-rotated around an axis (y) perpendicular to the guide field, which changes the wave function of this beam according to equation 6 as

$$\psi \rightarrow e^{i\chi} e^{-i\sigma_y \pi/2} |z\rangle = -i\sigma_y e^{i\chi} |z\rangle + e^{i\chi} |-z\rangle . \tag{8}$$

Thus, at the third crystal plate, two wave functions with opposite spin directions are superposed,

$$\psi_0 \propto (|z\rangle + e^{i\chi} |-z\rangle), \tag{9}$$

which gives a final polarization in the (xy)-plane depending on the nuclear phase-shift, χ,[24] where

$$P = \frac{\langle \psi_0 | \vec{\sigma} | \psi_0 \rangle}{I_0} = \begin{pmatrix} \cos \chi \\ \sin \chi \\ 0 \end{pmatrix} . \tag{10}$$

Therefore, a pure initial state can be transferred to a pure final state behind the interferometer whose direction is perpendicular to both of the spin states existing before superposition. The related experiment was performed in 1983 by Summhammer *et al.*[25] The measured results show a complete agreement with the theoretical expectations (FIGURE 3).

This experiment was repeated in a second version where the static dc-flipper was replaced by a Rabi-type resonance flipper. This represented a time-dependent interaction, and besides causing the spin inversion, it also caused an exchange of the Zeeman

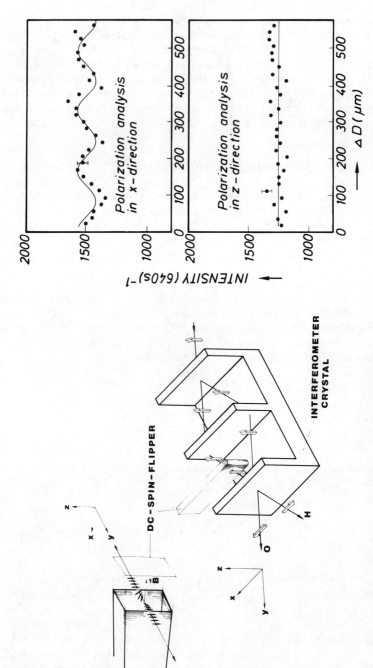

FIGURE 3. Sketch of the experimental situation and results of the static spin-superposition experiments. (Based on Summhammer et al.[25])

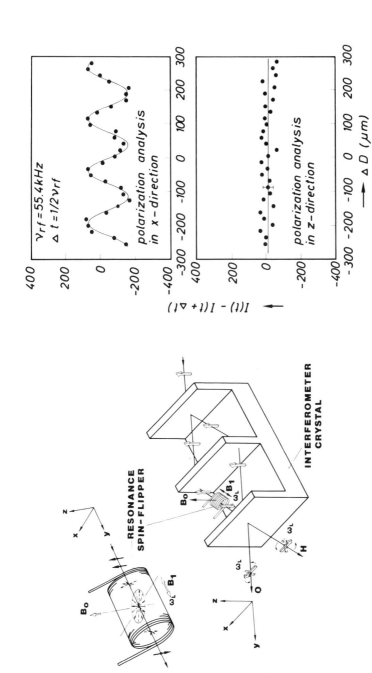

FIGURE 4. Sketch of the experimental situation and results of the time-dependent spin-superposition experiment with a Rabi-type neutron spin-flipper. (Based on Badurek *et al.*[30])

energy, $\hbar\omega_L = 2\mu B_0$, between the neutron and the resonator system.[26] The flipping efficiency for such a resonance system can be taken from Alvarez and Bloch,[27]

$$P_{12} = \frac{\sin^2\left[\frac{\mu B_1 t}{2\hbar}\sqrt{1 + \left(\frac{2(B_0 + \hbar\omega/2\mu)}{B_1}\right)^2}\right]}{1 + \left(\frac{2(B_0 + \hbar\omega/2\mu)}{B_1}\right)^2}, \tag{11}$$

which yields to two independent resonance conditions ($B_0 \gg B_1$),

$$\omega = \omega_L = \frac{2|\mu|B_0}{\hbar} \quad \text{and} \quad \frac{|\mu|B_1 l}{\hbar v} = \pi. \tag{12}$$

Here, $t(=1/v)$ is the time-of-flight of neutrons through the resonance coil of length, l, where the static field, B_0, and the oscillating field with the amplitude B_1 act on the neutron. It should be noticed that the flipping efficiency is independent from the phase of the flipper field. The width of the frequency resonance curve ($\sim B_1/B_0$) is in our case rather large because both the guide field and the amplitude of the resonance field are on the order of 20 G. The resonance frequency in an oscillating field is somewhat shifted towards higher frequencies due to the Bloch-Siegert effect[28] ($\omega_r = \omega_L[1 + (B_1^2/16B_0^2)]$) because the nonresonant component of the field contributes to an effective guide field. Therefore, ω_L has to be replaced by ω_r.[29] The associated energy transfer has been experimentally verified by using a high resolution backscattering instrument and a rather high magnetic guide field to achieve $\Delta E < 2\mu B_0$.[30] Thus, spin inversion and energy exchange has to be accounted for in calculating the wave function,

$$\psi \longrightarrow e^{i\chi}e^{i(\omega - \omega_r)t}|-z\rangle, \tag{13}$$

which gives a final polarization,

$$\vec{P} = \begin{pmatrix} \cos(\chi + \omega_r t) \\ \sin(\chi + \omega_r t) \\ 0 \end{pmatrix}, \tag{14}$$

and which now rotates with the Larmor frequency in the (xy)-plane without being driven by a magnetic field (FIGURE 4). Therefore, we used a stroboscopic measuring method to observe the polarization in time channels, Δt, synchronously with the phase of the oscillating flipper field (FIGURE 4).[31] Again, agreement with the theoretical prediction has been achieved, thus indicating that coherence can be preserved even when an energy exchange exists between the neutron and the apparatus.

These results gave rise to questions of whether a beam path detection could be possible besides the observation of the interference pattern. Our answer is "no" because, on the one hand, a single added or absorbed photon of the resonance circuit cannot be observed due to the uncertainty relation between the photon number (N) of the oscillating field and of its phase (φ), which is required for the stroboscopic measurement. This uncertainty relation already gives a reliable explanation for the impossibility of a simultaneous path and interference detection in the most simple, but incorrect form $[(\Delta N)^2(\Delta\varphi)^2 > \frac{1}{4}]$. However, it should be used and discussed in the more correct form,[32,33]

$$(\Delta N)^2 \frac{(\Delta S)^2 + (\Delta C)^2}{\langle S \rangle^2 + \langle C \rangle^2} \geq \frac{1}{4}, \tag{15}$$

where S and C are given by the creation and annihilation operators in the forms, $C = (a_- + a_+)/2$ and $S = (a_- + a_+)/2i$, whose matrix elements couple coherent Glauber states.

In addition, we now have to discuss whether the second possibility of observing the energy change of the neutron is feasible for a path detection. The answer is again "no" because it would be feasible only if the energetical width, ΔE, of the beam is smaller than the Zeeman energy ($\Delta E < \hbar\omega_r = 2\mu B_0$), which is a condition that contradicts the uncertainty relation for the beam properties, $\Delta E \Delta t \geq \hbar/2$, if one includes the requirement for the stroboscopic measurement ($\Delta t < 1/\omega_r$). It must also be discussed separately to what extent the argument given above holds for the case where two high magnetic field resonance flippers and very monochromatic beams ($\Delta E < \hbar\omega_r$) are used in an opposite operation mode or in the same mode acting on both beams, which would compensate for the energy shift.

DOUBLE COIL EXPERIMENT

The group of J. P. Vigier proposed a further experiment with two separate resonance coils, where there is one coil in each path (FIGURE 5).[34,35] They claim that an energy exchange inherently shows the particle properties of the neutron, and together with the self-interference characteristics of the experiment and the inseparability of a photon, they conclude that the neutron behaves inside the interferometer as a particle *and* as a wave. However, the complementary principle of the Copenhagen interpretation explains it as a particle *or* a wave. Unfortunately, the theoretical predictions about the outcome of a related experiment are the same. Therefore, a decision about various interpretations seems to be difficult, but the reader is referred to Vigier's contribution to this conference.

Three different modes of operation of the two resonance coils have been tested for this purpose:

(a) constant phase of both flippers, where

$$\psi_0 \to e^{i(\omega-\omega_r)t}\left|-z\right\rangle + e^{i\chi} e^{i(\omega-\omega_r)t}\left|-z\right\rangle ,$$

$$I_0 \propto 1 + \cos\chi ; \tag{16}$$

(b) with a distinct phase relation, Δ:

$$\psi_0 \to e^{i(\omega-\omega_r t)t}\left|-z\right\rangle + e^{i\chi}e^{i\Delta}e^{i(\omega-\omega_r)t}\left|-z\right\rangle ,$$

$$I_0 \propto 1 + \cos(\chi + \Delta) ; \tag{17}$$

(c) with random phase relation, $\Delta(t)$, where the average $\int \cos\Delta(t)\, dt$ over the measuring interval equals zero:

$$\psi_0 \rightarrow e^{i(\omega - \omega_r)t} \mid -z\rangle + e^{i\chi} e^{i\Delta(t)} e^{i(\omega - \omega_r)t} \mid -z\rangle ,$$

$$I_0 = \text{const.} \tag{18}$$

Experiment (c) does not show interference, but it contains all coherence phenomena that can be recovered by a phase-correlated measurement, $I = I(\Delta)$.

We performed the related measurements very recently and the results show the expected behavior (FIGURE 6). This indicates again that interference persists even if a certain finite energy exchange takes place inside the interferometer. The final polarization is now in the $\mid -z\rangle$ direction, as it has been tested by a separate

RESONANCE FLIPPER

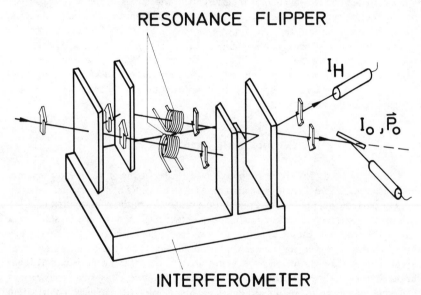

INTERFEROMETER

FIGURE 5. Experimental arrangement of two resonance flippers in a skew symmetrically cut interferometer. The polarization analyzer in the emerging O-beam was used for the Vigier-type experiments only.

polarization analyzer system placed behind the entire assembly. The experimental details and a more profound data evaluation will be given in a forthcoming paper.[36]

QUANTUM BEAT EFFECTS

A slight modification of the double coil experiment that was previously discussed permits the observation of characteristic beat effects. In this case, the frequency of the two resonators are chosen to be slightly different, which yields a wave function as

$$\psi_0 \rightarrow e^{i(\omega - \omega_{r1})t} \mid -z\rangle + e^{i\chi} e^{i(\omega - \omega_{r2})t} \mid -z\rangle \tag{19}$$

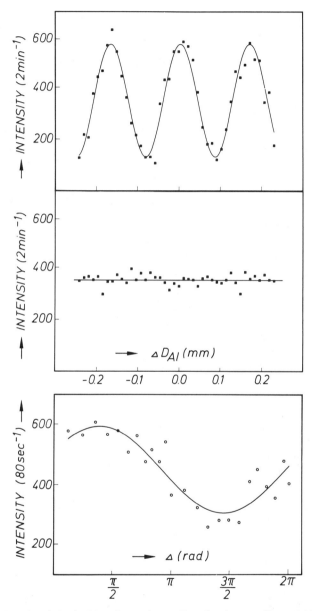

FIGURE 6. Results of the double coil experiment. Top: Synchronous flipper fields with ν_r = 71.90 kHz and variable nuclear phase-shift, χ; Middle: two slightly fluctuating mutually independent flipper fields with ν_r = 71.92 ± 0.02 kHz and variable nuclear phase-shift, χ; Bottom: constant nuclear phase-shift and variable phase-difference, Δ, between both flipper fields (ν_r = 71.90 kHz).

and an intensity modulation,

$$I_0 \propto (1 + \cos[\chi + (\omega_{r_1} - \omega_{r_2})t]) . \tag{20}$$

The difference between the two frequencies can be kept very small and stable by means of digital frequency synthesizers. This frequency difference causes a temporal intensity modulation approaching a macroscopic time scale, as is shown in FIGURE 7, where the modulation period is 48 s. This can also be interpreted as a measurement of an energy difference, $\hbar(\omega_{r_1} - \omega_{r_2})$, between the left and the right beam. The entire period shown in FIGURE 7 corresponds to an energy difference of $\Delta E = 8.6 \times 10^{-17}$ eV, and because the sensitivity of the phase determination is about $1/20$th of the whole period, it can be stated that a sensitivity of about $\Delta E = 4 \times 10^{-18}$ eV has been achieved. This extremely

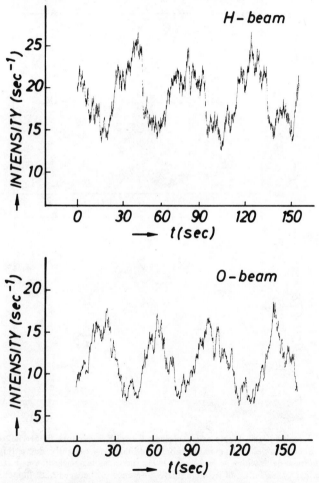

FIGURE 7. Ratemeter readout in the quantum beat experiment when a frequency difference of 0.02 Hz persists between the two flipper fields ($\nu_{r_1} = 71.89980$ kHz, $\nu_{r_2} = 71.89978$ kHz). The beating period corresponds to an energy difference of 8.6×1^{-17} eV.

high resolution is decoupled from the monochromaticity of the beam, which in the present experiment was only $\Delta E/E \sim 2.5\%$. The experimental details and the whole data evaluation will be given in a separate paper.[34]

In addition, whereas the usual determination of the neutron energy (Bragg-diffraction or time-of-flight) is essentially based on measurements of lengths, here it is reduced to a measurement of frequencies that can be done very precisely. This extremely high sensitivity may challenge further investigations about the electric charge, the electric dipole moment, and the polarizability of the neutron, and about radiation damping effects due to multiple scattering in condensed matter. The expected sizes of these effects have been discussed elsewhere.[37]

DISCUSSION

All of the results obtained so far agree completely with the formalism of quantum mechanics. The related measurements put quantum mechanical phenomena on a macroscopic scale in space and/or time. In observing the interference pattern event by event, it seems that each neutron carries information about the physical situation in both widely separated beam paths. Although the experiments belong to the region of self-interference, the interference pattern contains ensemble properties too. There is only self-interference, but many neutrons with the same or a similar history are required to form the interference pattern. Our experiments have shown that a finite energy transfer does not necessarily have to be a measuring process associated with a collapse of the wave field as long as it is below the limits of the uncertainty relation. There are often several equivalent possibilities for the explaination of the results: (a) The 4π-symmetry experiment can be explained either by an index of refraction formalism if the initial spins are assumed to be parallel or antiparallel to the magnetic field, or likewise, by the rotation of the polarization vector when the axis of quantization is chosen within the (xy)-plane; (b) The spin-superposition experiment raised the question of whether the superposition state knows the beam path of the individual neutrons when the final polarization is analyzed in the z-direction; (c) The quantum beat effect can be explained equivalently by the associated small energy difference or by a slowly varying phase difference between the two flipper fields. Therefore, it may be worthwhile to consider a certain unification of various quantities. There are situations where the interference pattern looks like an incoherent mixture of the intensity from both beams, but by applying a proper measuring method, the internal coherence effects can be recovered.

We tried to perform unbiased experiments and therefore we did not want to interfere with any epistemological interpretation of quantum mechanics. The only statement that should be made is that a decision between the various interpretations seems to be difficult or even impossible as long as their predictions about the outcome of a specific experiment are equal.

ACKNOWLEDGMENTS

We would like to express our thanks for the hospitality of the Institute Laue Langevin at Grenoble and for the cooperation within the Dortmund-Grenoble-Vienna interferometer group. Fruitful discussions with J. P. Vigier, as well as the support from A. Rumpf and the technical assistance from G. Schmid, are gratefully acknowledged.

REFERENCES

1. RAUCH, H., W. TREIMER & U. BONSE. 1974. Phys. Lett. **A47:** 369.
2. PETRASCHECK, D. 1976. Acta Phys. Austriaca **45:** 217.
3. BAUSPIESS, W., U. BONSE & W. GRAEFF. 1975. J. Appl. Crystallogr. **9:** 68.
4. BONSE, U. & H. RAUCH, Eds. 1979. Neutron Interferometry. Oxford Univ. Press (Clarendon). London/New York.
5. GREENBERGER, D. M. & A. W. OVERHAUSER. 1979. Rev. Mod. Phys. **51:** 43.
6. KLEIN, A. G. & S. A. WERNER. 1983. Rep. Progr. Phys. **46:** 259.
7. WERNER, S. A. 1986. This conference.
8. DEWDNEY, C. 1985. Phys. Lett. **109A:** 377.
9. RAUCH, H., A. ZEILINGER, G. BADUREK, A. WILFING, W. BAUSPIESS & U. BONSE. 1975. Phys. Lett. **54A:** 425.
10. WERNER, S. A., R. COLELLA, A. W. OVERHAUSER & C. F. EAGEN. 1975. Phys. Rev. Lett. **35:** 1053.
11. AHARONOV, Y. & L. SUSSKIND. 1967. Phys. Rev. **158:** 1237.
12. BERNSTEIN, H. J. 1967. Phys. Rev. Lett. **18:** 1102.
13. EDER, G. & A. ZEILINGER. 1976. Nuovo Cimento **34B:** 76.
14. RAUCH, H., A. WILFING, W. BAUSPIESS & U. BONSE. 1978. Z. Phys. **B29:** 281.
15. BYRNE, J. 1978. Nature **275:** 188.
16. BERNSTEIN, H. J. & A. V. PHILLIPS. 1981. Sci. Am. **245:** 121.
17. ZEILINGER, A. 1981. Nature **294:** 544.
18. SILVERMAN, M. P. 1980. Eur. J. Phys. **1:** 116.
19. JORDAN, T. F. 1983. Phys. Rev. **96A:** 457.
20. BADUREK, G., H. RAUCH, A. ZEILINGER, W. BAUSPIESS & U. BONSE. 1976. Phys. Rev. **D14:** 1177.
21. BADUREK, G., H. RAUCH, A. WILFING, U. BONSE & W. GRAEFF. 1979. J. Appl. Crystallogr. **12:** 186.
22. WIGNER, E. P. 1963. Am. J. Phys. **31:** 6.
23. MEZEI, F., Ed. 1980. Lect. Notes Phys. **128.**
24. ZEILINGER, A. 1979. In Neutron Interferometry. U. Bonse & H. Rauch, Eds.: 141. Oxford Univ. Press (Clarendon). London/New York.
25. SUMMHAMMER, J., G. BADUREK, H. RAUCH, A. ZEILINGER & U. KISCHKO. 1983. Phys. Rev. **A27:** 2532.
26. DRABKIN, G. M. & R. A. ZHITNIKOV. 1960. Sov. Phys. JETP **11:** 729.
27. ALVAREZ, L. W. & F. BLOCH. 1940. Phys. Rev. **57:** 111.
28. BLOCH, F. & A. SIEGERT. 1940. Phys. Rev. **57:** 522.
29. KENDRICK, H., J. S. KING, S. A. WERNER & A. ARROT. 1970. Nucl. Instrum. Methods **79:** 82.
30. ALEFELD, B., G. BADUREK & H. RAUCH. 1981. Z. Phys. **B41:** 231.
31. BADUREK, G., H. RAUCH & J. SUMMHAMMER. 1983. Phys. Rev. Lett. **51:** 1015.
32. JACKIW, R. 1968. J. Math. Phys. **9:** 339.
33. CARRUTHER, P. & M. M. NIETO. 1968. Rev. Mod. Phys. **40:** 411.
34. DEWDNEY, C., P. GUERET, A. KYPRIANIDIS & J. P. VIGIER. 1984. Phys. Lett. **102A:** 291.
35. VIGIER, J. P. 1985. Pramana J. Phys. **25:** 397.
36. BADUREK, G., H. RAUCH & D. TUPPINGER. 1986. Submitted to Phys. Rev. A.
37. RAUCH, H. 1979. In Neutron Interferometry. U. Bonse & H. Rauch, Eds.: 161. Oxford Univ. Press (Clarendon). London/New York.

Neutron Interferometry at Missouri

Recent Developments[a]

SAMUEL A. WERNER

*Physics Department
and Research Reactor Facility
University of Missouri-Columbia
Columbia, Missouri 65211*

INTRODUCTION AND OVERVIEW

In 1967, I ran across Ulrich Bonse and Michael Hart's paper in the library of the scientific laboratory, Ford Motor Company, in which the invention and initial testing of the perfect-silicon-crystal X-ray interferometer is described.[1] A year earlier, I had studied the paper by Batterman and Cole[2] on dynamical theory on X-ray diffraction, and was therefore able to see the inherent beauty of the Bonse-Hart device. I also was able to understand, at least qualitatively, the potential difficulties in making it work. With my background in neutron scattering research, it was natural to start thinking about using this device with thermal neutrons and about various experiments one might be able to carry out with it. My first idea was to put a magnetic field on one leg of the interferometer and look for phase-shifts caused by the Zeeman "potential energy," $-\vec{\mu} \cdot \vec{B}$. I took this idea to A. W. Overhauser. He was very enthusiastic about it. During the course of our conversation, the idea struck him that the gravitational potential energy difference, mgH, due to the Earth acting on the two beams in an interferometer separated by a height, H (a few cm), may be of the same order of magnitude at $\vec{\mu} \cdot \vec{B}$ (for a few hundred gauss). A quick calculation showed this to be the case. A month or so later, the very nice paper by Herbert Bernstein appeared, in which he described the neutron phase-shifts expected to be induced by a magnetic field in the language of a spinor rotation of fermions.[3]

I was very busy with other experiments at the time (and A. W. Overhauser was involved with his theory of SDWs and CDWs); however, we did work out the formulas for the experiment we now call gravitationally induced quantum interference, and I worked out my own theoretical version of how a neutron interferometer would work. In 1970, I went off to Sweden on sabbatical leave, and shortly after my return to Michigan, Overhauser accepted a position at Purdue University. He discussed our ideas of neutron interferometry there with Roberto Colella, who is an expert on X-ray diffraction physics. We did not, however, pursue our ideas experimentally, and in 1974, the important paper by Rauch, Treimer, and Bonse appeared.[4] They had demonstrated the neutron application of the Bonse-Hart interferometer. However, better late than never, we machined our first Si-crystal interferometer and tested it with X rays at Purdue. By the end of summer 1975, we had successfully carried out a preliminary

[a]This work was supported by the Physics Division, National Science Foundation, Grant No. PHY-8410683.

gravity experiment,[5] and also completed a spinor rotation experiment[6] at the University of Michigan Research Reactor. In August 1975, I joined the physics department at the University of Missouri and initiated a major program in neutron interferometry in Columbia.

Since that time, a large number of interesting neutron interferometry experiments have been carried out worldwide.[7] The following is a list of the experiments carried out by my group:

(1) Change of sign of the wave function of a fermion during a 2π-precession (1975).[6]

(2) Gravitationally induced quantum interference (1975, 1980, 1986).[5,8,9]

(3) Effect of the Earth's rotation on the quantum mechanical phase of the neutron (Neutron Sagnac Effect, 1979).[10]

(4) Measurement of the longitudinal coherence length of a neutron beam (1983).[11]

(5) Search for a phase-shift of a neutron beam in passing through moving matter with stationary boundaries (Null Fizeau Effect, 1985).[12]

(6) Search for quaternions in quantum mechanics: Is the neutron-nuclear scattering amplitude a pure complex number, or can it be a quaternion number? (Done in 1984.)[13]

(7) Measurement of the energy-dependent scattering length of ^{149}Sm in the vicinity of the first half Breit-Wigner resonance (1982).[14]

(8) Precision measurement of the scattering amplitude of ^{235}U (1986).[15]

The next section of this paper is devoted to a discussion of our neutron interferometry experiments on the role of gravity and inertia in quantum mechanics. We are currently pursuing a new experiment in which the full-360-degree symmetry of the neutron interference induced by the gravitational field of the Earth is observed. This experiment is motivated, in part, by the acceleration-induced interference experiments of Wroblewski and Bonse, and by their theoretical calculations indicating an important in-crystal gravitation-induced dynamical-diffraction effect on the observed phase-shifts.[16] In the last section, I give a summary of our ideas for future experiments, along with new instrumentation plans and concepts for large-scale neutron interferometry.

EFFECT OF GRAVITY AND INERTIA ON NEUTRON INTERFERENCE

In most experimentally accessible phenomena in physics, gravity and quantum mechanics do not simultaneously play an important role. A neutron quantum interference experiment, for which the outcome necessarily depends upon both Planck's constant, h, and the gravitational constant, G, in an inseparable way, was first carried out by Colella, Overhauser, and Werner.[5] A more detailed experiment was subsequently performed by Staudenmann et al.[8] I begin by reviewing the theoretical background and results of this experiment and the neutron Sagnac experiment.

A diagram of the three-crystal LLL interferometer is shown in FIGURE 1. This is a monolithic device fabricated from a perfect single-crystal Si ingot. A nominally collimated, monochromatic beam ($\Delta\lambda/\lambda \approx 0.01$) is directed along the line SA and is coherently split in the first Si slab by Bragg reflection (220 lattice planes). These two coherent beams are again split in the second crystal slab in the regions near points B and C. Two of these beams overlap and interfere near point D in the third Si slab. If the beam traversing the path ACD is phase-shifted by increasing the optical path length (via some interaction, in this case, gravity) relative to the beam traversing the path ABD, the counting rates in detectors C_2 and C_3 will change according to the formulas,[8]

$$I_2 = \gamma - \alpha \cos (\Delta\beta) \tag{1}$$

and

$$I_3 = \alpha[1 - \cos (\Delta\beta)]. \tag{2}$$

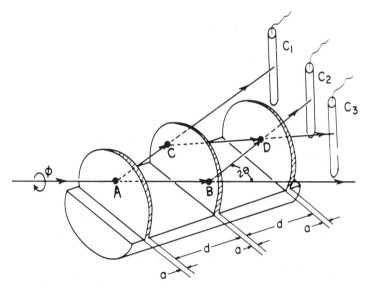

FIGURE 1. Schematic diagram of the LLL interferometer and the ^{3}He-detectors ($\frac{1}{2}$ inch diameter) used in our experiments at Missouri. The dimensions are $a = (2.464 \pm 0.002)$ mm and $d = (34.518 \pm 0.002)$ mm. In the gravity experiments, the interferometer is turned through angles ϕ about the incident beam. When $\phi = 0$, the parallelogram ABDC is horizontal.

Here, $\Delta\beta$ is the phase-shift, and the constants, α and γ, depend upon the incident flux, the crystal structure, and the neutron-nuclear scattering length of Si.

Because the distances involved in this interferometer are small compared to the Earth's radius, R, the Hamiltonian governing the neutron's motion in our laboratory's coordinate frame may be written as

$$H = \frac{\mathbf{p}^2}{2m_i} + m_g\vec{g} \cdot \vec{r} - \vec{\omega} \cdot \vec{L}. \tag{3}$$

Here, m_i is the neutron's inertial mass, m_g is the neutron's gravitational mass, and $\vec{g}$ is the acceleration due to gravity. The $\mathbf{p}$ is the neutron's canonical momentum, $\vec{\omega}$ is the angular rotation velocity of the Earth, and $\vec{L} = \vec{r} \times \vec{p}$ is the angular momentum of the neutron's motion about the center of the Earth. One finds from Hamilton's equations that the canonical momentum is related to the neutron velocity, $\dot{\vec{r}}$, by

$$\vec{p} = m_i \dot{\vec{r}} + m_i \vec{\omega} \times \vec{r}, \tag{4}$$

as expected. In order to calculate the phase-shift, $\Delta\beta$, in an interferometer experiment, we associate a de Broglie wave of wave-vector, $\vec{k}$, with the canonical momentum, $\vec{p} = \hbar\vec{k}$. The phase difference for the neutron wave traversing the path ACD in FIGURE 1 relative to ABD is then given by

$$\Delta\beta = \frac{1}{\hbar} \int_{ACD} \vec{p} \cdot d\vec{r} - \frac{1}{\hbar} \int_{ABD} \vec{p} \cdot d\vec{r} = \frac{1}{\hbar} \oint \vec{p} \cdot d\vec{r}. \tag{5}$$

Inserting the momentum (equation 4) into this line integral around the closed path ACDBA, we find that the phase-shift involves two terms,

$$\Delta\beta = \Delta\beta_{grav} + \Delta\beta_{sagnac}. \tag{6}$$

For a horizontally directed incident beam, the first term due to gravity is given by

$$\Delta\beta_{grav} = -2\pi m_i m_g (g/h^2)\lambda\, A \sin\phi \equiv -q_{grav} \cdot \sin\phi, \tag{7}$$

and the second term, analogous to the optical Sagnac effect[17] due to the Earth's rotation, is given by

$$\Delta\beta_{sagnac} = (4\pi m_i/h)\, \vec{\omega} \cdot \vec{A}, \tag{8}$$

where $\vec{A}$ is the normal area vector of the interferometer parallelograms (ACDBA), and λ is the neutron wavelength.[18] The derivations and discussion here have assumed that the trajectories between the crystal slabs are straight rather than parabolic curves. This is a good approximation. The angular deviation from a straight line over the distances in the interferometer is of order 0.01 arc seconds (for $\lambda = 1.4$Å neutrons), while the Darwin width for the Si interferometer crystals is ~0.1 arc seconds.

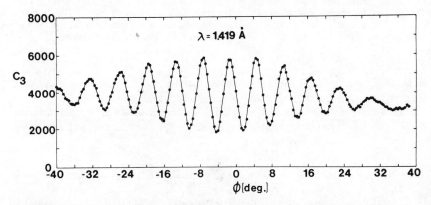

FIGURE 2. Gravitationally induced quantum interferogram. The neutron wavelength is $\lambda = 1.419$Å. The counting time was about 7 min per point (Staudenmann et al., reference 8).

FIGURE 3. Photograph of the rotator assembly, interferometer, detectors, and Benelex neutron shield box used in the gravity experiments. The size of the aluminum box in which the interferometer is mounted is ~25 cm × 25 cm × 20 cm.

The experimental procedure involves turning the interferometer, including the entrance slit and the ^{3}He-detectors, about the incident beam line AB as shown in FIGURE 1. Neutrons are counted for a preset length of time for each angular setting, ϕ. This procedure allows neutrons on the path CD to be somewhat higher above the surface of the Earth than for the beam path AB. The difference in the Earth's gravitational potential between these two levels causes a quantum mechanical phase-shift of the neutron wave on the trajectory ACD relative to ABD. The accumulated phase on the rising path AC is equal to the accumulated phase on the opposite rising path BD.

FIGURE 2 shows data taken by Staudenmann *et al.*[8] for incident neutrons of wavelength 1.419Å. Because the interferometer is extremely sensitive to strain, microphonics, and temperature gradients, this experiment was carried out by setting the LLL device on two felt strips in a "V-shaped" groove in a metallic cradle (which limited the angular rotation angle, ϕ, to ± 40 degrees). The interferometer is mounted inside of a metallic box and bolted rigidly to the rotator mechanism that is mounted inside of a heavy Benelex box as shown in FIGURE 3. The entire assembly is mounted on a set of four vibration-isolation pads. The frequency of the oscillations in FIGURE 2 was obtained by Fourier transforming the data. The peak of the Fourier transform occurs at $q = 60.3$ radians. This number is to be compared with theory. The incident beam for this experiment was oriented nearly exactly along a north-south line. For this orientation, equation 8 can be written as

$$\Delta\beta_{\text{sagnac}} = (4\pi m_i \omega A/h) \cos \theta_L \cos \phi = q_{\text{sagnac}} \cdot \cos \phi. \tag{9}$$

Using a colatitude angle, $\theta_L = 51.37°$, and $g = 980.0$ cm/sec^2 at Columbia, Missouri, along with the dimensions of the interferometer given in FIGURE 1, we find for $\lambda = 1.419$Å neutrons,

$$q_{\text{grav}} = 56.4 \text{ radians} \quad \text{and} \quad q_{\text{sagnac}} = 1.45 \text{ radians}. \tag{10}$$

There is an additional effect on the measured phase-shifts, $\Delta\beta$, due to bending (or warping) of the interferometer under its own weight as it is turned about the incident beam line (which is not an axis of elastic symmetry of the device). This effect was measured, *in situ*, with X rays. It was found experimentally that

$$\Delta\beta_{\text{bend}} = - (34.6/\lambda) \sin^2 \theta_\beta \sin \phi = - q_{\text{bend}} \cdot \sin \phi, \tag{11}$$

where θ_B is the Bragg angle for Si(220) at wavelength, λ. We have no first principles explanation of this result. For $\lambda = 1.419$Å neutrons, this formula gives $q_{\text{bend}} = 3.3$ radians. Equations 7, 9, and 11 show that the total phase-shift consists of three terms; it can be written in the form,

$$\Delta\beta = q \sin (\phi - \phi_o), \tag{12}$$

where

$$\phi_o = \tan^{-1}\left(\frac{q_{\text{sagnac}}}{q_{\text{grav}} + q_{\text{bend}}}\right) \tag{13}$$

and

$$q^2 = (q_{\text{grav}} + q_{\text{bend}})^2 + q_{\text{sagnac}}^2. \tag{14}$$

Although q_{sagnac} is 2.5% of q_{grav}, its effect on the measured frequency of oscillation, q, is small because it must be added in quadrature to q_{grav}. For $\lambda = 1.419$Å, the predicted value of q is 59.7 radians, which is within 1% of the measure value of 60.3 radians. A set of measurements at nine wavelengths between 1Å and 2Å were carried out. The resulting data were fitted with the theory outlined above, yielding a quantum mechanical measurement of the neutron mass,

$$(m_i m_g)^{1/2} = (1.675 \pm 0.003) \times 10^{-24} \text{g}, \tag{15}$$

that agrees with the rest mass of the neutron obtained from mass spectroscopy to within the limits of error.

The neutron Sagnac effect was detected separately using a vertically directed beam as shown in FIGURE 4.[19,20] The phase-shift was measured as a function of the interferometer orientation angle, ϕ, about the vertical axis using a phase rotator technique (not described here). A photograph of the apparatus for this experiment is shown in FIGURE 5. From symmetry, it is apparent that there is no ϕ-dependent gravity-induced phase-shift for this geometry. However, the angle between the axis of rotation of the Earth, $\vec{\omega}$, and the normal area vector, $\vec{A}$, is varied as the interferometer takes on various orientations specified by the angle, ϕ, thus changing the phase-shift

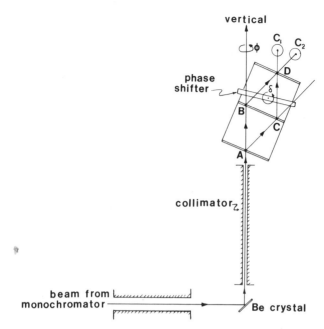

FIGURE 4. Schematic diagram of the configuration of the apparatus for vertical-beam experiments designed to measure the neutron Sagnac effect (Werner *et al.*, reference 10).

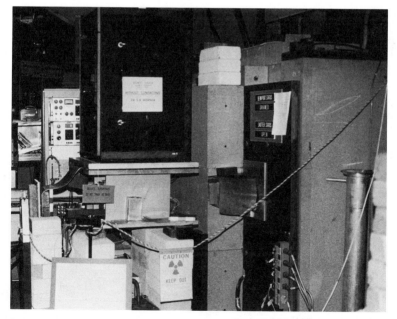

FIGURE 5. Photograph of the apparatus for the neutron Sagnac effect (Werner *et al.*, reference 10).

due to the Earth's rotation predicted by equation 8. In terms of the colatitude angle, θ_L, at the point on the Earth's surface where the experiment was done (Columbia, Missouri) and the angle, ϕ, the Sagnac phase-shift for this geometry is given by

$$\Delta\beta_{\text{sagnac}} = (4\pi m_i/h)\omega A \sin\theta_L \cdot \sin\phi. \tag{16}$$

The experimental results are shown in FIGURE 6. When the normal area vector points west or east, the phase-shift is zero, while when it is directed north or south, it is 95° or −95°, respectively. This result is in reasonable agreement with equation 16, which predicts it should be +92° and −92° for the north and south orientations, respectively. It is interesting to note that the results of this experiment depend only upon the inertial mass of the neutron, m_i, while the results of the gravity experiment depend upon the product, $m_i m_g$. Therefore, one can interpret the combination of the two experiments as independent measurements of the inertial and gravitational neutron masses obtained from quantum mechanical interference.

As mentioned earlier, the operation of the interferometer entails very sensitive strains. Mounting techniques involving glues, waxes, and epoxies of many varieties were found to be unsatisfactory. J-L. Staudenmann suggested and tested a technique that utilizes double-sticky-back plastic tape. This technique was used for holding the interferometer in the Sagnac effect experiment above. With this method for holding the interferometer to its metallic cradle, we have recently made our first attempts to obtain full-360° gravitationally induced quantum interferograms.[21] The results of an experiment carried out at $\lambda = 1.407$Å are shown in FIGURE 7. It is noted that in addition to the rapid gravity-induced oscillations (and the damping of these oscillations

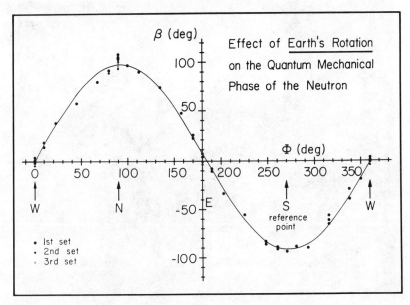

FIGURE 6. A plot of the phase-shift, β, due to the Earth's rotation as a function of the orientation, ϕ, of the interferometer shown in FIGURE 4 (Staudenmann *et al.*, reference 8).

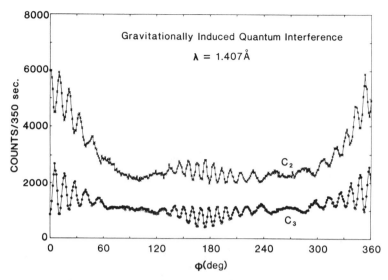

FIGURE 7. First full-360° rotation gravitationally induced quantum interferogram (H. Kaiser, M. Arif, and S. A. Werner, July 1985).

observed also in earlier experiments), there is an overall gradual decrease of intensity as the interferometer is rotated from 0° to 180°. This is due to a neutron optics variation of intensity passing through the interferometer as it is rotated from the parallel configuration ($\phi = 0°$), with respect to the monochromatic, to the antiparallel configuration ($\phi = 180°$). This variation can be shown to follow the formula,[22]

$$f(\phi) = \left[\frac{(1 - \epsilon)^2 \alpha^2 + \epsilon^2 \eta^2}{\beta^2 \sin^2 \phi + \alpha^2 (\cos \phi - \epsilon)^2 + \epsilon^2 \eta^2} \right]^{1/2}, \tag{17}$$

where α and β are the angular collimations (FWHM) of the incident beam in the horizontal and vertical planes, respectively, η is the mosaic width (FWHM), and $\epsilon = \tan\theta_B/\tan\theta_m$ (where θ_B and θ_m are the Bragg angles of the interferometer and monochromatic, respectively).

   This function has been experimentally measured by inserting a ruled aluminum plate across the beams (which destroys the transverse coherence of the beams), and also by adding the counting rates in the detectors C_2 and C_3 together. A measurement of this kind is shown in FIGURE 8, along with a fit to the functional form of equation 17. This neutron optics effect is reasonably well understood. The data of FIGURE 7 can therefore be corrected for this effect by scaling it with the function, $f(\phi)$. We have chosen to make this correction to the data, point-by-point, using the results of FIGURE 8. The interferograms shown in FIGURE 9 are the result of this procedure. The two patterns for C_2 and C_3 display the expected 180° phase difference required by equations 1 and 2. This data "looks" beautiful. However, the frequency of oscillation is about 27% lower than that which the theory for gravity-induced interference predicts. We have carried out X-ray measurements again to monitor the bending effects. We

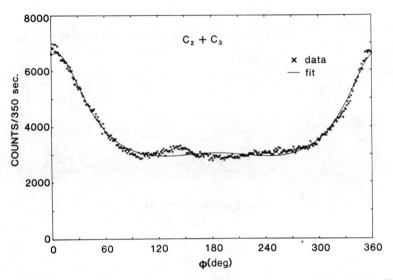

FIGURE 8. Measurement of the neutron-optics, geometrical correction function, $f(\phi)$, described by equation 17 and the discussion in the text. The solid line is a best fit to the data, with $\alpha = 0.39°$, $\beta = 0.46°$, and $\eta = 0.35°$.

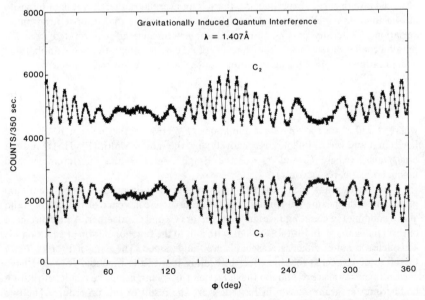

FIGURE 9. Full-360° gravitationally induced interference pattern corrected for the neutron-optics geometrical effect described in the text and plotted in FIGURE 8 (Werner *et al.*, reference 9).

find that these effects are quite large for this method of mounting the interferometer, and thus account for the discrepancy in the measured oscillation frequency.

We are now confronting this strain-induced mounting problem in various systematic ways. We have designed a new interferometer with strain-relief grooves, as shown in FIGURE 10.[23] This interferometer will be machined in the next several months. It will be rigidly mounted to the metallic cradle with a bracket that inserts into the lower groove. The upper groove isolates the interferometer crystal slabs from the strain induced by the rigid mount. It is hoped that this technique will allow us to approach our goal of carrying out a full-rotation gravitationally induced quantum interference experiment at a 0.1% level of precision.

To this point, we have tacitly assumed that neutrons propagate straight across each of the three-crystal slabs of the interferometer, and that the appropriate area, A, in

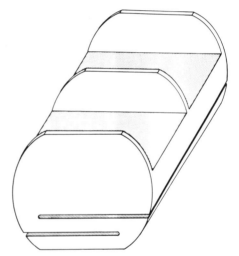

FIGURE 10. Schematic drawing of a new interferometer with two strain-relief grooves to be used in our next series of gravity experiments.

equation 7 is

$$A_o = 2d(d + a) \tan \theta_B, \qquad (18)$$

where d is the distance between the crystal slabs and a is their thickness. This is the appropriate formula for neutrons satisfying the Bragg condition exactly. However, for incident neutrons that fall within the Darwin width, but are slightly off the exact Bragg condition, the trajectories for neutrons corresponding to the α- and β-branches of the dispersion surface split and follow the dashed straight lines in FIGURE 11. The consequence of this fact for the three-crystal LLL interferometer is that it is actually an 8-path interferometer. There are three slightly different areas that must be considered, namely, A_o, $A_o + \delta A$, and $A_o - \delta A$, where

$$\delta A = 2a (a + d) \tan \theta_B. \qquad (19)$$

Thus, for an interferometer consisting of slabs of infinitesimal thickness, a, $\delta A/A_o$

approaches zero as a/d becomes small. In general, however, a quantitative understanding of the effects of gravity on the interferograms must utilize a dynamical-diffraction, intensity-weighted sum of these three different areas. M. A. Horne has recently developed this approach in analyzing our gravity interference experiments.[24] Numerical calculations appropriate to the dimensions of our interferometer reveal that the predicted oscillation frequency (for $\lambda = 1.419$Å neutrons) is 3.9% higher than our original prediction based upon A_o alone. From Horne's calculation, it is also possible to understand (at least qualitatively) the loss of contrast with increasing rotation angle, ϕ, as displayed by the data of FIGURES 2 and 9.

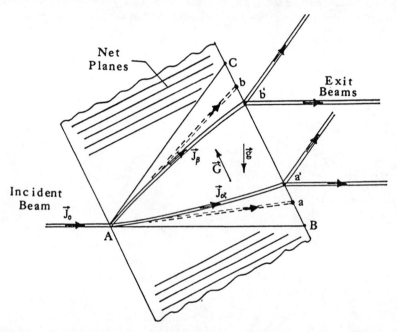

FIGURE 11. Schematic diagram of the trajectories of the neutron in a perfect crystal (Laue geometry) appropriate to the α-branch and β-branch of the dispersion surface. The trajectories are straight lines (Aa and Ab) if the gravitational force is neglected; they are hyperbolas (Aa' and Ab') if they are under the influence of gravity.

In addition to the effects of interferometer area just described, there are other more subtle gravitationally induced dynamical-diffraction effects. In free space (just above the surface of the Earth), it is well known that neutrons follow a classical parabolic trajectory.[25] It is natural to inquire about the effect of the Earth's gravity on the trajectory of the neutron inside the perfect crystal slabs of the interferometer. This is a rather complicated, but interesting mathematical physics problem. In the neutron Hamiltonian, one must add the slowly varying gravitational potential energy, $m\vec{g}$, to the rapidly varying periodic potential, $V(\vec{r})$, of the crystal lattice. Solving the resulting Schrödinger equation within the eikonal approximation reveals that the trajectories corresponding to the α- and β-branches of the surfaces are hyperbolic, as illustrated in FIGURE 11.[26] In connection with analyzing the results of their acceleration-induced neutron interference experiment, Bonse and Wroblewski extended these calcualtions for a single crystal to encompass the three-crystal LLL interferometer. This theory incorporates the interferometer area effects of Horne and the hyperbolic trajectories effects in a self-consistent and unified manner. Applying the results of this calculation to our gravity experiment, the predicted oscillation frequency is 4.3% higher than our original prediction based upon straight trajectories and the zeroth order area, A_o.

I believe that the theoretical analyses of Horne and of Bonse and Wroblewski are sound and correct. However, the results of the Staudenmann-Werner-Colella-Overhauser (SCOW) experiment were found to be in agreement with the simplified theory to better than 1%. Consequently, the motivation for a new generation gravitationally induced quantum-interference experiment, along with a more sophisticated analysis of the data, is substantial.

NEW IDEAS AND FUTURE PLANS

I would like to conclude this paper by first describing our ideas of a possible experimental pathway for the construction of large-scale (~ 1 meter) interferometers. I will then give a list of our agenda of ideas for future experiments.

Consider the following question: If we bring a massive body up close to the interferometer, is the gravitational potential sufficient to cause a measurable phase-shift? To get an idea of the answer to this question, suppose that we have an interferometer for which the path lengths are 10 cm, and suppose that we are sensitive to phase-shifts of 0.1 deg (0.00174 rad). For a potential, V, applied to one of the beams over a distance, S, the phase-shift is

$$\Delta\beta = kSV/2E, \tag{20}$$

where $\vec{k}$ is the neutron wave-vector ($2\pi/\lambda$) and E is its energy. For $\lambda = 1.4$Å ($E = 0.0472$ eV), our sensitivity to a potential is then

$$V = \Delta\beta \frac{2E}{kS} = 3.7 \times 10^{-14} \text{ eV}. \tag{21}$$

Let us compare this number with the gravitational potential of a neutron at the center of a homogeneous sphere of radius, R, and density, ρ, which is given by the formula,

$$V_{\text{sphere}} = -2\pi Gm\rho R^2. \tag{22}$$

For $R = 1$ m and $\rho = 13.6$ g/cm^3, we have

$$V_{\text{sphere}} = -6.0 \times 10^{-14} \text{eV}. \tag{23}$$

This potential is therefore of the same order as our current sensitivity in neutron interferometry. The difficulty in performing this "Neutron Cavendish Experiment" is one of geometry; one needs the gravitational potential of this sphere (or other massive bodies) to act preferentially on only one beam. Clearly, if we could build an interferometer of linear dimensions of one meter, the necessary beam separation for this type of experiment would be sufficient.

How can one envision making an interferometer this large? Single crystals of silicon can be grown that are 10 cm in diameter and perhaps 1 meter long. In order to increase the 10-cm dimension to 1 meter also, we suggest the scheme shown in FIGURES 12 and 13. The steps are the following:

(1) Machine and etch the Si interferometer (one piece) shown in FIGURE 12. Test it with X rays and neutrons.

(2) Split it into two pieces as shown. This leaves only two degrees of freedom: relative rocking angle and relative tilt.

(3) Machine a robust track out of Invar or black marble to high precision ($\sim \pm 0.0001''$).

(4) Separate the two Si pieces and mount them rigidly to the track with clamp-in strain-relief grooves (FIGURE 13).

(5) Adjust angles by bending the track (probably with piezoelectrics). Accuracy and stability required: $N \pm 0.01$ seconds of arc.

(6) Once a Bragg reflection from the second Si crystal is found, we know that the distance constraints ($\sim 1\ \mu m$) on the path lengths are automatically met.

(7) Monitor with high intensity X rays simultaneously.

A large-scale device of this type would open up neutron interferometry to a whole new realm of sensitivity, precision, and tiny effects.

The following is a list of the experiments that are currently on our future agenda. Our ideas and progress on some of them are rather well developed, while on others, our ideas are quite embryonic:

(1) High precision full-rotation gravity experiment.

(2) Measurement of the energy dependence of scattering lengths in the epithermal range at a pulsed neutron source (IPNS).

(3) Coherence-length measurements in the time domain.

(4) Search for an Aharonov-Bohm effect of the type described by Casher and Aharonov.[27]

(5) Cross-correlation Wheeler–delayed-choice experiment.

(6) Coherence enhancement by post-interferometer filtering.

(7) Neutron Cavendish experiment.

(8) Neutron Michelson-Morley experiment.

(9) Gravitationally induced neutron-nuclear absorption.

(10) New neutron interferometric search for strongly interacting gauge vector bosons.[28]

This is a very ambitious and exciting program for the future. It is clear that some of these ideas will "bear fruit" in the next few years, while others may prove to be beyond our current technologies. We are not the only group interested in these concepts, and no doubt other laboratories will adopt alternative experimental techniques to pursue some of these phenomena.

ACKNOWLEDGMENTS

Our current group at Missouri (Helmut Kaiser, Muhammed Arif, Ron Berliner, and myself) has had a close and productive collaboration for several years with Tony

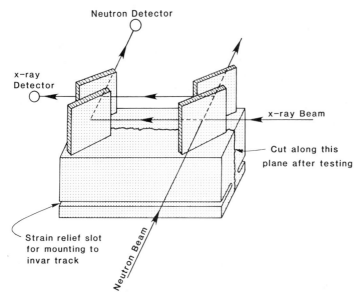

FIGURE 12. Schematic diagram of the single Si-crystal interferometer ingot that is to be subsequently cut as shown to make a large-scale interferometer (as shown in FIGURE 13) consisting of two pieces.

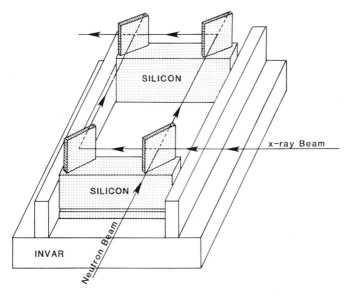

FIGURE 13. Large-scale interferometer concept. The dimensions could be as large as 1 meter × 1 meter.

Klein, Geoff Opat, and their students at the University of Melbourne, Australia. Several of the ideas listed above are theirs, and success in these experiments will depend upon our mutual efforts and good luck. A formal collaboration between our group and Helmut Rauch and Anton Zeilinger's group in Vienna, Austria, is currently being initiated. I have benefited from enlightening interactions and discussions with many friends and colleagues, especially Albert Overhauser (Purdue), Ulrich Bonse (Dortmund), Clifford Shull (MIT), Michael Horne (Stonehill, MIT), Daniel Greenberger (CCNY), and Herbert Bernstein (Hampshire). I am particularly indebted to Jean-Louis Staudenmann (Iowa State), who worked with me in carrying out the Sagnac effect experiment.

NOTES AND REFERENCES

1. BONSE, U. & M. HART. 1965. Appl. Phys. Lett. **6:** 155.
2. BATTERMAN, B. W. & H. COLE. 1964. Rev. Mod. Phys. **36:** 681.
3. BERNSTEIN, H. J. 1967. Phys. Rev. Lett. **18:** 1102.
4. RAUCH, H., W. TREIMER & U. BONSE. 1974. Phys. Lett. **47A:** 425.
5. COLELLA, R., A. W. OVERHAUSER & S. A. WERNER. 1975. Phys. Rev. Lett. **34:** 1472.
6. WERNER, S. A., R. COLELLA, A. W. OVERHAUSER & C. F. EAGEN. 1975. Phys. Rev. Lett. **35:** 1053. A similar experiment was carried out at nearly the same time at the I.L.L., Grenoble, France: RAUCH, H., A. ZEILINGER, G. BADUREK, A. WILFING, W. BAUSPIESS & U. BONSE. 1975. Phys. Lett. **54A:** 425. The same principle was demonstrated by Fraunhofer diffraction at a Bloch wall: KLEIN, A. G. & G. I. OPAT. 1976. Phys. Rev. Lett. **37:** 238.
7. See: 1979. Conference proceedings. *In* Neutron Interferometry. U. Bonse & H. Rauch, Eds. Oxford Univ. Press (Clarendon). London/New York. For comprehensive reviews, see: KLEIN, A. G. & S. A. WERNER. 1983. Neutron optics. Rep. Prog. Phys. **46:** 259; WERNER, S. A. & A. G. KLEIN. 1986. Recent advances in neutron optics. *In* Neutron Scattering, chap. 4. D-L. Price & K. Sköld, Eds. Academic Press. New York. To be published.
8. STAUDENMANN, J-L., S. A. WERNER, R. COLELLA & A. W. OVERHAUSER. 1980. Phys. Rev. **A21:** 1419.
9. WERNER, S. A., H. KAISER, M. ARIF, H-C. HU & R. BERLINER. 1986. Physica. To be published.
10. WERNER, S. A., J-L. STAUDENMANN & R. COLELLA. 1979. Phys. Rev. Lett. **42:** 1103.
11. KAISER, H., S. A. WERNER & E. A. GEORGE. 1983. Phys. Rev. Lett. **50:** 560.
12. ARIF, M., H. KAISER, S. A. WERNER, A. CIMMINO, W. A. HAMILTON, A. G. KLEIN & G. I. OPAT. 1985. Phys. Rev. **A31**(rapid communication): 1203.
13. KAISER, H., E. A. GEORGE & S. A. WERNER. 1984. Phys. Rev. **A29:** 2276. An experiment of this type was suggested by: PERES, A. 1979. Phys. Rev. Lett. **42:** 683.
14. WORD, R. E. & S. A. WERNER. 1980. Phys. Rev. **B26:** 4190.
15. KAISER, H., M. ARIF, S. A. WERNER & J. O. WILLIS. 1986. Physica. To be published.
16. BONSE, U. & T. WROBLEWSKI. 1983. Phys. Rev. Lett. **51:** 1401.
17. SAGNAC, M. G. 1913. C. R. Acad. Sci. (Paris) **157:** 708 and 1410.
18. The formula in equation 8 was obtained by PAGE, L. A. (1975. Phys. Rev. Lett. **35:** 543) using wave-optical arguments. An interesting derivation has been given by DRESDEN, M. & C. N. YANG (1979. Phys. Rev. **D20:** 1846), in which the phase-shift for a rotating interferometer is obtained from the point of view of a Doppler shift due to a moving source and moving reflecting crystals.
19. WERNER, S. A., J-L. STAUDENMANN & R. COLELLA. 1979. Phys. Rev. Lett. **42:** 1103.
20. The vertical geometry for this experiment was first suggested by: ANANDAN, J. 1977. Phys. Rev. **D15:** 1448.
21. A brief preliminary description of these new experiments was given at the International Conference on Neutron Scattering, Santa Fe, New Mexico (August 1985). See reference 9.

22. The derivation of this formula will be given in a future paper.
23. This design was suggested to us by Ulrich Bonse, University of Dortmund.
24. HORNE, M. A. 1986. Shull Festschrift Paper. To be published in Physica B.
25. DOBBS, J. W. T., J. A. HARVEY, D. DAYA & H. HORSTMANN. 1965. Phys. Rev. **139**: 756.
26. WERNER, S. A. 1980. Phys. Rev. **B21**: 1774.
27. AHARONOV, Y. & A. CASHER. 1984. Phys. Rev. Lett. **53**: 319.
28. This experiment is motivated by a suggestion by WU, T. T. & C. N. YANG (1975. Phys. Rev. **D12**: 3845). A first-level search was made by: ZEILINGER, A., M. A. HORNE & C. G. SHULL. 1983. Proc. Int. Symp. of Quantum Mechanics, Tokyo, pp. 389–393. OPAT, G. I. has suggested a new version of the experiment (Preprint available, 1985).

Three Gedanken Experiments on Complementarity in Double-Slit Diffraction

ANTON ZEILINGER

Atominstitut der Österreichischen Universitäten
Schüttelstraße 115
A-1020 Wien, Austria
and
Department of Physics
Massachusetts Institute of Technology
Cambridge, Massachusetts 02139

INTRODUCTION

The conceptual development of the foundations of modern physics is signified by numerous gedanken experiments that are purported to demonstrate some specific features of a given theory. The role of gedanken experiments was particularly important in relativity theory and in quantum mechanics, where due to technological limitations, many fundamental experiments were not yet possible in the early years of the theory. However, it is interesting to note that the conclusions drawn from such gedanken experiments are sometimes unwarranted. This will be discussed in the present paper for three different gedanken-experiment versions of the classic paradigmatic example of quantum physics, namely, the double-slit experiment.

In the first section, we will analyze the role of the detector slit size on the outcome of the double-slit experiment. In the second section, we will discuss Landé's approach to quantum mechanics, and show that gedanken experiments can be conceived that reveal his particle approach to be at least incomplete. In the third section, we will show that an experiment proposed by Prosser to demonstrate that the individual particles in a double-slit experiment always follow well-defined paths will not give conclusive results in Prosser's sense if Nature obeys quantum mechanics. From these discussions, the Copenhagen interpretation rises unscathed.

THE RELATION BETWEEN DETECTOR SIZE
AND INTERFERENCE PATTERN

Since the early days of quantum physics, the double-slit diffraction experiment has served as the paradigmatic example of the epistemologically strange features of quantum phenomena. In this experiment, the complementarity between two different possible types of information can be seen in a very clear way. Here, the two complementary types of information are the information about the path the particle (photon, electron, neutron, etc.) took and the information contained in the interference pattern. Most prominent among the discussions of the double-slit experiment is that between Einstein and Bohr at the Fifth Solvay Congress.[1] There, Einstein proposed a version of the double-slit arrangement where he thought that information about the slit that the particle passed could be obtained without destroying the interference pattern. Thus, he purported to show that quantum mechanics is internally inconsistent. Specifically, Einstein proposed to exploit a determination of the momentum transferred from the particle to the slit diaphragm in order to obtain information about the particle's path. In his classic reply, Bohr demonstrated that a certain minimum control of the momentum of the diaphragm is necessary in order to determine the path. This via Heisenberg's indeterminacy relations implies a minimum uncertainty in the diaphragm's position that is just enough to make the interference pattern disappear.

More recently, in a careful quantitative analysis of the Einstein gedanken experiment, Wooters and Zurek[2] did show that intermediate cases are possible where one can obtain some, as yet incomplete, information on slit passage, while still retaining an interference pattern with significant interference contrast. This kind of

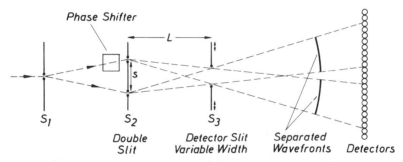

FIGURE 1. Principle of a double-slit diffraction experiment demonstrating the role of the detector slit width in creating the interference pattern. In the wide slit case shown, the diffraction at the detector slit is too small to result in significant overlap between the two slit wave fronts at large distances. For a small enough slit, these wave fronts will overlap at any distance, resulting in interference.

analysis was recently extended[3] to Mach-Zehnder type interferometers, where both the information contained in the interference pattern and the information about the particle's path were formulated in an information theoretic way that permitted a quantitative continuous transition between the extreme cases of maximum information of either type.

In this section, I will analyze another specific case where a continuous transition between observation of slit passage and observation of the interference pattern can be obtained. The experiment proposed simply consists of arranging a slit of variable width (FIGURE 1) behind the double slit and then observing the spatial intensity distribution behind that slit as a function of slit width. In addition, the experiment is proposed to employ a phase-shifter so as to permit a continuous variation of the relative phase between the amplitudes which pass through the two slits in the double-slit diaphragm. Alternatively, we may contemplate scanning the detector slit across the detector slit plane. Finally, the detection of the particles is supposed to be performed using a bank of individual detectors (FIGURE 1) with small enough spacing to resolve any structure in the intensity distribution.

Analyzing the proposed experiment, we expect, qualitatively, that for large slit width, diffraction at the detector slit will be negligible and radiation coming from the two slits in the double-slit diaphragm will separate again after some distance behind the detector slit. Thus, with a wide enough dectector slit, the slit passage information can be obtained after the particle has passed through the whole experimental setup. On the other hand, if the detector slit is small, diffraction at it may not be neglected anymore and the double-slit passage information is lost because at a small enough detector slit, the loss of angular definition due to slit diffraction can certainly be larger than the angular separation of radiation coming from the two slits in S_2.

In contrast, if we wish to observe the double-slit interference pattern, this also places a limit on the detector slit width. Specifically, the width of that slit should be smaller than or equal to the distance between the minima and the maxima in the interference pattern, that is,

$$\delta \lesssim \lambda L/2s. \tag{1}$$

Diffraction at such a slit produces a single slit pattern of angular full-width at half-maximum:

$$\Delta\theta = \frac{\lambda}{\delta} \gtrsim \frac{2s}{L}. \tag{2}$$

However, this is just twice the angular separation of the two slits as seen from the detector slit. This implies that although we may now observe interference either by scanning the detector slit across the beam or by changing the optical thickness of the phase-shifter plate, we have no possibility of knowing through which of the two slits in S_2 a specific particle registered by one of the detectors actually passed through. If we make the detector slit broad enough, detection of a particle can be correlated to slit passage because particles passing through the lower (upper) slit will be registered by a detector in the upper (lower) half (FIGURE 1). This latter statement may be operationally verified through covering either slit and observing that the above-mentioned correlation between slit passage and detectors holds. In addition, in that case, the observed intensity distribution with both slits open is just the algebraic sum of the two distributions with either slit open, independent of the phase-plate setting. Clearly, if the slit width has some intermediate value, the diffraction patterns of the two slits in S_2 will only partially overlap due to detector slit diffraction. Hence, some information (though partial) about the path the particle took may be obtained, and simultaneously, a (partially faded) interference pattern would appear. This is just another case of a manifestation of intermediate wave-particle behavior.[2-4]

In order to get a more quantitative understanding of the intermediate wave-particle behavior in the experiment proposed, various calculations in the Fraunhofer approximation were performed. FIGURE 2 shows the total intensity per slit width unit as a function of detector slit width where the detector slit is centered with respect to the double slit. The two curves in FIGURE 2 show the intensity with zero phase difference and with a phase difference, π, introduced by the phase-shifter. As expected, the interference contrast, defined as

$$C = |\,[I(\chi = 0) - I(\chi = \pi)]/[I(\chi = 0) + I(\chi = \pi)], \qquad (3)$$

is maximal for a narrow detector slit and vanishes if the detector slit is a multiple of the distance between the maxima of the double-slit pattern. This interference contrast is shown in FIGURE 3 together with the fraction of particles landing on the "correct" side after the detector slit. This latter number is defined as the fraction of particles that, with only the lower (upper) slit open, arrive in the upper (lower) half of the observation plane behind the detector slit, and is an indication of the correctness of interpreting a particle count in a detector in the upper (lower) half as being caused by a particle that has passed through the lower (upper) slit. FIGURE 3 shows that these two quantities are complementary.

FIGURE 2. Total intensity passing through a variable-width centered detector slit with no phase-shift ($\chi = 0$) and maximum phase-shift ($\chi = \pi$) introduced between the two waves incident on the two narrow slits of the double-slit assembly. The intensity is normalized to unit detector slit width, which is expressed in multiples of the interference fringe spacing.

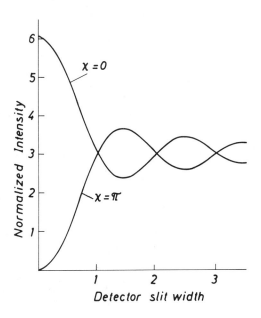

The experiment proposed here is easily realizable with either photons or very cold neutrons.[5] Clearly, one could even go a step further and change the width of the detector slit at a time when the particle is well under way and has already passed the double-slit diaphragm. This represents a simple realization of a delayed-choice experiment as proposed by Wheeler.[6]

Concluding this section, we note that the common jargon is to say that the interference pattern is produced by the double slit and then is detected by scanning it or registering it with a detector with enough spatial resolution to resolve its structure. Equally well, we could say that it is only the diffraction in the detector system, as shown above, that brings the interference pattern into existence by obliterating the

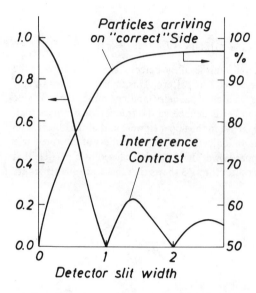

FIGURE 3. Interference contrast in a double-slit experiment as a function of detector slit width. This is complementary to slit passage information, characterized here by the fraction of particles arriving at the "correct" side, thus permitting slit passage inference.

information about the particle's path. This reminds us of the Copenhagen interpretation, which would take neither position, but would only state that the interference pattern is a property of the whole apparatus, including double slit and detector slit. That interpretation would certainly not even conceptually admit the existence of a double-slit pattern unless the detector was actually arranged so as to permit its observation.

The analysis of the influence of detector slit width also sheds new light on the double-slit experiment using a multiplate assembly as proposed by Wooters and Zurek[2] in the appendix of their paper. We leave the application of the ideas of this present paper to that gedanken experiment to the interested reader.

A DOUBLE-SLIT DIFFRACTION GEDANKEN EXPERIMENT ON LANDÉ'S THEORY OF MATTER DIFFRACTION

Diffraction of matter is usually regarded as being the most impressive argument supporting the wave nature of particles. The concept of a wave-particle duality that results from this wave nature of particles has for a long time now presented itself as a severe problem for saving Anschaulichkeit[7] in physics. This situation has repeatedly led to attempts at new interpretations of quantum mechanics or to new searches for more intuitively obvious (anschauliche) foundations. As an example, Landé has presented a "unitary particle theory of matter diffraction," in which he claims[8] not to need the wave nature of particles in order to explain diffraction. According to that theory, there are, besides the conservation laws of energy, angular momentum, and linear momentum, three axiomatic rules governing the possible changes of these quantities. Diffraction is governed by the quantum rule that states that a system having the linear periods, l_i, in its spatial Fourier decomposition is entitled to change its linear momentum in amounts,

$$\Delta p_i = h/l_i, \tag{4}$$

where h is Planck's constant. According to Landé, this rule was discovered by Duane, and he therefore calls it Duane's rule. Using that rule, Landé successfully explains the Bragg maxima in crystal diffraction because a crystal has structural Fourier components of periods, $l_i = a/n_i$, where a is its lattice constant. This, together with Duane's rule and momentum conservation, gives Bragg's law.

Turning now to the phenomenon of double-slit diffraction, Landé realizes that a screen with slits has as its spatial Fourier transformation, "a characteristic continuous spectrum of l values representing a Fourier integral. Each l component then entitles the diffractor as a whole unit to impart impulses $p = h/l$ to an incident particle with a probability proportional to the intensity of the corresponding l component in the l spectrum."[7] Landé then goes on to reason that the difference between the two-slits-open case and the case of one slit covered is the fact that the l spectrum is different in the two cases, and therefore, the momentum changes of a particle interacting with the diffractor as a whole are different in the two cases.

This ability of Duane's rule to give the correct diffraction maxima certainly justifies that Landé's theory be given further attention. On the experimental side, there is no doubt that diffraction of particles at simple macroscopic objects gives the results predicted by standard wave mechanics (FIGURE 4). The solid curve in FIGURE 4 shows the calculations of the diffraction pattern based on a Fresnel-Kirchhoff approach. The agreement is certainly impressive, and for the case of the single-slit and the double-slit

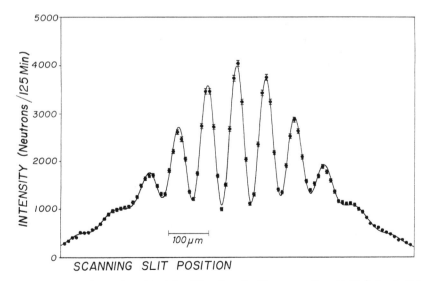

FIGURE 4. Experimental results of the diffraction of cold neutrons ($\lambda = 18.45$ Å, bandwidth ± 1.4 Å) at a two-slit diaphragm (openings of 22 μm and 23 μm, respectively, separated by a 104 μm wide absorber). The solid line represents the calculated result based on standard scalar Fresnel-Kirchhoff theory.

arrangements, it is unknown to us whether Landé's theory would result in an equally good agreement with experiment. That there are problems to be expected even in these cases results from the fact that Duane's rule does not make any allowance for the influence of the distance between the diffracting object and the observation plane on the diffraction pattern. In other words, there is no room for a difference between Fresnel and Fraunhofer diffraction in that theory.

A specific problem arises therefore for Landé's theory out of the existence of diffraction patterns that only exist within the domain of Fresnel diffraction and that vanish in the Fraunhofer limit. Of those, the best-known phenomenon is that of diffraction at a straight absorbing edge. There, diffraction maxima arise without the existence of any maxima in the spectrum of the spatial Fourier transform of the diffractor, which is a semi-infinite absorbing plane. For example, the position of the

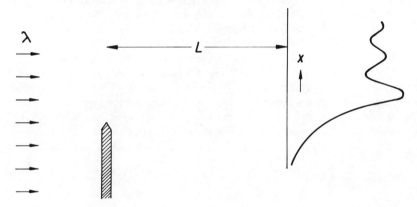

FIGURE 5. Principle of the diffraction at a straight absorbing edge. This type of diffraction disappears in the Fraunhofer limit and therefore cannot be explained as a momentum transfer.

first maximum (see FIGURE 5) scales like

$$x = \sqrt{\lambda L}. \tag{5}$$

This equation has two properties of significance for Landé's theory. Firstly, the diffraction pattern increases only with the square root of the distance from the absorbing edge to the observation plane. This makes it impossible to identify a specific momentum change as caused by the absorbing edge to be responsible for a specific diffraction maximum. Secondly, the diffraction pattern disappears in the Fraunhofer limit, that is, at infinity. Curiously, this fact now agrees with Duane's rule, leaving the diffraction pattern observed at finite distances unexplained.

In order to demonstrate the insufficiency of Duane's rule in explaining all diffraction phenomena, we turn to the double-slit diffraction experiment discussed in the previous section where a phase-shifter is employed in front of one of the diffracting slits. This phase-shifter causes a sidewards deflection of the double-slit diffraction pattern such that, within the Fraunhofer approximation, the maxima will occur at angles, α, fulfilling

$$\sin \alpha = \frac{\lambda}{d} (n + \chi/2\pi), \tag{6}$$

where n is an integer and χ is the phase-shift due to the phase-shifter. This implies that a particle diffracted by this assembly into one of the maxima experiences the momentum change, $\Delta p = p \sin \alpha$, of

$$\Delta p = nh/s + \chi h/2\pi s. \tag{7}$$

The first term in that equation is in agreement with Duane's rule because it reflects the spatial Fourier components of the double-slit screen itself. In order to explain not only the first term in the last equation that way, we have to search for a spatial periodicity of

$$l = 2\pi d/\chi \tag{8}$$

in the whole diffractor (which includes the double-slit screen and the phase-shifter). Clearly, periodicities of that kind cannot be identified in the experimental setup. Specifically, for $n = 0$, the momentum transfer has to be attributed to the phase-shifter alone, thus implying that there the phase-shifter should have a spatial periodicity of l, which is now proportional to the slit separation distance, s. This is certainly untenable. Furthermore, we note that the spatial periodicity required by equation 8 cannot have any explanation in either the thickness or the crystalline structure of the phase-shifter. We demonstrate this with the specific example of a neutron experiment. There, the phase-shift due to a phase-shifter of thickness, D, is

$$\chi = - \lambda D \sum_i N_i b_{ci}, \tag{9}$$

where N_i is the number of nuclei of type i per unit volume and b_{ci} is their coherent neutron scattering length. Therefore, the phase-shift, and hence the spatial Fourier component, l, can be continuously varied by altering the composition of the phase-shifter independent of its thickness or crystalline structure. Furthermore, equation 9 together with equation 8 would imply that the spatial periodicity of the diffractor was a function of the neutron wavelength, λ, used. This is certainly untenable.

We, therefore, have to conclude that as successful as the Duane-Landé approach is in explaining simple diffraction patterns, it breaks down in more complicated cases.[9] This implies that this theory is at least incomplete. The incompleteness corresponds to the property that it does not contain a principle equivalent to and as powerful as the superposition principle of quantum mechanics. In fact, the situation seems to be the reverse one, with Duane's rule being a consequence of the superposition principle in simple cases and in the Fraunhofer limit. Nevertheless, Landé's approach is conceptually interesting; however, in view of the present paper, it should only be taught to students[10] with great care and caution.

THE RELATION BETWEEN ENERGY FLOW AND THE
INTERFERENCE PATTERN

In a very interesting paper, Prosser[11] presents explicit solutions of Maxwell's equations for the case of diffraction of photons at a double-slit assembly. Of particular interest are the results for the phase and the energy flow lines. The latter lines (shown explicitly in Prosser's paper) have a certain undulatory character resulting in weaving trajectories that enable the light energy to be redistributed in the form of a diffraction pattern. The flow lines bunch together in such a way as to give rise to the interference pattern; at interference maxima, they are closer together, while at minima, they are further apart. Another feature of the flow lines is that no flow line crosses the symmetry plane between the two slits. This latter feature could already be deduced from symmetry considerations. It is also seen from the property that the lines of constant phase cut the symmetry plane at right angles, which immediately leads to an energy flow parallel to that plane.

This detailed description of double-slit interference in terms of an energy flow leads Prosser then[12] to propose that one could (in interpreting quantum reality) go beyond the Copenhagen interpretation. This latter interpretation usually is viewed as implying that quantum mechanics does not offer any possibility of a detailed description of quantum processes, but that, in contrast, one has to be content with the fact that the theory only allows one to make statistical predictions for individual measurement results given specific initial conditions, with no interpretation whatsoever of what goes on in between.

Going beyond the Copenhagen interpretation, Prosser proposes that the motion of individual photon wave packets may be interpreted as an energy flow that can be represented by the motion of a group of flow lines. If the spacing of the flow lines is proportional to the intensity of the field, then this leads to a rather natural interpretation of the interference pattern because the flow lines are bunched together at the maxima. Therefore, if we have a source emitting photons in well-defined directions over a certain lateral distance, then each individual photon will follow a well-defined path, which is a point that certainly goes beyond the Copenhagen interpretation. The whole diffraction pattern is then obtained as the sum over many individual photons tracing out the various individual flow lines. Thus, it is argued by Prosser that this interpretation does not require the Huygens principle because interference and diffraction can be interpreted in terms of the undulations of the photon trajectories. This latter point seems to overlook the fact that in order to calculate the energy flow directions, the solutions of the Maxwell equations are needed, which implies the Huygens principle because of the formal equivalence between the wave equation and the Feynman path integral approach to quantum mechanics. Yet, even with that limitation, the interpretation proposed by Prosser is still of significant conceptual interest and, in that sense, it is very similar to the quantum potential approach[13] if it is also assumed that individual particles follow well-defined paths. There too, the calculation of these paths requires knowledge of the complete solution of the Schrödinger equation.

In view of the possible future developments of the theory, it is certainly important to have various different interpretations at hand; even those that presently give the same experimental predictions are important. The viewpoints suggested by a specific interpretation could more easily lead to further developments of the theory (if there is any further development possible at all) than others. It is, therefore, of interest that Prosser proposes an explicit experiment that would discriminate between his interpretation and the Copenhagen interpretation.

This difference starts from the fact that no energy flow line ever crosses the plane of symmetry between the two slits. It follows, therefore, according to Prosser, that photons on the right-hand side of the interference pattern must have come through the right slit, and analogously for the left-hand side. So far, this conclusion is not yet significant because, for monochromatic radiation, the slit through which the photon

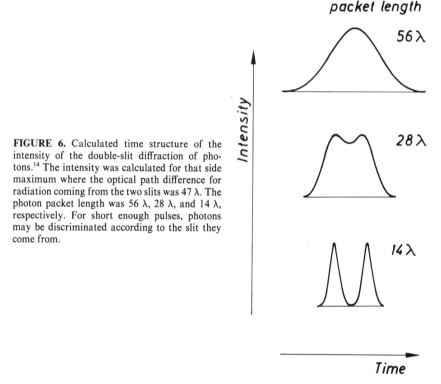

FIGURE 6. Calculated time structure of the intensity of the double-slit diffraction of photons.[14] The intensity was calculated for that side maximum where the optical path difference for radiation coming from the two slits was 47 λ. The photon packet length was 56 λ, 28 λ, and 14 λ, respectively. For short enough pulses, photons may be discriminated according to the slit they come from.

passed cannot be observed in any way as long as the interference pattern is observable. This point is shared by both interpretations. However, if we now turn to nonmonochromatic radiation, it is known and again accepted by both interpretations that the interference pattern will vanish if the wavelength spread is large enough. We may now perform an experiment to determine slit passage by using timed photon pulses and measuring their flight time from the source to an off-axis positioned detector. For that specific arrangement, Prosser concludes that whatever the width of the photon pulse, there will always be only one pulse observed at the detector. To him, this follows from the fact that a pulse can be considered to be a superposition of monochromatic components, and for each of the components, the statement separately holds that no flow line crosses the symmetry plane. This would call more conventional discussions of the double-slit problem into question because according to them the photon in that situation sometimes passes through one or the other slit.

To demonstrate that this conclusion does not follow from the formalism, a simple computer simulation of the experiment proposed by Prosser was performed where plane wave packets of varying lengths were incident on a double-slit assembly and where a detector was arranged at a position off-axis on one side of the symmetry plane. In the computer simulation, the time structure of the wave packet at the detector was calculated. FIGURE 6 shows three characteristic results, and it is evident from these results that, for a narrow enough wave packet, photons will be detected at arrival times corresponding to the two different flight times through the two slits. This clearly is at variance with Prosser's conclusion.

The result obtained can be brought into accordance with the energy flow model when we realize that the energy flow gives only the net flow across an interface and that there is certainly no net flow across the symmetry plane of the double-slit assembly. Nevertheless, there can be a significant number of photons crossing that plane as long as the net flow vanishes.

In conclusion, we therefore notice that none of the three gedanken experiments provides any compelling reason to assign a realistic description to individual particle behavior in the double-slit experiments. Hence, there is no need to go beyond the Copenhagen interpretation.

NOTES AND REFERENCES

1. BOHR, N. 1949. *In* Albert Einstein: Philosopher–Scientist. P. A. Schilpp, Ed.: 200. The Library of Living Philosophers. Evanston, Illinois.
2. WOOTERS, W. K. & W. H. ZUREK. 1979. Phys. Rev. **D19:** 473.
3. ZEILINGER, A. 1986. Physica **137B:** 235. Recently, a similar analysis has been performed by Greenberger (this volume).
4. BARTELL, L. S. 1980. Phys. Rev. **D21:** 1698.
5. ZEILINGER, A. 1986. *In* The Investigation of Fundamental Interactions with Cold Neutrons. G. L. Greene, Ed.: 112. NBS Special Publication no. 711. U. S. Department of Commerce, Washington, D.C.
6. WHEELER, J. A. 1978. *In* Mathematical Foundations of Quantum Theory. A. R. Marlow, Ed.: 9. Academic Press. New York.
7. The problem of proper translation of "Anschaulichkeit" into English is well known (see, e.g., MILLER, A. I. 1986. Imagery in Scientific Thought. MIT Press. Cambridge, Massachusetts); for our purposes, "intuitive understanding through visualizability" seems proper.
8. LANDE, A. 1975. Am. J. Phys. **43:** 701; 1976. Ann. Phys. (Leipzig) **33:** 88.
9. NARTONIS, D. K. 1974. Br. J. Philos. Sci. **25:** 329.
10. GORDON, R. 1981. Am. J. Phys. **49:** 300.
11. PROSSER, R. D. 1976. Int. J. Theor. Phys. **15:** 169.
12. PROSSER, R. D. 1976. Int. J. Theor. Phys. **15:** 181.
13. BOHM, D. J., C. DEWDNEY & B. B. HILEY. 1985. Nature **315:** 294.
14. ZEILINGER, A. & J. KAMESBERGER. In preparation.

Electron Interferometry Applied to Objects of Atomic Dimensions

HANNES LICHTE

Institut für Angewandte Physik
Universität Tübingen
D 7400 Tübingen, Federal Republic of Germany

QUANTUM INTERFERENCE USED FOR MEASUREMENT

In the year 1954, Möllenstedt and Düker[1] developed the electrostatic electron biprism allowing the production of two beam electron interference fields (FIGURE 1). It consists of a metallized quartz filament about 1 μm in diameter positioned between two electrodes on ground potential, and it works as follows: The wave front of an electron wave leaving the electron source is divided into two partial waves, and if a positive voltage of several volts is applied to the filament, these partial waves are deflected towards each other and overlap downstream to give rise to a cosine interference pattern.

Electron interference is understood as a phenomenon of a one-particle wave function. As we have only one particle in a wave, we would see an interference pattern of this wave function only if we could repeat the experiment very often under identical conditions and sum up all events on the same detector. Instead, we use an ensemble of electrons with slightly varying wave numbers, k [distribution $w(k)$], and slightly varying positions, q, of origin at the electron source described by the intensity distribution, $i(q)$ (FIGURE 2). Arriving at the detector one-by-one, the corresponding intensities are averaged, and due to the slight mismatching given by $w(k)$ and $i(q)$, the resulting interference pattern is somewhat modulated in contrast and phase. Following the theory of partial coherence used in light optics, this modulation is given by the degree of coherence equal to the Fourier transform of $i(q)$ if one considers lateral coherence, and equal to the Fourier transform of $w(k)$ if longitudinal coherence is taken into account.[2] For most applications, longitudinal coherence of usual electron sources is very good, whereas the conditions for lateral coherence, unfortunately, have to be satisfied with great care at the expense of intensity at the plane of observation.

A mutual phase-shift of the two partial waves results if they are propagating through an electrical potential $V(r)$ field and a magnetic vector potential $A(r)$ field (FIGURE 3). Following Glaser,[3] the effect of these fields can be expressed in terms of wave optics by the index of refraction:

$$n(\vec{r}, \vec{s}) = \sqrt{1 + \frac{V(\vec{r})}{U_o} - \frac{e}{\mathrm{p}_o}(\vec{A}(\vec{r}), \vec{s})},$$

where e is the electron charge, eU_o is the kinetic energy of the electrons, $\mathrm{p}_o = \sqrt{2emU_o}$ is their momentum in field free space ($V = U_o$), and $\vec{s}$ is the tangent unit vector to the geometrical electron trajectories. Hence, the phase difference between the two partial

175

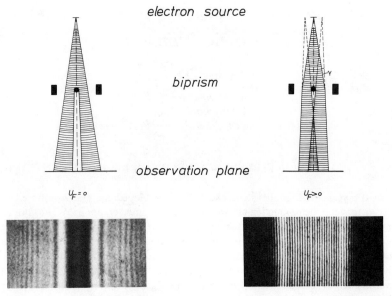

FIGURE 1. The electron biprism. The wave front of an electron wave emitted from the electron source is divided into two parts by the filament. If a positive voltage is applied to the filament, the two partial waves overlap to give rise to a sinusoidal interference pattern.

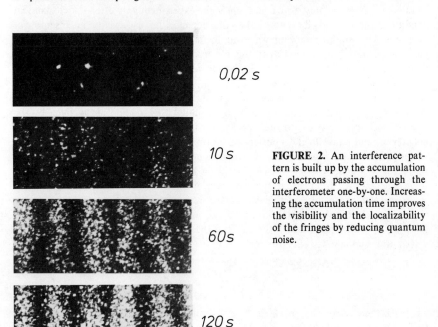

FIGURE 2. An interference pattern is built up by the accumulation of electrons passing through the interferometer one-by-one. Increasing the accumulation time improves the visibility and the localizability of the fringes by reducing quantum noise.

waves amounts to

$$\Delta\rho = \frac{p_o}{\hbar}\left[\int_{\sigma_1} nds - \int_{\sigma_2} nds\right],$$

where the integrals are taken along the paths, σ_1 and σ_2, in the interferometer, respectively.

Taking into account this phase-shift, $\Delta\rho$, and the degree of coherence, $\mu = |\mu| \exp (i\vartheta)$, an interference pattern is formed in the plane of observation with an intensity

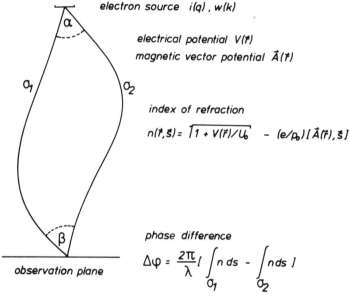

electron source $i(q)$, $w(k)$

electrical potential $V(\vec{r})$

magnetic vector potential $\vec{A}(\vec{r})$

index of refraction

$$n(\vec{r},\vec{s}) = \overline{\sqrt{1 + V(\vec{r})/U_o}} \; - (e/p_o)[\vec{A}(\vec{r}),\vec{s}]$$

phase difference

$$\Delta\varphi = \frac{2\pi}{\lambda}[\int_{\sigma_1} n\,ds - \int_{\sigma_2} n\,ds\,]$$

observation plane

FIGURE 3. Electron waves propagating through a spatial distribution of the potentials, V and A, sum up a mutual phase difference, $\Delta\rho$, that can be calculated using the index of refraction, n, and that can be determined by measuring the lateral displacement of the fringes.

distribution,

$$I(x) = 2I_o\left[1 + |\mu| \cos\left(\frac{2\pi}{d}x + \Delta\rho + \vartheta\right)\right],$$

where I_o is the common intensity of both waves. This is a field of parallel straight fringes of spacing, d, and contrast, $|\mu|$, shifted sideways by $\Delta\rho$ and ϑ, with respect to the optical axis. Thus, the fringe displacement is a very easily accessible measure for the phase of an electron wave.

Because, when compared to "classical" scattering experiments, a quantum mechanical interference measurement is extremely sensitive, and because no knowledge other than the data of the interference pattern is needed to measure the phase-shift, the electron biprism has turned out to be the heart of a great variety of experiments:

— Measurement of the wavelength,[4] coherence properties,[5–10] and Doppler shift[11] of electron waves.
— Investigation of the Aharonov-Bohm effect.[12,13]
— Measurement of the flux quantization in superconducting hollow cylinders.[14,15]
— Mapping of magnetization in thin films.[16,17]
— Michelson-type interferometer for the determination of surface height structures of bulk material.[18,19]
— Measurement of the mean inner potential of thin films[20] and of the potential distribution at p-n-junction.[21]
— Realization of electron interference microscopy[22,23] and electron off-axis holography.[24–27]

In the following, I should like to focus your attention on recent experiments in electron interference microscopy or holography that we have undertaken for the investigation of atomic structures using the electron biprism.

ELECTRON INTERFERENCE MICROSCOPY

In order to investigate fine details of micro-objects by electron interferometry, we have to use the electron biprism in combination with an electron microscope

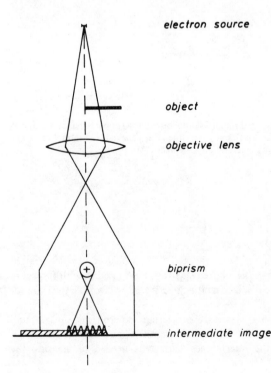

electron source

object

objective lens

biprism

intermediate image

FIGURE 4. Principal setup of an electron interference microscope. In the image plane, by the action of the biprism, a plane reference wave is superimposed on the image wave to show its phase modulation produced by the object.

 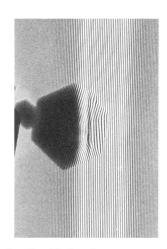

FIGURE 5. Left: Electron image of a MgO-crystal side by side with the reference wave, and separated from each other by the shadow of the biprism filament. Filament voltage $U = 0$ volt. Right: Interference micrograph of the MgO-crystal taken with $U = 7.5$ volts. The strong phase modulation of the electron wave transmitted through the crystal can be determined by measuring the fringe displacement.

(FIGURE 4): The object plane that is only partially covered by the object under investigation is coherently illuminated by an electron wave emitted from the field emission electron source. The part of the wave transmitted through the object ("object wave") is, in general, modulated in amplitude and in phase according to the object structure, while another part passing by the object remains a plane wave. Consequently, we find in the image plane (due to the imaging properties of the objective lens), the image wave of the object side by side with a plane reference wave. Applying a positive voltage to the filament of the biprism, the image wave and the reference wave overlap each other. The resulting interference fringes are modulated in contrast and position by the amplitude and phase of the image wave, respectively. This can be seen in FIGURE 5.

If the objective lens is free from aberrations, then object wave and image wave agree completely. In modern electron microscopes, this is true, unless details smaller than 2 nm of the object are to be resolved in the image. Consequently, an evaluation of the image plane interference pattern gives exact quantitative information about the amplitude and the phase of the object wave, and hence, about the object structure (either magnetic or electrical) if atomic resolution is not required.

At this point, holography enters the stage. As to their basic physics, there is no difference between electron interferometry and electron holography. The difference lies in the procedure of reading the information contained in the fringe pattern. If the deviation from a straight line of single fringes due to a phase-shift is measured, the method is called interferometry. Usually, only several fringes are needed, and hence, the coherence requirements are not much more stringent than in ordinary microscopy.

If the degree of coherence is sufficiently high to produce interference patterns with a large number of fringes (e.g., 200), the spatial modulation of the image wave may be evaluated by holography (FIGURE 6): A photographic plate exposed to the interference pattern suitably magnified in the electron microscope forms the hologram. In order to reconstruct the image wave, this hologram is put on a light optical bench and illuminated with an expanded laser wave. Due to diffraction by the fringes, the light wave is split into three diffracted waves (order, $+1, 0, -1$), One of them, for example, $+1$, can be shown to be a light optical copy of the image wave in the electron microscope. In the back focal plane of a collecting lens, its Fourier spectrum is separated from the others by means of an aperture. The transmitted wave forms its inverse Fourier transform (that is, the image wave) in the final image plane.

The advantage of holography as compared to conventional transmission microscopy is the following: Loosely speaking, behind the reconstruction lens of the light optical bench, we are virtually behind the objective lens of the electron microscope. Without being restricted by all of the technological problems arising if one wants to

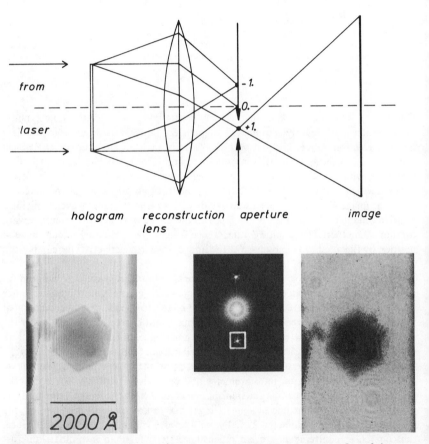

FIGURE 6. Light optical reconstruction of a wave recorded in a hologram. One of the waves diffracted at the grating of the interference fringes is isolated in the back focal plane of the reconstruction lens by means of an aperture. The reconstructed wave is formed in the image plane.

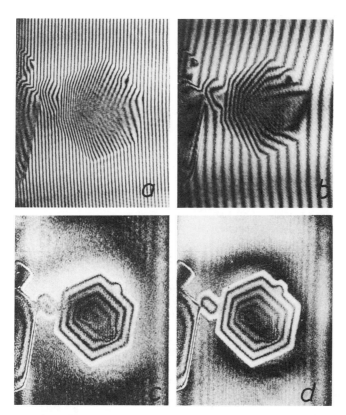

FIGURE 7. Effect of manipulations in the Fourier spectrum of the reconstructed wave: (a), (b) "holographic interferometry" by adding a coherent light wave differing in inclination for (a) and (b); (c) dark field imaging using a central beam stop; (d) Zernike phase contrast by means of an appropriate phase plate.

manipulate the spectrum of the electron wave in the electron microscope itself, we can instead, by light optical means, intervene in the spectrum of the reconstructed wave. We can intercept some range of spatial frequencies and/or apply appropriate phase plates to yield Zernike phase contrast. Furthermore, we can add a coherent reference wave for mapping the phase distribution, etc. These facilities have been demonstrated in several experiments (for example, by Wahl,[25] Hanßen[27] and co-workers, and Tonomura et al.[26]). Examples are given in FIGURE 7. However, because of some specific problems, electron holography has not yet been applied very successfully to the investigation of atomic structures.

INTERFERENCE MICROSCOPY WITH ATOMIC RESOLUTION

In principle, electron microscopy aims at the determination of atomic structures, that is, the distribution of the electrical potential or, equivalently, of the electron density in matter. To attain this high goal, we have to clear away the barrier set up by the aberrations of electron lenses, and thus, electron interference microscopy or holography may be expected to contribute to the solution of these problems.

Description of Lens Aberrations

An ideal optical lens can be treated as a phase-shifting device that converts a spherical wave emerging from an object point into a spherical wave converging to the corresponding image point. Using a real lens, the wave front in image space is not spherical, that is, it does not converge to a sharp image point. Consequently, the image is blurred. For theoretical considerations, in the back focal plane of the lens, the aberrated wave front is described by a phase factor, $\exp [i\chi(R)]$, where the "wave aberration" χ is a measure of the distance between the real and the spherical wave front, and R is a measure of the spatial frequency as well as the radial coordinate in the back focal plane. Taking spherical aberration and defocusing Δz into account, the wave aberration is given by

$$\chi(R) = k[0.25 \, C_s \, (R/k)^4 - 0.5 \, \Delta z \, (R/k)^2],$$

where C_s is the coefficient of spherical aberration of the lens and k is the wave number. Consequently, the image wave in the image plane can be written as

$$b(r) = o(r) x \, \text{FT} \, (\exp [i\chi(R)]),$$

where $o(r)$ denotes the object wave, x is the convolution, and FT is the Fourier transform.

As an example, let us consider the transfer of a harmonically modulated weak phase grating described by the object wave,

$$o(r) = \exp [i \, \rho_0 \cos (R_o r)] \text{ with } \rho_0 \ll 2\pi.$$

In the image plane of an ideal lens, we obtain the image wave, $b(r) = o(r)$. However, in the presence of a wave aberration, the image wave becomes

$$b(r) = 1 + i \, \rho_o \cos (R_o r) \exp [i\chi(R_o)],$$

with the amplitude,

$$A(r) = 1 - \rho_o \sin [\chi(R_o)] \cos (R_o r),$$

and the phase,

$$\phi(r) = \rho_o \cos [\chi(R_o)] \cos (R_o r).$$

Depending on the value of $\chi(R_o)$ for the spatial frequency, R_o, of the grating, the information about the object may be found in the phase, $\phi(r)$, of the image wave, $[\chi(R_o) = 0, \pi, \ldots]$, or in its amplitude, $A(r)$ $[\chi(R_o) = \pi/2, 3/2\pi, \ldots]$, or partially in the phase and the amplitude if $\chi(R_o)$ is in between. In ordinary electron microscopy, only the amplitude of the image wave is observed as $A(r)^2$, and the phase is lost (FIGURE 8). Hence, the image of an object containing not only one, but many spatial frequencies, R, may be strongly dissimilar from the object. Because we measure both the amplitude and the phase simultaneously in interference electron microscopy, no information is lost; however, the amplitude and phase measured in the image wave are scrambled with respect to the object wave. Using modern optical techniques, by deconvolution with FT(exp $[i\chi(R)]$), they can be restored. Consequently, electron interference microscopy together with this procedure correcting for the aberration enables us to determine the nonaberrated object wave in atomic dimensions, even though we have no aberration-free objective lenses at hand.

Electron Image Plane Interferograms in Atomic Dimensions

Atomic dimensions are given by the lattice spacings of crystals and the mutual distances of atoms in molecules covering a range from about 1 nm to about 0.1 nm. In order to investigate such structures, a lateral resolution of better than 0.05 nm is

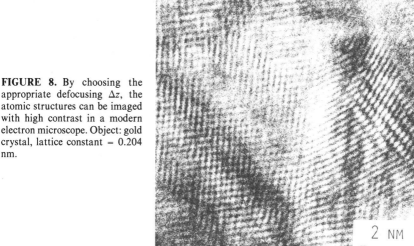

FIGURE 8. By choosing the appropriate defocusing Δz, the atomic structures can be imaged with high contrast in a modern electron microscope. Object: gold crystal, lattice constant = 0.204 nm.

2 NM

desirable. Then, the spacing of the interference fringes with respect to the object must be at least twice as narrow.

Depending on their atomic number, single atoms produce a phase-shift of the object wave of several 2π with a bell-shaped distribution that is several hundredths of a nanometer in width; this was calculated using the Hartree-Byatt model for atomic potential distributions. Evidently, single atoms are strong phase objects. Unfortunately, though, the wave aberration of the objective lens reduces the corresponding phase modulation of the image wave by a factor of about 100 in comparison to the object wave. In effect, single atoms produce only weak phase-shifts in the image wave. To detect the corresponding fringe shift in the interference pattern, the quantum noise in the fringes must be suppressed by collecting a sufficient number of electrons in the interferogram, and the contrast of the fringes must be as high as possible. Following

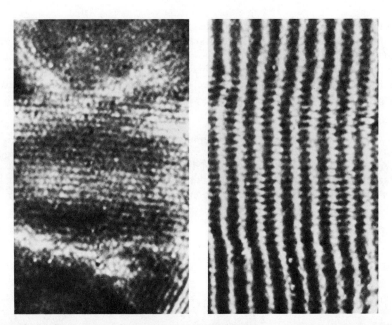

FIGURE 9. Reconstruction of a graphite crystal from a hologram with a fringe spacing of 0.16 nm. Left: Using a Zernike phase plate, the lattice planes with a spacing of 0.34 nm are discernible with high contrast. Right: Adding a coherent light wave to the reconstructed wave reveals, quantitatively, the phase modulation by the crystal. Unfortunately, the phase-shift due to single lattice planes is very weak.

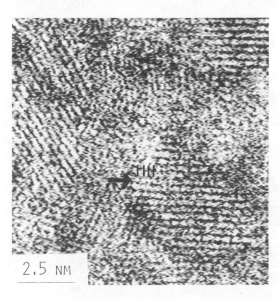

FIGURE 10. Image of uranium-oxide crystals reconstructed from an electron hologram with a fringe spacing of 0.08 nm. Single atomic sites are found, for example, near the arrow.

Walkup and Goodman,[29] the accuracy of phase determination, $\delta\rho$, from an interferogram with a fringe contrast, V, can be estimated to be

$$\delta\rho = \frac{\sqrt{2}}{V \cdot \sqrt{N}},$$

where N is the number of electrons per resolved picture element. The electron dose for

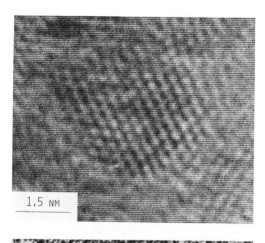

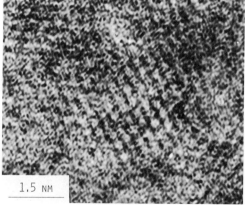

FIGURE 11. To obtain optimum resolution in the reconstructed wave, the interference fringes must be as narrow as possible. Top: The smallest fringe spacing (0.05 nm) reported up-to-date should make possible a resolution of 0.1 nm at best. Object: uranium-oxide crystals. Bottom: At present, the granularity in the reconstructed wave due to the noise of the fringes prohibits this good resolution to be found with weak objects. Single lattice components can hardly be recognized.

safely detecting a phase-shift of $2\pi/30$ combined with a lateral resolution of 0.2 nm is approximately 20 e/nm. Because such a high electron dose gives rise to radiation damage of sensitive objects, we may run into physical limits of structure analysis using electrons.

Electron interferometry in atomic dimensions constitutes a challenge to modern electron optics technology. This is so because of its extreme demands with respect to the coherence of the electron gun and the electrical stability of all electron lenses and deflectors, as well as to the mechanical stability of the microscope and the tranquility of the environment.

The following experiments have been performed using a Philips EM 420 ST electron microscope equipped with a field emission electron gun providing a very coherent electron beam. For our experiments in electron interferometry, we inserted an electron biprism and attached an image intensifier as a very helpful tool for controlling the adjustment. The microscope is installed in an environment with a very low level of mechanical vibrations and ac-stray fields. In addition, it is advisable to carry out such experiments at times with reduced disturbance level (for example, at night and on weekends).

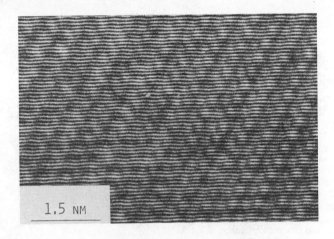

FIGURE 12. Interferogram of the finest details investigated by electron interferometry up-to-date. Compared to FIGURE 11, the signal/noise ratio is improved by reducing the noise at the expense of resolution and by using a stronger object (niobium-oxide single crystal). In the image wave, a phase modulation of about $\pi/2$ due to single lattice components is oberved. Bottom: In the Fourier spectrum of the wave reconstructed from this hologram, reflections are found that correspond to spacings of 0.165 nm in the object.

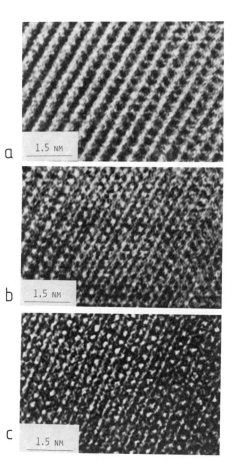

FIGURE 13. Images obtained from the hologram of FIGURE 12 (top) by manipulation of the Fourier spectrum of the reconstructed wave: (a) no manipulation; (b) Zernike phase contrast achieved by means of an appropriate phase plate; (c) dark field image using a central beam stop. Details smaller than 0.2 nm can easily be found.

Results

In our first steps, we have tried to find the limits of electron interference experiments in high resolution domains given by the modern electron optics technology. Right at the beginning, we just wanted to see what happens, and we took interferograms of graphite crystals that are often used in electron microscopy for testing the resolution of microscopes. At that time, we achieved a fringe spacing of 0.16 nm that limited the lateral resolution to 0.32 nm at best. FIGURE 9 shows that by holographic reconstruction of the interferogram, the lattice of the graphite crystal with a spacing of 0.34 nm is clearly resolved. Adding a coherent reference wave, we find a strong phase-shift by the contours of the crystal, but at first sight, alas, we hardly find any clearly visible phase modulation by the lattice planes (they do, though, produce a strong image contrast). The explanation is that the Zernike phase-contrast mechanism is extremely sensitive to phase variations down to $2\pi/100$, whereas the corresponding fringe shift cannot, for the most part, be detected by the naked eye.

Meanwhile, we learned to optimize the electron optical parameters of the microscope for a further reduction of the fringe spacing. In FIGURE 10, an image reconstructed from an interferogram with a fringe spacing of 0.08 nm is shown resolving the lattice of uranium-oxide crystals with a lattice constant of about 0.28 nm. In fact, the resolution is sufficient to recognize single atomic sites, but the noise increases considerably, which leads to an undesirable granulation. This gets even worse when the fringe spacing is reduced to 0.05 nm (FIGURE 11): In the highly enlarged detail of such an interferogram, one sees the noise due to the single electrons. Accordingly, in the corresponding part of the reconstructed image, we can expect a resolution of 0.1 nm at best, but, nevertheless, the single atoms of the very thin crystal can hardly be recognized in the noisy background. However, this is only a technical problem arising from the shortcomings of the photographic plate and it can be overcome very simply: By enhancing the magnification of the interference pattern in the electron microscope, the number of electrons per fringe can be increased without reaching the saturation density of the photographic plate.

By a slight modification of the electron microscope, the magnification was brought to its maximum value and things got considerably better (FIGURE 12). In the interferogram of a niobium-oxide crystal, the noise in the fringes of 0.075 nm spacing is reduced significantly. In addition, because the niobium-oxide crystal is chosen not as thin as the uranium crystals in the former interferogram, the phase in the image wave is clearly modulated. Due to this high signal/noise ratio, the image wave is reconstructed with reduced granularity, and single lattice components can be discerned with a lateral resolution of better than 0.2 nm (FIGURE 13).

Using the facilities for digital image processing installed in our institute,[30] we can furthermore reconstruct the object wave by correcting the aberrations still inherent in the images seen in FIGURE 13. Right now, this procedure is being tested.

ACKNOWLEDGMENTS

I would like to thank K-H. Herrmann, F. Lenz, and G. Möllenstedt for many valuable discussions. A complete list of references concerning electron interferometry up to 1981 can be found in reference 31.

REFERENCES

1. MÖLLENSTEDT, G. & H. DÜKER. 1954. Naturwissenschaften **42:** 41.
2. BORN, M. & E. WOLF. 1975. Principles of Optics. Pergamon. Oxford/New York.
3. GLASER, W. 1952. Grundlagen der Elektronenoptik. Springer-Verlag. Wien.
4. MÖLLENSTEDT, G. & H. DÜKER. 1956. Z. Phys. **145:** 377.
5. BRAUN, K. J. 1972. Untersuchungen der Kohärenzeigenschaften von Elektronenwellen mit dem Elektroneninterferometer. Diplomarbeit. Universität Tübingen.
6. SPEIDEL, R. & D. KURZ. 1977. Optik (Stuttgart) **49:** 173.
7. MÖLLENSTEDT, G. & G. WOHLAND. 1980. Proc. 7th Europ. Conf. on Electron Microscopy, Den Haag, vol. 1, p. 28.
8. WOHLAND, G. 1981. Messung der Kohärenzlänge von Elektronen im Elektroneninterferometer mit dem Wien-Filter. Thesis. Universität Tübingen.
9. LENZ, F. & G. WOHLAND. 1984. Optik (Stuttgart) **67:** 315.
10. SCHMID, H. 1985. Ein Elektronen-Interferometer mit 300 μm weit getrennten kohärenten Teilbündeln zur Erzeugung hoher Gangunterschiede und Messung der Phasenschiebung

durch das magnetische Vektorpotential bei metallisch abgeschirmtem Magnetfluß. Thesis. Universität Tübingen.

11. MÖLLENSTEDT, G. & H. LICHTE. 1978. Proc. 9th Int. Conf. on Electron Microscopy, Toronto, vol. I, p. 178.
12. MÖLLENSTEDT. G. & W. BAYH. 1962. Phys. Bl. **18**: 299.
13. MÖLLENSTEDT, G., H. SCHMID & H. LICHTE. 1982. Proc. 10th Int. Congr. on Electron Microscopy, Hamburg, vol. I, p. 433; TONOMURA, A. *et al.* 1983. Proc. Int. Symp. on Foundations of Quantum Mechanics, Tokyo, p. 20.
14. WAHL, H. 1970. Optik (Stuttgart) **30**: 508.
15. BOERSCH, H. & B. LISCHKE. Z. Phys. **237**: 449.
16. TONOMURA, A. 1972. Jpn. J. Appl. Phys. **11**: 493.
17. TONOMURA, A., T. MATSUDA, H. TANABE, N. OSAKABE, J. ENDO, A. FUKUHARA, K. SHINAGAWA & H. FUKIWARA. 1982. Phys. Rev. **B25**: 6799.
18. MÖLLENSTEDT, G., H. LICHTE & H. WAHL. 1972. Z. Phys. **249**: 456.
19. LICHTE, H. 1980. Optik (Stuttgart) **57**: 35.
20. MÖLLENSTEDT, G. & M. KELLER. 1957. Z. Phys. **148**: 34.
21. MERLI, P. G., G. F. MISSIROLLI & G. POZZI. 1974. J. Microsc. **21**: 11.
22. MÖLLENSTEDT, G. & R. BUHL. 1957. Phys. Bl. **13**: 357.
23. FAGET, J. & C. FERT. 1957. C. R. Acad. Sci. Paris **244**: 2368.
24. MÖLLENSTEDT, G. & H. WAHL. 1968. Naturwissenschaften **55**: 340.
25. WAHL, H. 1975. Bildebenenholographie mit Elektronen. Habilitationsschrift. Universität Tübingen.
26. TONOMURA, A., T. MATSUDA & J. ENDO. 1979. Jpn. J. Appl. Phys. **18**: 9.
27. HANβEN, K. J. 1982. Advances in Electronics and Electron Physics, vol. 59, p. 1. Academic Press. New York/London.
28. For example, see: REIMER, L. 1984. Transmission Electron Microscopy. Springer-Verlag. Berlin/Heidelberg/New York/Tokyo.
29. WALKUP, J. F. & J. W. GOODMAN. 1973. J. Opt. Soc. Am. **63**: 399.
30. FRANKE, F. J., K-H. HERRMANN, H. LICHTE & R. SCHILLING. 1985. Optik Suppl. **1**: 22.
31. MISSIROLLI, G., G. POZZI & U. VALDRE. 1981. J. Phys. **E14**: 649.

The Nonlocal Character of the Conductance in the Weakly Localized Limit

G. J. DOLAN AND D. J. BISHOP

AT&T Bell Laboratories
Murray Hill, New Jersey 07974

The quantum corrections to conductance were predicted by Thouless[1] and by Abrahams *et al.*[2] The corrections were studied in quantitative detail by Al'tshuler and Aronov,[3] and others.[4-7] The electron phase coherence required for the effects is characterized by a length scale that is typically $\tilde{L} \sim 1$ μm in size at temperatures ~ 1 K where the experiments are done. Modern lithographic techniques make such a scale accessible to direct probes of a sample's spatial characteristics, and several experiments, in a variety of geometrical configurations, have been directed toward this end. Here, we explicitly demonstrate the nonlocal nature of the conductance at such a length scale in a configuration that is intended to show that adding probes to a specimen disturbs, potentially seriously, the interference effects one may wish to measure in experiments on small samples. Some earlier experiments[8] have pointed peripherally toward such effects in other configurations, and recently, the problems have been considered specifically in theoretical work by Büttiker *et al.*[9] and by Doucot and Rammal.[5] The results here and the latter theoretical work specifically deal with the weak localization or "backscatter" interference terms that are seen in experiments on macroscopic systems. However, the conclusions are also relevant to those interference terms observable only in mesoscopic ($\sim\tilde{L}$) systems.[9]

Our experiment consists of a comparison of the properties of quasi-one-dimensional lithium thin-film "wires" for two cases (FIGURE 1). The case of a long, uniform wire has been studied in detail theoretically[3,5] and experimentally[6,7] in recent work, and is well understood. Along with such a sample, we have studied the case where small tabs are placed along a wire, which is a case specifically considered by Doucot and Rammal. This case is closely related to the problem of a small wire with voltage leads attached, but, on the other hand, it retains sufficient similarity to the uniform wire case that a comparison is informative. Intuitively (if one has local intuition), one would expect negligible changes in the resistance for the second case so long as the tab or probe width was small compared to the probe spacing, as it is in our experiment ($\sim\frac{1}{40}$). The changes we observe are in fact small, but they are larger than the percentage change in the ordinary resistivity produced by the tabs. They also have a dependence on the electron coherence range that is qualitatively in agreement with the localization theory of nonlocal conductivity.

In the uniform wire case, the small backscatter interference correction to the resistance can be expressed as a temperature and field dependent fractional change in the ordinary resistance:

$$\frac{\Delta R}{R_0} = \frac{e^2}{\pi \hbar} \frac{R\square}{w} \tilde{L}(T, H). \tag{1}$$

Here, $\tilde{L}(T, H)$ is a phase-breaking "length" dependent on temperature, magnetic field, and spin-dependent scattering:

$$\tilde{L}(T, H) = (\tfrac{3}{2})[L_i^{-2} + (\tfrac{4}{3})L_{SO}^{-2} + L_H^{-2}]^{-1/2} - (\tfrac{1}{2})(L_i^{-2} + L_H^{-2})^{-1/2}, \tag{2}$$

where the magnetic length is $L_H \equiv \sqrt{3}\Phi_0/\pi H w$ for a wire of dimension, w, transverse to

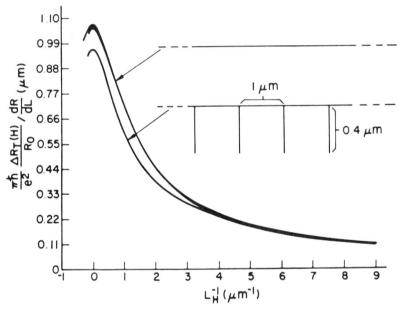

FIGURE 1. The coherence distance functon, $\tilde{L}$, versus the magnetic length, L_H, for wire samples with and without side-arms.

the field, and $\Phi_0 \equiv hc/2e$ is the paired-electron quantum of magnetic flux. In fact, it is the separate terms in the function $\tilde{L}$ that are really the lengths of the coherence.

The samples were lithium wires with $w = 26 \pm 2$nm, $L_i = =1.4 \pm 0.1$ μm, $L_{SO} = 1.78 \pm 0.05$ μm, and $R\square = 0.9 \pm 1$ Ω. FIGURE 1 shows the negative magnetoresistance for the samples at $T = 1.5$ K. The resistance change is divided by $(e^2/\pi \hbar)R\square/w$ to produce $\tilde{L}$ as defined in equation 1. The magnetic field scale is in units of L_H^{-1}. The top curve represents the uniform wire case. There were five such samples on the experimental chip, and within the evident noise, the curves for all were identical. This indicates the reliability of the sample formation procedure. The lower curve is the magnetoresistance for a sample on the same chip, but with tabs attached as in the figure. The tabs have a length of 0.4 μm and a width equal to the wire width with an accuracy ~10 nm. At $H = 0$, this curve is suppressed approximately 10% below the uniform wire curve with the difference vanishing at high fields. The difference vanishes at large fields where the range of coherence, $\tilde{L}$, becomes small. It is clear that the difference cannot be accounted for by the classical explanation based only on the geometry of the wire; in fact, it involves the range of coherence as well.

A quantitative prediction of the effect is contained in the theory of Doucot and Rammal, who calculated the magnetoresistance for a wide variety of normal metal networks and of a wire with tabs. FIGURE 2 shows the magnetoresistance their calculations predict for the geometry of FIGURE 1, but with different tab spacings, a. The deviations from the wire ($a = \infty$) result become significant as the spacing becomes

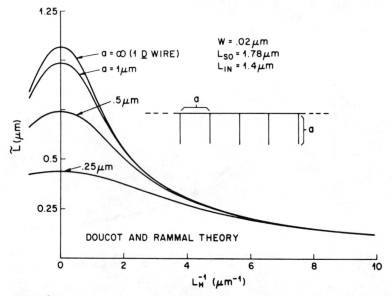

FIGURE 2. $\tilde{L}$ from the theory of Doucot and Rammal for the experimental configuration of FIGURE 1.

comparable to $\tilde{L}$. The deviation at $a = 1$ μm is ~10% in approximate agreement with FIGURE 1. Of course, the effect increases for smaller a.

Physically, the suppression of ΔR in the presence of the tabs represents a corresponding suppression of the amplitude of the interference of backscattered electron states. The addition of arms to the wire provides more sites to scatter to and from, which thereby reduces the backscatter interference amplitude and reduces the correction to the conductance. Our experiment explicitly demonstrates the nonlocal character of the weak localization corrections to conductance. This nonlocality must be considered in measurements made on systems with small-scale structure, and such details as the size and nature of voltage probes on a small sample may have significant impact. In a quantitative experiment, the nature of the boundary conditions associated with the probes must be considered. One effective way of doing this, namely, by designing an experiment with particularly simple boundary conditions, is demonstrated in reference 10. The theoretical formalism of Doucot and Rammal provides, in principle, a more general solution by explicitly solving the boundary-value problem in particular cases.

ACKNOWLEDGMENTS

We gratefully acknowledge helpful discussions with our colleagues, E. Abrahams, M. Büttiker, and particularly, B. Doucot and R. Rammal, who generously provided prepublication information on their work.

REFERENCES

1. THOULESS, D. J. 1977. Phys. Rev. Lett. **39:** 1167.
2. ABRAHAMS, E., P. W. ANDERSON, D. C. LICCIARDELLO & T. V. RAMAKRISHNAN. 1979. Phys. Rev. Lett. **43:** 718.
3. AL'TSHULER, B. L. & A. G. ARONOV. 1981. JETP Lett. **33:** 499.
4. LEE, P. A. & T. V. RAMAKRISHNAN. 1985. Rev. Mod. Phys. **57:** 287; AL'TSHULER, A. G. & A. G. ARONOV. Electron-electron interaction in disordered conductors. *In* Modern Problems in Condensed Matter Physics. A. L. Efros & M. Pollack, Eds. North-Holland. Amsterdam. In press. These articles review the extensive work on weak localization.
5. DOUCOT, B. & R. RAMMAL. 1985. Phys. Rev. Lett. **55:** 1148; and paper to be published.
6. SANTHANAM, P., S. WIND & D. E. PROBER. 1984. Phys. Rev. Lett. **53:** 1179.
7. LICINI, J. C., G. J. DOLAN & D. J. BISHOP. 1985. Phys. Rev. Lett. **54:** 1585.
8. DOLAN, G. J., J. C. LICINI & D. J. BISHOP. 1986. Phys. Rev. Lett. **56:** 1493.
9. MASDEN, J. T. & N. GIORDANO. 1982. Phys. Rev. Lett. **49:** 819; WEBB, R. A., S. WASHBURN, C. P. UMBACH & R. B. LAIBOWITZ. 1985. Phys. Rev. Lett. **54:** 2696; LICINI, J. C., D. J. BISHOP, M. KASTNER & J. MELNGALIS. To be published; BÜTTIKER, M., Y. IMRY & R. LANDAUER. 1983. Phys. Lett. **96A:** 365; GEFEN, Y., Y. IMRY & M. YA. AZBEL. 1984. Phys. Rev. Lett. **52:** 139; BÜTTIKER, M., Y. IMRY & M. YA. AZBEL. 1984. Phys. Rev. **A30:** 1982.
10. BISHOP, D. J. & G. J. DOLAN. 1985. Phys. Rev. Lett. **55:** 2911.

Flux-Sensitive Effects in Normal Metal Loops

MARKUS BÜTTIKER

IBM Thomas J. Watson Research Center
Yorktown Heights, New York 10598

INTRODUCTION

In this paper, we are concerned with coherent quantum mechanical electron transport in disordered normal metal structures and the role of inelastic events in bringing about electrical resistance. The wave nature of electrons plays an important role whether we study transport through a periodic lattice, which is governed by Bloch electrons, or whether we consider transport in disordered systems where we deal with localized wave functions. However, a striking manifestation of coherent transport can be expected when we form the conductor into a loop (or other multiply connected geometry) and study the sensitivity of the conductor to the flux through the hole. In the absence of inelastic scattering events, such a loop exhibits coherent transport phenomena that we tend to associate only with superconductors. The key phenomena (on which we expand in this paper) is that such structures support circulating, persistent currents.[1,2] It is of interest, then, to understand the effect of inelastic relaxation on these coherent transport phenomena and to study the transition from coherent to lossy and resistive behavior.

The study of electron transport is a central topic of solid-state physics. Much of this discussion has been carried out within the general framework of the linear response theory as advanced by Kubo[3] and Greenwood.[4] In this approach, transport coefficients are expressed in terms of time-dependent equilibrium correlation functions. We, however, pursue a different approach (one that has been put forward by Landauer[5]) that expresses transport coefficients in terms of stationary scattering properties of the sample. We start this paper with a brief discussion of Landauer's approach to resistance, and discuss the connection between inelastic events and resistance. This is followed by a discussion of the normal metal structures shown in FIGURE 1. We first treat a closed loop without inelastic events (FIGURE 1a), but with disorder, and then point out the existence of persistent currents.[1] The onset of resistance in such a loop[2,6,7] will be discussed using the model[7] of FIGURE 1b. The geometry of FIGURE 1c allows the study of the Aharonov-Bohm effect in normal metal loops. Reference 8, using weak localization theory, predicted Aharonov-Bohm resistance oscillations with period, $hc/2e$, and higher harmonics. Oscillations with this period have been seen in a number of ingenious experiments.[9,10] On the other hand, references 11–13, invoking the Landauer formula, predicted resistance oscillations with a fundamental period, hc/e. These predictions are not contradictory, but apply to physically distinct situations. Experiments have now demonstrated oscillations with period, hc/e, in a striking and clear fashion in single normal metal loops,[14–16] in semiconductors,[17] and in short series of loops.[18] For an extended discussion of the experiments of references 14 and 15, we refer the reader to reference 19.

RESISTANCE AND IRREVERSIBILITY

Landauer studied the resistance of an obstacle in an otherwise perfect wire.[5,20] The perfect wire connects to reservoirs, as shown in FIGURE 2. A complete spatial separation between elastic scattering and inelastic scattering is assumed. Scattering at the obstacle is elastic; inelastic processes occur only in the reservoirs. The reservoirs

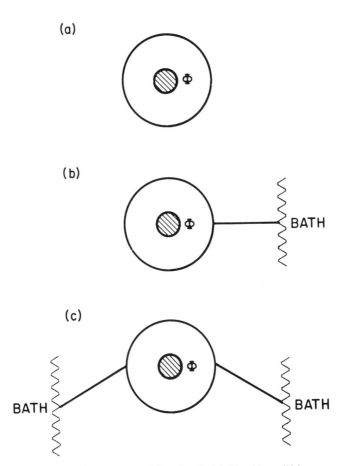

FIGURE 1. Normal metal loops penetrated by a flux, Φ. (a) Closed loop; (b) loop connected to a single lead and (c) to two leads. The reservoirs act as a source and a sink of carriers and of energy.

have the property that they absorb all carriers traveling toward them and that they reemit carriers with a phase and energy that is unrelated to that of the absorbed carriers. A current is imposed if the reservoirs have differing chemical potentials. The resistance is determined by studying the currents and the densities associated with the wave functions at the Fermi energy. In a one-dimensional wire, the obstacle is characterized by the transmission probability, $T(E)$, for carriers to traverse the sample. For zero temperature, Landauer finds a resistance,[5,20]

$$\mathcal{R} = \left(\frac{2\pi\hbar}{e^2}\right)\left(\frac{1 - T(E_F)}{T(E_F)}\right),$$ (1)

where E_F is the Fermi energy. Equation 1 can also be applied to calculate the resistance of a series of obstacles if the transmission through such a sequence is coherent and can be characterized by a transmission probability.[20] This has been used to find the dependence of the conductance of a one-dimensional disordered wire on the length of the wire,[20] and has also been used to develop the modern scaling theory for one-dimensional conductance.[21]

Equation 1 depends only on the elastic, static scattering properties of the sample. This might give the impression that it is the elastic scattering at the barrier that leads to resistance. However, reference 1 emphasizes that this is not correct. The scattering at the barrier at the Fermi energy is described by four wave functions; in addition to the two wave functions describing waves of unit amplitude incident on the sample from the

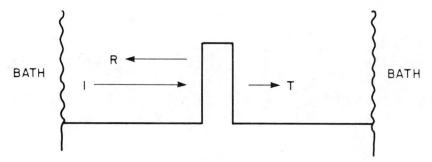

FIGURE 2. Barrier connected to ideal leads connected to reservoirs.

left or from the right, there are the complex conjugate (time-reversed) wave functions that describe waves of intensities, T and $R = 1 - T$, incident from both reservoirs. However, these later two wave functions, which require coherent incident streams from both reservoirs, are not realized in the arrangement of FIGURE 2 because the reservoirs cause phase randomization. It is the elimination of these two wave functions that gives rise to a positive resistance. Thus, the phase-randomizing reservoirs in FIGURE 2 are essential to obtain a positive resistance.[1]

It is worth noting that if the reservoirs, which we can picture as large blocks of normal metal, are replaced by superconductors, then the resulting SNS-microbridge exhibits no resistance if the inelastic scattering length is large compared to the length of the metal wire.[22,23]

We should emphasize that the system discussed here has very particular properties not commonly associated with discussions of resistance. The Joule heat due to the resistance (equation 1) is produced only in the reservoirs and not in the sample. While real systems do not, of course, exhibit the clear-cut separation of elastic and inelastic scattering assumed here, the spatial separation of elastic scattering and inelastic relaxation is, nevertheless, a real physical feature of systems that exhibit an inelastic scattering length that is large compared to the dimension of the obstacle.[24] It is this spatial separation that leads to an apparent deviation from the Onsager relations.[25] The measurements on Au loops and wires in references 14 and 15, as well as in earlier experiments,[26] indeed exhibit a pronounced asymmetry in the conductance if the magnetic field is reversed.

THE CLOSED NORMAL METAL LOOP

The connection between resistance and irreversibility discussed above raises the question asked in reference 1: What happens if we eliminate the reservoirs that introduce irreversible effects into our system? We can eliminate the reservoirs by forming the ideal wires that connect to the obstacle into a loop. To study transport, we apply a magnetic flux, Φ. For simplicity, we assume that the flux is entirely confined to the hole of the loop (see FIGURE 1a). This system is now completely described by a Hamiltonian with a vector potential, A, and a nonuniform potential, $V(x)$, due to the obstacle in the loop. Here, x is the coordinate along the loop. If we assume that the loop is circular, then the component of the vector potential along x is related to the flux, Φ, by $A = \Phi/L$, where L is the circumference of the loop. The motion of electrons in the loop is, therefore, governed by the Hamiltonian,

$$H = \frac{1}{2m} [p - (e\Phi/cL)]^2 + V(x). \tag{2}$$

As pointed out in reference 1, electrons circuiting the loop in the presence of a flux, Φ, behave like electrons traversing an infinite periodic structure with a potential, $V(x + L) = V(x)$; that is, a lattice with a unit cell equal to the circumference of the loop. The electronic states of such a lattice are Bloch functions, $\psi_{n,k} = e^{ikx}u_{n,k}(x)$, $u_{n,k}(x + L) = u_{n,k}(x)$, with energy, $E_n(k)$. The Schrödinger equation of the periodic lattice can be mapped onto equation 2, and this yields $k = -k_o\Phi/\Phi_o$, where $k_o = 2\pi L$ is the width of the Brillouin zone of the periodic lattice and $\Phi_o = hc/e$ is the single-charge flux quantum. The eigenfunctions of equation 2 are the $u_{n,k}(x)$ with k determined by the flux. The energy spectrum of equation 2 (shown in FIGURE 3) is given by the bands, $E_n(k)$. The eigenstates of the normal metal loop are thus given by a ladder of Bloch states with k selected by the flux. We have, at most, one electron per band (two if we take spin into account). The mapping discussed above now allows us to apply the usual solid-state schemes to calculate the quantities that we are interested in. Consider first a constant flux, Φ. The current in the loop is given by

$$I(k) = -\frac{e}{L} \sum_{n=1}^{N} v_n(k), \tag{3}$$

where n labels all occupied states up to the Fermi energy. The velocities in successive bands alternate, but, typically, higher lying bands have a larger velocity. Thus, typically, the current in equation 3 is determined by the highest occupied state. From this, we obtain a persistent current that is a periodic function of k and therefore of the flux, with a period, Φ_o. The current vanishes at the center of the Brillouin zone ($k = 0$) and at the boundary of the Brillouin zone ($k = \pm k_o/2$).

For weak disorder along the loop, the bands, $E_n(k)$, closely follow a free electron spectrum, $E \simeq k^2$. In this case, the persistent current given by equation 3 has a magnitude, $I \simeq ev_F/L$. For a metal with a lattice constant of $a \simeq 2 \cdot 10^{-8}$ cm forming a loop consisting of 10^4 atoms, this yields a current, $I \simeq 10^{-7}$ A. With increasing disorder in the loop, the bands, $E_n(k)$, become flatter, and the velocities in equation 3 become smaller. Consequently, with increasing disorder, the persistent current decreases.

Next, consider a flux that increases linearly in time, $\Phi = -cFt$, where F is the field induced in the loop. Using Bloch's law, $\hbar dk/dt = -eF$, yields a lattice vector that increases linearly with time, $k = -\omega t/L$. Here, $\omega = eU/\hbar$ (with $U = FL$) is a Josephson frequency with a single charge. Due to the induced electric field, F, the carriers in the loop are pushed in synchronism through the Brillouin zone. If k varies

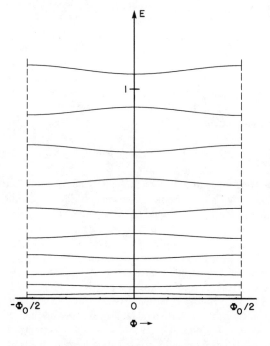

FIGURE 3. Energy spectrum of the closed loop of FIGURE 1a as a function of flux, Φ. The energy scale is $10^3 E_0$, with $E_0 = \hbar^2/2mL^2$. L is the circumference of the loop.

slowly enough, the gaps in FIGURE 3 confine the carriers to the bands, and Zener tunneling can be neglected. In the presence of a linearly increasing flux, we have, therefore, an oscillatory, Josephson-like current that is periodic in time with a period, $2\pi/\omega$. The time-averaged Josephson current, $I(k_o\omega t)$, vanishes because $\int dk v_n(k) = 0$ when integrated over the whole Brillouin zone. Therefore, there is no Joule heat associated with this current. Bloch[27] shows that persistent currents and Josephson currents always occur together; we cannot have one without the other.

We have neglected transitions into higher lying unoccupied states. This requires that the energy, $\hbar\omega$, is small compared to the gaps in FIGURE 3. For a loop of 10^4 atoms, the gaps are of the order of $E_F/N \sim 10^{-4}$ eV for $E_F \sim 1$ eV, which correspond to frequencies of the order of 10^{12} Hz. Even for frequencies that are high enough to induce transitions to higher unoccupied states, we expect this Hamiltonian system to exhibit complete phase coherence and to be completely reversible.[28] This system stores energy and has no mechanism to dissipate it.

Subsequently, we illustrate our results for the example of a loop with a single point scatterer characterized by an energy-independent transmission probability, T. FIGURE 3 shows the energy spectrum for such a loop with $T = 0.1$. The energy levels[29] are given by $E_n = E_0[\phi_n^2 + 2(-1)^n \phi_n \sqrt{T} \cos(2\pi\Phi/\Phi_0)]$, where $E_0 = \hbar^2/2mL^2$ and $\phi_n = (2n - 1)(\pi/2)$.

ONSET OF RESISTANCE

The effect of inelastic events on the coherent phenomena discussed in the previous section has been the subject of two recent publications. Landauer and Büttiker[6] have considered a closed loop in which the electronic degrees of freedom are weakly coupled to nonelectronic degrees of freedom. This work has been reviewed and extended in reference 2. Here, we expand on a model introduced in reference 7. Reference 7 considered the normal metal structure shown in FIGURE 1b. A current lead is connected to the loop and permits exchange of carriers between the loop and the reservoir. In contrast to the closed loop studied in reference 6, the number of carriers in the loop of FIGURE 1b is not a constant of motion. The model of reference 7 invokes the same spatial separation of elastic and inelastic scattering as we used in the discussion of the resistance of an obstacle in a wire (see FIGURE 2). Scattering in the loop and the lead is elastic. Inelastic scattering occurs only in the reservoir. The reservoir continuously injects carriers into the lead. These carriers travel towards the junction with the lead and the loop. At the junction, the carriers are either reflected and travel back to the reservoir, or they enter the loop. Eventually, a carrier in the loop will escape into the lead and reach the reservoir. In the reservoir, the carriers are scattered inelastically and reemitted into the lead with a phase and energy that is unrelated to the value of these quantities upon incidence. We have, thus, a model that describes an irreversible system, yet all the calculations can still be done by solving an elastic scattering problem. A particular example of such a loop was treated in reference 7. Here, we go on to give a simple discussion of the properties of this system without repeating these calculations.

We first describe the junction between the lead and the loop in more detail.[12] Suppose a carrier circling in the loop and approaching the junction has a probability, ϵ, to escape from the loop into the lead. A carrier approaching the junction from the lead has then a probability, $1 - 2\epsilon$, to be reflected at the junction and a probability, 2ϵ, to enter the loop. In the case, $\epsilon = 0$, the loop and the lead are disconnected. Carriers can neither enter nor escape from the loop. The electron levels in the loop, therefore, are the same as in the closed loop; that is, we have an energy spectrum as shown in FIGURE 3. If we allow ϵ to be nonzero, but small, the loop and the lead are only weakly coupled. The effect of weak coupling is to broaden the energy levels. The electron states in the loop acquire a finite lifetime. The level broadening is determined by the rate of escape of a carrier from the loop into the lead, and is proportional to an attempt frequency times the probability, ϵ, to tunnel from the loop into the lead. Thus, each state, E_n, in the loop is characterized by a lifetime, τ_n, that is proportional to ϵ^{-1}.

Let us assume a temperature such that kT exceeds the width of the levels, $\hbar/\tau_n$. Because the reservoir injects carriers into the lead according to the Fermi distribution, the levels in the loop are, in equilibrium, occupied with a probability, $f_n = f[E_n(k)]$. (If kT is smaller than the width of the energy level, we cannot characterize the occupation of the state by a single occupation probability, but have to take into account the variation of the occupation probability within a single broadened energy level.[7]) Suppose that the system has, through the action of some force, been driven away from equilibrium. If the actual occupation probability, ρ_n, is less than the equilibrium occupation probability, f_n, then carriers from the lead penetrating into the loop will drive the occupation probability toward the equilibrium value. If the occupation probability exceeds f_n, then carriers leak out of the state into the lead and into the reservoir. Thus, the temporal change of the actual occupation probability, ρ_n, is proportional to the imbalance between the actual occupation probability and the equilibrium occupation probability. The rate of change is determined by the lifetime of the state. Therefore, the time dependence of the occupation probabilities in this system is simply

$$\partial \rho_n / \partial t = - \frac{1}{\tau_n} (\rho_n - f_n). \tag{4}$$

The circulating current in the loop is now given by

$$I = - \frac{e}{L} \sum_n \rho_n \upsilon_n. \tag{5}$$

For a time-independent flux, $\rho_n = f_n$, and equation 5 gives the temperature-dependent persistent current of the weakly coupled loop. For the model discussed in reference 7, we found that this current decreases monotonically with increasing temperature and that the fundamental period remains Φ_0.

Consider next the case where the flux increases linearly in time, $d\Phi/dt = -cU$. According to Bloch's law, $k = -\omega t/L$, where $\omega = eU/\hbar$. Now, the equilibrium occupation probabilities are time-dependent, $f_n(t) = f(E_n[k(t)])$, and through equation 4, they give rise to time-dependent occupation probabilities, ρ_n. For simplicity, we take from now on the lifetime, τ_n, to be independent of flux and, thus, independent of time. We can then proceed as in reference 6 and expand E_n and f_n in Fourier series:

$$E_n(k) = \sum_{m=0}^{\infty} \Delta_{nm} \cos m\omega t, \tag{6}$$

$$f_n(k) = \sum_{m=0}^{\infty} g_{nm} \cos m\omega t. \tag{7}$$

Substituting f_n into equation 4, we solve for $\rho_n(t)$. Using this result to evaluate equation 5, and taking into account that $\upsilon_n = \hbar^{-1} dE_n/dk$, yields a time-averaged current,

$$\langle I \rangle = (e^2/L^2) \sum_n (\tau_n/m_n^*)U. \tag{8}$$

The bracket denotes a time average over a period of $2\pi/\omega$. Here, we have introduced the effective mass weighted by the actual distribution function,

$$\frac{1}{m_n^*} = \frac{1}{k_0} \int \frac{dk\, d^2E_n}{\hbar^2\, dk^2}\, \rho_n = -\frac{L^2}{2\hbar^2} \sum_m \frac{m^2 \Delta_{nm} g_{nm}}{1 + m^2 \omega^2 \tau_n^2}. \tag{9}$$

Note that the effective mass as defined in equation 9 depends on the temperature and is a function of the induced voltage, U. Equation 8 is a dc current accompanying the Josephson current. The dc current voltage characteristic is shown in FIGURE 4 (using the spectrum shown in FIGURE 3). At $U = 0$, for a constant flux, we have a branch due to the persistent currents; that is, equation 5 with $\rho_n = f_n$. We move up and down this branch as a function of flux, typically reaching the maximum current when $\Phi = \Phi_0/4$ and reaching the minimum when $\Phi = -\Phi_0/4$. Equation 8 gives the second branch shown in FIGURE 4, which exists for nonzero voltage, $U = \hbar\omega/e$. We have evaluated

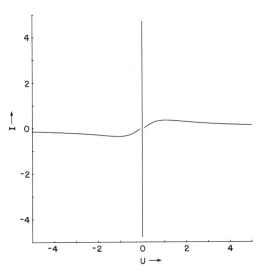

FIGURE 4. The dc current voltage characteristic of a normal metal loop with inelastic scattering for the model of FIGURE 1b and the spectrum shown in FIGURE 3 ($kT = 40E_0$). Current is in units of $e\hbar/mL^2$, and voltage is in units of $\hbar/e\tau$.

this branch for the loop of FIGURE 3 coupled with the junction invoked in references 7 and 12 to an ideal lead. We find[29] a lifetime, $\tau_n = \hbar/(\epsilon E_0 \phi_n)$, where $E_0 = \hbar^2/2mL^2$ and $\phi_n = (2n - 1)\,(\pi/2)$. The Fermi energy has been taken halfway between the tenth and eleventh energy level (for $\Phi = 0$). The temperature is $kT = 40E_0$, which is of the order of the width of the energy bands adjacent to the Fermi energy. Equation 8 exhibits a maximum at a voltage, $U = \hbar\omega/e = \hbar/e\tau$, where τ is a typical relaxation time; in our example, it is given by $\tau = \hbar/(10\pi\epsilon E_0)$.

The dc current (equation 8) vanishes for $\tau = 0$ and $\tau = \infty$, and peaks in between. There are other related problems in which the low-frequency transport peaks at an intermediate relaxation rate. Thermally activated escape from a metastable state is an example.[30] Another example comes from one-dimensional localization. In the absence of inelastic scattering, the carriers are confined to localized states. In the presence of intense inelastic scattering, current flow is impeded by inelastic scattering. A maximum current flow occurs for an intermediate scattering rate.[31,32] Furthermore, it is worth pointing out that transport in a single narrow conduction band, such as in a superlattice,[33] gives rise to a dc current that depends on the voltage and the scattering rate as a single term of equation 8. In this latter case, electron-electron interactions render the branch of the dc-characteristic, where dI/dV is negative, unstable against the formation of dipole domains.[34]

Of special interest is the slope of the dc current near the origin, which yields the dc conductance of the loop,

$$G_J = \langle I \rangle / U = e \langle I \rangle / \hbar \omega = (e^2/L^2) \sum_n (\tau_n/m_n^*). \tag{10}$$

The index, J, here emphasizes that this conductance characterizes a current accompanying Josephson oscillations. The effective mass in equation 10 is the zero frequency limit of equation 9; that is, the effective mass that is obtained by replacing the actual distribution function, ρ_n, by the equilibrium distribution function, f_n. Note that the effective mass, as defined in equation 9, is infinite if the level is completely filled ($f_n = 1$) or completely empty ($f_n = 0$). The conductance, G_J, diverges as τ_n tends to infinity, thus indicating that we are approaching a state without resistance. It should, however, be emphasized that the range over which $G_J U$ agrees well with equation 8 becomes smaller as the lifetime increases. For $U > \hbar/e\tau$, the effective mass (equation 9) diverges as τ tends to infinity. This implies that linear response is valid only for voltages, $U = \hbar\omega/e$, that are smaller than $\hbar/e\tau$.

It is interesting to compare this result with that of Greenwood (equation 30 of reference 4). Greenwood is interested in the resistance of a wire, not of a loop. However, he imposes periodic boundary conditions and applies a linearly increasing flux. His system is equivalent to a loop. In the presence of a constant induced voltage, he also finds a contribution to the current given by equation 5 (that is, an alternating Josephson-like current), and names it a "ripple current." However, because he considers only electronic degrees of freedom, and because he lets the density matrix evolve accordingly, the Josephson current is zero when averaged over a period, $2\pi/\omega$. Despite the fact that no dissipative mechanism is invoked, he finds a conductance and, thus, resistance. In Greenwood's calculation, the occupation probabilities change because of field-induced transitions into higher levels. One might think that such transitions (or, equivalently, Zener tunneling) provide a dissipative mechanism, and this seems to be the view of Lenstra and van Haeringen.[35] However, in a Hamiltonian system, such transitions are coherent and represent energy storage. By a suitable procedure, the system can be brought back into the original state as pointed out by Landauer.[28] Our key point is that inelastic phase-randomizing events are needed to obtain resistance.

We can elucidate the physics further by considering the response of the loop to an oscillating flux superimposed on a static flux, $\Phi = \Phi_1 + \Phi_2 \cos \Omega t$. We assume Φ_2 to be small compared to the flux quantum, Φ_0. Such a flux induces a time-dependent voltage, and via Bloch's law, this gives rise to a time-dependent k vector, where $k = k_1 + k_2 \cos \Omega t$, with $k_1 = k_0 \Phi_1/\Phi_0$ and $k_2 = k_0 \Phi_2/\Phi_0$. We now determine ρ_n to first order in k_2 using equation 4, and calculate the current to this order using equation 5. We then determine the Joule heat, $\langle I(t)U(t) \rangle$, averaged over a period, $2\pi/\Omega$. Dividing this by the time-averaged induced voltage, $\langle U^2 \rangle$, yields an ac conductance,

$$\alpha(\Omega, \Phi_1) = \frac{e^2}{L^2} \sum_n \frac{\tau_n v_n^2}{1 + \tau_n^2 \Omega^2} \left(-\frac{df}{dE} \right) \bigg|_{E=E_n}. \qquad (11)$$

Again, we find that the zero-frequency conductance diverges as the lifetime of the states tends to infinity. FIGURE 5 shows the zero-frequency limit of equation 11 for the spectrum of FIGURE 3 for two different temperatures. If the temperature is small

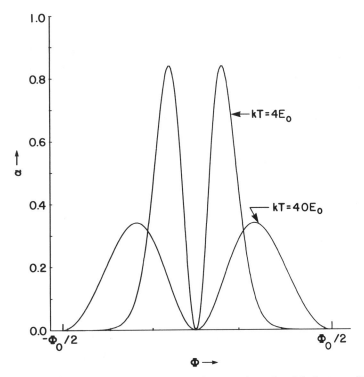

FIGURE 5. Zero-frequency limit of the ac conductance (equation 11) for two different temperatures, $kT = 4E_0$ and $kT = 40E_0$. Conductance is in units of $e^2/\hbar\epsilon$. The ϵ measures the coupling strength between the loop and the lead.

compared to the bandwidth of the energy levels adjacent to the Fermi energy, α exhibits a double peak either at the center of the Brillouin zone or at the boundary of the Brillouin zone, depending on where the gap, $E_{n+1}(\Phi) - E_n(\Phi)$, is minimal. As the temperature rises and kT exceeds the width of the energy levels, the flux dependence is determined by the square of the velocity in equation 11. The square of the velocity exhibits a strong second harmonic, and as shown in FIGURE 5, the periodicity of the ac conductance changes from hc/e to $hc/2e$ as the temperature increases. This crossover is the main subject of a paper by Imry and Shiren.[36] The main part of their investigation is based on the Greenwood formula. Dissipation is introduced into the loop, using a scheme of Czycholl and Kramer,[37] which was also invoked by Thouless and Kirkpatrick.[31] Because the Greenwood result (equation 30 of reference 4) does not contain the current (equation 5), this approach yields a result that is different from equation 11. In this approach, it is the field-induced transitions from one level, E_n, to another level, E_m, that give rise to the absorption of power. Because such field-induced transitions do not take place until the applied field is almost in resonance with the energy difference, $E_n - E_m$, these transitions give only a small contribution to the power absorption at low frequencies that is proportional to $1/\tau$. In contrast, the contribution given by equation 11 due to motion along the bands is proportional to τ. Field-induced transitions[36] between levels give rise to a conductance that peaks at $\Phi = 0$ or at $\Phi = \Phi_0/2$, which is in contrast to our result[2,7] that yields maxima away from the center or the boundary of the "Brillouin zone."

We can highlight the difference between the processes contained in the Greenwood formula and that of equation 11 by considering the ac conductance as a function of frequency for a fixed temperature and flux, Φ_1. Field-induced transitions give rise to peaks in the ac conductance at the frequencies, $(E_n - E_m)/\hbar$, where $n \neq m$. Centered at zero frequency, $\Omega = 0$, there is an additional peak, given by equation 11, that is not contained in the Greenwood formula. This zero-frequency peak is due to the motion of the carriers along the energy levels.

In the approach of reference 7, both the motion of the carriers along the bands, as well as the field-induced transitions, are taken into account. The derivation of the low-frequency result (equation 11) from the general result of reference 7 is the subject of reference 36. We stress here the similarity of the results (equations 9–11) to those obtained in references 2 and 6. However, the model in FIGURE 1b is an open system. Both in the presence of a linearly increasing flux and in the presence of an oscillating flux, we have an oscillating current in the lead connecting the loop and the reservoir.[7] In many ways, the open system is simpler than the closed loop. In the closed loop, it is the total energy of a configuration that determines the probability of the system to be in an excited state. (For a closed loop, these probabilities are not Fermi functions.[2,6]) In the loop connected to a reservoir (discussed here), we deal with single particle excitations and, consequently, with Fermi occupation probabilities.

The low frequency limit of the ac conductance as given by equation 11 is not the same as the dc conductance accompanying the Josephson current (equation 10). This is in contrast to what we are used to when considering the conductance of large systems (i.e., systems with a dense level of energy states). As pointed out in reference 2, however, the two are related. It turns out that the ac conductance integrated over the whole "Brillouin zone" is equal to the dc conductance (equation 10):

$$G_J = (1/\Phi_0) \int_{-\Phi_0/2}^{\Phi_0/2} d\Phi \alpha(\Phi, 0). \tag{12}$$

This relation between the two conductances is valid even when we consider the flux dependence of the lifetime. In this case, it is $d/dk(\tau_n v_n)$ that has to be weighted with the distribution function, f_n. Finally, we emphasize that the small signal conductance, α, and G_J bear no direct relationship to the recent experiments of references 9 and 14 on cylinders and loops with two attached leads. The two-terminal conductance that is relevant for these experiments is the subject of the next chapter.

AHARONOV-BOHM EFFECT

Consider now the loop shown in FIGURE 1c that is connected to two current leads. If the two reservoirs are at the same chemical potential and if the leads are weakly coupled to the loop, then this structure behaves the same way as the loop with a single lead.[2] (Because carriers in the loop now have two ports to escape from the loop, the broadening of the energy levels is enhanced compared to the loop connected to a single lead.) The interesting new features that can be studied in the geometry of FIGURE 1c arise if we consider transport through the loop. If the leads coupled to the loop are assumed to be perfect, we are back to the situation considered in FIGURE 2; however, instead of a barrier, the obstacle is now a loop penetrated by a flux. We can, therefore, ask what the resistance of this obstacle is, invoking equation 1. To do so, we have to determine the transmission probability for carriers incident in one lead to traverse the loop and exit through the other lead. Such a calculation for a one-dimensional loop was carried out by Gefen et al.[11] Because of the enclosed flux and because the waves are coherent through the loop despite elastic scattering (disorder), the transmission probability depends on the flux. Therefore, using equation 1, the resistance is a function of the flux, Φ. Reference 11 finds that $\mathcal{R}(\Phi)$ is periodic in the flux with a fundamental period, Φ_0.

Reference 11 investigated the case of strong coupling between the loop and the leads. It is, however, instructive to consider the limit of weak coupling.[12] Weak coupling means that carriers in the loop have only a small probability to escape into the leads. As indicated above, the density of states in the loop is then sharply peaked at or near the energies of the closed loop. This has the consequence that the transmission probability as a function of energy can be represented by a series of Breit-Wigner resonances,[12]

$$T(E, \Phi) = \sum_n T_{res,n} \frac{(\hbar/2\tau_n)^2}{[E - E_n(\Phi)]^2 + (\hbar/2\tau_n)^2}, \qquad (13)$$

where $E_n(\Phi)$ is the energy spectrum shown in FIGURE 3, and $T_{res,n}$ is the value of the transmission probability at resonance. To evaluate the resistance at zero temperature, we have to take the transmission probability at the Fermi energy, E_F. Then, only the bands immediately adjacent to the Fermi energy matter. Suppose the Fermi energy is between two bands, N and $N + 1$. If the energy difference between these two bands is minimal at $\Phi = 0$, the transmission probability, T, is maximal for $\Phi = 0$ and is minimal at $\Phi_0/2$. If the energy difference between the two levels is maximal at $\Phi = 0$, the transmission probability is minimal at $\Phi = 0$ and maximal at $\Phi_0/2$. If the Fermi energy intersects an energy level, then the transmission probability is maximal at the flux, $\pm \Phi_1$, for which $E_n(\Phi_1) = E_F$. In this case, the transmission probability reaches only a local minimum (or maximum) at $\Phi = 0$ and $\Phi_0/2$.

To compare the conductance of the loop of FIGURE 1c with our results for the loop connected to a single lead, we also consider the case where $kT > \hbar/\tau$. In this limit, we find

$$G \simeq \frac{e^2}{2\pi\hbar} \int dE \left(-\frac{df}{dE}\right) T(E, \Phi) \simeq \frac{e^2}{4} \sum_n \frac{1}{\tau_n} \left(-\frac{df}{dE}\right)\Bigg|_{E=E_n}. \qquad (14)$$

Note that the two-terminal conductance, G (equation 14), is inversely proportional to the lifetime of the electron states of the loop. In contrast, the conductance of the dc current accompanying the Josephsen current, G_J (equation 10), and the ac conductance, α (equation 11), are proportional to τ. The conductance of carriers through the loop, G, is smaller when the leads are coupled to the loop more weakly. On the other

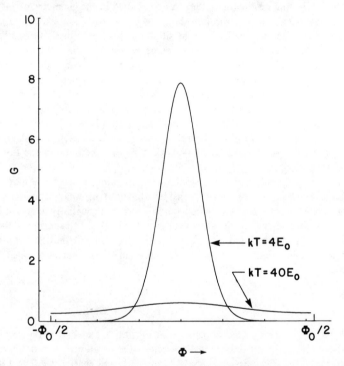

FIGURE 6. Two-terminal conductance of a normal metal loop (see FIGURE 1c) for two different temperatures, $kT = 4E_0$ and $kT = 40E_0$. Conductance is in units of $e^2\epsilon/\hbar$.

hand, the conductance associated with the motion of the carriers around the loop is *better* when the coupling of the loop to the leads is weaker. The conductance, G, (equation 14), is shown in FIGURE 6 for the same loop (spectrum) as was used in FIGURES 3–5. In the second expression of equation 6, we have also assumed that $T_{res,n}$ is independent of the flux and of order unity. For $kT > \hbar/\tau$, G is sensitive to the flux only through the dependence of the occupation probabilities on the energies, $E_n(\Phi)$. The conductance thus becomes insensitive to the flux if kT exceeds the width of the energy bands, $E_n(\Phi)$. The tight-binding spectrum that we have used here does not give rise to a transition from a conductance that is periodic with hc/e at low temperatures to a conductance that is periodic with period, $hc/2e$, at higher temperatures. Detailed studies of the temperature dependence of the two-terminal conductance are given in references 38 and 39.

Several papers[38-40] have treated ensemble averages of the two-terminal conductance and have shown that ensemble averaging leads to a conductance that is periodic with $hc/2e$. These results are relevant if we consider a one-dimensional array of loops in series. We assume that the phase breaking length is of the order of a circumference of a loop, but consecutive loops in the array are far enough apart so that there is no coherence between the loops. To find the total resistance of the array, we can then add the resistances of the single loops. (Strictly speaking, this is not correct because we also obtain a contribution to the total resistance due to the inelastic events that randomize the phase between consecutive loops.[32]) The resistance of a single loop is characterized by a transmission probability, $T(E_F, \Phi)$. As discussed above, the behavior of the transmission probability depends on the location of the Fermi energy with respect to the energy levels in the specific loop. The phase of the hc/e oscillations is either 0 or π. For some of the loops in the array, the Fermi energy, E_F, lies within a band, and $T(E_F, \Phi)$ reaches a maximum away from the symmetry points. In this case, the Fourier transform of $T(E_F, \Phi)$ has a substantial $hc/2e$ component. The phase of this $hc/2e$ oscillation is also not fixed, but, predominantly, it is such that the conductance is minimal for zero flux. Thus, if we add the single-loop resistances of an array consisting of N loops, we find the following results: Because each loop contributes an hc/e oscillation with a phase that is either zero or π, the amplitude of the resistance oscillations with period, hc/e, increases like $\sqrt{N}$. The flux-insensitive part of the resistance and the contribution to the resistance with period, $hc/2e$, increase proportional to N. Thus, the ratio of the hc/e amplitude and the total resistance decreases like $1/\sqrt{N}$ for a large number of loops. Therefore, in a large array of loops, the hc/e period is averaged to zero, and only a periodicity of $hc/2e$ and higher harmonics can be seen. The dependence on N of the Fourier amplitudes of the resistance oscillations of a series of loops has also recently been observed.[18]

The predictions of hc/e oscillations in references 11–13 and the prediction of $hc/2e$ oscillations in reference 8 are thus both correct, but they apply to distinct physical situations. Reference 8 employed a formalism that took an ensemble average at the outset.[38] In contrast, references 1 and 11–13 did not invoke ensemble averaging, but studied the properties of a specific sample. Whether a single sample effectively incorporates averaging[38,39] depends on the temperature and the size of the sample with respect to the inelastic scattering length.

In this paper, we have discussed persistent currents and Josephson-like currents in the metal structures of FIGURE 1. Persistent currents survive even a limited amount of inelastic events. In the presence of inelastic scattering, the time-dependent coherent phenomena are accompanied by resistive currents. We have distinguished three conductances (equations 10, 11, and 14) that are associated with current flow around the loop or through the loop. The experimental success with the Aharonov-Bohm effect in single loops raises the prospects that, in the future, other coherent phenomena in such small systems (such as the persistent currents and the low-frequency resistance phenomena discussed in the bulk of this paper) will be observed.

ACKNOWLEDGMENTS

Discussions with R. Landauer and Y. Imry have been important for this work. I thank R. Webb, S. Washburn, C. Umbach, C. van Haesendonck, and R. Laibowitz for many discussions of the experimental results, and for their interest in the work presented here.

REFERENCES

1. BÜTTIKER, M., Y. IMRY & R. LANDAUER. 1983. Josephson behavior in small normal one-dimensional rings. Phys. Lett. **96A:** 365.
2. BÜTTIKER, M. 1985. Quantum oscillations in normal metal loops. *In* SQUID '85. Proceedings of the Third International Conference on Superconducting Quantum Interference Devices, Berlin (West), June 23, 1985. H. D. Hahlbohm & H. Lübbig, Eds.: 529–560. de Gruyter. Berlin/New York.
3. KUBO, R. 1957. Statistical-mechanical theory of irreversible processes. J. Phys. Soc. Jpn. **12:** 570–586.
4. GREENWOOD, D. A. 1956. The Boltzmann equation in the theory of electrical conduction in metals. Proc. Phys. Soc. **71:** 585–596.
5. LANDAUER, R. 1957. Spatial variation of currents and fields due to localized scatters in metallic conduction. IBM J. Res. Dev. **1:** 223–231.
6. LANDAUER, R. & M. BÜTTIKER. 1985. Resistance of small metallic loops. Phys. Rev. Lett. **54:** 2049–2052.
7. BÜTTIKER, M. 1985. Small normal-metal loop coupled to an electron reservoir. Phys. Rev. **B32:** 1846–1849.
8. AL'TSHULER, B. L., A. G. ARONOV & B. Z. SPIVAK. 1981. The Aharonov-Bohm effect in disordered conductors. Sov. Phys. JETP Lett. **33:** 94–97.
9. SHARVIN, D. YU. & YU. V. SHARVIN. 1981. Magnetic-flux quantization in a cylindrical film of a normal metal. JETP Lett. **34:** 272–275.
10. DOLAN, G. J. & D. J. BISHOP. The nonlocal character of the conductance in the weakly localized limit. This volume; GIJS, M., C. VAN HAESENDONCK & Y. BRUYNSERAEDE. 1984. Resistance oscillations and electron localization in cylindrical Mg films. Phys. Rev. Lett. **52:** 2069–2072; PANNETIER, B., J. CHAUSSY, R. RAMMAL & P. GANDIT. 1984. Magnetic flux quantization in the weak-localization regime of a nonsuperconducting metal. Phys. Rev. Lett. **53:** 718–721; GORDON. J. M. 1984. Quantum phase sensitivity to macroscopic boundaries: Al cylinders and wires. Phys. Rev. **B30:** 6770–6773.
11. GEFEN, Y., Y. IMRY & M. YA. AZBEL. 1984. Quantum oscillations and the Aharonov-Bohm effect for parallel resistors. Phys. Rev. Lett. **52:** 129–132.
12. BÜTTIKER, M., Y. IMRY & M. YA. AZBEL. 1984. Quantum oscillations in one-dimensional normal-metal rings. Phys. Rev. **A30:** 1982–1989.
13. BÜTTIKER, M., Y. IMRY, R. LANDAUER & S. PINHAS. 1985. Generalized many-channel conductance formula with application to small rings. Phys. Rev. **B31:** 6207–6215; STONE, A. D. 1985. Magnetoresistance fluctuations in mesoscopic wires and rings. Phys. Rev. Lett. **54:** 2692.
14. WEBB, R. A., S. WASHBURN, C. UMBACH & R. A. LAIBOWITZ. 1985. Observation of h/e Aharonov-Bohm oscillations in normal metal rings. Phys. Rev. Lett. **54:** 2696–2699.
15. WASHBURN, S., C. P. UMBACH, R. B. LAIBOWITZ & R. A. WEBB. 1985. Temperature dependence of the normal-metal Aharonov-Bohm effect. Phys. Rev. **32:** 4789–4792.
16. CHANDRASEKHAR, V., M. J. ROOKS, S. WIND & D. E. PROBER. 1985. Observation of Aharonov-Bohm electron interference effects with periods h/e and $h/2e$ in individual micron-size, normal metal rings. Phys. Rev. Lett. **55:** 1610–1613.
17. DATTA, S., M. R. MELLOCH, S. BANDYOPADHYAY, R. NOREN, M. VAZIRI, M. MILLER & R. REIFENBERGER. 1985. Novel interference effects between parallel quantum wells. Phys. Rev. Lett. **55:** 2344–2347.
18. UMBACH, C. P., C. VAN HAESENDONCK, R. B. LAIBOWITZ, S. WASHBURN & R. A. WEBB.

1986. Direct observation of the self-averaging of the Aharonov-Bohm effect in normal metals. Phys. Rev. Lett. **56:** 386–389.

19. WEBB, R. A., S. WASHBURN, C. P. UMBACH & R. B. LAIBOWITZ. 1985. In search of magnetic flux quantization in normal metal rings. *In* SQUID '85. Proceedings of the Third International Conference on Superconducting Quantum Interference Devices. H. D. Hahlbohm & H. Lübbig, Eds.: 561–584. de Gruyter. Berlin.
20. LANDAUER, R. 1970. Electrical resistance of disordered one-dimensional lattices. Philos. Mag. **21:** 863–867.
21. ANDERSON, P. W., D. J. THOULESS, E. ABRAHAMS & D. S. FISHER. 1980. New method for a scaling theory of localization. Phys. Rev. **B22:** 3519–3526.
22. BARDEEN, J. & J. L. JOHNSON. 1972. Josephson current flow in pure superconducting–normal-superconducting junctions. Phys. Rev. **B5:** 72–78.
23. BÜTTIKER, M. & T. M. KLAPWIJK. 1986. Flux sensitivity of a piecewise normal and superconducting metal loop. Phys. Rev. **B33:** 5114–5117.
24. LANDAUER, R. 1978. Electrical conductivity in inhomogeneous media. *In* Electrical Transport and Optical Properties in Inhomogeneous Media. J. C. Garland & D. B. Tanner, Eds.: 2–45. AIP. New York.
25. BÜTTIKER, M. & Y. IMRY. 1985. Magnetic field asymmetry in the multichannel Landauer formula. J. Phys. **C18:** L467–472; SIVAN, U. & Y. IMRY. 1986. Multichannel Landauer formula for thermoelectric transport with application to thermopower near the mobility edge. Phys. Rev. **33:** 551–558.
26. UMBACH, C. P., S. WASHBURN, R. B. LAIBOWITZ & R. A. WEBB. 1984. Magnetoresistance of small, quasi-one-dimensional, normal-metal rings and lines. Phys. Rev. **B30:** 4048–4051.
27. BLOCH, F. 1968. Simple interpretation of the Josephson effect. Phys. Rev. Lett. **21:** 1241–1243.
28. LANDAUER, R. 1986. Zener tunneling and dissipation in small metal loops. Phys. Rev. **B33:** 6497–6499.
29. BÜTTIKER, M. Onset of resistance in small normal metal loops. Preprint.
30. BÜTTIKER, M., E. P. HARRIS & R. LANDAUER. 1983. Thermal activation in extremely underdamped Josephson-junction circuits. Phys. Rev. **B28:** 1268–1275.
31. THOULESS, D. J. & S. KIRKPATRICK. 1981. Conductivity of the disordered linear chain. J. Phys. **C14:** 235–244.
32. BÜTTIKER, M. 1986. Role of quantum coherence in series resistors. Phys. Rev. **B33:** 3020–3026.
33. ESAKI, L. & R. TSU. 1970. Superlattice and negative differential conductivity in semiconductors. IBM J. Res. Dev. **14:** 61–65.
34. BÜTTIKER, M. & H. THOMAS. 1979. Bifurcation and stability of dynamical structures at a current instability. Z. Phys. **B34:** 301–311.
35. LENSTRA, D. & W. VAN HAERINGEN. 1985. On the theory of conductance in a one-dimensional statically disordered system. Physica **128B:** 26–38.
36. IMRY, Y. & N. S. SHIREN. 1986. Energy averaging and the flux-periodic phenomena in small normal metal rings. Phys. Rev. **B33:** 7992–7997.
37. CZYCHOLL, G. & B. KRAMER. 1979. Nonvanishing zero temperature static conductivity in one-dimensional disordered systems. Solid State Commun. **32:** 945–951.
38. MURAT, M., Y. GEFEN & Y. IMRY. 1986. Ensemble and temperature averaging of quantum oscillations in normal metal rings. Phys. Rev. **B34:** 659–668.
39. STONE, A. D. & Y. IMRY. 1986. Ensemble and temperature averaging of quantum oscillations in normal metal rings. Phys. Rev. Lett. **56:** 189–192.
40. LI, Q. & C. M. SOUKOULIS. 1986. Quantum oscillations in one-dimensional metal rings: average over disorder. Phys. Rev. **B33:** 7318–7321.

Magnetic Monopoles and Dipoles in Quantum Mechanics[a]

HARRY J. LIPKIN[b] AND MURRAY PESHKIN[c,d]

Argonne National Laboratory
Argonne, Illinois 60439-4843
and
Weizmann Institute of Science
Rehovot, Israel

Magnetic monopole charges present a peculiar challenge to quantum mechanical theories. Even the simplest problem of one moving electric charge interacting with one externally fixed magnetic charge has the feature that the angular momentum in the crossed electric and magnetic fields is independent of the distance between the two charges. That makes both for singular behavior at zero distance and for a kind of lack of separability at infinite distance. Formally, the trouble shows up as the nonexistence of a vector potential to describe the Lorentz force. This is no obstacle to classical mechanics because the equations of motion can be obtained from Newton's laws, but with no vector potential, there is no Lagrangian or Hamiltonian, and the usual ways of quantizing the theory do not work.

Dirac[1] first addressed the quantum theoretical problem in 1931. He showed that for quantized values of the electric and magnetic charges e and g which obey

$$eg/c = n\hbar/2, \tag{1}$$

n being an integer, he could introduce a singular vector potential that served as the basis for a quantum mechanical theory with particles that can be interpreted as magnetic monopoles. Since Dirac's original work, there have been many developments of the theory, and some formulations have removed or substantially hidden the singular strings.[2,3] However, the main physical obstacles have remained, and we still have no satisfactory theory of particles interacting with fields and no practical ability to deal with several electrons interacting with several monopoles. In terms of its impact upon experiment, the theory can really make only two claims. Equation 1 tells us what value of g to seek, and the singularity at the origin results in spin flips at high energy, which may imply baryon number changes under the assumptions of grand unified theories.[4]

In this paper, we first consider the force on and the energy of a "di-monopole," the limiting case of a dipole made from two monopoles at zero separation and finite magnetic moment, interacting with an externally fixed magnetic field whose source is

[a]This work was supported in part by the U.S. Department of Energy, Nuclear Physics Division, under Contract No. W-31-109-ENG-38, and in part by the Minerva Foundation, Munich, Germany.
[b]H. J. Lipkin's permanent address is the Weizmann Institute of Science, Rehovot, Israel.
[c]M. Peshkin's permanent address is the Argonne National Laboratory, Argonne, Illinois 60439-4843.
[d]This paper was presented at the conference by M. Peshkin.

an electric current. Our original motivation was to see how the experimental signature of a di-monopole differs in quantum theory from the signature of an ordinary magnetic dipole whose magnetic moment arises from a circulating electric current or from some form factor that behaves like a circulating current.[5] In fact, we found that we do not know how to deal with di-monopoles near electric currents in quantum mechanics, and that the obstacle is again the lack of an appropriate classical Hamiltonian from which to begin. We also found that when the same ideas were applied to the problem of a single monopole coexisting with an external electric current, they led to interesting contradictions. These contradictions illuminate the nonexistence of the Hamiltonian for the monopole without a flux string in a novel way that is physically different from and in some respects more general than the impossibility of defining a vector potential. This is illustrated by a simple "toy model" for the nonrelativistic motion of a monopole around an electric current.

In the simplest example of the Dirac procedure, a spinless monopole charge g is fixed at the origin, and we wish to describe the nonrelativistic motion of a spinless electron nearby. Classically, the equation of motion is determined by the Lorentz force:

$$m\dot{\mathbf{v}} = (e/c)\,\mathbf{v} \times \mathbf{B} = (eg/c)\,\mathbf{v} \times \mathbf{r}/r^3. \tag{2}$$

To do quantum mechanics, we want a Hamiltonian,

$$H = \left(\frac{1}{2m}\right)[\mathbf{p} - (e/c)\mathbf{A}]^2, \tag{3}$$

but there is no vector potential $\mathbf{A}$ whose curl equals the monopole field $\mathbf{B}$, even if the origin where $\nabla \cdot \mathbf{B} \neq 0$ is excluded[3] from the region where we require $\mathbf{B} = \nabla \times \mathbf{A}$. Dirac solved that problem for quantized values of the charges by introducing his now famous singular vector potential,

$$A_\phi = g(1 - \cos \theta)/r \sin \theta; \qquad A_r = A_\theta = 0. \tag{4}$$

Dirac's vector potential does not really represent a pure monopole field. Its curl contains a delta function singularity along the negative z-axis that physically represents a string of magnetic flux $\Phi = 4\pi g$, running from minus infinity to the origin. Dirac's monopole can be regarded as the end of a current-carrying solenoid that is semi-infinite in length and infinitesimal in diameter. However, for quantized values of eg/c, Dirac showed that the flux string or solenoid has no physical reality in the sense that it can be moved from the negative z-axis to any other line connecting infinity with the origin by a gauge transformation.

Dirac's trick does not apply to the di-monopole, even if we are prepared to go the limiting case through quantized values of g. A vector potential can be had by connecting the monopole-antimonopole pair with a flux string or solenoid, but then what we actually have is an ordinary dipole whose source is circulating currents.

However, the difficulty is more general than that. Imagine a di-monopole placed at the origin in a stationary external magnetic field $\mathbf{B}$, and oriented as shown in FIGURE 1. The x-component of force on the di-monopole is given by

$$F_x = \lim\{g[\mathbf{B}_x(0, y, 0) - \mathbf{B}_x(0, -y, 0)]\} = \mu\partial\mathbf{B}_x/\partial y, \tag{5}$$

where the limit means $y \rightarrow 0$, $g \rightarrow \infty$ with finite $2gy = \mu$. Alternatively, we could try to get the force from a Hamiltonian by introducing the potential energy suggested by classical mechanics,

$$V = -\mu B_y. \tag{6}$$

Then the force would be given by

$$F_x = -\partial V/\partial x = \mu \partial B_y/\partial x. \tag{7}$$

Equation 7 for the force F_x is not the same as the correct expression in equation 5 unless $(\nabla \times \mathbf{B})_z = 0$. Thus, a Hamiltonian based on this V will be inconsistent with the correct equation of motion unless the current density vanishes at the origin.

This paradox results from an ambiguity in the definition of the energy of a di-monopole in the magnetic field generated by an electric current. The potential energy of a monopole in a magnetic field cannot be defined uniquely in a region where

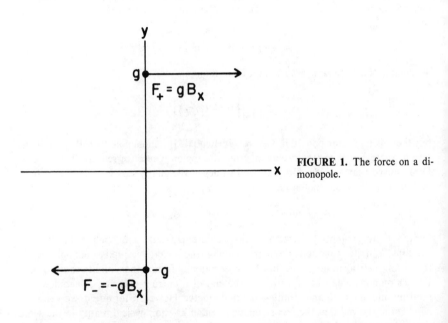

FIGURE 1. The force on a di-monopole.

electric currents are present, and the energy needed to move a monopole-antimonopole pair from one point to another depends upon the path chosen for the motion. That path dependence does not vanish in the limiting case of a di-monopole. Suppose a monopole-antimonopole pair are moved from $-x$ to $+x$. If they move along the paths shown in FIGURE 2a, the work done agrees with equation 5, but if they move along the paths shown in FIGURE 2b, the work done agrees with equation 7. The difference between the two results is just the work done in carrying one monopole around the loop defined by the four corners, as shown in FIGURE 3. If the current density j_z at the loop is finite, this energy difference remains finite in the di-monopole limit.

The paradox can be illuminated in one way by examining the energy in the magnetic fields. The total magnetic field is the sum of an external magnetic field, $\mathbf{B}_{ext}$,

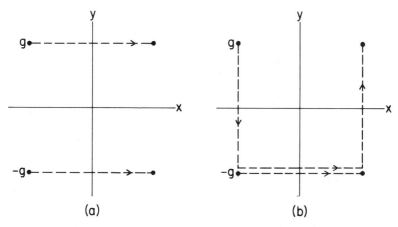

FIGURE 2. Virtual displacement of a di-monopole by two different paths to the same final configuration.

and the dipole field, $\mathbf{B}_{dip}$. The interaction energy between the two fields is given by the integral of the cross-term in the energy density, $(\mathbf{B}_{ext} \cdot \mathbf{B}_{dip})/4\pi$. First, suppose the dipole field is an ordinary one due to a current loop. If the external field is produced by currents, this can be integrated by parts to obtain the familiar $\mathbf{j}_{dip} \cdot \mathbf{A}_{ext}$ interaction. However, if the external field is produced by magnetic charges, then $\mathbf{B}_{ext}$ is irrotational and the interaction energy vanishes.

Next, suppose the dipole field is due to a static di-monopole. Then a magnetostatic potential M can be defined so that $\mathbf{B}_{dip} = -\nabla M$. Now if all fields vanish sufficiently rapidly at infinity, the interaction energy can be integrated by parts to give an energy

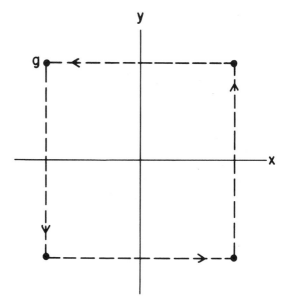

FIGURE 3. Circuit of a monopole that is equivalent to the difference between the virtual displacements of FIGURES 2a and 2b.

density proportional to $M \nabla \cdot \mathbf{B}_{\text{ext}}$. If $\mathbf{B}_{\text{ext}}$ is produced by magnetic charges, this is just the magnetostatic energy of the di-monopole in the field of all the other magnetic charges. However, this magnetic interaction energy vanishes when the external field is produced by electric currents instead of by magnetic charges. This is another manifestation of the impossibility of defining a Hamiltonian for a di-monopole interacting with electric currents in a consistent way.

A simple model involving only a monopole rather than a di-monopole illustrates all the physical principles involved when magnetic sources move in a solenoidal magnetic field whose source is an electric current. Here, we can easily see how the troubles of the Hamiltonian theory arise from simple physical considerations that do not involve formalistic problems such as the existence or nonexistence of a vector potential. Consider a magnetic charge that moves freely on a circle of radius r in the xy plane. A long resistanceless wire along the z-axis connects two capacitor plates far from the circle where the monopole moves. The dynamical variables are the charge q on the capacitor, the angle coordinate θ of the monopole on its circle, and their time derivatives. The current $\dot{q}$ in the wire is the source of a magnetic field in the θ direction,

$$B_\theta(t) = 2\dot{q}(t)/rc, \tag{8}$$

and the moving magnetic charge is in turn the source of an electric force on the current. These interactions are described by the Lagrangian

$$\mathcal{L} = (\tfrac{1}{2})I\dot{\theta}^2 + (\tfrac{1}{2})L\dot{q}^2 - \left(\frac{1}{2C}\right)q^2 - (2g/c)q\dot{\theta}, \tag{9}$$

where $\mathcal{L}$ is the self-inductance of the wire, C is the capacitance of the two plates, and $I = mr^2$. The corresponding Hamiltonian,

$$H = \left(\frac{1}{2L}\right)\mathrm{p}_q^2 + \frac{1}{2}L\omega^2 q^2 + \frac{1}{2I}\mathrm{p}_\theta^2 + \frac{4g}{Ic}q\mathrm{p}_\theta, \tag{10}$$

equals the conserved total energy,

$$E = \frac{1}{2}L\dot{q}^2 + \frac{1}{2C}q^2 + \frac{1}{2}I\dot{\theta}^2. \tag{11}$$

The solutions of the equations of motion are

$$q(t) = q_0 + \frac{i_0}{\omega}\sin\omega(t - t_0) \tag{12}$$

and

$$\dot{\theta}(t) = -\frac{c}{2gC}q_0 + \frac{2g}{\omega Ic}i_0\sin\omega(t - t_0), \tag{13}$$

where

$$\omega^2 = \frac{1}{L}\left(\frac{1}{C} + \frac{4g^2}{Ic^2}\right), \tag{14}$$

and q_0 and i_0 are constants. In general, energy flows between the magnetic charge and the electrical system with frequency ω.

We can use these results to treat the motion of a monopole in an externally fixed magnetic field produced by a stationary current. That case is represented in our model by the limit $L \rightarrow \infty$, $\omega \rightarrow 0$, while $L\omega^2$ remains finite as do q_0 and i_0. C may be finite or infinite. For any finite time t, the current and magnetic field approach the constant values

$$\lim \{\dot{q}(t)\} = i_0 \, ,$$

$$\lim \{B_\theta(t)\} = 2i_0 \, /rc, \tag{15}$$

but the energy of the electrical system,

$$E_q = \frac{1}{2} L\dot{q}^2 + \frac{1}{2C} q^2, \tag{16}$$

approaches

$$\lim \{E_q\} = \frac{1}{2} Li_0^2 + \frac{1}{2} (L\omega^2) q_0^2 + (L\omega^2) q_0 i_0 (t - t_0) \tag{17}$$

for finite values of $(t - t_0)$.

The first term on the right-hand side of equation 17 is an infinite constant amount of energy. The last term represents a finite amount of energy that is exchanged between the magnetic charge and the fixed external magnetic field in which the magnetic charge moves. This term compensates the kinetic energy of the magnetic charge to conserve the total energy of the interacting system.

Because of the last term in equation 17, it is impossible to obtain a Hamiltonian function of θ and p_θ by subtracting equation 17 from the full Hamiltonian in the external field limit. When the variables of the electrical system are included in the dynamical description, the Hamiltonian theory works correctly. However, the Hamiltonian does not separate into an electrical part and a magnetic-charge part, even in the limit where the inertia of the electrical system becomes infinite and the magnetic field becomes fixed. This is so because the energy of the electrical system is then infinite and a finite amount of energy passes between the magnetic charge and the current as the magnetic charge moves.

All these results for the external field cases are physically correct. However, they cannot be expressed in terms of a Hamiltonian with the interactions of the monopole described by a local interaction involving only the dynamical variables of the monopole and the electromagnetic fields or potentials at the position of the monopole. Newton's laws using only the field and monopole variables describe the motion correctly, but there is no Hamiltonian description without including the interaction with the current source, and that interaction must be nonlocal. Therefore, the ordinary ways of doing quantum mechanics do not work. The interaction terms in the Lagrangian (equation 9) and the Hamiltonian (equation 10) between the monopole and the electrical system involve the product of the monopole velocity or canonical momentum and the charge q. The charge q is a variable that is far away from the monopole, and the interaction is manifestly nonlocal. Because the magnetic field at the position of the monopole is proportional to the current and therefore to the variable $\dot{q}$, the variable q can be expressed as a time integral of the magnetic field or vector potential at the position of the monopole. This gives an interaction that is local in space but nonlocal in time, and is equally unsatisfactory.

One could perhaps evade the paradox by attaching a flux string to the monopole so that the string winds around the current and $\theta = 0$ is not physically the same as $\theta = 2\pi$. That is what happens if the Lagrangian, $\mathcal{L}$, of equation 9 is replaced by

$$\mathcal{L}' = \mathcal{L} + \frac{d}{dt}(q\theta) = \frac{1}{2} I\dot{\theta}^2 + \frac{1}{2} L\dot{q}^2 - \frac{1}{2C} q^2 + \frac{2q}{c} \dot{q}\theta. \tag{18}$$

The equations of motion are unchanged and the interaction term now has the form of the product of the monopole coordinate θ and the current variable that is proportional to the field at the position of the monopole. However, the variable θ is not a legitimate operator because it is not single valued. It carries additional information beyond the actual position of the monopole; namely, a kind of winding number describing the number of times the monopole has moved around the current. That represents the motion of a monopole carrying a string, with the string winding and unwinding around the current as the monopole moves back and forth.

The above example suggests that the introduction of a singular string may not be harmless even when the Dirac quantization condition is obeyed.

REFERENCES

1. DIRAC, P. A. M. 1931. Proc. R. Soc. London **A133**: 60.
2. LIPKIN, H. J., W. I. WEISBERGER & M. PESHKIN. 1969. Ann. Phys. **53**: 203.
3. WU, T. T. & C. N. YANG. 1975. Phys. Rev. **D12**: 3845; 1976. Nucl. Phys. **B107**: 365.
4. CALLAN, G. C., JR. 1982. *In* Magnetic Monopoles. R. A. Carrigan, Jr. & W. P. Trower, Eds.: 92. Plenum. New York/London; and references therein.
5. JACKSON, J. D. 1977. The nature of intrinsic dipole moments. CERN report no. 77-17, theory division; BLOCH, F. 1936. Phys. Rev. **50**: 259; SCHWINGER, J. 1937. Phys. Rev. **51**: 544.

A Possible Test of the Topological Effect in Quantum Mechanics

AKIRA INOMATA

Department of Physics
State University of New York at Albany
Albany, New York 12222

INTRODUCTION

The topological nature of the Aharonov-Bohm effect has long been recognized.[1,2] The presence of an infinitely long solenoid containing magnetic flux makes the physical arena of a charged particle multiply connected. When the particle encircles the solenoid once, its wave function will acquire a phase factor of exp $[iq\Phi/\hbar c]$, where q is the charge carried by the particle and Φ is the flux confined in the solenoid. The interference due to the flux-dependent phase difference has been unambiguously demonstrated by experiment.[3]

In earlier papers,[4] we have formulated the Aharonov-Bohm effect by means of path integration and have pointed out that the interference term contains not only the flux-dependent effect, but also a nontrivial effect that depends on how many times the particle has moved around the solenoid. Subsequently, Deaver and Donaldson[5] have made measurements on a superconducting ring that twice encircles a long solenoid and have shown that the flux confined in the solenoid is quantized with $\Delta\Phi = \Phi_0/2$, where Φ_0 is the fundamental fluxoid, hc/q ($q = 2e$ for a superconducting ring). Then, anticipating that an N-turn ring would show flux states with $\Delta\Phi = \Phi_0/N$, they have claimed that this demonstrates the winding-number dependence of the Aharonov-Bohm effect that we have proposed. However, the number of turns of the ring is not quite the same as the topological winding number. In a superconducting ring, the states of all winding numbers are contributing to flux quantization, and the number of turns of the ring can be treated as the winding number only when the contributions from the higher winding numbers are suppressed by some means.[6] Other possible bound-state experiments have also been considered for detecting the winding-number dependence.[7]

In this paper, we propose a quantum interference experiment to detect the winding-number dependence associated with the Aharonov-Bohm effect. The setup for this experiment is similar to that proposed by Silverman for the determination of angular momentum of the charged particle-solenoid system.[8] In the next section of this paper, we briefly describe how the propagator for such a system can be derived by path integration. Then, in the third section, we discuss the complementary relation between the angular momentum and the winding number. Finally, the last section is devoted to explaining the proposed interference experiment.

PATH INTEGRAL FORMULATION OF THE AHARONOV-BOHM EFFECT

The idealized setup for the measurement of the Aharonov-Bohm effect consists of the particle source, the detector, and an impenetrable solenoid with confined magnetic flux. In a two-dimensional formulation, the circular cross section of the solenoid cuts out the impenetrable region from the background space. In doing so, the physical arena for a charged particle becomes multiply connected. The magnetic field, $\mathbf{B}$, is zero outside the solenoid, but the vector potential is given by

$$\mathbf{A} = (\Phi/2\pi)\nabla\theta. \tag{2.1}$$

The Lagrangian for a particle of mass, M, and charge, q, moving outside the solenoid is[9]

$$L(\mathbf{r}, \dot{\mathbf{r}}) = \tfrac{1}{2}M\dot{\mathbf{r}}^2 - (q\Phi/2\pi c)\dot{\theta}, \tag{2.2}$$

which does not accommodate any information of the multiply connectedness of the background space. An appropriate tool of describing a particle in a multiply connected space is Feynman's path integral.[9] According to Feynman's prescription, the propagator is given as a sum over all possible paths,

$$K(\mathbf{r}'', \mathbf{r}'; \tau) = \lim_{N\to\infty} \int \prod_{j=1}^{N} \exp\left[\frac{i}{\hbar}(S_j + S_j^c)\right] \prod_{j=1}^{N}\left[\frac{M}{2\pi i\hbar\epsilon}\right] \prod_{j=1}^{N-1} d\mathbf{r}_j, \tag{2.3}$$

where $\mathbf{r}_j = \mathbf{r}(t_j)$, $\mathbf{r}' = \mathbf{r}_0$, $\mathbf{r}'' = \mathbf{r}_N$, and $\epsilon = t_j - t_{j-1} = \tau/N$. The short time actions in equation 2.3 are expressed in polar coordinates as

$$S_j = \tfrac{1}{2}M(\mathbf{r}_j^2 + \mathbf{r}_{j-1}^2)/\epsilon - M(\mathbf{r}_j\mathbf{r}_{j-1}/\epsilon)\cos(\Delta\theta_j) + \xi\hbar\Delta\theta_j \tag{2.4}$$

and

$$S_j^c = (\hbar/i)\ln\Theta(\mathbf{r}_j - R), \tag{2.5}$$

where $\xi = q\Phi/(2\pi\hbar c) = \Phi/\Phi_0$ and

$$\Theta(r - R) = \begin{cases} 1 & \text{for } r > R, \\ 0 & \text{for } r \leq R, \end{cases}$$

with R being the radius of the solenoid. The second action (equation 2.5) represents the constraint that the solenoid is impenetrable. We now rewrite equation 2.4 within a valid approximation for path integration as[4]

$$S_j = \frac{M}{2\epsilon}(\mathbf{r}_j^2 + \mathbf{r}_{j-1}^2) - \frac{M}{\epsilon}\mathbf{r}_j\mathbf{r}_{j-1}\cos\left[\Delta\theta_j + \frac{\xi\hbar\epsilon}{M\mathbf{r}_j\,\mathbf{r}_{j-1}}\right] - \frac{\xi^2\hbar^2}{2M\mathbf{r}_j\mathbf{r}_{j-1}}. \tag{2.6}$$

Using the asymptotic relation,

$$\exp\left[z\cos\left(\theta + \frac{i\lambda}{z}\right) - \frac{\lambda^2}{2z}\right] \sim \sum_{m=-\infty}^{\infty} e^{im\theta} I_{m+\lambda}(z), \tag{2.7}$$

we find

$$\exp\left[\frac{i}{\hbar}\sum_{j=1}^{N}S_j\right]$$

$$= \prod_{j=1}^{N}\left\{\sum_{m_j=-\infty}^{\infty}[\exp(im_j\Delta\theta_j)I_{|m_j-\xi|}(Mr_jr_{j-1}/i\hbar\epsilon)]\exp[iM(r_j^2+r_{j-1}^2)/2\hbar\epsilon]\right\}. \quad (2.8)$$

Completing the angular integration of equation 2.3 by using equation 2.8, we obtain

$$K(\mathbf{r}'',\mathbf{r}';\tau) = \sum_{m=-\infty}^{\infty}\exp[im(\theta''-\theta')]Q_{m-\xi}(\mathbf{r}'',\mathbf{r}';\tau), \quad (2.9)$$

where

$$Q_\lambda(\mathbf{r}'',\mathbf{r}';\tau) = \lim_{N\to\infty}(2\pi)^{N-1}\int\prod_{j=1}^{N}\{\exp[iM(r_j^2+r_{j-1}^2)/2\hbar\epsilon]$$

$$\times I_\lambda(Mr_j\,r_{j-1}/i\hbar\epsilon)\Theta(r_j-R)\}\prod_{j=1}^{N}[M/2\pi i\hbar\epsilon]\prod_{j=1}^{N-1}(r_j dr_j). \quad (2.10)$$

In this way, the radial and angular variables are separated. As is obvious, the summation parameter, m, corresponds to the angular quantum number. The constraint is included in the radial part. To extract information of the multiply connected background, we define the following integral:

$$K_\varphi(\mathbf{r}'',\mathbf{r}';\tau) = \frac{1}{2\pi}\int_{-\infty}^{\infty}\sum_{m=-\infty}^{\infty}\exp[im(\theta''-\theta')+i\lambda\varphi]Q_{m+\lambda-\xi}d\lambda. \quad (2.11)$$

It is easy to show that

$$K(\mathbf{r}'',\mathbf{r}';\tau) = \int K_\varphi(\mathbf{r}'',\mathbf{r}';\tau)d\varphi. \quad (2.12)$$

If we change the integration variable in equation 2.12 from λ to $\lambda-m+\xi$, then

$$K_\varphi = \frac{1}{2\pi}\int_{-\infty}^{\infty}\exp[im(\theta''-\theta'-\varphi)+i(\lambda+\xi)\varphi]Q_\lambda d\lambda. \quad (2.13)$$

Furthermore, we use Poisson's sum formula,

$$\sum_{m=-\infty}^{\infty}\exp(im\theta) = 2\pi\sum_{n=-\infty}^{\infty}\delta(\theta+2\pi n),$$

to express equation 2.13 in the form,

$$K_\varphi = \sum_{n=-\infty}^{\infty}\delta(\theta''-\theta'-\varphi+2\pi n)e^{i\xi\varphi}\int_{-\infty}^{\infty}e^{i\lambda\varphi}Q_\lambda(\mathbf{r}'',\mathbf{r}';\tau)d\lambda. \quad (2.14)$$

Substitution of equation 2.14 into equation 2.12 yields

$$K(\mathbf{r}'',\mathbf{r}';\tau) = \sum_{n=-\infty}^{\infty}K_n(\mathbf{r}'',\theta'';\mathbf{r}',\theta';\tau), \quad (2.15)$$

where

$$K_n(r'', \theta''; r', \theta'; \tau) = \exp\left[i\xi(\theta'' - \theta' + 2\pi n)\right]$$

$$\times \int_{-\infty}^{\infty} \exp\left[i\lambda(\theta'' - \theta' + 2\pi n)\right] Q_\lambda(r'', r'; \tau)\,d\lambda. \quad (2.16)$$

The n-th propagator (equation 2.16) represents the contribution from the class of paths encircling the solenoid n times. In the limit of $R \to 0$, that is, when the solenoid is considered extremely thin, the radial integration of equation 2.10 can be carried out, with the result being[4]

$$Q_\lambda(r'', r'; \tau) = \frac{M}{2\pi i\hbar\tau} \exp\left[i(r'^2 + r''^2)M/2\hbar\tau\right] I_{|\lambda|}(r'r''M/i\hbar\tau). \quad (2.17)$$

Substituting equation 2.17 into equation 2.16, we obtain

$$K_n = (M/2\pi i\hbar\tau) \exp\left[i(r'' - r')^2 M/2\hbar\tau\right]$$

$$\times \exp\left[i\xi(\theta'' - \theta' + 2\pi n) + \tfrac{1}{2}ia(\theta'' - \theta' + 2\pi n)^2\right], \quad (2.18)$$

where $a = r'r''M/(\hbar\tau)$. The superposition of K_n and $K_{n'}$ leads to the interference,

$$|K_n + K_{n'}|^2 = |K_n|^2 + |K_{n'}|^2 + 2\mathrm{Re}(K_n^* K_{n'})$$

$$= (M/2\pi\hbar\tau)^2 \cos^2\left[\pi(n - n')\{\xi + a\bar{\theta} + a\pi(n + n' + 1)\}\right], \quad (2.19)$$

where $\theta'' - \theta' = \bar{\theta} + \pi$. The interference depends not only on the relative position of the detector and the solenoid, but also on the winding numbers. However, the topological shift will disappear if $n + n' + 1 = 0$. For the two-slit interference experiment, $n = 0$ and $n' = -1$, so there is no observable topological shift. For the winding numbers, see FIGURE 1.

COMPLEMENTARITY BETWEEN THE ANGULAR MOMENTUM AND THE WINDING NUMBER

As we have seen in the preceding section, the propagator for a charged particle moving outside the solenoid can be given in two different forms: namely,

$$K(r'', r'; \tau) = \sum_{m=-\infty}^{\infty} \tilde{K}_m(\vec{r}'', \vec{r}'; \tau) \quad (3.1)$$

with

$$\tilde{K}_m(r'', r'; \tau) = e^{im(\theta'' - \theta')} Q_{m-\xi}(r'', r'; \tau), \quad (3.2)$$

and

$$K(r'', r'; \tau) = \sum_{n=-\infty}^{\infty} K_n(r'', r'; \tau) \quad (3.3)$$

with

$$K_n(r'', r'; \tau) = e^{i\xi(\theta'' - \theta' + 2\pi n)} \int_{-\infty}^{\infty} \exp\left[i\lambda(\theta'' - \theta' + 2\pi n)\right] Q_\lambda(r'', r'; \tau)\,d\lambda. \quad (3.4)$$

Obviously, $\tilde{K}_m$ and K_n satisfy the following relations:

$$-i\frac{\partial}{\partial\theta}\tilde{K}_m(r,\theta;r',\theta';\tau) = m\tilde{K}_m(r,\theta;r',\theta';\tau) \tag{3.5}$$

and

$$i\frac{\partial}{\partial\eta}K_n(r'',\theta;r',\theta;\tau) = n K_n(r'',\theta;r',\theta;\tau), \tag{3.6}$$

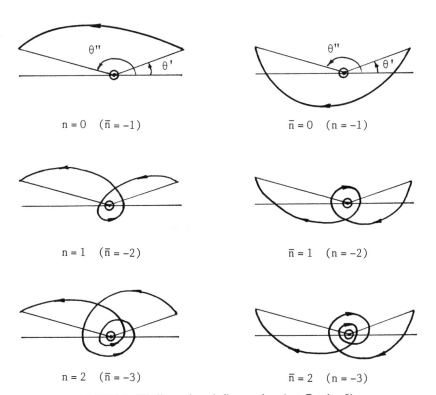

$n = 0$ $(\bar{n} = -1)$ $\bar{n} = 0$ $(n = -1)$

$n = 1$ $(\bar{n} = -2)$ $\bar{n} = 1$ $(n = -2)$

$n = 2$ $(\bar{n} = -3)$ $\bar{n} = 2$ $(n = -3)$

FIGURE 1. Winding and unwinding numbers $(n + \bar{n} + 1 = 0)$.

where $\eta = -2\pi\xi = -q\Phi/(hc)$. As $-i\partial/\partial\theta$ is the coordinate realization of the angular momentum operator, $\hat{L}_\theta$, $i\partial/\partial\eta$ may be regarded as a realization of an operator, say $\hat{W}_\eta$, whose discrete eigenvalues are the winding numbers. Because the two expressions (equations 3.1 and 3.3) are related by Poisson's formula, the two set of integers, m and n, cannot coexist. In other words, $\hat{L}_\theta$ and $\hat{W}_\eta$ cannot simultaneously be diagonalized. They are complementary to each other. In fact, ξ is part of the kinetic angular momentum, $\hat{K}_\varphi = \hat{L}_\theta - \hbar\xi$, whereas the winding number is the discrete part of the angular variable, $\varphi = \theta + 2\pi n$. The complementary nature of n and m is a reflection of the complementary relation between $\hat{\theta}$ and $\hat{L}_\theta$.

INTERFERENCE EXPERIMENT FOR THE
WINDING-NUMBER DEPENDENCE

Next, we consider a possible test for the winding-number effect. Because the angular quantum number, m, and the winding number, n, cannot be measured at the same time, it is necessary to choose a setup for which the information of angular momentum is unimportant. What we have pointed out as the topological shift is the winding-number dependence of the interference in the Aharonov-Bohm experiment. However, it is technically difficult to separate two homotopically inequivalent classes

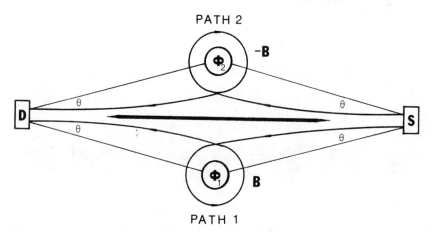

FIGURE 2. Double solenoid interference experiment.

of paths around a single solenoid. Therefore, we borrow the idea of the double solenoid interference setup proposed by Silverman for other purposes.[8]

The setup is schematically shown in FIGURE 2. A collimated beam of charged particles from the source, S, splits into two coherent beams. Each beam enters into a time-independent magnetic field and encircles a solenoid placed in the middle of the B-field. For each beam, we apply the result obtained in equation 2.18. For path 1, if the beam encircles n times about the solenoid, the propagator is given by

$$K_n = (M/2\pi i\hbar\tau) \exp\left[i\xi_1(\pi - 2\theta + 2\pi n) + \tfrac{1}{2}ia(\pi - 2\theta + 2\pi n)^2\right]. \quad (4.1)$$

For path 2, after $\bar{n}$ revolutions clockwise,

$$K_n = (M/2\pi i\hbar\tau) \exp\left[i\xi_2(\pi + 2\theta - 2\pi n - 2\pi)\right.$$

$$\left. + \tfrac{1}{2}ia(\pi + 2\theta - 2\pi n - 2\pi)^2\right]. \quad (4.2)$$

Upon recombination of the two beams, the forward beam intensity at D will be

$$I = |K_n + K_{\bar{n}}|^2 = I_0 \cos^2 [\xi_1(n + \tfrac{1}{2}) + \xi_2(\bar{n} + \tfrac{1}{2}) - \theta(\xi_1 + \xi_2)$$
$$+ 2\pi a \theta(\bar{n} - n) + a\pi^2(n + \bar{n} + 1)(n - \bar{n})], \quad (4.3)$$

where $\xi_1 = \Phi_1/\Phi_0$ and $\xi_2 = \Phi_2/\Phi_0$. For the winding and unwinding numbers, see FIGURE 1. The interference (equation 4.3) now depends on the winding numbers of the two beams as well as the flux generated in the two solenoids. From the observation of a periodic variation of the interference, we would be able to detect the winding-number effect.

For instance, we set $\xi_2 = 0$. Furthermore, let us make θ very small. Then, we have

$$I = I_0 \cos^2 [\xi_1(n + \tfrac{1}{2}) + a\pi^2(n + \bar{n} + 1)(n - \bar{n})]. \quad (4.4)$$

If $n = \bar{n}$, then only the flux-dependent term of equation 4.4 contributes to the interference, and a destructive interference should occur when ξ_1 becomes an odd integer. However, the destructive interference will be disrupted as soon as the value of n is changed. Let $\mathbf{B} = 0$. Then, $n = \bar{n} = 0$. If $\mathbf{B} \neq 0$ so that $n \neq 0$, then n becomes different from $\bar{n}$. Because $\xi_2 = 0$, there is no winding about ξ_2 and hence $\bar{n} = 0$ regardless of whether the B-field vanishes or not. Consequently, the second term of equation 4.4 starts to contribute to the interference. Thus, by switching on $\mathbf{B}$, we can change the winding number, n, from zero to a nonzero integer. Therefore, any change in interference will indicate the winding-number dependence of the Aharonov-Bohm interference.

REFERENCES

1. BOHM, D. & B. J. HILEY. 1978. Nuovo Cimento **52A**: 295.
2. GREENBERGER, D. M. 1981. Phys. Rev. **D23**: 1460.
3. TONOMURA, A. *et al.* 1982. Phys. Rev. Lett. **48**: 1443; 1983. Phys. Rev. Lett. **51**: 331.
4. BERNIDO, C. C. & A. INOMATA. 1980. Phys. Lett. **77A**: 384; 1981. J. Math. Phys. **22**: 715.
5. DEAVER, B. S. & G. B. DONALDSON. 1982. Phys. Lett. **89A**: 178.
6. INOMATA, A. 1983. Phys. Lett. **95A**: 176.
7. GERRY, C. C. & A. INOMATA. 1986. *In* Fundamental Questions in Quantum Mechanics. L. M. Roth & A. Inomata, Eds.: 199. Gordon & Breach. New York.
8. SILVERMAN, M. 1983. Phys. Rev. Lett. **51**: 1927.
9. INOMATA, A. & V. J. SINGH. 1978. J. Math. Phys. **19**: 2319.

General Relativistic Effects on Superconductors

JEEVA ANANDAN

Department of Physics and Astronomy
University of South Carolina
Columbia, South Carolina 29208
and
Laboratoire de Physique
Institut Henri Poincaré
F-75231 Paris, France

I. INTRODUCTION

During the past several decades, a series of fascinating phenomena in superconductors have been discovered. These phenomena show that the electron pairs, called Cooper pairs, that are responsible for superconductivity are in the same quantum mechanical state, described by a wave function, $\psi(\vec{x}, t)$, that has appreciable value throughout the superconductor that normally has macroscopic dimensions. This naturally raises the question of what effects the two long-range fields (namely, the electromagnetic and gravitational fields) have on a superconductor. The effect of the electromagnetic field has been studied extensively.[1,2] Indeed, a superconducting device (the SQUID) provides the most sensitive measurement of this field. This gives an additional reason for studying the effect of gravity because the extreme sensitivity of superconducting devices may enable us for the first time to test relativistic gravitational effects on a charged quantum mechanical system (the Cooper pair).

Gravitational effects on a superconducting circuit and a superconducting Josephson interferometer were studied by DeWitt[3] and Papini,[4] respectively. When space-time curvature effects are locally negligible, as is usually the case, both these effects may be regarded as being due to the rotation of the apparatus relative to the local inertial frame; the former effect is then called the London moment.[1] General relativistic phenomenological equations for a superconductor that generalize the Ginzburg-Landau equation have been proposed by Meier and Salie[5] and the author.[6] However, these equations seem to be more complex than necessary to study the effect of gravity or rotation.

In the next section, we will formulate what appears to be the simplest theory[7] (which is consistent with general relativity and quantum mechanics) that is sufficient to study all the effects considered here. The treatments in the first two subsections of the next section are valid for all conductors, and the third subsection in the next section specializes to superconductors. These principles are then applied in the third section for the stationary situation. The electromagnetic field inside a superconductor due to gravity and rotation, and the effect of gravity on superconducting circuits and Josephson junctions are obtained. Experiments of the type to be discussed in this section were previously considered by Brady,[8] but he did not have a general relativistic theory to predict the outcome of all such experiments. The nonstationary situation corresponding to the influence of gravitational radiation on superconducting circuits[9,10] is considered in the final section.

II. THE BASIC PRINCIPLES

Statistical Mechanics in a Gravitational Field

Because we are concerned with the effect of gravity on the conducting electrons in a conductor, it would be useful to first discuss statistical mechanics in a gravitational field. The basic principle of nonrelativistic statistical mechanics is that the probability of a subsystem having N particles with energy, E, in thermal and diffusive equilibrium with a reservoir at temperature, T, and electrochemical potential, μ, is proportional to the Gibb's factor, $\exp [(\mu N/kT) - (E/kT)]$, where k is Boltzmann's constant. As is well known, in the absence of the gravitational field, this implies that T and μ are constant throughout a system that is in thermal and diffusive equilibrium.

It is easy to convince oneself that this is not valid in the presence of a gravitational field (that is, treated general relativistically) by means of the following gedanken-experiment. Consider two gases that are separated by a height, H, in a stationary gravitational field and that are in thermal equilibrium by means of exchange of radiation. However, when radiation emitted by the lower gas with frequency, ω_2, reaches the upper gas, its frequency is redshifted to $\omega_1 = \omega_2 (1 - gH/c^2)$. Because the temperature is like the average kinetic energy (which now includes the rest-mass energy), the temperatures, T_1 and T_2, of the upper and lower gases are therefore related by $T_1 = T_2 (1 - gH/c^2)$. If the gases are also in diffusive equilibrium, then μ/kT (the coefficient of N in the Gibb's factor) must be the same for the two gases. Therefore, μ must vary in the same way as T, and hence $\mu_1 = \mu_2 (1 - gH/c^2)$.

Now, for a gas to be in equilibrium in a gravitational field, it is necessary for the latter to have a timelike Killing vector field, ξ^μ, and the average 4-velocity of the gas, $t^\mu \propto \xi^\mu$, as in the above example. Also, the macroscopically averaged electromagnetic field, $F_{\mu\nu}$, should be invariant along ξ^μ. A gauge can then be chosen so that the vector potential, A_μ, satisfies $(L_\xi A) = 0$, where L_ξ is the lie derivative with respect to ξ. Then, $\mu = \zeta + eA_\mu t^\mu$, where e is the charge of each particle in the gas and ζ is the chemical potential (including the rest-mass energy), as measured by observers whose 4-velocity field is t^μ. Finally, let T be the temperature measured using thermometers by the same observers. Thus, the above arguments show that when the gas is in thermal and diffusive equilibrium, T and μ are not constant; however, $\tilde{T} \equiv \Lambda^{1/2}T$ and $\tilde{\mu} \equiv \Lambda^{1/2}\mu = \Lambda^{1/2}\zeta + eA_\mu\xi^\mu$ are constants where $\Lambda = \xi^\mu\xi_\mu$. On choosing a coordinate system such that $\xi^\mu = (1, 0, 0, 0)$, the metric coefficients, $g_{\mu\nu}$, are independent of time and $\Lambda = g_{oo}$. In general, Λ includes the effect of space-time curvature. However, if curvature effects are negligible, then the apparatus may be regarded as having an acceleration, g, relative to a local inertial frame, and thus, $\Lambda = (1 + gz/c^2)^2$, where z is the height above some fixed point. Also, $\zeta \simeq mc^2 + \zeta_n$, where m is the mass of the particle and ζ_n is the nonrelativistic chemical potential. Hence, $\tilde{\mu} \simeq mc^2 + \zeta_n + mgz + eA_o$ in the above coordinate system if the curvature effects are negligible.

A special case of such a gas is the conduction electrons in a metal. Here, let $t^\mu =$

$\Lambda^{-1/2}\xi^\mu$ be the 4-velocity of the metal. Define

$$f_\nu = \Lambda^{-1/2}\partial_\nu\tilde{\mu}, \tag{2.1}$$

which is the apparent force on the conduction electrons for an observer who is at rest with respect to the metal. Because[7] $\partial_\mu\Lambda^{1/2} = -\Lambda^{1/2}t^\nu\nabla_\nu t^\mu$, where ∇_ν is the space-time covariant derivative, and $\partial_\nu(A_\mu\xi^\mu) \equiv (L_\xi A)_\nu + F_{\nu\mu}\xi^\mu = \Lambda^{1/2}F_{\nu\mu}t^\mu$, where $F_{\mu\nu} = \partial_\mu A_\nu - \partial_\nu A_\mu$, it follows that $f_\nu = \partial_\nu\zeta - \zeta a_\nu + eE_\nu$, where $a^\mu = t^\nu\nabla_\nu t^\mu$ is the acceleration of the metal relative to the local inertial frames, and $E^\mu = F^\mu_\nu t^\nu$ is the electric field as measured by observers at rest relative to the metal. Because, during equilibrium, $\tilde{\mu}$ is constant,

$$f_\nu \equiv \partial_\nu\zeta - a_\nu\zeta + eE_\nu = 0. \tag{2.2}$$

Similarly, in the nonrelativistic limit considered above, during equilibrium, $\vec{0} = \nabla\tilde{\mu} = \nabla\zeta_n - m\vec{g} - e\vec{E}$, where $\vec{g}$ is the acceleration due to gravity ($g^i = -a^i$) and $\vec{E} = (E^1, E^2, E^3)$. Hence, even in the absence of a current, the electric field in a metal may be nonzero. Equation 2.2 modifies the prediction of Schiff and Barnhill,[11] which corresponds to the special (though unrealistic) case of $\partial_\mu\zeta = 0$.[12]

The General Relativistic Ohm's Law

To get a further physical feeling for the $\tilde{\mu}$ (introduced in the previous subsection, and which may be called the gravito-electrochemical potential), consider two neutral conductors at rest in a stationary gravitational field. Suppose that initially they were in contact so that $\tilde{\mu}$ was the same for both of them. Now, suppose that they are separated, with each being insulated from its environment, and one is raised to a height, H, relative to the other. If the two conductors are now connected by a conducting wire, will a charge flow between them? Even though the two conductors have the same value for μ, they have different values for $\tilde{\mu}$. Hence, a positive charge from the top conductor, which has the higher value of $\tilde{\mu}$, will momentarily flow to the lower conductor until $\tilde{\mu}$ is the same for both. On the other hand, if we connect the earth and the moon by a wire, then, neglecting the tidal forces, no charge will be exchanged between them because the moon and the earth are freely falling. In this approximation, the pseudoforce (equation 2.1) is zero at the earth and the moon.

Having realized that a variation of $\tilde{\mu}$ drives a current through a stationary conductor, we now formulate the general relativistic generalization of Ohm's law. Consider a thin circuit carrying a steady current at rest in a stationary gravitational field. It follows from the general relativistic charge conservation law, $\nabla_\mu j^\mu = 0$, that the current I that is measured by a local observer using, say, an ammeter, is not constant along the wire, in general. However, $\tilde{I} = \Lambda^{1/2}I$ is constant.[13,14] Then, the change in the gravito-electrochemical potential across a piece of wire with resistance, R, is[7,14]

$$\Delta\tilde{\mu} = e\tilde{I}R, \tag{2.3}$$

where e is the charge of the current carrier, which in a metal is the electron. In general, R is not the same as the resistance in the absence of gravity because of the compression or stretching of the metal by gravity. However, if R is determined independently by local measurements, then equation 2.3 can be used to predict the current if the voltage is given, and vice versa.

In making this prediction, it should be noted that the voltage measured by a voltmeter whose linear dimensions are negligible is the change in μ across the voltmeter. Hence, if two voltmeters are connected across the same portion of a conductor, as shown in FIGURE 1, by wires whose resistances are negligible, then their readings would be $V_1 = \Delta \tilde{\mu}/\Lambda_1^{1/2}$ and $V_2 = \Delta \tilde{\mu}/\Lambda_2^{1/2}$, where Λ_1 and Λ_2 are the values of Λ at the respective voltmeters. Hence, $V_1/V_2 \simeq 1 - gH/c^2$, where H is the height between the voltmeters. It should be noted that, in general, Λ_2/Λ_1 also has a contribution from the space-time curvature that we have neglected. Thus, the general relativistic Ohm's law (equation 2.3), in principle, contains information of the curvature, and, therefore,

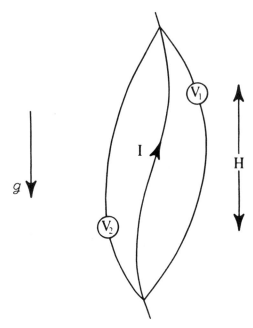

FIGURE 1. Two voltmeters at different heights will measure different voltages across the same conductor.

goes beyond the equivalence principle. We shall see in the third section that the above-mentioned difference in the measured voltages is experimentally measurable in the laboratory. However, in this case, the curvature effects are negligible, and the experiment would test the relativistic equivalence principle.

Superconductors

Because a superconductor has no resistance, equation 2.3 implies that $\tilde{\mu}$ must be constant in a superconductor, including even the case when it carries the supercurrent of the Cooper pairs. The "wave function," $\psi(x^\mu)$, of the Cooper pairs may be assumed to satisfy a general relativistic generalization of the Ginzburg-Landau equation proposed previously,[6] which implies that the supercurrent density,

$$j_\mu = \frac{ie\hbar}{m^*}\left\{\psi^*\left(\partial_\mu + i\frac{2e}{\hbar c}A_\mu\right)\psi - \psi\left(\partial_\mu - i\frac{2e}{\hbar c}A_\mu\right)\psi^*\right\},$$

satisfies the conservation law, $\nabla_\mu j^\mu = 0$, where ∇_μ is the space-time covariant derivative and m^* is the mass of the Cooper pair. Therefore, if we write $\psi = \chi e^{i\phi}$, where χ and ϕ are real, then $j_\mu = 2n^*e/m^* p_\mu$, where $p_\mu = -\hbar\partial_\mu\phi - 2e/cA_\mu$ and $n^* = \chi^2$ is the density of Cooper pairs. Hence,

$$\partial_{[\mu}j_{\nu]} + \frac{2n^*e^2}{m^*c}F_{\mu\nu} - \frac{2e}{m^*}\partial_{[\mu}n^*p_{\nu]} = 0, \tag{2.4}$$

where [ ] represents antisymmetrization. When the last term is negligible, equation 2.4 becomes the covariant generalization of London's equations.[1,2]

However, any supercurrent flows only on the surface within the penetration depth. Thus, in the interior of the superconductor,[7]

$$p^\mu = \frac{2}{c}\zeta t^\mu, \tag{2.5}$$

where t^μ is the 4-velocity of the superconductor. For the stationary situation that will be considered in the next section, $\xi^\mu = \Lambda^{1/2} t^\mu$ is a Killing field. An expression for ζ in equation 2.5 using the general relativistic Ginzburg-Landau equation has been obtained.[6]

Physically, it is reasonable to interpret ζ as the chemical potential (including the rest-mass energy) because 2ζ is like the effective mass of the Cooper pair and p_μ is like the energy momentum. Also, equation 2.5 implies $2\zeta = p_\nu t^\nu c$ or

$$-\hbar\frac{d\phi}{d\tau} = \frac{2}{c}\mu, \tag{2.6}$$

where the electrochemical potential, μ, is equal to $\zeta + eA_\mu t^\mu$, and $d/d\tau = t^\mu\partial_\mu$ is the derivative with respect to proper time along the world-lines of the superconductor. Hence, equation 2.6 is like de Broglie's equation for the rate of change of phase of a massive particle (the Cooper pair) in its rest frame, but it is modified to include the electromagnetic interaction. Because $\tilde{\mu}$ is constant along a superconducting wire in the stationary situation, the frequency, $\omega \equiv -c\,d\phi/d\tau = (2\Lambda^{-1/2}/\hbar)\,\tilde{\mu}$, is not constant in general. Indeed, for a uniform gravitational field, $\vec{g}$, $\omega = \omega_o(1 - gz/c^2)$, where ω_o is a constant and z is the height above a fixed horizontal level. This is the "gravitational redshift" of a massive, charged particle, and superconductivity provides the opportunity of testing it in the laboratory for the first time by means of the Josephson effect, which we shall describe shortly. It may also be noted that if the rest-mass energy contribution is subtracted away from equation 2.6, then one obtains the Josephson equation, which can therefore be used to justify the interpretation given to ζ above.

Because ψ must be single-valued, on integrating equation 2.5 around a closed curve, γ, in the interior of the superconductor,

$$\frac{2e}{\hbar c} \int_\Sigma F_{\mu\nu} \frac{d\sigma^{\mu\nu}}{2} + \frac{2}{\hbar c} \oint_\gamma \zeta t_\mu dx^\mu = 2\pi n, \tag{2.7}$$

where n is an interger and Σ is a surface spanned by γ. The manner in which equation 2.7 generalizes the usual condition for the quantization of the fluxoid has been discussed elsewhere.[10]

Finally, suppose that a current, I, passes through a Josephson junction, that is, a thin normal conductor or insulator separating two superconductors. Then,[15]

$$I = I_o \sin \Delta\phi^*, \tag{2.8}$$

where I_o is constant and $\Delta\phi^* = -1/\hbar \int_C p_\mu dx^\mu$, with C being the shortest geodesic across the Josephson junction consisting of events that are simultaneous with respect to the junction. Hence, in the stationary situation, $L_\xi(\Delta\phi^*) = 1/\hbar \int (L_\xi p)_\mu dx^\mu$, where L_ξ in the lie derivative with respect to the Killing field, $\xi = 1/c\, d/dt$. Using the identity, $(L_\xi p)_\mu = \partial_\mu(p_\nu \xi^\nu) - 2\partial_{[\mu} p_{\nu]}\xi^\nu$, along with equations 2.5 and 2.1,

$$\frac{1}{c}\frac{d}{dt}(\Delta\phi^*) \equiv L_\xi(\Delta\phi^*) = -\frac{2}{\hbar c}\int_C \partial_\mu(\Lambda^{1/2}\zeta)\,dx^\mu - \frac{2e}{\hbar c}F_{\mu\nu}\xi^\nu dx^\mu$$

$$= -\frac{2}{\hbar c}\int_c \Lambda^{1/2}f_\mu dx^\mu = -2\frac{\Delta\tilde{\mu}}{\hbar c}. \tag{2.9}$$

Because the variation of Λ across the Josephson junction is negligible, equation 2.9 may also be written as

$$\frac{d}{d\tau}(\Delta\phi^*) \equiv L_t(\Delta\phi^*) = \frac{2}{\hbar c}(\zeta_1 - \zeta_2) - \frac{2e}{\hbar c}\int_C E_\mu dx^\mu = \frac{-2\Delta\mu}{\hbar c}, \tag{2.10}$$

where τ is the proper time at the junction, $E_\mu = F_{\mu\nu}t^\nu$ is the electric field in the rest frame of the junction, and ζ_1 and ζ_2 are the values of ζ on the two sides of the junction.

It follows from equations 2.8 and 2.10 that an alternating current of frequency,

$$\omega = \frac{2\Delta\mu}{\hbar}, \tag{2.11}$$

where $\Delta\mu = \int c f_\mu dx^\mu$, would flow across the junction (the ac Josephson effect). Hence, the junction would emit radiation with the same frequency, ω.

III. THE STATIONARY SITUATION

According to general relativity or Newtonian gravity, the gravitional field influences the geometry of space-time by modifying the local inertial frames. Hence, a body whose linear dimensions are small compared to the radius of curvature can, nevertheless, experience the effect of the gravitational field in the following way: Suppose that the body has no acceleration or rotation relative to the distant stars as determined by telescopes attached to the body. Then, in general, it would have an acceleration and a rotation relative to the local inertial frames if there was a nearby gravitating object. The precise relationship between these local inertial frames and the source of gravity is determined by the field equations of Einstein or Newton.

However, there are two possible ways in which Einstein's theory can be distinguished from Newton's theory. First, the local inertial frames predicted by the two theories may be incompatible. For example, the inertial frames near a rotating body undergo a slight precession because of the Lense-Thirring field,[16] and this does not occur in Newtonian gravity (unless it is supplemented by Mach's principle, which, however, is not a complete theory). Another example is the oscillation and precession of local inertial frames in a gravitational wave (as observed in a Fermi-normal coordinate system), which also has no Newtonian analog. Secondly, the local inertial frames are Minkowskian in general relatively, whereas they are Galilean in Newton's theory. Hence, by verifying that the above body is accelerating relative to a local Minkowski space-time and not a local Galilean space-time, Newtonian gravity can be refuted. In this sense, general relativity can be tested without directly measuring curvature. For example, if the laboratory is found to be accelerating and rotating relative to a common local Minkowski space-time, then the only way in which these local Minkowski space-times around the surface of the earth can be meshed together is by means of a curved Riemannian space-time. We shall, therefore, now consider the effect of rotation and acceleration on superconductors, restricting ourselves to the stationary situation.

The Effect of Uniform Rotation on a Relativistic Superconductor

It follows from equation 2.5 that in the interior of the superconductor,

$$F_{\mu\nu} = \frac{2}{e} \partial_{[\nu} \zeta t_{\mu]} + \frac{2}{e} \zeta \partial_{[\nu} t_{\mu]}. \tag{3.1}$$

Hence, the magnetic field in the rest frame of the superconductor, in its interior, is[7]

$$B^{\mu} = \frac{1}{2} \eta^{\mu\nu\rho\sigma} F_{\rho\sigma} t_{\nu} = -\frac{2}{ec} \zeta \Omega^{\mu}, \tag{3.2}$$

where $\Omega^{\mu} = (\frac{1}{2})c\eta^{\mu\nu\rho\sigma}(\nabla_{\nu} t_{\rho})t_{\sigma}$ is the local angular velocity of the superconductor. Equation 2.3 generalizes the London moment[1] that corresponds to the approximation, $\zeta \simeq mc^2$. However, an experimentalist has to make a cavity in order to measure the magnetic field in a superconductor. Furthermore, the magnetic field that he/she would then measure is different from equation 3.2, as can be seen by the argument in the following paragraph.

For simplicity, consider a long circular cylinder of radius, R, rotating in Minkowski space-time with constant angular velocity, $\vec{\Omega}$, about its axis (FIGURE 2). Then, equation 2.7 on choosing γ to be a closed curve at constant time in the interior of the superconductor implies

$$\frac{2e}{\hbar c} \int_{\Sigma} \vec{B} \cdot d\vec{s} + \frac{2}{\hbar c^2} \zeta \oint_{\gamma} \vec{u} \cdot d\vec{r} = 2\pi n, \tag{3.3}$$

where $\vec{u} = \vec{\Omega} \times \vec{r}$ is the velocity of the superconductor assuming that $u/c \ll 1$. Now, the electric field of the dipole layer in the inside surface of the cylinder gives rise to a magnetic field, $\vec{B}_d = (1/c)\vec{u} \times \vec{E} = -(\vec{E} \cdot \vec{r}/c)\vec{\Omega} = (ER/c)\vec{\Omega}$. Hence, the magnetic flux in equation 3.3 is $\int_\Sigma \vec{B} \cdot d\vec{s} = \int_\Sigma \vec{B}_o \cdot d\vec{s} + (ER/c)\Omega 2\pi Rd$, where $\vec{B}_o$ is the magnetic field inside the cavity and d is the thickness of the dipole layer.

By Maxwell's equations, $\vec{B}_o$ is constant inside the cavity. Thus, equation 3.3 reads $nhc/2 = (eB_o + 2eV\Omega/c + 2\zeta\Omega/c)S$, where $S = \pi R^2$ is the area of Σ, and $V = Ed$ is the electrostatic potential inside the superconductor in a gauge in which $V = 0$ in free space. In the special case when $n = 0$,

$$\vec{B}_o = -\frac{2}{ec}\mu\vec{\Omega}, \tag{3.4}$$

where μ is the electrochemical potential in the above gauge (i.e., $\mu = mc^2 - W$, where W is the work function).[7,17-19] This argument can be easily generalized to a cylinder of arbitrary cross section to yield equation 3.4 again. The deviation of equation 3.4 from

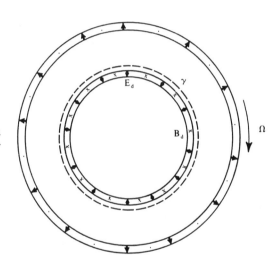

FIGURE 2. The cross section of a rotating cylindrical superconductor.

the prediction of London,[1] which corresponds to the approximation of $\mu \simeq mc^2$, should be experimentally observable.[19] This would be the first ever direct measurement of ζ.

As already mentioned, if the superconductor is placed on a platform that is nonrotating relative to the distant stars as determined by telescopes, then, in general, it would rotate with respect to the local inertial frames if a nearby rotating body was present because of the general relativistic Lense-Thirring field.[16] For example, if the rotating body is the earth (which is approximately spherically symmetric), then the angular velocity of the local inertial frames relative to the distant stars at position, $\vec{r}$, from the center of the earth is

$$\vec{\Omega} = \frac{4GM_eR_e^2}{5c^2}\left[-\frac{\vec{\Omega}_e}{r^3} + \frac{(\vec{\Omega}_e \cdot \vec{r})\vec{r}}{r^5}\right], \tag{3.5}$$

where M_e, R_e, and $\vec{\Omega}_e$ are the mass, radius, and angular velocity of the earth, respectively, and G is the gravitational constant. Hence, the magnetic field, $\vec{B}_o$, inside a superconducting circuit that is at rest on the platform can be obtained from equations 3.4 and 3.5. The platform may be on a satellite or on the earth and moving so that its angular velocity relative to the distant stars has no component normal to the plane of the circuit as determined by telescopes.

If the circuit consists of 1000 turns around a circle of radius 1 m, the magnetic flux enclosed by it is $\sim 10^{-6}\Phi_o$, where $\Phi_o = hc/2e$. Such fluxes have been measured before; however, in the present case, there are two serious problems arising from the very large inductance of the circuit and the difficulty of shielding it without canceling the above flux. These problems appear to make this experiment unfeasible at present.

The Effect of Gravity or Uniform Acceleration on a Superconductor

Suppose now that the superconductor has an acceleration, a^μ, in Minkowski space-time such that its typical dimension is $\ell \ll c^2/g$, where $g = (-a_\mu a^\mu)^{1/2}$.

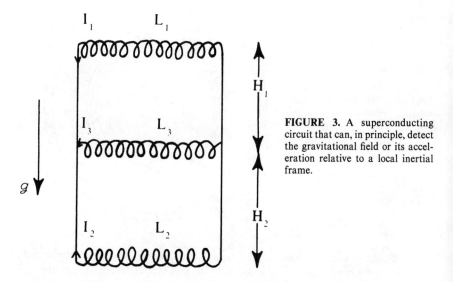

FIGURE 3. A superconducting circuit that can, in principle, detect the gravitational field or its acceleration relative to a local inertial frame.

Alternatively, one may consider the superconductor at rest in a gravitational field with $\ell \ll$ the radius of curvature, so that it has uniform acceleration, $a^\mu = t^\nu \nabla_\nu t^\mu$, relative to the local Minkowski space-time. Several superconducting devices that can, in principle, detect a^μ in either case were considered previously.[7] Here, we shall discuss only two such devices.

Consider first a superconducting circuit consisting of three horizontal solenoids with inductances, L_1, L_2, and L_3, connected in parallel and carrying currents, I_1, I_2, and I_3, respectively, as shown in FIGURE 3, at rest in a gravitational field. The diameters of the solenoids are small compared to the distances, H_1 and H_2, between adjacent solenoids. Initially, the circuit is in the horizontal plane so that $I_1 + I_2 + I_3 = 0$. Suppose that it is now brought into a vertical plane. Assuming that there is no leakage of flux lines and no changes in the inductances, the changes in the currents, δI_1, δI_2, and δI_3, satisfy

$$L_1 \delta I_1 - L_3 \delta I_3 = 0, \qquad L_3 \delta I_3 - L_2 \delta I_2 = 0 \tag{3.6}$$

on using equation 2.7. However, because it is $\tilde{I}$ that is constant along each wire (see the section on the general relativistic Ohm's law), charge conservation at the junction requires $(I_1 + \delta I_1)(1 + gH_1/c^2) + I_3 + \delta I_3 + (I_2 + \delta I_2)(1 - gH_2/c^2) = 0$ or

$$\delta I_1 + \delta I_2 + \delta I_3 = -I_1 gH_1/c^2 + I_2 gH_2/c^2. \tag{3.7}$$

Solving equations 3.6 and 3.7 gives

$$\delta I_j = \frac{L_k L_\ell}{L_1 L_2 + L_2 L_3 + L_3 L_1} \left(I_2 \frac{gH_2}{c^2} - I_1 \frac{gH_1}{c^2} \right), \tag{3.8}$$

where (j, k, ℓ) = any permutation of $(1, 2, 3)$.

It is easiest to detect δI_3 when $-I_1 = I_2 = I$, say. Then, $I_3 = 0$ and

$$\delta I_3 = \frac{L_1 L_2 I}{L_1 L_2 + L_2 L_3 + L_3 L_1} \frac{g(H_1 + H_2)}{c^2}. \tag{3.9}$$

If the circuit is rotated about the solenoid, L_3, then δI_3 will oscillate with the same frequency. Also, in the limiting case of $L_3 \to 0$, equation 3.8 is in agreement with reference 7. Even though the quantum mechanical condition (equation 2.7) was used in these derivations, the same results will be obtained for a hypothetical perfect conductor, which is not a superconductor. This is because the magnetic flux through such a circuit cannot change since if it were to change, then the corresponding electric field would drive an infinite current. Thus, equation 3.6 and therefore equation 3.8 are also valid in this more general case.

Consider now two Josephson junctions connected in parallel, with H being the height between them. If an electrochemical potential difference is applied across them (say, by means of a battery), then each junction radiates with frequency, ω, which according to equation 2.11 is $\omega = 2(\Lambda^{-1/2}/\hbar)\Delta\tilde{\mu}$. This ω is the frequency measured by a local observer at the junction, at rest with respect to this junction. However, because $\tilde{\mu}$ is constant in the superconductor (see the section entitled SUPERCONDUCTORS), $\Delta\tilde{\mu}$ across both junctions must be the same. Hence, if ω_1 and ω_2 are the frequencies of the upper and the lower junctions, then $\omega_1/\omega_2 = \Lambda_2^{1/2}/\Lambda_1^{1/2} \simeq 1 - gH/c^2$.

This is true basically because equation 2.6 and the condition that $\tilde{\mu}$ is constant (which follows from the general relativistic Ohm's law) imply that the frequency of the Cooper pair wave function decreases with height, and ω_1 is therefore "redshifted" relative to ω_2. Alternatively, the Josephson junction may be regarded as a voltmeter that measures the potential difference, $\Lambda^{-1/2}\Delta\tilde{\mu}$, across the junction by the frequency of radiation. As mentioned previously (see FIGURE 1), two voltmeters connected across the same two points would measure different voltages, depending on their heights, which explains the difference between ω_1 and ω_2.

If the microwaves are brought together at a detector, however, there would be no frequency difference between them owing to the redshift of the microwaves because of the Einstein effect that compensates for the above effect. The latter has already been observed by Pound and Rebka.[20] Hence, this null experiment together with the

Pound-Rebka result and the Josephson equations would imply that the potential differences, $\Delta\mu_1$ and $\Delta\mu_2$, at the upper and the lower junctions are related according to

$$\Delta\mu_1 = \Delta\mu_2(1 - gH/c^2). \tag{3.10}$$

Thus, such an experiment would confirm the variation of the potential difference with height mentioned above. Also, on using equation 2.6, this would confirm the "redshifting" of the Cooper pair wave function mentioned above.

Now, let γ be a closed curve through the interior of the circuit perpendicular to t^μ everywhere. Then, because

$$\oint_\gamma p_\mu dx^\mu = -2\frac{e}{c}\int_\Sigma F_{\mu\nu}d\sigma^{\mu\nu}/2$$

where Σ is a surface spanned by γ, on using equation 2.5,

$$-\Delta\phi_1^* + \Delta\phi_2^* = \frac{2e}{\hbar c}\int_\Sigma F_{\mu\nu}\frac{d\sigma^{\mu\nu}}{2},$$

where $\hbar\Delta\phi_1^*$ and $-\hbar\Delta\phi_2^*$ are the contributions of $\int p_\mu dx^\mu$ for the two Josephson junctions in which equation 2.5 is not valid. Hence, from equation 2.9 or 2.10, the change in magnetic flux during a given time interval is

$$\Delta\left(\int_\Sigma F_{\mu\nu}\frac{d\sigma^{\mu\nu}}{2}\right) = \frac{c}{e}\int_0^T (\Delta\tilde{\mu}_1 - \Delta\tilde{\mu}_2)\, dt = \frac{c}{e}\int_0^\tau \left[\Delta\mu_1 - \Delta\mu_2\left(1 - \frac{gH}{c^2}\right)\right] d\tau, \quad \text{(3.11)}$$

where $\tau = \Lambda_1^{1/2}T$ is the proper time elapsed at the upper junction. Equations 3.10 and 3.11 imply that the magnetic flux should be constant in time for the above experiment. Because the general relativistic time dilation in a gravitational field was assumed in deriving equation 3.11, and because equation 3.10 would be confirmed by the observed equality of the frequencies of microwaves at the detector, the additional observation that the magnetic flux is constant would confirm the time dilation.

Consider now the time reversal of the above experiment: suppose that the junctions are coupled to microwave radiation from a common source, and there is no battery. Experiments of this type have been performed previously by Clark[21] and Tsai et al.,[22] but they were not sensitive enough to test the gravitational effect to be described now. Due to the gravitational redshift of the microwave, the potential differences, $\Delta\mu_1$ and $\Delta\mu_2$, at the upper and the lower junctions, which are proportional to the microwave frequencies at these junctions according to the Josephson equations, are related by equation 3.10. Then, equation 3.11 implies that the magnetic flux does not change with time. The experimental confirmation[23] of this null result would confirm the equation (equation 2.9 or 2.10) used to derive equation 3.11. The essential aspect of equation 2.9 that is needed to get the null result is the dependence on the height of the frequency of the Cooper pair wave function or the potential difference as discussed above, which, therefore, would be tested by this experiment. If the Cooper pair frequency does not redshift, for example, the integrand on the right-hand side of equation 3.11 should be replaced by $\Delta\mu_1 - \Delta\mu_2$; then, on using equation 3.10, the magnetic flux and, therefore, the current in the circuit would increase linearly with time.

Suppose now that the two Josephson junctions are coupled to two independent microwave sources that have the same frequency and that are near the respective junctions. Then, $\Delta\mu_1 = \Delta\mu_2$. Therefore, according to equation 3.11, when the apparatus is horizontal, the magnetic flux in the circuit would remain constant and this would verify that the frequencies are the same. However, if it is brought into a vertical plane, then the magnetic flux will increase linearly with time according to

$$\Delta\left(\int_\Sigma F_{\mu\nu} \frac{d\sigma^{\mu\nu}}{2}\right) = \frac{c}{e} \frac{gH}{c^2} \int_0^\tau \Delta\mu_1 d\tau. \tag{3.12}$$

This effect has no Newtonian analog even though the Cooper pair, being massive, can be coupled to gravity within Newtonian physics (unlike the photon in the Pound-Rebka experiment). For $H = 1$ m, $gH/c^2 = 1.1 \times 10^{-16}$. It is possible to make a hydrogen maser whose frequency is stable to this accuracy with some difficulty. However, it may be easier to do this experiment by using a common microwave source and Doppler-shifting one of the microwaves to compensate for the gravitational redshift so that they have the same frequency at the junctions. Then, the velocity, v, of the Doppler-shifting source satisfies $2v/c = gH/c^2$ or $v = 1.7 \times 10^{-8}$ m/sec per m height.[24] More generally, equation 3.11 then yields

$$\Delta\left(\int_\Sigma F_{\mu\nu} \frac{d\sigma^{\mu\nu}}{2}\right) = \frac{\hbar c}{e} \int \Delta\omega \, dt,$$

where $\Delta\omega = 2v\omega/c$ is the Doppler shift of the frequency, ω; thus, varying v, this effect can be tested. This $\Delta\omega$ may be directly measured by the beat frequency when the Doppler-shifted and unshifted microwaves are interfered.

The advantage of the last two experiments over the preceding one is that non-null results are predicted by relativistic gravity as opposed to the null result for the latter experiment. Also, in the above-proposed experiment, with independent microwave sources, Newtonian physics would predict a null result, whereas in the other two experiments, it would be necessary to assume the Pound-Rebka result[20] to distinguish between the results predicted by relativistic gravity and Newtonian physics.

Discussion: The Action and the Relativistic Equivalence Principle

According to the Feynman path integral formulation of quantum mechanics, the phase of the probability amplitude to go from one space-time point, P, to another, Q, is approximately $S_c/\hbar$, where S_c is the action for the classical path, C, joining P and Q, provided $S_c/\hbar \gg 1$. Thus, the action has a direct physical significance and is observable in quantum mechanics (unlike in classical physics). Once the action is determined experimentally, then it can also be used to describe quantum processes for which the action $S \sim \hbar$.

For example, the nonrelativistic action of a free particle, $S_{\text{free}} = -\int \frac{1}{2}mv^2 dt$, implies the de Broglie equation, and the confirmation of it by Davisson and Germer may therefore be regarded as confirmation of the chosen S_{free}. If the particle interacts with the electromagnetic field, then the action is $S_{\text{EM}} = S_{\text{free}} - e/c \int A_\mu dx^\mu$, which implies the celebrated Aharonov-Bohm effect.[25] The confirmation of this effect amounts to a measurement of S_{EM} up to a total divergence. For a particle in a gravitational field, the nonrelativistic action is $S_{\text{NR,grav}} = -\int \frac{1}{2}mv^2 dt - \int mU dt$, where U is the Newtonian gravitational potential. An experiment performed by Colella, Overhauser, and Werner (COW)[26] that measures the phase-shift in neutron interference due to the gravitational field may be regarded as confirmation and measurement of $S_{NR,grav}$. However, this experiment is not yet sensitive enough to measure the relativistic corrections.

Now, the relativistic action of a massive free particle is $S_R = -mc \int d\tau$, where τ is the proper time along the path of integration. The strong principle of equivalence implies that the same form of action is valid in the presence of gravity. To lowest order then, S_R gives $S_{NR,grav}$. Because the weak equivalence principle is not valid in quantum physics,[27,28] it is reasonable to ask what experimental evidence there is for the strong equivalence principle. It is, therefore, important to observe S_R and not just its approximation, $S_{NR,grav}$.

If the particle is interacting with an electromagnetic field as well as with a gravitational field, its relativistic action is

$$S_{R,EM} = -mc \int d\tau - \frac{e}{c} \int A_\mu dx^\mu. \tag{3.13}$$

Equation 2.5 follows from equation 3.13 if we take the phase to be $S_{R,EM}/\hbar$, and if we take m to be $2\zeta/c^2$, the effective mass. Hence, the prediction for the relativistic correction to the magnetic field in a rotating superconductor (in the subsection on uniform rotation) is ultimately based on equation 3.13, and, therefore, its experimental observation is a confirmation of equation 3.13. Similarly, the experimental confirmation of the predictions for the Josephson interferometer (in the section on the effect of gravity and uniform acceleration) based on equation 2.5 may be regarded as observation of equation 3.13 via the phase. This would be the first confirmation of equation 3.13 for a charged particle in a gravitational field. Also, the COW experiment[26] confirmed the Newtonian equivalence principle for a quantum mechanical system for the first time. The experiments described in this section then would test for the first time the relativistic equivalence principle or the assumption that the laboratory is accelerating relative to a local Minkowski space-time (as opposed to a local Galilean space-time) for a quantum mechanical particle, a charged particle, and a massive particle (namely, the Cooper pair).

IV. THE EFFECT OF GRAVITATIONAL RADIATION ON SUPERCONDUCTORS

The two essential ingredients of general relativity are the description of gravity by a curved Riemannian space-time geometry, and the prediction of the interaction between the matter distribution and this geometry using Einstein's field equations. In the previous section, some experiments were considered to test the first ingredient by using superconductors. We will now consider the second ingredient.

As is well known, the experimental detection of electromagnetic waves, which established the electromagnetic field as a dynamical entity having its own independent degrees of freedom, was a very important confirmation of Maxwell's equations, Also, these degrees of freedom, when subject to the laws of quantum mechanics, gave photons. Similarly, the detection of gravitational waves would be a profound confirmation of general relativity, apart from its suggestive value in introducing gravitons.

Superconducting devices that can, in principle, detect gravitational radiation have been proposed previously.[9,10] The best such device seems to be a superconducting circuit in the form of a square with a diagonal. There are solenoids on the diagonal and the two adjacent sides that are bisected by this diagonal. For simplicity, it may be assumed that the circuit is appropriately weighted so that its center of mass is at the center of the square, and that, initially, current flows only along the outer circuit. If a gravitational wave passes perpendicular to the circuit, then its tidal forces would, in general, stretch and compress the two solenoids alternatively. This would force an alternating current to flow along the diagonal because of the quantization of fluxoid in each subcircuit.

It is convenient to assume that the center of mass of this circuit is freely falling. A more general case that includes the case of the apparatus being at rest in the laboratory (which has acceleration and rotation relative to the local inertial frames) has been treated previously.[10] However, no essential difference has been obtained as far as the effect of the gravitational wave is concerned, so we may as well assume that the center of mass is freely falling. Then, a Fermi-normal coordinate system may be chosen around the world-line of the center of mass, with the apparatus assumed to be at rest in this coordinate system in the absence of the gravitational wave. The latter would then make the metric coefficients time-dependent and it would also cause an oscillation of the apparatus in this coordinate system. We shall also assume that the curvature is entirely due to the gravitational wave.

If the frequency of the gravitational wave $\omega \ll$ the gap frequency of the superconductor, then the London equations (equation 2.4) and equation 2.5 can be assumed to be valid in the present nonstationary situation. Then, the resulting general relativistic quantization of fluxoid (equation 2.7) can be written approximately in the above coordinate system as[10]

$$\frac{2e}{\hbar c} \int_{\Sigma} \vec{B} \cdot d\vec{s} + \frac{2}{\hbar c} \oint_{\gamma} \zeta g_{oi} dx^i + \frac{2}{\hbar c^2} \oint_{\gamma} \zeta v^i dx^i = 2\pi n, \tag{4.1}$$

where γ is a curve through a closed superconducting subcircuit at constant time and $\vec{v}$ is the velocity field of the superconductor on this curve. Because $g_{oi} = (2/3) R_{ojik} x^j x^k$, the second term in equation 4.1 is due to the "magnetic components," R_{oijk}, of the gravitational wave. The velocity, v^i, in the third term is due to the zero-point oscillation, the thermal fluctuation, and the oscillation of the apparatus primarily due to the "electric components," R_{oioj}, of the gravitational wave.

The latter oscillation can be easily computed for the simple case of each solenoid being uniformly wound around uniform insulating cylinders that are long compared to their diameters so that the solenoids vibrate like Weber bars. Suppose that the axis of a given solenoid is along the x-axis in the interval, $0 \le x \le \ell$, in the absence of the gravitational wave. Neglecting damping forces, the displacement, $u(x, t)$, parallel to the axis of a particle in the cylinder due to the tidal forces of the gravitational wave satisfies

$$\frac{\partial^2 u}{\partial t^2} - v_s^2 \frac{\partial^2 u}{\partial x^2} = -\frac{\omega^2}{2} A \left(x - \frac{\ell}{2} \right) \sin (\omega t + \beta),$$

where A is the amplitude of the gravitational wave, v_s is the velocity of sound in the cylinder, and β is a constant. This has the exact solution,[10,29]

$$u(x, t) = \frac{A}{2} \left\{ \frac{\ell}{2} - x + \frac{\sin k\left(x - \dfrac{\ell}{2}\right)}{k \cos \dfrac{k\ell}{2}} \right\} \sin (\omega t + \beta), \qquad (4.2)$$

where $k = \omega/v_s$. However, we can also write

$$u(x, t) = \sum_n C_n u_n(x) \sin (\omega t + \beta), \qquad (4.3)$$

where the functions, $u_n(x) = \sqrt{2/\ell} \cos (k_n x)$, with $k_n = \pi n/\ell$, are orthonormal in the interval $[0, \ell]$. Hence,[9]

$$C_n = \int_0^\ell dx\, u_n(x) \frac{A}{2} \left\{ \frac{\ell}{2} - x + \frac{\sin k\left(x - \dfrac{\ell}{2}\right)}{k \cos \dfrac{k\ell}{2}} \right\} = \sqrt{\frac{2}{\ell}} \frac{\omega^2 A(1 - [1 - (-1)^n])}{2k_n^2 (\omega^2 - \omega_n^2)},$$

where $\omega_n = k_n v_s$ are the resonant frequencies.

Suppose that each outer solenoid has a diameter of about 1 m, a magnetic field of $B_o \sim 2$ teslas, $\ell \sim 1 m$, and $\omega \sim 10^3$ Hz. Then, the contribution to the first and second terms in equation 4.1 due to the gravitational wave are, respectively, $2e/\hbar c \int \vec{B}_o \cdot d\vec{s} \times A \sim 10^{17} A$ and $2\zeta/\hbar c \oint \frac{2}{3} R_{\text{olim}} x^\ell x^m dx^i \sim (L/\lambda_c) (\ell^2/\lambda^2) A \sim 10^5 A$, where L is the length of wire and $\lambda_c = h/mc$ is the Compton wavelength of the electron. Also, from equation 4.3, the major contribution to $v/c = (1/c) \partial u/\partial t$ by the gravity wave is $\omega^3 A\ell/c(\omega^2 - \omega_1^2) \sim 10^{-5} A$ if $\omega_1 \sim 10^3$ Hz. Hence, the second and third terms are negligible compared to the first term in equation 4.1 so that the magnetic flux is conserved.

On the other hand, for neutral superfluid helium, equation 4.1 is valid without the first term and $\zeta = mc^2$, where m is the mass of the helium atom. It is seen from the above argument that the proposal made previously[30] to detect gravitational waves by the effect of the "magnetic components" on a superfluid interferometer is not useful in general because the oscillations of the apparatus due to the tidal forces have a much bigger effect for an actual interferometer. It is amusing, nevertheless, to consider a hypothetical apparatus that is ideally rigid, that is, the velocity of sound approaches the velocity of light. Then, $\omega_1 \sim \pi c/\ell \sim 10^9$ Hz so that $v/c \sim 10^{-17} A$. Hence, the contribution from the tidal forces that depend on the "electric components," R_{oioj}, is $2/\hbar c^2 \oint \zeta v^i dx^i \sim 10^{-2} A$ for Cooper pairs and $\sim 10 A$ for helium in an apparatus whose geometry is similar to the above superconducting device. Therefore, this contribution is negligible compared to the contribution from the "magnetic components," and the previous analysis[30] can be used.

The changes in the inductances of the solenoids can be computed using equation 4.2 or 4.3. An advantage of the present Fermi-normal coordinate system for the superconducting detector is that the general relativistic Maxwell equations take the form of the ordinary Maxwell equations. This makes it relatively easy to determine the change in the magnetic flux, δF_3, in the diagonal solenoid due to the effect of the gravitational wave:[10]

$$\delta F_3 = -\frac{2L_1L_2L_3IA}{L_1L_2 + L_2L_3 + L_3L_1}\left(1 - \frac{2\tan\frac{k\ell}{2}}{k\ell}\right)\sin(\omega t + \beta), \qquad (4.4)$$

where L_1, L_2, and L_3 are the inductances of the outer solenoids and the diagonal solenoids, respectively. By measuring δF_3, the gravitational wave can, in principle, be determined.

The sensitivity of this device has been discussed previously.[9,10] A major problem is thermal noise. To overcome this, it may be necessary to make the cylinders (around which the solenoids are wound) very massive. Alternatively, we may join each of the other solenoids to a very massive Weber bar along its axis so that when the bar expands, the solenoid contracts and vice versa. Then, the superconducting device acts as a transducer, as we shall see now.

Assuming that the solenoids stretch or contract uniformly, the fractional changes in their inductances are

$$\frac{\delta L_1}{L_1} = -\frac{\delta\ell_1}{\ell_1}, \qquad \frac{\delta L_2}{L_2} = -\frac{\delta\ell_2}{\ell_2},$$

where $\delta\ell_1$ and $\delta\ell_2$ are the changes in their lengths, ℓ_1 and ℓ_2. However, because the Weber bars are at right angles and assuming that they have the same length d, $\delta\ell_1 = \delta\ell_2$. We also have the quantization conditions for the fluxes through two of the closed subcircuits:

$$L_1I_1 + L_3(I_1 - I_2) = n_1\Phi_o,$$

$$L_2I_2 - L_3(I_1 - I_2) = n_2\Phi_o,$$

where $\Phi_o = h/2e$, and I_1 and I_2 are the currents through L_1 and L_2. On assuming that there is no leakage of flux lines and $\ell_1 = \ell_2 = \ell$, then after some algebra,

$$\delta F_3 = \frac{\delta\ell_1}{\ell_1}\frac{2L_1L_2L_3I}{L_1L_2 + L_2L_3 + L_3L_1}, \qquad (4.5)$$

where we have set $I_1 = I_2 = I$. Now, $\delta\ell_1/\ell \sim A(d/\ell)\sin(\omega t + \beta)$. Therefore, the expression 4.5 is bigger than the expression 4.4 by the approximate factor, d/ℓ. Hence, by making d large and ℓ small, the sensitivity can be correspondingly increased. However, when ℓ is small compared to the diameter of the solenoid, the assumption above that states that the solenoid is long is, of course, no longer valid and the result should be computed again.

ACKNOWLEDGMENTS

I thank Ron Drever for emphasizing the importance of thermal noise in the superconducting gravity wave detector and for a useful discussion. Parts of this paper are also to be published in the proceedings of the conference on the Fundamental Aspects of Quantum Theory, Como, September 4–11, 1985.

NOTES AND REFERENCES

1. LONDON, F. 1950. Superfluids I. Wiley. New York.
2. See, for example: VAN DUZER, T. & C. W. TURNER. 1981. Principles of Superconductive Devices and Circuits. Elsevier. New York/Oxford.
3. DEWITT, B. S. 1966. Phys. Rev. Lett. **16:** 1092.
4. PAPINI, G. 1967. Phys. Lett. **24A:** 32.
5. MEIER, W. & N. SALIE. 1980. *Abstract in* The Ninth International Conference on General Relativity and Gravity, Jena, vol. 2.
6. ANANDAN, J. 1985. *In* Quantum Concepts in Space and Time. C. J. Isham & R. Penrose, Eds. Oxford Univ. Press. London/New York.
7. ANANDAN, J. 1984. Phys. Lett. **105A:** 280.
8. BRADY, R. M. 1982. Ph.D. thesis. Univ. of Cambridge. This thesis assumes that the current in a wire is constant in a gravitational field, which violates charge conservation in general relativity, as can be seen, for example, from reference 14.
9. ANANDAN, J. 1985. Phys. Lett. **110A:** 446.
10. ANANDAN, J. 1986. Proceedings of the Fourth Grossman Meeting on General Relativity, Rome 1985. R. Ruffini, Ed. North-Holland. Amsterdam.
11. SCHIFF, L. I. & M. V. BARNHILL. 1966. Phys. Rev. **151:** 1067.
12. See also: DESSLER, A. J. *et al.* 1968. Phys. Rev. **168:** 737; HERRING, C. 1968. Phys. Rev. **171:** 1361.
13. ANANDAN, J. 1984. Gen. Rel. Grav. **16:** 33.
14. ANANDAN, J. 1984. Class. Quantum Grav. **1:** L51.
15. JOSEPHSON, B. D. 1964. Rev. Mod. Phys. **36:** 216.
16. LENSE, J. & H. THIRRING. 1918. Phys. Z. **29:** 156.
17. A similar argument due to B. D. Josephson was quoted by: ANDERSON, P. W. 1967. Progress in Low Temperature Physics. C. J. Gorter, Ed. North-Holland. Amsterdam. However, it is not clear if this prediction is for the magnetic field in the interior or in the space inside a cavity of the superconductor.
18. A prediction in agreement with equation 3.4 was made by: BRADY, R. M. 1982. J. Low Temp. Phys. **49:** 1. However, his equation (equation 3.3) used to obtain this result can be written in the present notation as $\hbar(\partial\phi/\partial x^\nu) = [-2(mc^2 - W)/c]t_\nu$, which disagrees with equation 2.5 of the present paper and is not gauge invariant.
19. CABRERA, B., H. GUTFREUND & W. A. LITTLE. 1982. Phys. Rev. **B25:** 6644. These authors predict a value for $\vec{B}_o$ that differs from equation 3.4. This work seems to imply, in the present formalism, $p^\mu = 2mc\gamma t^\mu$ in the interior of a superconductor, which appears to disagree with equation 2.5 because $mc^2(\gamma - 1)$ is the average kinetic energy of electrons on the Fermi surface. Moreover, the last equation yields $-\hbar d\phi/d\tau = (2/c) \cdot (mc^2\gamma + eA_\mu t^\mu)$, which also seems to disagree with the Josephson equation (equation 2.6). It, therefore, appears to imply that a Josephson junction can radiate even when there is no electrochemical potential difference across the junction, which would violate conservation of energy. See also: FELCH, S. B. *et al.* 1985. Phys. Rev. **B31:** 7006.
20. POUND, R. V. & G. A. REBKA. 1960. Phys. Rev. Lett. **4:** 337.
21. CLARKE, J. 1968. Phys. Rev. Lett. **21:** 1566.
22. TSAI, J-S., A. K. JAIN & J. E. LUKENS. 1983. Phys. Rev. Lett. **51:** 316.
23. An experiment of this type has recently been performed by: JAIN, A. K. & J. E. LUKENS. 1986. Bull. Am. Phys. Soc. **31:** 495. I thank James Lukens for informing me of this experiment prior to publication.
24. H. A. Farach has suggested to me that such a small velocity can be achieved by uniformly changing the temperature of a rod to which the Doppler-shifting device is attached. Also, T. Datta has suggested the use of the piezoelectric effect on a crystal (namely, its change in size when an electric field is applied) to obtain the same low velocity. A variation of 10

volts/sec of the potential difference across a suitable crystal would be sufficient to get $v \sim 10^{-8}$ m/sec.

25. AHARONOV, Y. & D. BOHM. 1959. Phys. Rev. **115:** 485.
26. COLELLA, R., A. W. OVERHAUSER & S. A. WERNER. 1975. Phys. Rev. Lett. **34:** 1472.
27. GREENBERGER, D. 1986. Ann. Phys. **47:** 116.
28. GREENBERGER, D. & A. W. OVERHAUSER. 1980. Sci. Am. **242:** 66; 1983. Rev. Mod. Phys. **55:** 875.
29. WEBER, J. 1960. Phys. Rev. **117:** 306.
30. ANANDAN, J. 1981. Phys. Rev. Lett. **47:** 463; 1984. Phys. Rev. Lett. **52:** 401.

Quantum Measurement[a]

W. G. UNRUH[b]

Department of Physics
University of British Columbia
Vancouver, British Columbia, Canada V6T 2A6

The problem of quantum measurement theory has had a long and turbulent history. A dominant attitude among most physicists is to ignore the problem—to say that they will use quantum mechanics to calculate, and will leave the "philosophizing" to philosophers, or to physicists who have lost their taste or ability for "real" physics. Although the attitude has some justification in that it is difficult to point to any real discovery that arose out of the concerns having to do with quantum measurement theory, it is also an attitude that denys the main reason why many of us are physicists, namely, a desire to understand the universe around us, and not only to engage in a magical, though effective, manipulation of arcane symbols.

Recently, there has occurred the discovery of at least one hitherto unknown effect that arose out of the investigation of questions of quantum measurement theory. The effect is now known as acceleration radiation, which I discovered about ten years ago.[1] In the process of trying to understand the physical effects of gravity on a quantum field theory, a number of physicists were concerned with the notion of the creation of particles associated with the field by an external gravitational field. In so doing, they came up against the problem of exactly how to define what a particle is. In general, these attempts were directed at a generalization of the definition of particle that is used in a free flat spacetime theory; namely, that a particle is an elementary excitation from the "ground" state of the harmonic oscillator type system, which represents one of the "positive frequency" modes of the free field.

The operators of a linear system can always be written in terms of "creation" and "annihilation" operators; specifically, they can be written as combinations of the momentum, p, and the position operator, q, of the system of the form,

$$a = \alpha p + iq/\alpha,$$

$$a\dagger = \alpha p + iq/\alpha,$$

where a and $a\dagger$ obey the commutation relation,

$$[a, a\dagger] = 1$$

for arbitrary values of α. (I use units throughout in which $\hbar = c = G = k = 1$.)
One can define the "ground" state for these operators by

$$a|0\rangle = 0,$$

[a]This work was supported in part by the National Research Council of Canada, and the Canadian Institute for Advanced Research.
[b]W.G.U. is an LAC Minerals Fellow at the Canadian Institute for Advanced Research.

242

but the states so defined for the various values of α are not the same. If p and q are the momentum and position operators for some single mode of the field, then the first excited state, $a^\dagger|0\rangle$, would be defined as a one-particle state of the field. This definition of one-particle states depends on the value of α. Now, for a harmonic oscillator, the value of α can be uniquely chosen by demanding that the "ground" state also be a minimum energy state. The problem in a general relativistic context is that total energy is not a well-defined concept. The ambiguity in the choice of the factor, α, and thus in the notion of "ground" state or vacuum state is real. Although the mathematical formalism for quantum field theory in a background gravitational field is easy to set up, the physical interpretation in terms of particles seems to be beset by ambiguity.

In order to try to achieve a physical understanding of what a particle is, I asked myself the question of how one would actually measure the presence of a particle. The issue of using the physical process of measurement to define the mathematical object in the theory was to be the guiding principle. In particular, I defined a particle as something that a particle detector would detect. This tautology would have been rather useless if one did not already have an idea of what a particle is, at least in some circumstances, and how one would go about creating something that could detect those entities. This definition of a particle did focus attention on how one should go about trying to define the physical entities in the theory, namely, by looking at the way in which one goes about making measurements in the theory.

Let me briefly describe the sort of model particle detector that was used. Consider a system with two energy levels, labeled 0 and 1. This detector is to be taken as a well-localized object whose dimensions are much, much smaller than any radius of curvature of the spacetime; thus, one can ignore all curvature effects on the detector. The energy levels are defined in the rest frame of the detector, and any acceleration of the detector is taken to be equivalent to the imposition of an external gravitational field by Einstein's equivalence principle. Note that because of these assumptions, the energy levels of the detector are well defined. Now, start the detector off in its lowest energy state, state 0. If the detector is coupled to the field, that coupling could induce transitions from the 0 state to the 1 state. If such a transition does occur, define this as the detection by the detector of a particle of the field.

Now, this definition of a particle detector works perfectly well for those situations in which we feel we know what a particle is. In particular, if such a detector is placed at rest in flat spacetime, and the field is in the usual vacuum state, the detector will remain in its 0 state forever. A particle will never be detected. If now the field is put into an n-particle state (using the usual definition of particle for a free-field theory in flat spacetime), the probability that the detector will be excited is proportional to the number of particles present, and to the cross section of the detector to those particles present (e.g., if some of the particles do not pass over the point where the detector is located, the detector will not detect those particles).

Having defined the model for a particle detector, we can now use it to try to understand the physical content of the field theory that we are interested in. One rather surprising result arose when I asked the question as to what would happen if one took such a detector and accelerated it in a situation in which the field was placed in its vacuum state in flat spacetime. An unaccelerated detector would, as mentioned above, never be found in its excited state 1. The calculation was straightforward. Although I did the calculation in what are called Rindler coordinates for flat spacetime because the calculation there was easier for me, the result has nothing to do with any coordinate system. The calculation could have been (and has been[2]) equally well performed in the usual Minkowski coordinates.

The result I obtained was that the detector did become excited in this case. Furthermore, the excitation rate was just what one would have expected if one had placed the detector into a thermal bath in a gravitational field with g equal to the acceleration of the detector, and the temperature equal to

$$T = a/2\pi \; [\hbar/kc]. \tag{1}$$

This temperature corresponds roughly to 1 K for an acceleration of 10^{21}cm/sec^2. In spite of the extreme conditions necessary to produce a measurable effect, there has been a suggestion recently that one could interpret the spin depolarization of electrons in a synchrotron as a measurement of this effect.[3] The two states of the detector there are taken to be the states of the electron spin parallel or antiparallel to the magnetic field, while the acceleration is provided by the relativistic circular motion of the detector.

This is, thus, one example where some of the concerns that motivate quantum measurement theory have had a direct impact on the discovery of new phenomena. Other examples have occurred in the attempts to understand the behavior of gravity wave detectors in the limit where the quantum properties of the detectors become important.[4] Of course, these examples do not address the key issue of quantum measurement theory, namely, why, when the theory predicts probabilities, do our measurements produce actual values? What feature of the physical world that leads to the definite outcome of experiments are we missing in our theory? They do, however, illustrate that the concern over these questions of quantum measurement theory are not useless, but can lead to genuine insight and understanding of our theories of the physical world.

At this point, I would like to change topics in order to deliver a paean in praise of the Heisenberg representation over the usual Schrödinger representation when discussing issues of quantum measurement theory. Although the two are, of course, mathematically equivalent, I do not believe that they are equivalent in their evocative powers. In particular, I believe that in its mixing of dynamics and "knowledge," the Schrödinger representation has led to many fruitless discussions and debates, including discussions that are difficult to even formulate in the Heisenberg representation. Two questions that have been raised are:

(1) Whether, and how, one can take into account the outcomes of experiments made to the future of the experiment one is interested in.
(2) Along which spatial hypersurface should one consider the reduction of the wave packet to have taken place in the case of a relativistic theory?

In the Schrödinger representation, the development of the theory is all encoded in the wave function, or more generally, the density matrix. The physical attributes of a system, represented by an Hermitian operator, remain fixed. The image one has is that the system has various attributes or potential attributes, and the density matrix encodes those attributes that are made manifest at any one time. Because it is only the state (or density matrix) that changes, whether due to the dynamics of the system, or because of measurements one has made, one gets the feeling that the true physical entity is the wave function. Physical reality resides in the wave function and its changes. At this point, one runs up against the oft-repeated puzzle that the wave function can change in two very different ways: namely, due to the dynamic evolution of the system, or via the "reduction of the wave packet" that occurs when a measurement is made. Furthermore, because the wave function is the physical entity, this reduction is thought of as almost a physical event. Something in the real world out there changes. Because the only effect of physical dynamics is to change the wave function, any change must be due to some sort of physical process.

In the Heisenberg representation, on the other hand, it is the operators that are the dynamic entities. One can regard quantum mechanics as giving the physical entities in the world attributes, but attributes that are not simply represented mathematically by numbers, but by operators. That one could assign numbers to various attributes of physical bodies, and that these numbers are the important characteristics of the bodies, is, of course, a relatively recent historical development; that nature is not satisfied with such a simple representation is not entirely surprising.

In the course of time, it is these that change and develop according to the appropriate laws of motion. Having now described the behavior of the world in terms of the interplay between these operators, one must make a link with our knowledge of the world. The link to our knowledge is given by the wave function. This link is provided in two separate ways. In the first, it is the wave function that encodes our previous interactions with the world, but as we shall see, it does so only in some cases. In the second, it provides us with a way of calculating the probabilities of the outcomes of measurements made of some attribute of the system. During the dynamic evolution of the system, the operators (or attributes) of the system change. During a measurement, the wave function (representing our knowledge of the system) changes. By clearly separating these two aspects of the theory, the Heisenberg representation prevents confusion. The question as to the nature of the two different types of dynamics (namely, the unitary evolution type dynamics, and the measurement type) becomes unaskable. Dynamics is clearly different from measurement. One affects the operators, and the other affects the wave function.

I would like to suggest, however, a slight rewriting of the rules of quantum mechanics that does away also with the wave function as well. The wave function is, as mentioned, used to encode the knowledge that we have about the world, that is, knowledge derived from the outcome of other (often earlier) experiments. As I shall describe later, it handles this task well only if all of those other experiments occurred before the time of interest. Let me then reformulate the correspondence between the theory, along with the probabilities of the outcomes of an experiment slightly differently than usual.

Consider some operator, A, at some time, t. (Remember that, throughout, we are working in the Heisenberg representation, so the operators are time-dependent.) In the usual way, we can define the projection operators, $P_{A\alpha}$, as the projection operator onto the eigenstate of the operator, A, with eigenvalue, α. In the usual description of quantum mechanics, if we make a measurement of A at t, and if the density matrix of the system before the time, t, is ρ, then the probability that the outcome will be α is given by

$$\text{Prob}_\alpha = \text{tr}(\rho P_{A\alpha}), \tag{2}$$

and the density matrix after the measurement is given by

$$\rho f = P_{A\alpha} \rho P_{A\alpha} / \text{Prob}_\alpha. \tag{3}$$

Let me now assume that there is a whole series of measurements that we wish to perform on the set of operators $\{A_i\}$ at the times, t_i (i.e., we measure A_i at the time, t_i). Let me define the operator,

$$R(\{\alpha_i\}) = P_{A_N\alpha_N} \cdots P_{A_1\alpha_1} \rho_I P_{A_1\alpha_1} \cdots P_{A_N\alpha_N}, \tag{4}$$

where ρ_I is some initial density matrix, and where the labeling of the operators is such that the times at which the various measurements are performed satisfy

$$t_1 \leq t_2 \leq \ldots \leq t_N. \tag{5}$$

Now let us say that we are interested in predicting the probability of the outcome of the j-th experiment, that is, the measurement of the operator, A_j, at time, t_j. Let us furthermore assume that the set of operators indexed by the set, $K = \{k'\}$, has not yet been measured (or that we do not know the outcomes of those experiments if they have been measured). Then, the probability of the outcome, α_j (where j is obviously in the set, K), will be given by

$$\text{Prob}(\alpha_j) = \frac{\sum\limits_{\alpha_{k'}; k' \in \{K'-\{j\}\}} \text{tr}[R(\{\alpha_1, \ldots, a_j, \ldots, \alpha_N\})]}{\sum\limits_{\alpha_{k'}; k' \in K'} \text{tr}[R(\{\alpha_1\})]}, \tag{6}$$

where for i not in the set, K', the value of α_i is taken as that which has been measured or determined. Now, if the set, K', includes only operators at times later than any operator whose index is not in K', this probability is just that given by the usual rules of quantum mechanics. For example, if $N \in K'$, and $N \neq j$, then we have as part of both the denominator and the numerator of the above expression,

$$\sum_{\alpha_N} \text{tr}(P_{A_N\alpha_N} [\ldots] P_{A_N\alpha_N}) = \sum_{\alpha_N} \text{tr}(P_{A_N\alpha_N} [\ldots]) = \text{tr}([\ldots]), \tag{7}$$

because of the cyclical nature of the trace operator, because P is a projection operator, $P^2 = P$, and because of the completeness of eigenvectors of the operator, A_N; that is,

$$\sum_{\alpha_N} P_{A_N\alpha_N} = \text{Identity}. \tag{8}$$

In a similar manner, all unmeasured operators at times later than any one measured operator will drop out of the sum in equation 6. Note that if the operators, A_i, have been measured for all i such that $t_i < t_j$, and if the operators, A_k, have not been measured for all k such that $t_k > t_j$, then we can write the probability as

$$\text{Prob}(\alpha_j) = \text{tr}(\rho' P_{A_j\alpha_j}), \tag{9}$$

with

$$\rho' = P_{j-1} \ldots P_1 \rho_I P_1 \ldots P_{j-1} / \text{tr}(P_{j-1} \ldots P_1 \rho_I P_1 \ldots P_{j-1}), \tag{10}$$

where ρ' is the "reduced" density matrix; that is, the effect on the calculation of the probability of obtaining α_j of all of the previous measurements is that given by the usual calculation using the new density matrix, ρ'. This process by which we replace the fact that we know the outcome of a number of previous measurements by using a new density matrix is what is known as the "reduction of the wave packet." Note that this has nothing to do with the dynamics of the physical system, which is all encoded in the time dependence of the operators.

However, the above expression (equation 6) is more general. It allows us to calculate the probability of an outcome if we know the outcome of a measurement made after the one we are interested in. Although this situation is rarely discussed in quantum measurement theory (see, however, other papers in this volume), it is a common practice in experimental physics. For example, in many particle physics experiments, the experimentalist is only interested in those events where some product of the reaction went through a certain detector. The experimentalist selects out only those experiments that meet some such requirement. The experimentalist's interest in the theory is now to calculate the probabilities of various possible reactions at the target, and these are reactions that obviously took place before the reaction product went through the given detector.

A specific example of such an experiment might be the following: A physicist measures the spin of a particle along the x-direction at 9 a.m. and finds it to be $+\frac{1}{2}$. At 11 a.m., the physicist measures it along the y-direction and finds it to be $+\frac{1}{2}$. A graduate student now comes in who had measured the spin along some direction at 10 a.m., and wants to know what the probabilities for the various possible outcomes of that experiment were. The physicist's first reply to such a question might be, "Because of my measurement at 9 a.m., the state of the spin just before the measurement at 10 a.m. was in an eigenstate of the x-spin operator, $|x = \frac{1}{2}\rangle$. Thus, the probability of getting $\frac{1}{2}$ in your experiment is given by

$$P_{1/2} = \langle x = \frac{1}{2} | \frac{1}{2} + S_\lambda | x = \frac{1}{2} \rangle, \tag{11}$$

where S_λ is the spin operator along the direction in which you measured the spin." The graduate student answers, "But surely that cannot be right. Suppose that I measured the y-component of the spin. Then your measurement at 11 a.m. means that I must with certainty have had the result of $\frac{1}{2}$, while your reasoning would give me only a probability of 50% of getting $\frac{1}{2}$. On the other hand, had I measured S_x, I would again with certainty have had the result of $\frac{1}{2}$."

One can readily see that, in fact, there is no state or density matrix for the system that one can use to calculate the desired probability. No density matrix can make the outcomes of either an S_x or an S_y be $\frac{1}{2}$ with certainty.

On the other hand, the probabilities for the various outcomes of the possible measurements at 10 a.m. are easily calculable. In the language most people would use, one would calculate this probability by assuming that this set of experiments had been carried out a very large number of times. At 9 a.m., S_x was found to be $\frac{1}{2}$. One can then calculate the probability that at 10 a.m., S_λ was measured to be either $\frac{1}{2}$ or $-\frac{1}{2}$, and we could thus calculate the number of times in which either of these results would be obtained. One can then calculate, for each member with that outcome, how many times the value of S_y at 11 a.m. had values of $\frac{1}{2}$ or $-\frac{1}{2}$. Now, out of the whole set of possible outcomes, we can select those, and only those, in which S_y was $\frac{1}{2}$ at 11 a.m. One can then count the number of cases in this subject where S_λ was $\frac{1}{2}$, and assign the probability to that outcome as that number of times divided by the total number of cases in which S_y was $\frac{1}{2}$.

After doing the calculation, one obtains

$$\text{Prob}(S_\lambda = \tfrac{1}{2}) = \frac{\text{tr}(P_{x1/2}P_{\lambda 1/2}P_{y1/2}P_{y1/2}P_{\lambda 1/2}P_{x1/2})}{\Sigma_\lambda\,(P_{x1/2}P_\lambda P_{y1/2}P_{y1/2}P_\lambda P_{x1/2})}, \tag{12}$$

where $P_{x1/2}$ is the projection operator, $|x\tfrac{1}{2}\rangle\,\langle x\tfrac{1}{2}|$, and similarly for y and λ. The sum in the denominator is over the two possible eigenvalues for S_λ. If S_λ is the spin in the direction, $n = (\cos\theta, \sin\theta, 0)$, then the answer for the probability turns out to be

$$\text{Prob}(S_\lambda = \tfrac{1}{2}) = (1 + \cos\theta + \sin\theta + \sin 2\theta/2)/(2 + \sin 2\theta). \tag{13}$$

Now, the expression (equation 12) for the probability is just that given by equation 6 restricted to this case. Because the initial measurement of S_x was a complete measurement on the system, the result is also independent of ρ_I. It is interesting to note that although the description of how I went about calculating the probability seemed to select out an order in time (from 9 to 11 a.m.) and seemed to treat the first measurement differently from the second, the result is actually completely symmetric. S_x and S_y enter into the expression in the identical manner.

Furthermore, the general expression (equation 6) is also completely symmetric with respect to the past and the future if one takes ρ to be the identity, or, equivalently, if one assumes that a subset of the operator, $P_1 \ldots P_{j-1}$, is a complete set of operators for the system. One can write

$$\text{tr}(P_N \ldots P_j \ldots P_1 P_1 \ldots P_j \ldots P_N) = \text{tr}(P_1 \ldots P_j \ldots P_N P_N \ldots P_j \ldots P_1). \tag{14}$$

Thus, this demonstrates that the measurement process is not time-asymmetric as is sometimes claimed. The only time-asymmetry is introduced by the setting of the initial condition with ρ_I, or by stating that the earlier measurements have been made, while the later ones have not.

Let us now consider another situation, namely, one in which A_j is defined at time, t_j, and A_{j+1} is defined at time, $t_{j+1} > t_j$. Let us furthermore assume that we know the outcome of the measurement on A_{j+1}. In general, in this situation the measurement on A_{j+1} is not equivalent (in its effect on the probabilities of the outcomes of the measurement of A_j) to replacing the density matrix by a reduced density matrix as in equation 10. However, if A_j and A_{j+1} commute, the effect is the same. In the expression for the probabilities for the various possible outcomes of the A_j measurement, one has terms of the form,

$$\text{tr}(\ldots P_{A_{j+1}\alpha_{j+1}}P_{A_j\alpha_j}\rho_{j-i}P_{A_j\alpha_j}P_{A_{j+1}\alpha_{j+1}}\ldots), \tag{15}$$

where ρ_{j-1} is the reduced density matrix from the previous $j-1$ measurements. Because the P's for A_j and A_{j+1} commute, however, this term may be written as

$$\text{tr}(\ldots P_{A_j\alpha_j}P_{A_{j+1}\alpha_{j+1}}\rho_{j-i}P_{A_{j+1}\alpha_{j+1}}P_{A_j\alpha_j}\ldots). \tag{16}$$

The density matrix,

$$\rho' = P_{A_{j+1}\alpha_{j+1}}\rho_{j-i}P_{A_{j+1}\alpha_{j+1}}, \tag{17}$$

can be used to calculate all of the probabilities for the outcomes of measurements of A_j. One, therefore, has here a situation in which the effect of a measurement after the present one can be represented by a "reduction" of the density matrix for the experiment of concern. Note that this is only true for the measurement of those operators that now commute with the operator measured at a later time.

One can apply this result immediately to the question about the effect of the measurement of one operator on another one that is spacelike separated from the first in a relativistic theory. In that case, the two operators must commute. We can thus always regard the effect of the measurement of the one on the other as a "reduction" of the density matrix.

Equation 6 thus represents a formulation of measurement in the Heisenberg representation that seems to me to clarify a number of issues that can lead to confusion in the Schrödinger representation.

REFERENCES

1. UNRUH, W. G. 1976. Phys. Rev. **D14:** 870; see also: UNRUH, W. G. & R. M. WALD. 1984. Phys. Rev. **D29:** 1047.
2. See, for example: SANCHEZ, N. 1981. Phys. Lett. **105B:** 375.
3. BELL, J. S. & J. M. LEINAAS. 1984. Nucl. Phys. **B212:** 131.
4. See, for example: CAVES, C. 1986. Phys. Rev. **D33:** 1643; CAVES, C. 1983. Quantum nondemolition measurements. *In* Quantum Optics, Experimental Gravitation, and Measurement Theory. P. Meystre & M. O. Scully, Eds. Plenum. New York; and references therein.

Progress in Back Action Evasion Experiments[a]

MARK F. BOCKO[b] AND WARREN W. JOHNSON[c]

[b]Department of Electrical Engineering
[c]Department of Physics and Astronomy
University of Rochester
Rochester, New York 14627

INTRODUCTION

The ultimate limit of our ability to gain information about the natural world is defined by the quantum noise that arises in the process of measurement. In most cases, the information being sought can be viewed as the magnitude and time-dependence of a generalized "force" or "signal" that acts on some part of a measurement system. Our ability to acquire useful information can then often be characterized by specifying the weakest signal that could be detected in the presence of the internal noise of the measurement.

It is, therefore, of great fundamental and practical interest to determine the origin and magnitude of the quantum noise that arises in the process of linear detection. Josephson-junction-based Superconducting QUantum Interference Devices (SQUIDs), quasi-particle heterodyne mixers, and Josephson junction parametric amplifiers are among the linear detectors that recently have achieved noise performances approaching a "quantum limit."[1-3] It is essential to understand the role of the quantum measurement process in the function of such devices in order to be able to make detailed predictions of the quantum noise. Alternatively, one may view such systems as a testing ground for the quantum theory of measurement.

The original motivation was to develop more sensitive detectors of gravitational radiation from the cosmos. Braginsky[4] was the first to suggest that a massive Weber bar[5] detector should be viewed as a macroscopic quantum oscillator, with the nature of which determining a "standard quantum limit" to antenna sensitivity. However, Braginsky,[6] as well as Caves, Thorne, and co-workers,[7] proposed novel measurement strategies that could circumvent the "standard quantum limit." These techniques are known collectively as Quantum NonDemolition or QND. In a QND measurement, one settles for partial information about the oscillator observables with the bonus of reduced fluctuations in the measured observables. Caves et al. made a realistic proposal for a system that should be able to perform a QND measurement. It was this definite proposal that sparked our interest to consider the possibility of experimental investigation.[8]

We will discuss the experiment under development in which we plan to continuously measure the amplitude and phase of a mechanical, macroscopic quantum oscillator. We have confined our investigation to an extremely simple linear detector

[a]This work was supported by the National Science Foundation.

with the hope that it may shed some light on the more general problem of the linear detection process. We also plan to implement the QND technique in an attempt to reduce the noise of this linear detector below the "standard quantum limit."[9] If the QND strategy works, it will have important applications—the first of which will be the improvement of future gravitational radiation antennae.

We present a classical model of an oscillator-transducer-amplifier chain, and conclude that two independent noise sources are required to realistically model the measurement process in such a system. In particular, we model the amplifier as an ideal current amplifier with a voltage noise source at the input and a purely additive current noise source at the output.[10] We show that both noise sources must be present or the model predicts an infinite sensitivity for some choices of parameters. We believe that this will also be a requirement of a quantum model for a measurement, and we conjecture that:

Any model of a continuous linear quantum measurement process must contain two separate sources of noise to adequately represent the effect of measurement.

We present experimental data that confirm all of the terms in the equations of the classical model. We have demonstrated both the forward coupling characteristics of the system, that is, how the output responds to the behavior of the mechanical oscillator, and the reverse coupling characteristics, or the effect of the measuring apparatus on the dynamics of the oscillator. Finally, we assess the prospects for achieving the experimental parameters necessary to reach the quantum domain.

LINEAR DETECTION AND THE "QUANTUM LIMIT"

A linear detector is distinguished from a square-law detector such as a photomultiplier in that the former responds to the amplitude and phase of an incoming signal and the latter has an output proportional to the magnitude squared of an incoming signal.

We begin by ignoring everything except the quantum nature of the system, which in this case is a simple harmonic oscillator. The question we ask is how accurately in a linear measurement can one determine a force that acts on the oscillator? We consider the simplest and most common version of the quantum measurement process, which we call a "one-shot measurement." The measurement process is broken down into three steps:

(1) Initial state preparation;
(2) Free evolution of the system;
(3) Collapse of the wave function.

Quantum mechanics allows us to calculate the distribution function for the results of measurements on an ensemble of identically prepared systems. The noise in the measurement is represented by the width of this distribution.

Before we continue, it is convenient to introduce the complex amplitude of the simple harmonic oscillator,

$$X_1 + jX_2 = (x + jp/m\omega)e^{j\omega t},$$

where x is the oscillator displacement, p is the momentum, m is the mass, ω is the angular frequency, and $j = (-1)^{1/2}$. If the systems are prepared in a familiar coherent state, then the distribution of measurement results will have equal scatter in the X_1 and X_2 values (see FIGURE 1). If one could prepare the system in some other state, for example, a squeezed coherent state, then the fluctuations in one component of the complex amplitude could be reduced below the coherent state level at the expense of an increase of fluctuations in the other phase. Hollenhorst gave an analysis of the results of one-shot measurements on a harmonic oscillator for a variety of initial states.[11]

The one-shot model of the measurement process is suggestive, but it does not realistically describe the measurement process in the experiments we envision in which one will continuously monitor a single quantum system. Before proceeding to describe the requirements of a quantum model that could adequately describe the continuous measurement process, we seek guidance from a classical model of such systems.

CLASSICAL MODEL

The proposal of Caves *et al.*[7] for a QND measurement scheme is a specific example of a parametric transducer. Our realization of their proposal is a bridge circuit with a resonant readout arm in which the movement of the mechanical oscillator causes an imbalance of the bridge (see FIGURE 2). The mechanical oscillator has a mass, m, an angular frequency, ω_1, and a relaxation time, τ_1. The electrical resonator is composed of the parallel combination of the two capacitors with the readout arm inductance, L, to give an angular frequency, $\omega_2 = (2CL)^{-1/2}$, and a relaxation time, τ_2. The coupling

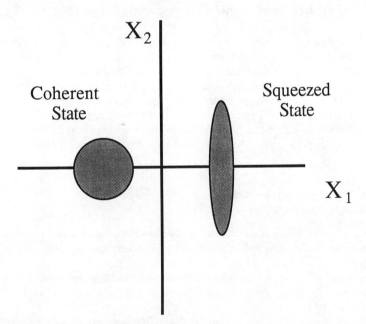

FIGURE 1. The distribution of expected values for a measurement of a harmonic oscillator's complex amplitude in a coherent state and a squeezed state.

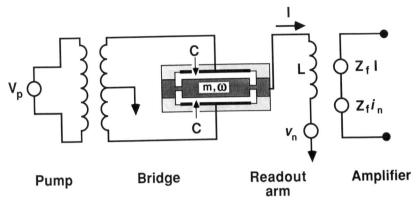

Pump **Bridge** **Readout arm** **Amplifier**

FIGURE 2. The parametric transducer. A mechanical resonator, shown here as a mass loaded diaphragm, is one plate of a three-plate capacitor. The electric fields created by the pump voltage across the capacitors couple the motion of the resonator to the bridge circuit. The bridge circuit is nominally balanced, so motion of the diaphragm causes a current to flow in the resonant readout arm. The readout current is amplified by a current amplifier with forward transfer impedance, Z_f.

between the mechanical and electrical oscillators is through a time-varying electric field furnished by an external pump. We represent this as

$$E_p(t) = E_0/2\{(1 - f) \cos (\omega_2 + \omega_1)t + (1 + f) \cos (\omega_2 - \omega_1)t\}.$$

When $f = 1$, the bridge is excited at the difference of the mode frequencies, and the device functions as a familiar parametric up-convertor; when $f = -1$, the device works as a phase-inverting up-convertor, and when $f = 0$, the coupling between the two oscillators is that suggested by Caves et al.[7,12] to perform a QND measurement. In terms of the complex amplitudes, X_1, X_2, of the mechanical oscillator and Q_1, Q_2 of the electrical resonator, the equations of motion are:

$$(d/dt + 1/2\tau_1) X_1 = f (E_0/4) (1/m\omega_1)Q_2 - [(f_S + f_L)/m\omega_1] \sin (\omega_1 t),$$

$$(d/dt + 1/2\tau_1) X_2 = -(E_0/4) (1/m\omega_1) Q_1 + [(f_S + f_L)/m\omega_1] \cos (\omega_1 t),$$

$$(d/dt + 1/2\tau_2) Q_1 = f (E_0/4) (1/L\omega_2) X_2 - (v_n/L\omega_2) \sin (\omega_2 t),$$

$$(d/dt + 1/2\tau_2) Q_2 = -(E_0/4) (1/L\omega_2) X_1 + (v_n/L\omega_2) \cos (\omega_2 t).$$

We have introduced the signal force, f_S, which acts on the mechanical oscillator, and the random variables, f_L and v_n, to represent, respectively, the Langevin force acting on the mechanical oscillator (with double-sided spectral density, $2kTm/\tau_1$) and the random voltage that drives the electrical resonator. The random voltage, v_n, has two contributions: the input noise of the amplifier and another Langevin term (with double-sided spectral density, $2kTL/\tau_2$) to model the Johnson noise of the electrical resonator. The physical temperature of the two oscillators is T.

As a first observation, note that when $f = 0$, the coupling between the two oscillators is nonreciprocal. Q_1 and Q_2 are the accessible output quantities, but Q_2 alone

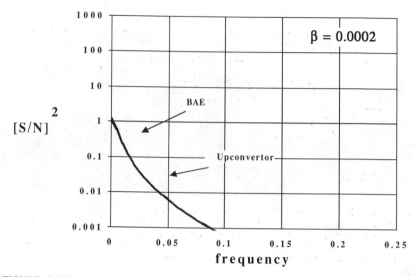

FIGURE 3. The calculated spectral density of the signal-to-noise ratio for the parametric up-convertor and the BAE scheme. An impulsive signal is assumed. The coupling strength is $\beta = 0.0002$.

contains information about the mechanical variables (specifically, X_1). Thus, one claims that X_1 is the measured system variable. Furthermore, we see that X_1 is isolated from the noise source, v_n, that excites the electrical oscillator. For this reason, the name of Back Action Evasion (BAE) is given to the $f = 0$ measurement strategy.

SPECTRAL SENSITIVITY MEASURE

How does one define a useful figure of merit for this classical model of a linear detector? To answer this, one must keep the original intention in mind. The purpose is to monitor for any changes in a force that may be acting on the mechanical oscillator. Therefore, we are led to two conclusions. First, because we are interested in detecting some signal in the presence of noise, the important quantity is the signal-to-noise ratio. The noise alone is an insufficient characterization. Secondly, because we are looking for changes in the force that acts on the system, we must have some measure of the self-correlation of the output data stream. Thus, we adopt the spectral density (the Fourier transform of the autocorrelation function) of the signal-to-noise ratio as the quantity sought for characterization. This quantity is also conveniently accessible experimentally.

We choose Q_2 as the measured output quantity, and calculate its response to an impulsive signal, $f_s = p_0\delta(t)$, as well as to the assumed sources of noise. In calculating the noise spectrum of Q_2, it must be remembered to include the contribution from the amplifier additive noise represented by i_n. We form the spectral density of the signal-to-noise ratio, denoted $(S/N)^2$, to find

$$(S/N)^2 = (N_s/N_n)\,(\beta\gamma/8\pi)\,[\,|J(y)|^2 + \alpha\beta\gamma/8 + \gamma^2|G_1(y)|^2]^{-1}.$$

·We have made the following definitions:

$$\alpha \equiv (T/T_n) \, (\omega_2/\omega_1) \, (1/\omega_1\tau_1),$$

$$\beta \equiv E_0^2 \, (\omega_2/\omega_1) \, (C/m\omega_1^2),$$

$$\gamma \equiv (\omega_2/\omega_1) \, \omega_2 C Z_n,$$

and

$$J(y) \equiv G_1(y) G_2(y) + f\beta/8$$

with

$$G_1(y) \equiv (jy + 1/2\omega_1\tau_1) \quad \text{and} \quad G_2(y) \equiv (jy + 1/2\omega_1\tau_2).$$

The noise temperature and noise impedance of the electronics are $T_n = (\,|i_n|\,|v_n|\,)/k$ and $Z_n = (\,|v_n|\,/\,|i_n|\,)$, with $|\ \ |$ denoting the square root of the double-sided spectral density. We have defined $N_s = p_0^2/2m\hbar\omega_1$ as the number of quanta that the impulsive force would impart to an initially unexcited mechanical oscillator, and $N_n = kT_n/\hbar\omega_2$ as the noise number of the electronics. The frequency, y, is normalized by ω_1.

To plot the curves in FIGURES 3 and 4, we assumed that there was no Brownian noise in the mechanical oscillator ($\alpha = 0$) and plotted $(S/N)^2$ as a function of the frequency, y. Compare the conventional $f = 1$ case to the BAE case of $f = 0$ in the limits of weak coupling ($\beta = 0.0002$) and strong coupling ($\beta = 0.2$) (see FIGURES 3 and 4, respectively). When the coupling is weak, the two measurement techniques have indistinguishable signal-to-noise spectra. When the coupling becomes strong, the signal-to-noise spectra differ radically in the two cases. In the BAE case, the signal-to-noise spectrum retains the same frequency dependence as the spectrum in the weak coupling limit, but it continually increases in magnitude in proportion to the

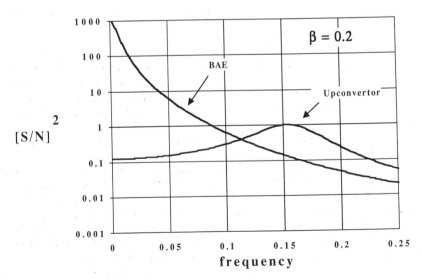

FIGURE 4. The same as FIGURE 3, but with $\beta = 0.2$.

coupling strength, β. It appears that in the BAE case, when $\alpha = 0$, the signal-to-noise spectrum increases without bound. In fact, there are second-order modulation terms left out of the equations here that determine a finite limit for the signal-to-noise ratio.[9]

The behavior of the system is much more complex for the conventional parametric up-convertor case of $f = 1$. One finds that the peak of the signal-to-noise spectrum linearly increases in proportion to β up to some maximum value. After this point, the signal-to-noise spectrum begins to broaden, and eventually, the position of the peak begins to shift in frequency. This behavior is a manifestation of the well-known dynamic damping and frequency pulling of parametric up-convertors.[13] The model indicates that the bandwidth over which useful information is distributed becomes wider as the coupling is increased. Thus, to make a meaningful comparison of the different cases, one must assume that the optimum sampling bandwidth is being used.

We have done an explicit calculation of the optimum figure of merit as a function of the parameters. In this calculation, the detection bandwidth is implicit, so the detailed knowledge gained from an examination of the signal-to-noise spectra is lost.[14] We find it convenient to express the result in terms of the number of quanta that would be deposited in the unexcited mechanical oscillator by an impulse that would give an integrated signal-to-noise ratio of unity. We call this quantity, the impulse noise number, N_I. The result may be expressed as

$$N_I = N_n/r,$$

where

$$1/r = (f^2 + 8\alpha\gamma/\beta)^{1/2}\{1 + (\beta/4\gamma^2)[(f^2 + 8\alpha\gamma/\beta)^{1/2} - f]\}^{1/2}$$

when $(\alpha\beta/2\gamma^3)(1 + f\gamma/\alpha) > 1$, and

$$1/r = (2)^{-1/2}(f^2 + 8\alpha\gamma/\beta)^{1/2} \times (\{1 - f(\beta/4\gamma^2) + [1 - (\beta/2\gamma^2)(f + \alpha/\gamma)]^{1/2}\}^{1/2}$$
$$+ \{1 - f(\beta/4\gamma^2) - [1 - (\beta/2\gamma^2)(f + \alpha/\gamma)]^{1/2}\}^{1/2})$$

when $(\alpha\beta/2\gamma^3)(1 + f\gamma/\alpha) < 1$.

We now return to an examination of the signal-to-noise spectra to make a further observation. In the absence of additive noise, the signal-to-noise spectra for the conventional and the BAE cases are identical. One may arrive at this result by making γ infinite and N_E zero, thus holding the product constant. Even more alarming is that as the coupling strength increases, the signal-to-noise ratio increases without bound. It is only when there is also a purely additive noise source that we obtain some limit for the sensitivity of the detector. BAE may then be used to improve the signal-to-noise ratio over that limit.

The elimination of the back-acting noise in a BAE measurement, though, is not the essential feature that distinguishes it from a conventional measurement. The reason why a BAE measurement works is that it allows one to retain a narrow sampling bandwidth even for strong coupling; thus, the amount of wideband additive noise in the filtered output may be kept small. Conversely, for a conventional measurement, when the coupling is strong, one is forced to use a much wider sampling bandwidth; consequently, it will suffer a greater contribution from the additive noise.

We draw two very important general conclusions from this illustration. First, the spectral distribution of the signal-to-noise ratio is the important factor in the determination of the figure of merit for a linear detector; spot signal-to-noise ratios are insufficient. Second, the full description of a linear detector requires two separate noise sources—one back-acting and the other purely additive.

EXPERIMENTAL TESTS

In summary, the experiments performed so far by several groups have proven the correctness of the classical model, but there is a large gap between the current achievements and the quantum noise regime.

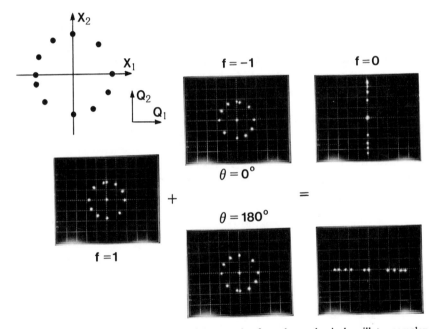

FIGURE 5. Experimental investigation of the mapping from the mechanical oscillator complex amplitude plane (X_1, X_2) onto the electrical mode complex amplitude plane (Q_1, Q_2) for the three types of parametric coupling discussed in the text. In the lower row, the phase of the sum frequency component of the pump is advanced 180 degrees.

The phase-sensitive nature of the forward coupling that is predicted for the BAE measurement has been demonstrated in electromechanical devices by our group at Rochester,[15] and the back action evasion behavior has been reported by Spetz *et al.*[16] and Bordoni *et al.*[17]

In FIGURE 5, we display the phase-sensitive forward coupling characteristic of a BAE measurement. We performed cryogenic experiments on a prototype gravitational radiation antenna transducer in which a mechanical oscillator with a frequency of 16 kHz was coupled to a superconducting radio frequency bridge with a frequency near 4 MHz. In a series of measurements, the mechanical oscillator was excited with varying phases, and the mapping of the excitation signal into the output from the bridge was monitored. We see that there is a one-to-one mapping from the mechanical oscillator to the output signal for the two conventional modes of operation, $f = \pm 1$, but that when $f = 0$, the mapping is degenerate and the information about one of the mechanical oscillator phases is lost. This demonstrates how, in a BAE measurement, one is able to measure a single component of an oscillator complex amplitude.

The data in FIGURE 6 show the effect of the reverse coupling on the measured oscillator for the parametric up-convertor mode of operation. We have plotted the relaxation time of the mechanical oscillator versus the coupling strength given by the pump voltage. We predict, from the equations of motion, that the relaxation time, τ, of the mechanical oscillator varies as

$$(\tau/\tau_1)^{-1} = 1 + 2f\beta_1(\omega_2/\omega_1)(\omega_1\tau_1)(\omega_2\tau_2)V_{pump}^2,$$

where β_1 is the value of β for a pump voltage of 1 volt peak-to-peak. In the conventional $f = 1$ case, we find the relaxation time decreases as β is increased, which is in agreement with the formula. The solid curve is the model prediction with the absolute coupling strength, β_1, adjusted to 2.07×10^{-6} for the best fit. We do not yet have an independent measure of β_1.

The estimated displacement sensitivity that has been reached so far is less than the sensitivity required to see the quantum fluctuations. FIGURE 7 is a plot of the noise spectrum of the bridge output under the best experimental conditions yet achieved. The noise spectrum has two peaks: a broad one that corresponds to the bridge resonance, and a narrow peak characteristic of the mechanical resonance. The large

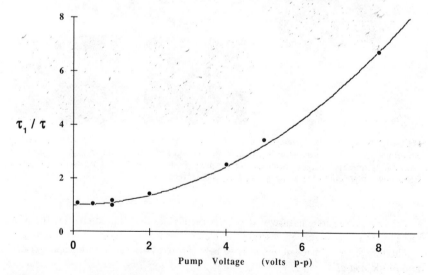

FIGURE 6. The measured relaxation time of the mechanical mode is plotted versus the pump voltage for the parametric up-convertor. This shows the influence of the transducer on the dynamics of the mechanical oscillator. The quantity plotted is the inverse of the relaxation time normalized to the uncoupled value.

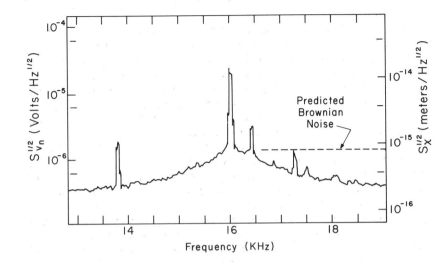

FIGURE 7. The measured noise spectrum from the output of the parametric transducer operated in the up-convertor mode. The central sharp peak is the mechanical oscillator resonance, and the broad peak is the resonance of the transducer electrical mode. The other sharp peaks are electromagnetic interference.

excitation of the mechanical oscillator is due to unwanted mechanical excitation from the environment, which could be eliminated by additional vibration isolation. The level of the noise in the broad peak translates to an equivalent position noise of 2×10^{-16} meters in the bandwidth of the mechanical oscillator. The mass is 0.8 grams and the frequency is 16 kHz, which gives a quantum limit of 8×10^{-19} meters; this is a factor of 250 less than the present sensitivity limit.

To close this section, we will discuss the relationship between a QND experiment and the generation of optical squeezed states. Recently, Slusher *et al.*[18] produced a squeezed, nearly minimum uncertainty state of the optical radiation field. They demonstrated that it is possible to prepare a state that, in one of its phases, has a distribution of measured field amplitudes that is more narrow than that of a minimum uncertainty coherent state. The essential difference between these optical experiments and a QND experiment is that in the QND experiment, one will make a continuous measurement on the same quantum system without destroying it. In the optical experiment, the quantum system is prepared in a special state and then a "one-shot" measurement is performed that destroys the state. Squeezed states will probably enter in the description of a QND experiment, but unlike the optical experiment, the QND experiment will allow us to address the quantum measurement problem by allowing repeated measurements.

TOWARD A QUANTUM MODEL OF A CONTINUOUS LINEAR MEASUREMENT

The one-shot model of the quantum measurement process outlined earlier may be an accurate description of atomic-beam–Stern-Gerlach-type experiments, but the classical model just presented suggests that a more sophisticated quantum model is required to describe a continuous measurement. We have seen from the classical model that as soon as one considers the possibility of multiple or continuous measurements of a system, a joint probability distribution function is required to describe the data. The simplest quantity to measure that gives such information is the two-point correlation function; one usually measures its Fourier transform, specifically, the power spectral density, as in FIGURE 7. In general, one may need even higher order correlation functions. A quantum theory should furnish the same description.

One model that gives such a description is the path integral approach of Caves.[19] He develops a general formulation and applies it to the continuous measurement of the position of a one-dimensional nonrelativistic quantum system. The application of the path integral formulation to predict the measurable quantities in the experiments described here remains to be understood.

There are other outstanding problems in a full quantum description of a continuous linear detection process. The first question is: "What does a linear detector detect?"

It is customary to assume that the measured quantum observables and their correlations are the same as the corresponding classical dynamical variables and their correlations. As an illustration of the potential pitfall in making such an assumption, we examine the treatment of the photodetection process by Mandel.[20] He considered the fluctuations in the photoelectron counts for two types of photon detectors. The first is a familiar photodetector (such as a photomultiplier) that operates by the ionization of an atom when a photon is absorbed from the radiation field. This detector "measures" the normally ordered combinations of the radiation mode annihilation and creation operators. In a second type of photon detector, which Mandel calls the "quantum counter," the radiation field is measured by a stimulated emission process with an atom in an excited state. In this device, the photoelectron counting correlations are given by the antinormally ordered creation and annihilation operators. The noise in the two types of photon detectors differ by the zero-point term.

Mandel shows that in the classical limit (i.e., a large number of photons per mode of the radiation field), the two types of photon detectors have identical photoelectron counting statistics. It is only in the limit of very weak radiation fields that the zero-point term becomes noticeable. The behavior of these two detectors is identical in the classical limit, but deviates greatly in the quantum regime. This underscores the necessity of a microscopic quantum picture of the linear amplifier to predict the quantum noise that arises in the measurement process.

A model of a quantum measurement with a linear detector must also account for the effects of large coupling between the system and apparatus. The classical model of the parametric up-convertor has shown how the dynamics of the measured system are strongly influenced by the coupling to the measurement apparatus. The absence of dynamic damping in the BAE scheme is the key to reducing the classical noise. We must also understand the differences between reciprocal and nonreciprocal coupling in the quantum model.

In a Langevin description of quantum noise, the effect of "zero-point fluctuations" is included by the addition of a "zero-point term" to the Langevin force. Aside from this feature, the calculations are purely classical, so our model may serve as a guide for a quantum Langevin calculation. We saw in the classical model that two sources of noise are required to give an acceptable description; thus, we conclude that a quantum Langevin model that contains a single noise source to account for the quantum noise is inadequate. This provides the motivation for our conjecture:

Any model for a continuous linear quantum measurement process must contain two separate sources of noise to adequately represent the effect of the measurement.

FUTURE PROSPECTS AND CONCLUSIONS

At present, there is scant experimental evidence upon which to base a quantum theory of the linear detection process. The correctness of the corresponding classical theory is well supported by experiments, but the sensitivity of these experiments falls short (by a factor of approximately 250) of that believed needed to see quantum effects. We are actively seeking to improve the experiments to the quantum level of sensitivity.

The major experimental obstacle to be overcome is thermal noise. The relevant combination of physical parameters is $T/\omega\tau$, where T is the physical temperature of the device and $\omega\tau$ is roughly the number of cycles in the mode decay time. The minimum requirements to reach the quantum noise level have been determined;[8] for the mechanical oscillator, it is $T/\omega\tau \leq 10^{-10}$, and for the electrical mode of oscillation, $T/\omega\tau \leq 10^{-7}$. These values have been achieved in other experiments,[21,22] but it is a formidable task to integrate these achievements into a working measurement system.

We have presented a classical model of a particular linear detector, along with experimental evidence that supports the model. The unusual feature of this linear detector is that it may be operated in a nonreciprocal mode, BAE, that improves the noise over a conventional measurement strategy. The important relationship between the classical model and possible quantum models is in the form of the predictions that the models must be capable of making. The time correlation of the output data stream is needed to characterize the noise of the measurement, and the classical model furnishes a prediction of this quantity in the form of a signal-to-noise spectral density. The conventional "one-shot" description of quantum measurements is inadequate for this purpose and we propose that an accurate quantum model must provide a similar description. Recently, such an approach has been undertaken by Caves.[19] Although a quantum Langevin description may make the required predictions of the correlation functions, the classical model shows the necessity of two separate noise sources in the description of a linear measurement. Thus, the quantum Langevin approach is inadequate to properly describe quantum noise for a linear detector. We also conclude that, in addition to these requirements, a suitable quantum model of linear detection must account in some way for back action and the difference between reciprocal and nonreciprocal coupling strategies.

The experimental possibility to construct linear detectors that have noise at or below the "quantum limit" will not only be of technological importance, but will also provide a unique testing ground for quantum measurement theory.

ACKNOWLEDGMENTS

We wish to thank David H. Douglass for his discussions and enlightening advice, and Robert Kaser for rescuing the nearly completed manuscript from destruction in the jaws of a malfunctioning computer network.

REFERENCES

1. CROMAR, M. W. & P. CARELLI. 1981. Appl. Phys. Lett. **38:** 723.
2. MCGRATH, W. R., A. V. RAISANEN, P. L. RICHARDS, R. E. HARRIS & F. L. LLOYD. 1985. IEEE Trans. Magn. **MAG-21:** 212.
3. CALANDER, N., T. CLAESON & S. RUDNER. 1982. J. Appl. Phys. **53:** 5093.
4. BRAGINSKY, V. B. & YU. I. VORONTSOV. 1975. Sov. Phys. Usp. **17:** 644.
5. WEBER, J. 1960. Phys. Rev. **117:** 306.
6. BRAGINSKY, V. B. & A. B. MANUKIN. 1977. Measurement of Weak Forces in Physics Experiments. D. H. Douglass, Ed. Univ. of Chicago Press. Chicago.
7. CAVES, C. M., K. S. THORNE, R. W. P. DREVER, V. D. SANDBERG & M. ZIMMERMANN. 1980. Rev. Mod. Phys. **52:** 341.
8. JOHNSON, W. W. & M. F. BOCKO. 1981. Phys. Rev. Lett. **47:** 1184.
9. BOCKO, M. F. & W. W. JOHNSON. 1982. Phys. Rev. Lett. **48:** 1371.
10. CLARKE, J., C. D. TESCHE & R. P. GIFFARD. 1974. J. Low Temp. Phys. **37:** 405.
11. HOLLENHORST, J. N. 1979. Phys. Rev. **D19:** 1669.
12. THORNE, K. S., R. W. P. DREVER, C. M. CAVES, M. ZIMMERMANN & V. D. SANDBERG. 1978. Phys. Rev. Lett. **40:** 667.
13. LOUISELL, W. H., A. YARIV & A. E. SIEGMANN. 1961. Phys. Rev. **124:** 1646.
14. PAPOULIS, A. 1977. Signal Analysis. McGraw–Hill. New York.
15. BOCKO, M. F. & W. W. JOHNSON. 1984. Phys. Rev. **A30:** 2135.
16. SPETZ, G. W., A. G. MANN & W. O. HAMILTON. 1984. Phys. Lett. **104A:** 335.
17. BORDONI, F., S. DEPANFILIS, F. FUGLINI, V. IAFOLLA & S. NOZZOLI. Proceedings of the Fourth Marcel Grossman Meeting on General Relativity. In press.
18. SLUSHER, R. E., L. W. HOLLBERG, B. YURKE, J. C. MERTZ & J. F. VALLEY. 1985. Phys. Rev. Lett. **55:** 2409.
19. CAVES, C. M. 1985. Quantum mechanics of measurements distributed in time. A path integral approach. California Institute of Technology preprint no. GRP-042.
20. MANDEL, L. 1966. Phys. Rev. **152:** 438.
21. MCGUIGAN, D. F., C. C. LAM, R. Q. GRAM, A. W. HOFFMAN, D. H. DOUGLASS & H. W. GUTCHE. 1978. J. Low Temp. Phys. **30:** 621.
22. STONE, J. L. & W. H. HARTWIG. 1968. J. Appl. Phys. **39:** 2665.

EPR Correlations and EPW Distributions

J. S. BELL

CERN CH-1211
Geneva 23, Switzerland

It is known that with Bohm's example of EPR correlations involving particles with spin, there is an irreducible nonlocality. The nonlocality cannot be removed by the introduction of hypothetical variables unknown to ordinary quantum mechanics. How is it with the original EPR example involving two particles of zero spin? Here, we will see that the Wigner phase-space distribution[1] illuminates the problem.

Of course, if one admits "measurement" of arbitrary "observables" on arbitrary states, it is easy to mimic[2] the EPRB situation. Some steps have been made towards realism in that connection.[3] Here, we will consider a narrower problem that is restricted to "measurement" of positions only on two noninteracting spinless particles in free space. EPR considered "measurement" of momenta as well as positions. However, the simplest way to "measure" the momenta of free particles is just to wait a long time and "measure" their positions. Here, we will allow position measurements at arbitrary times, t_1 and t_2, on the two particles respectively. This corresponds to "measuring" the combinations,

$$\hat{q}_1 + t_1\hat{p}_1/m_1 \quad \text{and} \quad \hat{q}_2 + t_2\hat{p}_2/m_2, \tag{1}$$

at time zero, where m_1 and m_2 are the masses, and the $\hat{q}$ and $\hat{p}$ are position and momentum operators, respectively. We will be content here with just one space dimension.

The times, t_1 and t_2, play the same roles here as do the two polarizer settings in the EPRB example. One can envisage then some analogue of the CHHS inequality[4,5] discriminating between quantum mechanics on the one hand and local causality on the other.

The QM probability of finding at times, t_1 and t_2, respectively, that there are particles at positions, q_1 and q_2, respectively, is

$$\rho(q_1, q_2, t_1, t_2)$$

with

$$\rho = |\psi(q_1, q_2, t_1, t_2)|. \tag{2}$$

The two-time wave function, ψ, satisfies the two Schrödinger equations:

$$i\hbar\,\partial\psi/\partial t_1 = H_1\psi = (\hat{p}_1^2/2m_1)\psi,$$

$$i\hbar\,\partial\psi/\partial t_2 = H_2\psi = (\hat{p}_2^2/2m_2)\psi, \tag{3}$$

with

$$i\hat{p}_1 = \hbar\partial/\partial q_1, \quad i\hat{p}_2 = \hbar\partial/\partial q_2.$$

For simplicity, we will consider the case of equal masses, and take units such that

$$m_1 = m_2 = \hbar = 1.$$

The same ρ (equation 2) can be obtained from the corresponding two-time Wigner distribution:

$$\rho = \iint \frac{dp_1}{2\pi} \frac{dp_2}{2\pi} W(q_1, q_2, p_1, p_2, t_1, t_2), \tag{4}$$

where

$$W = \iint dy_1 dy_2 e^{-i(p_1 y_1 + p_2 y_2)} \psi\left(q_1 + \frac{y_1}{2}, q_2 + \frac{y_2}{2}, t_1, t_2\right) \psi^*\left(q_1 - \frac{y_1}{2}, q_2 - \frac{y_2}{2}, t_1, t_2\right). \tag{5}$$

From equation 3,

$$(\partial/\partial t_1 + p_1 \partial/\partial q_1) W = (\partial/\partial t_2 + p_2 \partial/\partial q_2) W = 0; \tag{6}$$

that is, W evolves exactly as does a probability distribution for a pair of freely moving classical particles:

$$W(q_1, q_2, p_1, p_2, t_1, t_2) = W(q_1 - p_1 t_1, q_2 - p_2 t_2, p_1, p_2, t_1, t_2). \tag{7}$$

When W happens to be initially nowhere negative, the classical evolution (equation 7) preserves the nonnegativity. The original EPR wave function,[6]

$$\delta[(q_1 + \tfrac{1}{2}q_0) - (q_2 - \tfrac{1}{2}q_0)], \tag{8}$$

which is assumed to hold at $t_1 = t_2 = 0$, gives

$$W(q_1, q_2, p_1, p_2, 0, 0) = \delta(q_1 - q_2 + q_0) 2\pi \delta(p_1 + p_2). \tag{9}$$

This is nowhere negative, and the evolved function (equation 7) has the same property. Thus, in this case, the EPR correlations are precisely those between two classical particles in independent free classical motion.

With the wave function (equation 8), there is no nonlocality problem when the incompleteness of the wave function description is admitted. The Wigner distribution provides a local classical model of the correlations. Since the Wigner distribution appeared in 1932, this remark could already have been made in 1935. Perhaps it was. Perhaps, though, it was already anticipated that wave functions other than equation 8, with Wigner distributions that are not nonnegative, would provide a more formidable problem. We will see that this is so.

Consider, for example, the initial wave function,

$$(q^2 - 2a^2) e^{-q^2/(2a^2)}, \tag{10}$$

where

$$q = (q_1 + q_0/2) - (q_2 - q_0/2). \tag{11}$$

It could be made normalizable by including a factor,

$$\exp\{-[(q_1 + q_0/2) + (q_2 - q_0/2)]^2/(2b^2)\}. \tag{12}$$

However, we will immediately anticipate the limit, $b \to \infty$, and will consider only relative probabilities. By choosing the unit of length so that $a = 1$, this gives as the initial Wigner distribution,

$$W(q_1, q_2, p_1, p_2, 0, 0) = Ke^{-q^2}e^{-p^2}\{(q^2 + p^2)^2 - 5q^2 + p^2 + 11/4\}\delta(p_1 + p_2), \quad (13)$$

where K is an unimportant constant, and

$$p = (p_1 - p_2)/2. \quad (14)$$

This W in equation 13 is in some regions negative—for example, at $(p = 0, q = 1)$. It no longer provides an explicitly local classical model of the correlations. I do not know that the failure of W to be nonnegative is a sufficient condition in general for a locality paradox. However, it happens that equation 13 implies (besides the negative regions in the Wigner distribution) a violation of the CHHS locality inequality.

To see this, first calculate the two-time position probability distribution either from equations 4, 7, and 13, or from equation 2 and the solution of equation 3. The result is

$$\rho = K'(1 + \tau^2)^{-5/2}[q^4 + q^2(2\tau^2 - 4) + 3(1 + \tau^2) + (1 + \tau^2)^2] e^{-q^2/1+\tau^2}, \quad (15)$$

where K' is an unimportant constant, and

$$\tau = t_1 + t_2. \quad (16)$$

Then, calculate the probability, D, that $(q_1 + q_0/2)$ and $(q_2 - q_0/2)$ disagree in sign:

$$D(t_1, t_2) = \int_{-\infty}^{\infty} dq|q|\rho \quad (17)$$

$$= K''(\tau^2 + 2/5)/\sqrt{\tau^2 + 1}. \quad (18)$$

Finally, consider the CHHS inequality,

$$E(t_1, t_2) + E(t_1, t_2') + E(t_1', t_2) - E(t_1', t_2') \leq 2, \quad (19)$$

where

$$\left. \begin{aligned} E(t_1, t_2) &= [\text{probability of } (+, +)] \\ &+ [\text{probability of } (-, -)] \\ &- [\text{probability of } (+, -)] \\ &- [\text{probability of } (-, +)]. \end{aligned} \right\} \quad \begin{aligned} (20) \\ \\ (21) \end{aligned}$$

Using equation 21, equation 19 becomes

$$D(t_1, t_2) + D(t_1, t_2') + D(t_1', t_2) - D(t_1', t_2') \geq 0. \quad (22)$$

With

$$t_1' = 0, \quad t_2 = \tau, \quad t_1 = -2\tau, \quad t_2' = 3\tau, \quad (23)$$

and assuming (in view of equation 18)

$$D(t_1, t_2) = F(|t_1 + t_2|), \quad (24)$$

equation 22 gives (for τ positive)

$$3F(\tau) - F(3\tau) \geq 0. \tag{25}$$

However, this is violated by equation 18 when τ exceeds about 1. There is a real nonlocality problem with the wave function (equation 10).

Only some epsilonics will be added here. The essential assumption for equation 19 is (very roughly) that the measurement on particle 1 is irrelevant for particle 2, and vice versa. This follows from local causality[7] if we look for the particles only in limited space-time regions,

$$|q_1 + q_0/2| < L, |t_1| < T,$$

$$|q_2 - q_0/2| < L, |t_2| < T, \tag{26}$$

with

$$L \ll q_0, cT \ll q_0, \tag{27}$$

so that the two regions (equation 26) have spacelike separation. We must, however, make L large enough (when compared with b in equation 12) so that the particles are almost sure to be found in the regions in question. This is so because in passing from equation 20 to 21, it was assumed that the four probabilities in equation 20 add to unity; also, b in turn must be large compared with a, as was used to simplify the detailed calculations. Therefore, as well as equation 27, we specify

$$1 \gg a/b \gg (b/L)e^{-L^2/b^2}. \tag{28}$$

NOTES AND REFERENCES

1. WIGNER, E. P. 1932. Phys. Rev. **40:** 749.
2. BELL, J. S. 1965. Physics **1:** 195.
3. HORNE, M. A. & A. ZEILINGER. 1985. *In* Symposium on the Foundations of Modern Physics, Joensuu, Finland. P. Lahti & P. Mittelstaedt, Eds. World Scientific. Singapore. Also, see reference 9 below.
4. CLAUSER, J. F., R. A. HOLT, M. A. HORNE & A. SHIMONY. 1969. Phys. Rev. Lett. **23:** 880.
5. CLAUSER, J. F. & A. SHIMONY. 1978. Rep. Prog. Phys. **41:** 1881.
6. EINSTEIN, A., B. PODOLSKY & N. ROSEN. 1935. Phys. Rev. **47:** 779.
7. BELL, J. S. 1976. Theory of local beables. Preprint CERN-TH 2053/75. Reprinted in Epistem. Lett. **9:** 11 (1976) and in Dialectica **39:** 86 (1985). The notion of local causality presented in this reference involves complete specification of the beables in an infinite space-time region. The following conception is more attractive in this respect: in a locally causal theory, the probabilities attached to values of local beables in one space-time region, when values are specified for all local beables in a second space-time region that fully obstructs the backward light cone of the first, are unaltered by specification of values of local beables in a third region with spacelike separation from the first two (see reference 8 below).
8. The discussion has a new interest when the positions, q_1 and q_2, are granted beable status. Then, we can consider their actual values rather than "measurement results" at arbitrary times, t_1 and t_2. External intervention by hypothetically free-willed experiments is not involved.
9. See also: KHALFIN, L. A. & B. S. TSIRELSON. 1985. Joensuu proceedings (see reference 3); CETTO, A. M., L. DE LA PEÑA & E. SANTOS. 1985. Phys. Lett. **A113:** 304. These last authors invoke the Wigner distribution.

Decay of Quantum Coherence due to the Presence of a Heat Bath

Markovian Master-Equation Approach[a]

R. F. O'CONNELL,[b] C. M. SAVAGE,[c] AND D. F. WALLS[c]

[b]*Department of Physics*
Louisiana State University
Baton Rouge, Louisiana 70803

[c]*Department of Physics*
University of Waikato
Hamilton, New Zealand

INTRODUCTION

Presently, there is much interest in models of the measurement process. We use the technique of Markovian master equations to describe the interaction of various systems with an environment of harmonic oscillators. As described by Zurek,[1] we find that certain couplings tend to diagonalize the system's reduced density operator in the so-called pointer basis.

In general terms, we are considering a quantum system, S, on which one carries out measurements via a quantum apparatus, A, which is coupled to an environment, E. In the first stage of the measurement (as shown by von Neumann[2]), unitary evolution introduces correlations between the state vectors of S and A. (This is not destroyed by the presence of the environment.) Also, after the correlation has been established, the interaction between S and A is essentially negligible. However, when the measurement is completed, there is an apparent ambiguity as to which states the quantum system will find itself in; this in turn stems from the ambiguity in the choice of the preferred basis for A (the variables of A being "traced out" in the second stage of the measurement). Zurek argues that a natural choice of what is actually observed emerges by consideration of an interaction, H_{AE}, between A and E that establishes correlations between A and E. In essence, H_{AE} determines the so-called "pointer observable," P, as being the observable for which $[P, H_{AE}] = 0$. In other words, taking the environment, E, into account determines the mixture into which the S-A-E collapsed.

There has been a recent surge of activity in many different areas that focuses on the crucial role of the environment. For example, in condensed matter physics, Caldeira and Leggett[3] and many others have considered the effect of dissipation due to the environment on quantum tunneling of a macroscopic variable. Zeh[4] and Wigner[5] pointed out that it is virtually impossible to isolate a macroscopic body, which, in turn,

[a]This research was partially supported by the U.S. Office of Naval Research under Contract No. N 00014-86-K-0002.

led Wigner to remark "... that quantum mechanics' validity has narrower limitation [in] that it is not applicable to the detailed behavior of macroscopic bodies. ...." The analysis of Wigner was based on the consideration of a cubic centimeter of tungsten at the temperature of 3 K of intergalactic space. An example from the realm of atomic physics is the recent demonstration[6] that the absorption spectrum of light by atoms is affected by the ambient temperature,[7] and Ford, Lewis, and O'Connell[8] have emphasized the necessity of analyzing this problem by treating the atom-laser system as being immersed in a heat bath of blackbody radiation. Furthermore, their exact analysis showed that, at least for this particular problem, non-Markovian effects play a crucial role. In addition, this calculation demonstrated that one can supplement traditional quantum mechanical techniques with stochastic methods for the purpose of calculating environmental effects.

We turn now to a detailed look at how the reduced density matrix tends to become diagonalized in the pointer basis; thus, from henceforth, we will simply use S to denote the combined correlated system-apparatus. In a recent series of papers, Walls, Milburn, and Savage (WMS)[9–11] discussed concrete models of the quantum measurement process using a Markovian master-equation approach, and they showed that any macroscopic quantum coherence will be rapidly destroyed by its interaction with the environment. Thus, this provides a possible mechanism for the reduction of the wave function. Their starting point is a Hamiltonian describing a quantum system coupled to an environment of harmonic oscillators, and they find that certain couplings tend to diagonalize the system's reduced density matrix, ρ, in the so-called pointer basis of Zurek. These papers considered specific system-environment interaction Hamiltonians, H_{SE}. Here, we consider a more general system observable, O_S, in the expression for H_{SE} (while recognizing that it does not encompass all the situations considered by WMS). In particular, if O_S is chosen to be a constant of the motion or, less restrictively, a quantum nondemolition variable, then we show that the off-diagonal elements, ρ_{mn}, decay to zero at an exponential rate proportional to $(m - n)^2$.

Consider a quantum system coupled to an environment of harmonic oscillators so that the total Hamiltonian is

$$H = H_S + H_E + H_{SE},   \tag{1.1}$$

where H_S and H_E are, respectively, the free system and environment Hamiltonians. We take the system-environment interaction Hamiltonian to be

$$H_{SE} = \hbar O_S(\Gamma_E + \Gamma_E^+),   \tag{1.2}$$

where O_S is a system observable ($O_S = O_S^+$) and $\Gamma_E = \Sigma_i\, g_i a_i$ is the usual sum of environmental annihilation operators weighted by coupling strengths. In addition, $H_E = \Sigma_i \hbar \omega_i a_i^+ a_i$, as is usual.

If O_S is a constant of the system's free motion, $[O_S, H_S] = 0$, then the following interaction picture of the master equation for the system's reduced density operator may be derived (see also Louisell[12] and Lindblad[13]) as

$$\frac{\partial \rho}{\partial t} = \frac{\gamma}{2}(2O_S\rho O_S - O_S^2\rho - \rho O_S^2),   \tag{1.3}$$

where $\gamma/2$ is the damping constant. Actually, in equation 4.3 of reference 13, Lindblad has written down a result for $(\partial\rho/\partial t)$ that he argues is the most general time-homogeneous quantum mechanical Markovian master equation with a bounded Liouville operator; replacing V by O in Lindblad's equation (to conform to our notation) and setting $O^+ = 0$ results in our equation 1.3. Taking matrix elements in the basis of O_S, $O_S|m\rangle_S = m|m\rangle_S$, we have

$$\frac{\partial\rho_{mn}}{\partial t} = -\frac{\gamma}{2}(m-n)^2\rho_{mn}, \tag{1.4}$$

where $\rho_{mn} = \langle m|\rho|n\rangle$. The solution follows immediately:

$$\rho_{mn}(t) = \exp\left[-\frac{\gamma}{2}(m-n)^2 t\right]\rho_{mn}(o). \tag{1.5}$$

This solution has the remarkable property that the off-diagonal elements, ρ_{mn}, go to zero at an exponential rate given by $\gamma(m-n)^2/2$. In the case of nonzero temperatures, it may be verified that the corresponding rate is $\gamma(2\bar{n}+1)(m-n)^2/2$, where $\bar{n}$ is the average number of photons.

In the less restrictive case, where O_S is not a constant of the motion, but, instead, is a quantum nondemolition (QND) observable, the eigenvalues, m and n, are functions of time. Consequently, equation 1.5 is replaced by

$$\rho_{mn}(t) = \exp\left[-\frac{\gamma}{2}\int_0^t \{m(t)-n(t)\}^2 dt\right]\rho_{mn}(o). \tag{1.6}$$

O_S is an example of Zurek's pointer observable. The diagonalization of the reduced density operator in the pointer basis is due to the interaction Hamiltonian, H_{SE}, correlating different pointer eigenstates with nearly orthogonal environmental states. This can be seen explicitly for the preceding system by considering the approximate unitary evolution of an initial superposition of pointer eigenstates correlated with the vacuum state of the environment:

$$|\psi, t=0\rangle = (|m\rangle_S + |n\rangle_S)|\{o\}\rangle_E. \tag{1.7}$$

This is an eigenstate of the free Hamiltonian, so an approximate expression for the state at times, $t \ll \Omega^{-1}$, where Ω is the bath cutoff frequency, is

$$|\psi, t\rangle = \exp\{iO_S(\Gamma_E + \Gamma_E^+)t\}|\psi, t=0\rangle$$
$$= |m\rangle_S|\{-ik_j mt\}\rangle_E + |n\rangle_S|\{-ik_j nt\}\rangle_E, \tag{1.8}$$

where the environmental oscillators are in coherent states and we have used the result,

$$\exp[i(\alpha a^+ + \alpha^* a)]|O\rangle = |i\alpha\rangle. \tag{1.9}$$

Tracing the total density operator, $|\psi\rangle\langle\psi|$, over the environment yields the reduced density operator,

$$\rho(t) = |m\rangle\langle m| + |n\rangle\langle n| + \eta|m\rangle\langle n| + \eta^*|n\rangle\langle m|,$$

where

$$\eta = {}_E\langle\{-ik_jmt\}|\{-ik_jnt\}\rangle_E = \exp\left[-1/2\sum_j |k_j|^2(m-n)^2t^2\right]. \qquad (1.10)$$

Because it diagonalizes the system's density matrix in the pointer basis, the environment can be regarded as performing a measurement on the pointer observable. Choosing it to be a constant of the motion, $[O_S, H_S] = 0$, results in the particularly simple behavior of equation 1.5. Choosing it to be a QND observable results in equation 1.6. Examples of systems for which O is a QND variable are the harmonic oscillator coupled to its environment by the number observable, a^+a, or by the quadrature phase observable, $X_\theta = a^+e^{i\theta} + ae^{-i\theta}$, where each of which is a QND observable of the harmonic oscillator. Phase damping of a spin in a magnetic field may be modeled by coupling the QND observable, J_z, to a bath. The QND coupling for a free particle is via momentum.

Many examples of non-QND pointer observables have been considered by Walls, Milburn, and Savage,[9–11] and thus it is of interest to review the salient points of their results for comparison with the situation of QND pointer observables. In all cases, the system(-apparatus) is taken to be an harmonic oscillator (except for the case considered in the section entitled FREE PARTICLE, where the frequency of the oscillator is taken to be zero), and the environment is treated as an ensemble of harmonic oscillators. Thus, the basic choice remaining concerns the form for H_{SE}, and particularly, the choice of O_S in equation 1.2 for H_{SE}. In the next section, we discuss the results for coordinate-coordinate interaction in the rotating-wave approximation[9] so that $\hbar O_S = a$, and hence, O_S is not a QND observable. A similar remark applies in the third section of this paper to the case where $\hbar O_S = x$, where x is the coordinate of the system oscillator, which again is not a QND observable quantity. This system displays residual correlations over lengths of the order of its thermal de Broglie wavelength.[10] The zero frequency (or high temperature) limit of the corresponding master equation[11] is considered in the final section.

HARMONIC OSCILLATOR: AMPLITUDE DAMPING, ZERO TEMPERATURES

Consider the following harmonic oscillator Hamiltonian,[9]

$$H = \hbar\omega a^+a + a\Gamma^+ + a^+\Gamma + H_E, \qquad (2.1)$$

where Γ represents a reservoir operator. This reservoir coupling is equivalent to coordinate-coordinate coupling in the rotating-wave approximation in which high frequency terms are ignored. In the Born and Markov approximations (i.e., lowest order perturbation in the interaction with the bath is assumed and memory effects are neglected), the harmonic oscillator's reduced density operator satisfies the following Schrödinger picture master equation,[12]

$$\frac{\partial\rho}{\partial t} = -i\omega[a^+a,\rho] + \frac{\gamma}{2}(2a\rho a^+ - a^+a\rho - \rho a^+a), \qquad (2.2)$$

where we have taken a zero temperature environment. In order to obtain a suitable solution for ρ, we introduce the quantum characteristic function,

$$\kappa(\lambda) = \text{tr}(\rho e^{\lambda a^+} e^{-\lambda^* a}). \tag{2.3}$$

Because ρ satisfies equation 2.2, κ satisfies the equivalent equation,

$$\left\{ \frac{\partial}{\partial t} + \left(\frac{\gamma}{2} - i\omega \right) \lambda \frac{\partial}{\partial \lambda} + \left(\frac{\gamma}{2} + i\omega \right) \lambda^* \frac{\partial}{\partial \lambda^*} \right\} \kappa = 0. \tag{2.4}$$

The general solution of this equation is

$$\kappa(\lambda e^{-(\gamma/2 - i\omega)t}, \lambda^* e^{-(\gamma/2 + i\omega)t}), \tag{2.5}$$

where κ is chosen to fit the initial condition of $\kappa(t = 0)$. The density operator and the characteristic function corresponding to an initial superposition of coherent states are, respectively,

$$\rho(o) = \sum_{\alpha,\beta} N_{\alpha\beta} |\alpha\rangle \langle\beta| \tag{2.6a}$$

and

$$\kappa(o) = \sum_{\alpha,\beta} N_{\alpha\beta} \langle\beta|\alpha\rangle \, e^{\lambda\beta^* - \lambda^*\alpha}. \tag{2.6b}$$

With this initial condition, the solution to equations 2.4 and 2.2 are[9]

$$\kappa(t) = \sum_{\alpha,\beta} N_{\alpha\beta} \langle\beta|\alpha\rangle \exp\left\{ (\beta^* e^{i\omega t}\lambda - \alpha e^{-i\omega t}\lambda^*) \, e^{-\gamma t/2} \right\} \tag{2.7a}$$

and

$$\rho(t) = \sum_{\alpha,\beta} N_{\alpha\beta} \langle\beta|\alpha\rangle^{(1 - e^{-\gamma t})} |\alpha e^{-(\gamma/2 + i\omega)t}\rangle \langle\beta e^{-(\gamma/2 + i\omega)t}|. \tag{2.7b}$$

Thus, the off-diagonal elements are reduced by the factor, $\langle\beta|\alpha\rangle^{(1 - e^{-\gamma t})}$. The greater the separation of the initially superposed states, the more rapid and complete the reduction of coherence. After a few γ^{-1} of time, the initial coherent state superposition is reduced to a near diagonal mixture of coherent states.

HARMONIC OSCILLATOR COORDINATE OVERDAMPING

In this section, we consider the harmonic oscillator to be coupled via its coordinate, x, to the coordinates of the reservoir oscillators represented by X. The relevant Hamiltonian is[10]

$$H = \hbar\omega a^+ a + xX + H_E. \tag{3.1}$$

After taking the continuum limit for the number of bath oscillators and making the Born and Markov approximations, Agarwal[14] (see also Caldeira and Leggett,[15] and

Dekker[16]) obtained the Schrödinger picture master equation, which is

$$\frac{\partial \rho}{\partial t} = -i\omega[a^+ a, \rho] - \frac{i\gamma}{\hbar} [x, P\rho + \rho P] - \frac{2\gamma}{\hbar} (\bar{n} + \frac{1}{2}) \, m\omega[x, [x, \rho]], \qquad (3.2)$$

where P is the oscillator's momentum operator, m is its mass, and $\bar{n} = [\exp(\hbar\omega/kT) - 1]^{-1}$ is its mean occupation number when in equilibrium at temperature, T. Solving for the quantum characteristic function as in the previous section, Savage and Walls[10] obtained the Q function, $\langle z|\rho|z \rangle$, and from this, they also obtained an expression for the density operator. Taking coordinate basis matrix elements, they find in the heavily overdamped limit of $\gamma \gg \omega$,

$$\langle x - y|\rho|x + y \rangle = (2\pi\sigma_x^2)^{-1/2} \sum_{\alpha\beta} N_{\alpha\beta} \langle \beta|\alpha \rangle \times \exp\{-C^2(\beta^* - \alpha)^2 e^{-4\gamma t}\sigma_y^2\}$$

$$\times \exp\{-\frac{1}{2}\sigma_x^{-2} [x - C^{-1}(\beta^* + \alpha) \, e^{-(\omega^2/2\gamma)t}]^2\}$$

$$\times \exp\{-\frac{1}{2}\sigma_y^{-2} [y - C\sigma_y^2 (\beta^* - \alpha) \, e^{-2\gamma t}]^2\}. \qquad (3.3)$$

The variances of the diagonal, σ_x^2, and off-diagonal, σ_y^2, parts are

$$\sigma_x^2 = C^{-2}[1 + 2\bar{n}(1 - e^{-(\omega^2/\gamma t)})],$$

$$\sigma_y^2 = C^{-2} [1 + 2\bar{n}(1 - e^{-4\gamma t})]^{-1},$$

with

$$C = (2m\omega/\hbar)^{1/2}. \qquad (3.4)$$

As pointed out by Savage and Walls,[10] at high temperatures and after a time of a few γ^{-1}, the off-diagonal variance becomes $\hbar^2/(4mkT) = (\lambda_d/4\pi)^2$, where λ_d is the de Broglie wavelength associated with the oscillators mean kinetic energy at temperature, T. The spreading of the diagonal part occurs at a much slower rate determined by the quantity, ω^2/γ. Thus, for times, t, satisfying $\gamma/\omega^2 \gg t \gg 1/(4\gamma)$, the density operator has been substantially diagonalized in the coordinate basis without much thermal spreading of the diagonal matrix element. The off-diagonal variance can be made arbitrarily small by making the temperature or oscillator mass sufficiently high.

Thus, the overdamped oscillator described by the Hamiltonian in equation 3.1 provides a model of coordinate measurement on the harmonic oscillator. The diagonalization (otherwise referred to as collapse of the state vector) may occur without disturbing the initial diagonal coordinate distribution.

FREE PARTICLE

The zero frequency (or equivalently, the high temperature) limit of equation 3.2 yields the master equation for the coordinate damped free particle:[11]

$$\frac{\partial \rho}{\partial t} = \frac{i}{\hbar} \bigg/ [\vec{P}^2/2m, \rho] - \frac{i\gamma}{\hbar} [\vec{x}, \vec{P}\rho + \rho\vec{P}] - 2m\gamma kT\hbar^{-2}[\vec{x}, [\vec{x}, \rho]]. \qquad (4.1)$$

To solve this equation, Savage and Walls[11] introduced the quantum characteristic function,

$$\kappa(\vec{\lambda}, \vec{\mu}) = \text{Tr}(\rho e^{i(\vec{\lambda}\cdot\vec{x} + \hbar^{-1}\vec{\mu}\cdot\vec{P})}). \tag{4.2}$$

An interesting initial condition is the superposition of plane waves with wave vectors, $\vec{K}_1$ and $\vec{K}_2$. The corresponding initial wave function and the coordinate basis density matrix elements are, respectively,

$$\psi(\vec{x}) = \frac{1}{\sqrt{2}}(e^{i\vec{K}_1\cdot\vec{x}} + e^{i\vec{K}_2\cdot\vec{x}}) \tag{4.3a}$$

and

$$\langle\vec{x}|\rho|\vec{x} - \vec{\mu}\rangle = \tfrac{1}{2}e^{i\vec{K}_1\cdot\vec{\mu}}(1 + e^{i(\vec{K}_2-\vec{K}_1)\cdot\vec{x}}) + \tfrac{1}{2}e^{i\vec{K}_2\cdot\vec{\mu}}(1 + e^{i(\vec{K}_2-\vec{K}_1)\cdot\vec{x}}). \tag{4.3b}$$

Solving for $x(t)$ and inverting, we find[6]

$$\langle\vec{x}|\rho|\vec{x} - \vec{\mu}\rangle = \tfrac{1}{2}\exp\{-\tfrac{1}{2}mkT\hbar^{-2}(1 - e^{-4\gamma t})\vec{\mu}^2\}$$

$$\times \{e^{ie^{-2\gamma t}\vec{K}_1\cdot\vec{\mu}} + e^{ie^{-2\gamma t}\vec{K}_2\cdot\vec{\mu}} + e^{-\eta}e^{(i/2)e^{-2\gamma t(\vec{K}_1+\vec{K}_2)}\cdot\vec{\mu}}[e^{\vec{a}\cdot(\vec{K}_1-\vec{K}_2)} + e^{-\vec{a}\cdot(\vec{K}_1-\vec{K}_2)}]\}, \tag{4.4}$$

where we have introduced the quantities,

$$\eta = \frac{kT}{2\gamma^2 m}\left[\gamma t - \frac{3}{4} + e^{-2\gamma t} - \frac{1}{4}e^{-4\gamma t}\right]|\vec{K}_1 - \vec{K}_2|^2,$$

$$\vec{a} = \frac{kT}{2\gamma\hbar}(1 - 2e^{-2\gamma t} + e^{-4\gamma t})\vec{\mu}$$

$$+ i\left\{-\vec{x} + \tfrac{1}{2}\vec{\mu} + \frac{\hbar}{4\gamma m}(1 - e^{-2\gamma t})(\vec{K}_1 + \vec{K}_2)\right\}. \tag{4.5}$$

The first factor on the right-hand side of equation 4.4 tends to diagonalize the coordinate basis density matrix. For example, Savage and Walls[11] considered a neutron mass and environmental temperature of 100 K to enable this factor to be about $\exp[-(1 - e^{-4\gamma t})(10^{10}\vec{\mu})^2]$. Assuming a one percent decrease in particle momentum, we have $\gamma t \approx 0.05$ (see below) and the factor becomes $\exp[-(2 \times 10^9 \vec{N})^2]$. This factor is small for $|\vec{N}| \gg 10^{-9}$m, so quantum coordinate coherence extends over about 10^{-9} meters, which is, for example, much less than the width of a bubble-chamber track.

The first two terms in the second factor on the right-hand side of equation 4.4 describe a mixture of particles having momentum, $e^{-2\gamma t\hbar\vec{K}_1}$ and $e^{-2\gamma t\hbar\vec{K}_2}$. Thus, the environmental interaction damps the particle momentum.

The interference pattern of the initially superposed plane waves is revealed in the diagonal matrix elements ($\vec{\mu} = 0$ in equation 4.4),

$$\langle\vec{x}|\rho|\vec{x}\rangle = 1 + e^{-\eta}\cos\left[\vec{x}\cdot(\vec{K}_1 - \vec{K}_2) - \frac{\hbar}{4\gamma m}(1 - e^{-2\gamma t})(\vec{K}_1^2 - \vec{K}_2^2)\right], \tag{4.6}$$

where η is defined in equation 4.5. The factor, $e^{-\eta}$, reduces the visibility of the interference fringes.

The exponent, η, is always positive and increases with time. Being proportional to $|(\vec{K}_1 - \vec{K}_2)|^2$ means that the fringe visibility reduces rapidly with increasing separation in the wave-vector space of the initially superposed waves.

It is interesting to compare our expression for fringe visibility with an experiment in which electron interference fringes due to superimposed plane waves have been observed.[11] The electron wavelength was about 0.04 Å and the flight time was about 10^{-9} s. At room temperature, η is about

$$\eta \approx 10^{16}(\gamma t)^{-2}[\gamma t - \tfrac{3}{4} + e^{-2\gamma t} - \tfrac{1}{4}e^{-4\gamma t}]. \qquad (4.7)$$

Because the interference pattern was clearly visible, γt, which determines the momentum damping, would have to be exceedingly small ($\gamma t \approx 10^{-16}$) for the model to be consistent with experiment.

ACKNOWLEDGMENTS

R. F. O'Connell would like to thank G. W. Ford and J. T. Lewis, who originally brought to his attention the work of Lindblad (reference 13).

REFERENCES

1. ZUREK, W. H. 1981. Phys. Rev. **D24**: 1516; 1982. Phys. Rev. **D26**: 1862.
2. VON NEUMANN 1932. Mathematische Grundlagen der Quantenmechanik. Springer-Verlag. Berlin; 1955. Mathematical Foundations of Quantum Mechanics. Princeton Univ. Press. Princeton, New Jersey.
3. CALDEIRA, A. O. & A. J. LEGGETT. 1983. Ann. Phys. **149**: 374.
4. ZEH, H. Z. 1971. *In* Foundations of Quantum Mechanics. Proceedings of the International School of Physics "Enrico Fermi." B. d'Espagnat, Ed.: 263–273. Academic Press. New York.
5. WIGNER, E. P. 1983. *In* Quantum Optics, Experimental Gravity, and Measurement Theory. NATO Advanced Study Institute Series B, vol. 94. P. Meystre & M. O. Scully, Eds. Plenum. New York.
6. HOLLBERG, L. & J. L. HALL. 1984. Phys. Rev. Lett. **42**: 835.
7. COOKE, W. E. & T. F. GALLAGHER. 1980. Phys. Rev. **A21**: 588.
8. FORD, G. W., J. T. LEWIS & R. F. O'CONNELL. 1985. Phys. Rev. Lett. **55**: 2273; 1986. J. Phys. **B19**: L41.
9. WALLS, D. F. & G. J. MILLBURN. 1985. Phys. Rev. **A31**: 2403.
10. SAVAGE, C. M. & D. F. WALLS. 1985. Phys. Rev. **A32**: 2316.
11. SAVAGE, C. M. & D. F. WALLS. 1985. Phys. Rev. **A32**: 3487.
12. LOUISELL, W. N. 1973. Quantum Statistical Properties of Radiation. Wiley. New York.
13. LINDBLAD, G. 1976. Commun. Math. Phys. **48**: 119.
14. AGARWAL, G. S. 1971. Phys. Rev. **A4**: 739.
15. CALDEIRA, A. O. & A. J. LEGGETT. 1983. Physica **121A**: 587.
16. DEKKER, H. 1977. Phys. Rev. **A16**: 2126.

The Discrete Wigner Function[a]

WILLIAM K. WOOTTERS

Center for Theoretical Physics
The University of Texas at Austin
Austin, Texas 78712
and
Department of Physics and Astronomy
Williams College
Williamstown, Massachusetts 01267[b]

INTRODUCTION

In nonrelativistic quantum mechanics, any spatial quantum state, as opposed to a spin state, can be represented by a real function on classical phase-space known as the Wigner function.[1-4] The Wigner function has a number of special properties that make it a convenient object on which to base a formulation of quantum mechanics, but it is limited in that it applies only to continuous degrees of freedom such as position and not to inherently discrete degrees of freedom such as spin. The main purpose of this paper is to present a generalization of the Wigner function that applies to systems having only a finite number of orthogonal states.

As we shall see, when one writes the laws of quantum mechanics in terms of this generalized Wigner function, the theory looks quite different from what we are accustomed to. The familiar complex vector space is not in obvious view. Instead, the basic mathematical entity on which the theory is built is the phase-space, which in the simplest discrete cases is a two-dimensional vector space over a finite field. This formulation of quantum mechanics suggests an interesting way of viewing the relationship between quantum theory and ordinary probability theory: the latter is obtained from the former by collapsing the two-dimensional phase-space down to one dimension. We can also imagine starting from quantum theory and going the other direction: Do there exist systems whose phase-space is three-dimensional? We explore both of these points in the last two sections of this paper.

In generalizing the Wigner function, we are guided by the following property, which we would like to preserve to as great an extent as possible when we go to the discrete case. Consider the usual Wigner function of a spinless particle in one spatial dimension. Imagine a complete set of parallel lines in the two-dimensional phase-space. The equations for these lines are of the form, $aq + bp = c$, where a and b are constants, q and p are position and momentum, respectively, and c is a number that varies from line to line and takes all possible real values. Now integrate the Wigner function over each of these parallel lines. The result of the integration is a function of the one variable, c. Remarkably, this function is none other than the probability distribution one would obtain by measuring (on an ensemble described by the given Wigner

[a]This work was supported by NSF Grant No. PHY-8503890.
[b]This is W. K. Wootters' permanent address.

275

function) the observable, $a\hat{q} + b\hat{p}$. To be more precise, if the integrals over the parallel lines are done with respect to the measure $dq/|b|$ (or $dp/|a|$), and if $w(c)$ is the result of this integration, then $w(c)dc$ is the probability that the measured value of $a\hat{q} + b\hat{p}$ will lie between c and $c + dc$.

In the discrete case, the integration will be replaced by a summation, but the essential result will remain valid: the "projection" of the Wigner function along any direction in phase-space yields the probability distribution of some definite observable associated with that particular direction.

The problem of generalizing the Wigner function and related functions to spin systems has been considered before. However, most of this work has been focused on continuous functions of angle variables rather than on discrete functions. Continuous generalizations of the Wigner function have been introduced by Stratonovich[5] and by Cohen and Scully.[6] Another sort of continuous representation of spin states has been developed[7] on the basis of the coherent spin states of Radcliffe[8] and Atkins and Dobson.[9] Discrete distribution functions for spin-½ particles have been proposed recently by O'Connell and Wigner[10] and by Cohen and Scully.[6] The discrete Wigner function discussed in the present paper borrows much from these, but it differs in that it applies to arbitrary spin and is defined on an explicitly geometrical phase-space.

DEFINITION OF THE DISCRETE WIGNER FUNCTION

Let us begin by describing the "phase-space" for a system with N orthogonal states. For reasons that will become clear, it is simplest to start with the case where N is a prime number. In that case, the phase-space can be pictured as an $N \times N$ array of points. Each point is labeled by a vertical coordinate, a_1, and a horizontal coordinate, a_2, where a_1 and a_2 each take the values, $0, \ldots, N - 1$. The numbers, $0, \ldots, N - 1$, with addition and multiplication modulo N, constitute a mathematical field. This field plays the role that the real numbers play in the continuous case; in each case, the phase-space is a two-dimensional vector space over the appropriate field. In particular, one can define "lines" and "parallel lines" in the finite phase-space just as in the continuous case: The set of all points for which a_1 and a_2 satisfy $ma_1 + na_2 = r$, where m, n, and r are elements of the finite field, constitutes a line, and any two lines that differ only in the value of r are parallel. Two nonparallel lines intersect in exactly one point, and every two points determine a line. One can convince oneself that there are a total of $N(N + 1)$ lines in the $N \times N$ phase-space and that these lines can be grouped into $N + 1$ groups of N parallel lines. We can think of a set of parallel lines as defining a direction in phase-space (e.g., the vertical direction). Thus, there are exactly $N + 1$ different directions.

In order to define the discrete Wigner function, we are going to expand the density matrix, ρ, in terms of a certain complete set of mutually orthogonal $N \times N$ matrices. (Here "orthogonal" is used to mean that the trace of the product vanishes.) Let us call these matrices, A_α, and let the matrix A_α be associated with the point, $\alpha = (a_1, a_2)$, in phase-space. Once the A's are specified, the Wigner function, W, will be defined by the equation,

$$\rho = \sum_\alpha W_\alpha A_\alpha. \tag{1}$$

In order for the Wigner function to have the "projection property" discussed in the INTRODUCTION, it turns out to be sufficient that the A's have the following properties:

(i) $\operatorname{tr} A_\alpha = 1$;

(ii) $\operatorname{tr}(A_\alpha A_\beta) = N\delta_{\alpha\beta}$;

(iii) Consider any set of N parallel lines. For each line, find the average of all the A_α's for which α lies on that line. The N averages thereby obtained are a set of mutually orthogonal projection operators.

In the APPENDIX, we present a set of A's that have properties (i)–(iii). Let us take these as the A's used in equation 1 to define the Wigner function.

Equation 1 is an implicit definition of the Wigner function. An explicit expression for W in terms of the density matrix can be obtained from this definition by using property (ii):

$$W_\alpha = (1/N) \operatorname{tr}(\rho A_\alpha). \tag{2}$$

Also, properties (i), (ii), and (iii) of the A's lead to analogous properties of the real function W:

(i') $\Sigma_\alpha W_\alpha = 1$;

(ii') Given two states, W and W', the sum, $N\Sigma_\alpha W_\alpha W'_\alpha$, is equal to $\operatorname{tr}(\rho\rho')$, which in the case of pure states is equal to the squared modulus of the inner product of the two state vectors;

(iii') Consider any set of N parallel lines. As we have said, they define a direction in phase-space. For each line, find the sum of all W_α's for which α lies on that line. The N numbers thereby obtained are the probabilities of the outcomes of a definite measurement associated with that particular direction.

Property (iii') is the desired generalization of the projection property.

We now have the discrete Wigner function for prime N. Before we extend the definition to composite N, let us say a few more words about the prime case, beginning with a simple example. The spin of a spin-$\frac{1}{2}$ particle is a system for which $N = 2$. The phase-space is therefore a 2×2 array of points, and the Wigner function consists of just four real numbers, W_{00}, W_{01}, W_{10}, and W_{11}. The sums over the horizontal rows (i.e., $W_{00} + W_{01}$ and $W_{10} + W_{11}$) turn out to be the probabilities that the x-component of spin will be found to have the values of $+\frac{1}{2}$ and $-\frac{1}{2}$, respectively. Similarly, the vertical direction corresponds to the y-component of spin and the diagonal direction (the two diagonal lines are parallel in this geometry) corresponds to the z-component of spin. These are the only three directions in this phase-space.

For prime N greater than 2, the special measurements associated with the $N + 1$ directions are not so familiar as in the $N = 2$ case; however, they have shown up in the literature before, namely, in connection with the problem of state-determination.[11,12]

For any prime N, the $N + 1$ special measurements have an interesting property, which does not generalize to the nonprime case: Given any two of these measurements, every eigenstate of one of them is a "state of complete ignorance" with respect to the other; that is, it has an equal chance of giving any outcome when the other measurement is performed on it. This property follows from (i)–(iii) and the fact that any two nonparallel lines intersect in exactly one point. This fact about nonparallel lines has no analogue in the case where N is composite.

Systems with composite N are related to systems with prime N in the same way that, in the continuous case, particles in two or more spatial dimensions are related to particles in one dimension: the phase-space for composite N is the Cartesian product of phase-spaces for prime N. To be more specific, if $N = N_1 N_2 \ldots N_f$, where $N_1, \ldots, N_f$ are prime, then the phase-space for a system with N orthogonal states is the Cartesian product of the f phase-spaces appropriate for the numbers N_i. As before, a matrix A is associated with each point of the phase-space, and the Wigner function is defined in terms of the A's by equation 1. The A's in this case are simply the tensor products of the A's for the factor spaces:

$$A_{\alpha_1 \alpha_2 \ldots \alpha_f} = A_{\alpha_1} \otimes A_{\alpha_2} \otimes \ldots \otimes A_{\alpha_f}. \tag{3}$$

These A's have properties (i) and (ii), and they also have property (iii) if by "line" one understands the Cartesian product of f lines, one for each factor space. In the same sense, the Wigner function for the composite case has properties (i')–(iii').

QUANTUM MECHANICS IN TERMS OF THE WIGNER FUNCTION

It is well known how to write the basic laws of quantum mechanics for the continuous case in terms of the Wigner function.[1-4] Here we write the basic laws of the quantum mechanics of discrete systems in terms of the discrete Wigner function. There are essentially four rules we need: (1) the rule for deciding whether or not a given Wigner function represents a pure state; (2) the law of evolution; (3) the rule for computing expectation values of observables; (4) the prescription for forming composite systems from simple systems. Here is how these rules look:

(a) A given normalized Wigner function (i.e., $\Sigma_\alpha W_\alpha = 1$) represents a pure state if and only if it satisfies the equation,

$$W_\alpha = \Gamma_{\alpha\beta\gamma} W_\beta W_\gamma, \quad \text{where } \Gamma_{\alpha\beta\gamma} = (1/N) \, \text{tr} \, (A_\alpha A_\beta A_\gamma), \tag{4}$$

and where summation over repeated indices (i.e., over β and γ in the first equation) is understood. (Interesting fact: For prime $N > 2$, it turns out that $\Gamma_{\alpha\beta\gamma}$ is equal to $(1/N) \exp \left[(2\pi i/N)(\text{area of the triangle } \alpha\beta\gamma) \right]$, where the area is a signed area, measured in units of the area of a certain standard triangle.) Mixed states are weighted averages of pure states.

(b) The values of the Wigner function at the N^2 points of phase-space can be thought of as the components of a vector in an N^2-dimensional space. The transformations that take an initial W to a final W are linear transformations on this space. A transformation is allowed if and only if it satisfies two conditions: it must leave the normalization of W unchanged, and it must leave Γ invariant; that is, "$W_\alpha^{final} = Z_{\alpha\beta} W_\beta^{initial}$" is allowed if and only if

$$\sum_\alpha Z_{\alpha\beta} = 1 \quad \text{and} \quad Z_{\lambda\alpha} Z_{\nu\beta} Z_{\rho\gamma} \Gamma_{\alpha\beta\gamma} = \Gamma_{\lambda\nu\rho}. \tag{5}$$

One can show that such transformations are generated by a Hamiltonian in the following sense. The Hamiltonian, H, is a real function on phase-space, and the differential equation of evolution is

$$(i/\hbar)\,dW_\alpha/dt = \Gamma_{\alpha\beta\gamma}(H_\beta W_\gamma - W_\beta H_\gamma).\tag{6}$$

(c) Observables are represented by real functions on phase-space. The expectation value of an observable O is given by

$$\langle O \rangle = \sum_\alpha W_\alpha O_\alpha.\tag{7}$$

(d) If two systems are combined to make a composite system, the above rules apply to the composite, with Γ given by the product of the Γ's for the two subsystems:

$$\Gamma_{\alpha_1\alpha_2\beta_1\beta_2\gamma_1\gamma_2} = \Gamma_{\alpha_1\beta_1\gamma_1}\Gamma_{\alpha_2\beta_2\gamma_2}.\tag{8}$$

Those are the rules of quantum mechanics. Notice that the structure of the theory is determined largely by Γ. We defined Γ in terms of the A's, but this was not necessary. One can simply state directly what the components of Γ are and the theory will be well defined. In fact, it is enough to give the components of Γ for prime values of N. The Γ's for composite values of N can then be obtained using rule (d).

THE RELATIONSHIP BETWEEN QUANTUM THEORY AND CLASSICAL PROBABILITY THEORY

By "classical probability theory," we mean the theory that describes, for example, the expected result of a large number of throws of a weighted die. As in quantum theory, in classical probability theory there are pure states and mixed states: a die that is so heavily weighted that it always lands on the same face is in a pure state; any die that allows two or more possible outcomes is in a mixed state.

In this section, we want to write the basic rules of probability theory in such a way that they can be compared to the rules of quantum theory given in the preceding section; then we will do the comparison.

As before, let N be the number of possible outcomes of a complete measurement, and to begin with, let N be prime. We can define a "phase-space" for probability theory, which is a one-dimensional vector space over the field with N elements. Thus, there are N points in the phase-space. A state is represented by a real function W (the probability distribution) on the phase-space. The basic rules of the theory, which are analogous to the above rules of quantum theory, are the following:

(a′) A given normalized function W represents a pure state if and only if it satisfies the equation,

$$W_\alpha = \Gamma_{\alpha\beta\gamma}W_\beta W_\gamma, \qquad \text{where } \Gamma_{\alpha\beta\gamma} = \delta_{\alpha\beta}\delta_{\alpha\gamma}.\tag{9}$$

Mixed states are weighted averages of pure states.

(b′) There is no natural evolution of a discrete system in classical probability theory. Certainly, there can be no continuous evolution that preserves the purity of states. Therefore, in a sense there is no analogue of rule (b) above. On the other hand, if we simply apply rule (b) to the present situation, with Γ

as given in (a'), the result makes some sense: the only transformations, Z, that preserve the normalization of W and leave Γ invariant are the permutations of the points of phase-space. Thus, rule (b) actually requires in this case that there be no continuous evolution. In this trivial sense, the evolution rule applies as well to classical probability theory as it does to quantum theory.

(c') Observables are represented by real functions on phase-space. The expectation value of an observable O is given by

$$\langle O \rangle = \sum_{\alpha} W_{\alpha} O_{\alpha}. \tag{10}$$

(d') If two systems are combined to make a composite system, the above rules apply to the composite, with Γ given by the product of the Γ's for the two subsystems.

These rules are obviously just like those of quantum mechanics, but with two differences: the phase-space is one-dimensional and Γ is different. A consequence of these differences is this: from rule (a'), one can prove that every allowed function W, whether for a pure or mixed state, takes only nonnegative values, whereas in quantum mechanics, W can have negative values. For this reason, the W's of quantum theory cannot be thought of as probabilities. They can be called "pre-probabilities" because they can be summed to get genuine probabilities.

There is a very interesting connection between the Γ of classical probability theory and the Γ of quantum mechanics. The former can be obtained from the latter by "averaging over any direction in phase-space": Consider any complete set of N parallel lines in the two-dimensional phase-space. Assign one of these lines to each of the symbols, α, β, and γ. Now find the average of the quantum mechanical $\Gamma_{\alpha\beta\gamma}$ over all values of α, β, and γ such that each index lies on its assigned line. The result of this averaging is an object that again has three indices, but where each index now refers to a line, not a point. The N parallel lines can be thought of as the N points of a one-dimensional phase-space. Therefore, the indices of the averaged Γ can be thought of as taking values in such a space. When viewed in this way, the averaged Γ turns out to be the correct Γ for classical probability theory divided by N.

To put it another way, one can reduce the dimension of the vector space in which α, β, and γ take their values by simply averaging over some direction. The result of applying this reduction procedure to the correct two-dimensional (i.e., quantum mechanical) Γ is $1/N$ times the correct one-dimensional (i.e., classical) Γ, no matter which direction was averaged over. In this sense, quantum mechanics can be viewed as a generalization of classical probability theory. The rule for generalizing is this: add another dimension and choose Γ so that it reduces to the correct one-dimensional Γ in the above sense.

It is interesting to ask whether quantum mechanics is singled out uniquely by this property. That is, if we accept the form of rules (a) through (d) of the previous section, but do not specify Γ except to insist that it reduce as above, are we forced into quantum mechanics? The answer is no. There are many choices of Γ that satisfy this criterion. However, of all theories obtainable in this way, quantum mechanics has a particularly high degree of symmetry. I have analyzed thoroughly only the case where $N = 2$. In that case, quantum mechanics is picked out uniquely if, in addition to the "reduction criterion," Γ is required to have the following properties: (i) $\Gamma_{\alpha\beta\gamma}$ is invariant under any uniform translation of the points, α, β, and γ; (ii) interchanging any two indices of Γ is the same as taking the complex conjugate; (iii) Γ is such that the pure-state condition (a) of the previous section allows a continuum of pure states; (iv) Γ is such that there exist pure states of a pair of $N = 2$ systems in which the two systems are correlated. This last property is necessary in order for two $N = 2$ systems to be able to interact with each other.

It would be very interesting to investigate this question further. In particular, one would like to know to what extent quantum mechanics is picked out by the reduction criterion for values of N greater than two.

A THREE-DIMENSIONAL PHASE-SPACE?

Once we start talking about going from a one-dimensional to a two-dimensional phase-space, it is natural to ask whether there exist systems whose phase-space is three-dimensional. First, we should determine whether there exists an interesting theory involving a three-dimensional phase-space. If a theory of this sort exists, there is no guarantee that nature has chosen to use it, but the possibility is worth investigating.

Therefore, first notice that rules (a)–(d) can be applied as well to three or more dimensions as they can to two dimensions. The mathematical structure of the theory is completely determined once we specify Γ.

We have seen that the Γ for quantum mechanics reduces to that of classical probability theory upon averaging over any direction in phase-space and multiplying by N. Working by analogy, we now ask whether there is a three-dimensional Γ that reduces to the quantum mechanical Γ upon averaging over any direction and mutiplying by N.

Again, I have looked carefully only at the case where $N = 2$, for which the phase-space is a $2 \times 2 \times 2$ array of points. As before, it turns out that there are a number of theories that reduce in the prescribed way. However, there is one theory that has a particularly high degree of symmetry. Without going into any details, let me summarize some of the features of this theory: A pure state is specified by six real numbers and can be naturally represented by a point on a 6-sphere, or equivalently, by a unit vector in $\mathbf{R}^7$. Mixed states can therefore be represented by points in the interior of a 6-sphere. Every complete measurement on the system has, of course, two possible outcomes because N equals 2. The probability that one pure state will "become" another upon measurement is $\cos^2(\theta/2)$, where θ is the angle between the unit vectors representing the two states. The allowed group of transformations is a 14-dimensional group whose Lie algebra is G_2, the smallest of the five exceptional Lie algebras. Finally, a system described by this theory—let us call it a "cubon"—can be combined with ordinary quantum mechanical particles and other cubons to make a composite system, and there exist pure states of such composites in which a cubon is correlated with the rest of the system.

I offer no interpretation of the cubon. At this stage, there is a great deal of freedom in choosing a three-dimensional generalization of the two-dimensional theory. One would need a much tighter theoretical structure before believing that nature could not resist making use of the three-dimensional phase-space.

To summarize, we have found an analogue of the continuous Wigner function that is applicable to discrete quantum systems. In a formulation of the quantum mechanics of such systems based on this function, states and observables become real functions on a finite phase-space. The phase-space is either a two-dimensional vector space over a finite field or the Cartesian product of such spaces. By reducing the dimension of the phase-space, we arrive at classical probability theory; by augmenting the dimension, we arrive in the simplest case ($N = 2$) at a generalization of quantum mechanics that makes mathematical sense, but is as yet uninterpreted.

ACKNOWLEDGMENT

I would like to thank Ben Schumacher for many stimulating and enlightening conversations about phase-space and the Wigner function.

REFERENCES

1. WIGNER, E. P. 1932. Phys. Rev. **40:** 749.
2. MOYAL, J. E. 1949. Proc. Cambridge Philos. Soc. **41:** 99.
3. TATARSKII, V. I. 1983. Sov. Phys. Usp. **26:** 311.
4. HILLERY, M., R. F. O'CONNELL, M. O. SCULLY & E. P. WIGNER. 1984. Phys. Rep. **106:** 123.
5. STRATONOVICH, R. L. 1957. Sov. Phys. JETP **4:** 891.
6. COHEN, L. & M. O. SCULLY. 1986. Joint Wigner distribution for spin ½ particles. Found. Phys. **16:** 295.
7. See, for example: SRIRAM SHASTRY, B. & G. S. AGARWAL. 1978. Pramana **11:** 85.
8. RADCLIFFE, J. M. 1971. J. Phys. A: Math. Nucl. Gen. **4:** 313.
9. ATKINS, P. W. & J. C. DOBSON. 1971. Proc. R. Soc. London Ser. **A321:** 321.
10. O'CONNELL, R. F. & E. P. WIGNER. 1984. Phys. Rev. **A30:** 2613.
11. IVANOVIC, I. D. 1981. J. Phys. A: Math. Nucl. Gen. **14:** 3241.
12. WOOTTERS, W. K. 1986. Quantum mechanics without probability amplitudes. Found. Phys. **16:** 391.

APPENDIX

Here, we present, for every prime number N, a set of N^2 matrices that have properties (i)–(iii) (see the second section of this paper). Here, $\alpha = (a_1, a_2)$ represents a point in phase-space, and a_1 and a_2 take values from 0 to $N - 1$.

$$N = 2:\ A_\alpha = (1/2)[(-1)^{a_1}\sigma_x + (-1)^{a_2}\sigma_y + (-1)^{a_1+a_2}\sigma_z + I],\qquad \text{(A1)}$$

where the σ's are the Pauli matrices and I is the 2×2 identity matrix.

$$N > 2:\ (A_\alpha)_{k\ell} = \delta_{a_1,k+\ell}\exp\left[(2\pi i/N)a_2(k - \ell)\right],\ \text{where}\ k, \ell = 1, \ldots, N. \quad \text{(A2)}$$

Properties (i), (ii), and (iii) are all straightforward consequences of these expressions for the A's.

Joint Quantum Probabilities and the Uncertainty Principle

LEON COHEN[a]

IBM Thomas J. Watson Research Center
Yorktown Heights, New York 10598

INTRODUCTION

One of the standard arguments why position and momentum cannot be measured simultaneously goes something like this: If they could be measured simultaneously, then a joint distribution for them would have to exist; however, joint distributions cannot exist because according to the uncertainty principle, an arbitrarily small region in phase-space cannot be properly defined, and indeed, a simultaneous measurement would require the existence of a distribution at each point in phase-space. It is the purpose of this article to critically examine this argument with the consideration that well-defined positive distributions of noncommuting operators, which satisfy the quantum mechanical marginal distributions exactly, have been shown to exist and can be readily calculated.[1] We shall use position and momentum in most of our discussion because similar considerations hold for other pairs of noncommuting operators. A joint distribution, $P(q, p)$, must satisfy the individual quantum probability distributions for position and momentum:

$$\int_{-\infty}^{\infty} P(q, p)\, dp = |\psi(q)|^2, \tag{1.1}$$

$$\int_{-\infty}^{\infty} P(q, p)\, dq = |\phi(p)|^2, \tag{1.2}$$

where $\psi(q)$ is the position wave function and $\phi(p)$ is the momentum wave function.

Of course, there have been many other arguments besides the one mentioned above that have been used to argue that simultaneous measurement of noncommuting operators is impossible in quantum mechanics. A review and critical analysis of all these arguments has been given by Park and Margenau.[2]

An argument commonly given in support of the above view is that Wigner has shown that positive joint distributions do not exist.[3] Wigner was quite precise in stating that his proof applied only to the so-called bilinear distributions. However, many have assumed that the proof is generally true. The Wigner distribution has been used with immense success in almost every branch of physics[4] although, except for a Gaussian wave function, it is never positive definite. It has been argued that the fact that the Wigner distribution is not positive definite is a reflection of the uncertainty principle and the impossibility of joint measurement.

A penetrating analysis of the Wigner proof and its consequences has been given by Mugur-Schachter,[5] and it is particularly illuminating because at the time, an actual

[a]Permanent address: Hunter College of the City University, New York, New York 10471.

construction of the positive distributions was not available. She concludes that "Wigner's theorem has no bearing on a non-void class of joint distributions" and "it seems probable that this class is not reduced to the trivial distribution alone." By the "trivial distribution," it is meant the correlationless case. Indeed, joint distribution with correlations do exist and are easy to generate, as we will see below. The relationship between the uncertainty principle and joint distributions has been analyzed by Kuryshkin.[6] Kuryshkin and co-workers have constructed positive joint distributions, although their distributions do not satisfy the marginals. However, his arguments and analysis are equally valid. In the outstanding article of Ballentine[7] dealing with the statistical interpretation of quantum mechanics, the relation of joint distributions and the statistical interpretation has been discussed, although, again, at that time, it was not clear whether they existed.

JOINT POSITIVE DISTRIBUTIONS

Joint positive distributions satisfying the quantum mechanical marginals are easy to obtain:[1]

$$P(q, p) = |\psi(q)|^2 |\phi(p)|^2 \{1 + c\rho(u, v)\}, \tag{2.1}$$

where

$$u(q) = \int_{-\infty}^{q} |\psi(q')|^2 \, dq', \quad v(p) = \int_{-\infty}^{p} |\phi(p')|^2 \, dp', \tag{2.2}$$

and $\rho(u, v)$ is any function satisfying

$$\int_0^1 \rho(u, v) dv = 0, \quad \int_0^1 \rho(u, v) du = 0. \tag{2.3}$$

The c is a numerical constant in the range, $-1/\ell_2 < c < 1/\ell_1$, where $-\ell_1$ and ℓ_2 are the absolute minimum and maximum values of ρ in the unit square, respectively. To see that the marginals are satisfied, we integrate with respect to momentum,

$$\int_{-\infty}^{\infty} P(q, p) dp = |\psi(q)|^2 + c|\psi(q)|^2 \int_{-\infty}^{\infty} |\phi(p)|^2 \rho(u, v) dp \tag{2.4}$$

$$= |\psi(q)|^2 + c|\psi(q)|^2 \int_0^1 \rho(u, v) dv = |\psi(q)|^2, \tag{2.5}$$

where we have used the facts that $dv = |\phi(p)|^2 \, dp$ and that the range of u varies from zero to one as p goes from $-\infty$ to ∞; similarly for integration over position. We note that in the above demonstration, the value of the constant, c, did not enter. The role of c is to assure that the distribution is positive. Two simple ways to generate ρ's satisfying equation 2.3 are the following: Choose any function, $h(u, v)$, of two variables, and normalize it to one in the unit square,

$$\int_0^1 \int_0^1 h(u, v) = 1. \tag{2.6}$$

If we define

$$h_1(u) = \int_0^1 h(u, v) dv, \quad h_2(v) = \int_0^1 h(u, v) du, \tag{2.7}$$

then, the choice,

$$\rho(u, v) = h(u, v) - h_1(u)h_2(v) \qquad (2.8)$$

or

$$\rho(u, v) = h(u, v) - h_1(u) - h_2(v) = 1, \qquad (2.9)$$

will assure that equation 2.3 will be satisfied.

Joint distribution for operators other than position and momentum have been considered by Scully and myself, where both Wigner-type distributions and positive distributions have been constructed.[8] For the positive distributions, the generalization of the position-momentum case is straightforward. Consider two arbitrary operators, A and B, and let a and b stand for the random numbers associated with them. We seek a joint distribution of a and b such that

$$\int_{-\infty}^{\infty} P(a, b)da = |\phi^B(b)|^2, \quad \int_{-\infty}^{\infty} P(a, b)db = |\phi^A(a)|^2, \qquad (2.10)$$

where $\phi^A(a)$ and $\phi^B(b)$ are the state functions in the A and B representations,

$$\phi^A(a) = \int_{-\infty}^{\infty} v_a^*(q)\psi(q)dq, \quad \phi^B(b) = \int_{-\infty}^{\infty} w_b^*(q)\psi(q)dq, \qquad (2.11)$$

and $v_a(q)$ and $w_b(q)$ are the eigenfunctions of A and B with eigenvalues, a and b, respectively. The joint distributions of the variables, a and b, are

$$P(a, b) = |\phi^A(a)|^2 |\phi^B(b)|^2 \{1 + cp(u, v)\}, \qquad (2.12)$$

where now

$$u(a) = \int_{-\infty}^{a} |\phi^A(a')|^2 \, da', \quad v(b) = \int_{-\infty}^{b} |\phi^B(b')|^2 \, db' \qquad (2.13)$$

We should also mention that generalization to more than two variables is not straightforward, but has been given.[1]

Clearly, there are an infinite number of possible ways to choose ρ, and therefore an infinite number of distributions. That is reasonable because the marginals cannot uniquely determine the joint distribution. What we have given is an explicit construction of them. Finch and Groblicki[9] have shown that the above formulation encompasses all possible forms for the joint distributions. We should emphasize that from equation 2.2, it appears that the joint distribution depends only on the square of the wave functions. That is indeed the case if we assume that ρ and c are not functionals of the state functions. Now it is known that $|\psi(q)|^2$ and $|\phi(p)|^2$ do not determine the state, and hence, from a knowledge of the joint distribution, it would appear that the state is not determined. However, we have not imposed correlations, and their imposition by way of ρ and c may depend on the state. For example, we may want to impose predetermined values for the mixed moments,

$$\langle q^n p^m \rangle = \int_{-\infty}^{\infty} \psi^*(q)O(Q^n P^m)\psi(q)dq, \qquad (2.14)$$

where $O(Q^n P^m)$ is the quantum operator corresponding to $q^n p^m$. This will bring further information about the state function, and if enough information regarding the state is put into c and ρ, then the distribution will uniquely depend on the state. Such imposition will usually take the form of constraints by way of expectation values, and they can be incorporated in the following way: Suppose that in addition to the marginals, we wish to obtain a joint distribution that satisfies given expectation values of a set of functions, $r_i(x, y)$,

$$\langle r_i(q, p) \rangle = e_i, \quad i = 1, \ldots, K, \tag{2.15}$$

where the e's are given. There are many ways to impose such constraints, and the simplest is to parameterize ρ and choose the parameters so that the constraints are satisfied. A particularly convenient choice is to take a linear combination,

$$\rho(u, v) = \sum_{j=1}^{K} a_i \rho_i(u, v), \tag{2.16}$$

where each of the ρ_i's satisfies equation 2.3, and the a_i's are to be determined so that equation 2.15 is satisfied. Calculating the expectation values with the distribution given by equation 2.1, we have

$$\int_{-\infty}^{\infty} P(q, p) r_i(q, p) \, dq \, dp = e_i \tag{2.17}$$

$$= \int_{-\infty}^{\infty} |\psi(q)|^2 \, |\phi(p)|^2 \, r_i(q, p) \, dq \, dp$$

$$+ \sum_{j=1}^{K} a_j \int_{-\infty}^{\infty} \rho_j(u, v) r_i(q, p) |\psi(q)|^2 \, |\phi(p)|^2 dq \, dp, \tag{2.18}$$

which we rewrite as

$$e_i = e_i^0 + \sum_{j=1}^{K} R_{ij} a_j, \quad i = 1, \ldots, K, \tag{2.19}$$

where

$$e_i^0 = \int_{-\infty}^{\infty} |\psi(q)|^2 |\phi(p)|^2 r_i(q, p) \, dx \, dy, \tag{2.20}$$

$$R_{ij} = \int_{-\infty}^{\infty} \rho_j(u, v) r_i(x, y) |\psi(q)|^2 |\phi(p)|^2 \, dq \, dp. \tag{2.21}$$

e_i^0 are the expectation values of $r_i(q, p)$ with the correlationless distribution, and they are known because the marginals are known. Equation 2.19 is a linear equation for the a's that can be readily solved, and the range of c will depend on the a's. This still leaves an infinite number of distributions that can accommodate the constraints because a different set of ρ's will produce a different answer. How do we decide? Clearly, we cannot, and the more constraints imposed, the narrower will be the possibilities. An infinite number of constraints will, in general, fix the distribution. However, if not all information is given, one can, for example, use the principle of maximum entropy to choose among the remaining distribution.

If we have a joint distribution, then the ρ that produces it from its marginals can be obtained in the following way: From equation 2.1,

$$\rho(u, v) = \frac{1}{c} \left\{ \frac{P(q,p)}{|\psi(q)|^2 |\phi(p)|^2} - 1 \right\}, \tag{2.22}$$

which can be expressed in terms of u and v by inverting equation 2.2 and solving for q and p in terms of u and v and substituting into equation 2.22.

UNCERTAINTY PRINCIPLE AND JOINT DISTRIBUTIONS

There are many interpretations of the uncertainty principle, but there is universal agreement as to its mathematical statement. For the case of position and momentum, it relates the product of the standard deviations as defined in the usual manner of classical probability theory:

$$(\Delta q)^2 = \int_{-\infty}^{\infty} (q - \langle q \rangle)^2 |\psi(q)|^2 \, dq, \quad (\Delta p)^2 = \int_{-\infty}^{\infty} (p - \langle p \rangle)^2 |\phi(p)|^2 \, dp. \quad (3.1)$$

The remarkable aspect of the uncertainty principle, $\Delta q \Delta p > h/2$, is that it is true for any wave function. Now, suppose we have a joint distribution and wish to calculate the product, $(\Delta q)^2 (\Delta p)^2$. It would be

$$(\Delta q)^2 (\Delta p)^2 = \left\{ \int_{-\infty}^{\infty} \int_{-\infty}^{\infty} (q - \langle q \rangle)^2 P(q, p) dq dp \right\}$$

$$\cdot \left\{ \int_{-\infty}^{\infty} \int_{-\infty}^{\infty} (p - \langle p \rangle) P(q, p) dq dp \right\} \quad (3.2)$$

$$= \left\{ \int_{-\infty}^{\infty} (q - \langle q \rangle)^2 |\psi(q)| dq \right\} \left\{ \int_{-\infty}^{\infty} (p - \langle p \rangle)^2 |\psi(p)|^2 \, dp \right\}. \quad (3.3)$$

This is the usual starting point in the derivation of the uncertainty principle, and hence, the uncertainty principle follows. Of course, the results of equations 3.2 and 3.3 are obvious because the uncertainty principle depends only on the marginals. It does not relate $\langle (q - \langle q \rangle)^2 (p - \langle p \rangle)^2 \rangle$, but $\langle (q - \langle q \rangle)^2 \rangle \langle (p - \langle p \rangle)^2 \rangle$, and that is why only the marginals come in. Any joint distribution that yields the marginals will yield the uncertainty principle. The uncertainty principle has nothing to do with correlations between position and momentum. What it does say is that the marginals are functionally dependent. It implies that individual probability distributions for noncommuting observables cannot be chosen to be independent of each other. However, the fact that the marginals are related does not imply correlation between the random variables, and it has nothing to do with the existence of joint distributions or the impossibility of joint measurement.

BILINEARITY AND JOINT DISTRIBUTIONS

Historically, the quasi distributions that have been studied such as the Wigner[3] distribution and the Margenau-Hill[11] distribution are bilinear functionals of the wave function. The positive distributions given above are not, and it is worthwhile to contrast and examine the implications of bilinearity. There are an infinite number of bilinear distributions that satisfy the marginals,[11]

$$P(q, p) = \frac{1}{4\pi^2} \int_{-\infty}^{\infty} e^{-i\theta q - i\tau p + i\theta u} f(\theta, \tau) \psi^*(u - \tfrac{1}{2}\tau) \psi(u + \tfrac{1}{2}\tau) du \, d\tau \, d\theta, \quad (4.1)$$

where f is any function satisfying $f(0,\tau) = f(\theta,0) = 1$. If f is not taken to be a functional of the state, then equation 4.1 generates all possible bilinear distributions satisfying the quantum marginals. However, none of these distributions are positive definite for an arbitrary wave function. Are joint distributions, in general, bilinear to the square root of the marginals? Joint distributions arise all the time in quantum mechanics; for example, the square of any multidimensional wave function is a joint distribution. Now, if we take such a joint distribution and express it in terms of the marginals, will the answer be bilinear in the square root of the marginals? In general, no. The relationship is always a more complicated functional relationship than bilinearity. Indeed, it can always be put in the form given by equation 2.1, and the appropriate ρ can be calculated using equation 2.22. The simplest joint distribution, for example, is the correlationless distribution that is a product of its marginals and hence depends quadrilinearly on the square root of the marginals.

There are three basic reasons that there has been such an emphasis on bilinearity for joint quasi distributions in quantum mechanics. Historically, they were the first to have been found. Secondly, they are certainly the simplest functions satisfying the marginals, although they cannot be interpreted as probabilities. Thirdly, one can give a seeming derivation of them that on the surface is plausible. In the light of the positive distributions, it is worthwhile to reexamine the previous "derivations" of the quasi-quantum distributions. The usual derivations are based on the characteristic function and on the correspondence of mixed moments. The argument goes something like this: If there exists a joint distribution, then its characteristic function would be[10-12]

$$M(\theta, \tau) = \langle e^{i\theta q + i\tau p} \rangle = \int_{-\infty}^{\infty} \int_{-\infty}^{\infty} P(q, p) e^{i\theta q + i\tau p} dq dp, \tag{4.2}$$

and if we know the characteristic function, then we could get the distribution by Fourier inversion:

$$P(q, p) = \frac{1}{4\pi^2} \int_{-\infty}^{\infty} \int_{-\infty}^{\infty} M(\theta, \tau) e^{-i\theta q - i\tau p} d\theta. \tag{4.3}$$

However, the characteristic function is the expectation value of $e^{i\theta q + i\tau p}$, and quantum mechanics certainly gives us rules for calculation of expectation values. Now, what shall we take for $\langle e^{i\theta q + i\tau p} \rangle$? Shall we use $\langle e^{i\theta Q + i\tau P} \rangle$ or $\langle e^{i\theta Q} e^{i\tau P} \rangle$, or any other choice that reduces to the classical case when the operators, Q and P, are taken to be c numbers? Also, by expanding the characteristic function, it can be expressed in terms of the moments:

$$M(\theta, \tau) = \sum_{n,m=1}^{\infty} \frac{\theta^n \tau^m}{n! m!} \langle q^n p^m \rangle. \tag{4.4}$$

However, again, it is not obvious what to take for $\langle q^n p^m \rangle$. Depending on what we take to be the quantum counterpart to the mixed moments, we will get a different characteristic function and a different distribution function.[11] It has always been tacitly assumed that the operator corresponding to a classical quantity is independent of the wave function. This assumption leads to a characteristic function that is bilinear in the state, and hence, so is the distribution. However, as previously discussed, joint distributions and characteristic functions do not depend bilinearly on the square root of the marginals if the distribution function is proper, that is, positive definite. We are thus led to consider state-dependent correspondence rules. Also, we will give other reasons for the plausibility of considering state-dependent correspondence rules. Of course, for functions of position or momentum only, we do not expect the correspondence to be state-dependent, and we will see that this is the case.

STATE-DEPENDENT CORRESPONDENCE RULES

An operator whose expectation value in the usual quantum mechanical sense gives the characteristic distribution is

$$\hat{M}(\theta, \tau) = f(\theta, \tau)e^{i\theta Q + i\tau P}. \tag{5.1}$$

Now, if we take f to be independent of the wave function, we obtain the bilinear class of joint distributions. If we take

$$f(\theta, \tau) = \frac{M_q(\theta) M_p(\tau)\{1 + c\tilde{\rho}(\theta, \tau)\}}{\displaystyle\int_{-\infty}^{\infty} \psi^*(u - \tau h/2)e^{i\theta u}\psi(u + \tau h/2)\,du}, \tag{5.2}$$

where

$$\tilde{\rho}(\theta, \tau) = \int_{-\infty}^{\infty} \rho(u, v)e^{i\theta q + i\tau p}dq\,dp \tag{5.3}$$

and $M_q(\theta)$ and $M_p(\tau)$ are the characteristic functions of the marginals, then the characteristic function operator given by equation 5.2 will give the positive distributions of equation 2.1.

In general, the correspondence between classical functions and quantum operators is[11]

$$e^{i\theta q + i\tau p} \longrightarrow f(\theta, \tau)e^{i\theta Q + i\tau P}. \tag{5.4}$$

We now examine the consequences of this correspondence. Consider first the case where $\tau = 0$. That leads to

$$e^{i\theta q} \longrightarrow f(\theta, 0)e^{i\theta Q} = e^{i\theta Q} \tag{5.5}$$

or $g(q) \longrightarrow g(Q)$, where g is any function. Similar considerations apply to functions of momentum. Hence, for functions of position and momentum only, the standard replacement of q by Q still holds and is state-independent. Now, let us consider mixed moments. We have previously given a method to obtain the quantum operators from the classical counterpart. If $g(q, p)$ is the classical function, then the quantum operator, $G(Q,P)$, is[11]

$$G(Q,P) = \int_{-\infty}^{\infty} \int_{-\infty}^{\infty} \gamma(\theta, \tau) f(\theta, \tau)e^{i\theta Q + i\tau P}d\theta\,d\tau, \tag{5.6}$$

where

$$\gamma(\theta, \tau) = \frac{1}{4\pi^2} \int_{-\infty}^{\infty} \int_{-\infty}^{\infty} g(q, p)e^{-i\theta q - i\tau p}dq\,dp. \tag{5.7}$$

This assures that

$$\int_{-\infty}^{\infty} \psi^*(q)\, G(Q, P)\psi(q)dq = \int_{-\infty}^{\infty} \int_{-\infty}^{\infty} g(q, p)\, P(q, p)\, dq\, dp. \tag{5.8}$$

Consider, for example, the quantum operator corresponding to qp. Using the above, we have that

$$qp \rightarrow \frac{1}{2}\{QP + PQ\} - \frac{\partial f(\theta, \tau)}{\partial \theta \partial \tau}\bigg|_{0,0}. \tag{5.9}$$

Is it not plausible to insist that $qp \rightarrow \frac{1}{2}\{QP + PQ\}$, which would make the correspondence state independent?

We would like, though, to argue the contrary for the following reasons: Recently, the joint distributions for two spin components have been worked out and a certain aspect of that work has a bearing on our discussion.[8] Because each spin component has two possible outcomes, the joint distribution will have four possibilities, and therefore all we need is four conditions to fix the joint probabilities. The condition of normalization and the two marginal conditions give three. Now, the other condition must reflect correlations, and it certainly would seem plausible to take for the expectation value of the product of the two spin components, σ_x, σ_y, say, the symmetrized operator, $\frac{1}{2}(\sigma_x\sigma_y + \sigma_y\sigma_x)$. However, the imposition of this rule results in an improper distribution in the sense that it is not positive definite. With this example, we have isolated the quantum mechanical correspondence rule (for spin components at least) for a product of two operators because no other factors come in. Hence, the expectation value of a product of two observables cannot in general be the expected value of the symmetrized product of the operators if we want to get proper expectation values. Another example that would argue that for mixed moments we should take state-dependent operators, is to consider a situation where we expect the joint probability to be the correlationless case. For that case then, we would want $\langle qp \rangle = \langle q \rangle \langle p \rangle$. However, how can we get that? The only way is to make the correspondence state-dependent. To see that, take

$$f(\theta, \tau) = \frac{M_q(\theta)\, M_p(\tau)}{\int_{-\infty}^{\infty} \psi^*(u - \tau h/2)e^{i\theta u}\psi(u + \tau h/2)du}, \tag{5.10}$$

which is state-dependent. A straightforward, but lengthy calculation gives that

$$\frac{\partial f(\theta, \tau)}{\partial \theta \partial \tau}\bigg|_{0,0} = \frac{1}{2}\langle QP + PQ \rangle - \langle Q \rangle \langle P \rangle, \tag{5.11}$$

which upon substitution in equation 5.9 leads to $\langle qp \rangle = \langle q \rangle \langle p \rangle$. There is no way to achieve this unless the correspondence is state-dependent. We emphasize that we are not saying that in general we have the correlationless case, but we are pointing out that when we do have it, then the only way to obtain it is by assuming that the correspondence between classical functions and quantum operators is state-dependent.

CONCLUSIONS

The fact that we have been able to write proper joint distributions of noncommuting variables does not imply that quantum mechanics can be cast into a classical probability theory. It has been shown that quantum expectation values cannot be calculated in a consistent manner by way of phase-space integration, and that proof holds for the positive distributions also.[13-15]

Our analysis shows that the uncertainty principle has no bearing on the question of joint distributions, and if it is interpreted in a statistical sense, then it has no bearing on the question of joint measurability of noncommuting operators. What it does do is constrain the marginals. However, constraining the marginals has no bearing on joint distributions between the variables because, as we have shown, joint distributions can be constructed for any marginals whether they are functionally related or not. As mentioned, there are many arguments that have been given why one may not be able to measure two noncommuting observables simultaneously, but we have shown that the joint distribution argument does not hold.

REFERENCES

1. COHEN, L. & Y. I. ZAPAROVANNY. 1980. J. Math. Phys. **21**: 794; COHEN, L. 1984. J. Chem. Phys. **80**: 4277; J. Math. Phys. **25**: 2402; 1986. *In* Frontiers of Non-Equilibrium Statistical Physics. G. T. Moore & M. O. Scully, Eds. Plenum. New York; COHEN, L. & T. POSCH. 1985. IEEE Trans. Acoust. Speech Signal Process. **33**: 31.
2. PARK, J. L. & H. MARGENAU. 1971. *In* Perspectives in Quantum Theory. W. Yourgrau & A. van der Merwe, Eds. MIT Press. Cambridge, Massachusetts.
3. WIGNER, E. 1932. Phys. Rev. **40**: 749; WIGNER, E. 1971. *In* Perspectives in Quantum Theory. W. Yourgrau & A. van der Merwe, Eds. MIT Press. Cambridge, Massachusetts.
4. For a general review, see: HILLERY, M., R. F. O'CONNELL, M. O. SCULLY & E. P. WIGNER. 1984. Phys. Rep. **106**: 121; BALAZS, N. L. & B. K. JENNINGS. 1984. Phys. Rep. **104**: 347.
5. MUGUR-SCHACHTER, M. 1979. Found. Phys. **9**: 389; 1983. Found. Phys. **13**: 419.
6. KURYSHKIN, V. V. 1973. Int. J. Theor. Phys. **7**: 451; 1977. *In* The Uncertainty Principle and the Foundations of Quantum Mechanics. Wiley. New York.
7. BALLENTINE, L. E. 1970. Rev. Mod. Phys. **42**: 358.
8. COHEN, L. & M. O. SCULLY. 1986. Joint Wigner distribution for spin ½ particles. Found. Phys. **16**: 295; Wigner-type distributions for arbitrary operators. To be published.
9. FINCH, P. D. & R. GROBLICKI. 1984. Found. Phys. **14**: 549.
10. MEHTA, C. L. 1964. J. Math. Phys. **5**: 677; MARGENAU, H. & R. N. HILL. 1961. Prog. Theor. Phys. **26**: 722; GROENEWOLD, H. J. 1946. Physica **12**: 405; VON ROOS, O. 1960. Phys. Rev. **99**: 974; TAKABAYASI, T. 1954. Prog. Theor. Phys. **9**: 341.
11. COHEN, L. 1966. J. Math. Phys. **7**: 781; MARGENAU, H. & L. COHEN. 1967. *In* Quantum Theory and Reality. Mario Bunge, Ed. Springer-Verlag. New York; COHEN, L. 1973. *In* Foundations and Philosophy of Quantum Mechanics. C. A. Hooker, Ed.: 69. Reidel. Dordrecht; 1976. J. Math. Phys. **17**: 1863; 1978. J. Chem. Phys. **70**: 788.
12. MOYAL, J. E. 1949. Proc. Cambridge Philos. Soc. **45**: 99.
13. COHEN, L. 1966. Philos. Sci. **33**: 317.
14. SRINIVAS, M. D. & E. WOLF. 1975. Phys. Rev. **D11**: 1477.
15. GROBLICKI, R. 1983. J. Math. Phys. **24**: 841.

On Measurable Distinctions between Quantum Ensembles

M. P. SILVERMAN

Department of Physics
Trinity College
Hartford, Connecticut 06106

INTRODUCTION

In his graphic depiction of the Young two-slit experiment for electrons, Feynman characterized quantum interference as "a phenomenon which is ... *absolutely* impossible to explain in any classical way, and which has in it the heart of quantum mechanics. In reality, it contains the *only* mystery."[1] While many subsequent studies have helped penetrate more deeply the quantum "mystery," the principal distinction between quantum and classical mechanics is still the uniquely quantum mechanical interference phenomena described by linear superpositions of probability amplitudes.

Statistical uncertainty and probability have a role in both classical and quantum physics, although at different levels of fundamentality. An elementary constituent of a classical ensemble of particles can be endowed with dynamical variables that may not be known, but that are, in principle, knowable; their determination is not precluded by physical law. An elementary constituent (e.g., an atom) of a quantum ensemble cannot ordinarily be endowed with definite dynamical variables; the general quantal description—even of a single particle—is not in terms of the observable attributes themselves (e.g., energy or momentum), but in terms of probability amplitudes for the potential realization of these attributes. For a multiparticle quantum system, there may also be a statistical distribution of probability amplitudes over the elementary constituents whereupon the use of statistics as in classical physics becomes necessary.

This paper is concerned with the experimental distinguishability of a quantum ensemble, wherein which each constituent is endowed with definite, although statistically distributed, energy values, and another ensemble, where each constituent is in a linear superposition of energy eigenstates encompassing the same energy values as the first ensemble.

For simplicity, I consider an ensemble of effectively two-state atoms. Each atom, initially in its ground state, is subjected to an impulsive excitation at time, t_o, that prepares it in a linear superposition of two excited states. This is characterized by the state vector,

$$|\psi(t_o)\rangle = a_1|1\rangle + a_2|2\rangle. \tag{1}$$

The atoms are said to be coherently excited. The system constitutes a pure state whose density matrix in an energy representation has elements,

$$p_{ii}^o = |a_i|^2 \quad (i = 1, 2), \tag{2a}$$

$$p_{12}^o = |a_1 a_2| \exp(-i\Phi); \tag{2b}$$

292

the relative phase is

$$\Phi = \arg(a_2) - \arg(a_1). \tag{2c}$$

A measurement of the energy of the system at t_o would yield values, E_1, E_2, with probabilities, $|a_1|^2$, $|a_2|^2$, respectively; this is the same as if the system consisted of a mixture of definite states, that is, an ensemble of atoms distributed over $|1\rangle$, $|2\rangle$ with respective probabilities, $|a_1|^2$, $|a_2|^2$, and characterized by a density matrix with elements,

$$p_{ij}^o = |a_i|^2 \delta_{ij}. \tag{3}$$

Nevertheless, the two ensembles are quite different; quantum correlations that distinguish a superposition state from a mixture of definite states can be manifested by quantum interference effects in atomic fluorescence.

The excitation of individual atoms into states such as equation 1 does not necessarily mean that the ensemble as a whole will manifest quantum interference effects if subpopulations of constituents are in linear superpositions of eigenstates with different phases. It is of both practical and conceptual significance to ascertain to what extent the incursion of phase disorder extinguishes the coherence observable in an ensemble of mixed superposition states. As an experimental problem, the distinction between theoretically different quantum ensembles may be difficult. The experimenter is not presented in the laboratory with the elements of a density matrix, but, at best, with the ensemble of atoms and the source of excitation. For example, the theoretical possibility of quantum interference in light emission from coherently excited atoms was pointed out in the 1930s by Breit.[2] When observed in the 1960s, the modulated fluorescence ("quantum beats") was incorrectly attributed to electric field–induced Stark mixing of degenerate states,[3] rather than being correctly attributed to field-free decay of nondegenerate states.[4] In an astrophysical setting, the experimenter has control over neither the ensemble of atoms nor the source of excitation. The question has been raised, for example, of whether quantum interference amongst Zeeman states of atoms in the Crab Nebula is produced by optical pulsar NP 0531.[5] If so, one could determine, by a direct Doppler-free method, the magnitude of the magnetic field in an interstellar medium. The atoms of the nebula, however, do not comprise a pure superposition state; constraints on the direct observation of a modulated fluorescent intensity are severe. It would be useful to know whether an ensemble of mixed superposition states manifests in some way the quantum coherence within individual atoms.

In this paper, I consider atoms impulsively excited at an amplitude-modulated or constant rate; an impulsive excitation at random times is equivalent to a continuous excitation with random phases.[6] I show that so long as the relative phase of the superposed states (not to be confused with the possibly random phase of the source of excitation) is well defined in the ensemble, the quantum coherence is not entirely extinguished from the fluorescent intensity; however, observation may, depending upon experimental circumstances, be difficult. If the phase is a random variable, the light intensity does not reveal the coherent excitation of individual atoms; ensembles of mixed indefinite and mixed definite states would not be distinguishable by such a measurement.

It has been claimed[7] that a random distribution of phase still leads to manifestations of quantum interference in the power spectrum of intensity fluctuations. In the specified example,[8] however, the intensity fluctuations occurred in a stationary light beam transmitted through an atomic gas, not in spontaneous emission; the absorption of radiation produced, at any instant in time, a well-defined phase for the off-diagonal density matrix elements of the ensemble. Thus, the quantum phases did not vary randomly over the atoms of the ensemble. I have shown[9] that the measurement of correlated intensity fluctuations in spontaneous emission at two detectors by means of intensity interferometry[10] also manifests quantum interference of atomic states if, again, the quantum phases (even though they fluctuate) are common to all constituents of the sample at each instant in time. In both cases, the light was treated classically.

In this paper, I examine more generally the case of correlated intensity fluctuations from an ensemble of mixed superposition states from the perspectives of both the classical and quantum descriptions of the light field. The classically computed degree of second-order coherence contains a contribution to correlated intensity fluctuations from the radiative decay of coherently excited individual atoms that persists even if the relative phase is a random variable. The quantum degree of second-order coherence does not lead to this contribution. Within the framework of quantum optics, but not of classical optics, the two ensembles are physically equivalent.

The organization of this paper is as follows: The following section describes the density matrix and the measure of order of a system of decaying two-state atoms. In the third section, the time-evolution and fluorescent intensity of an ensemble of such atoms subjected to an impulsive interaction over an indefinite period of time are examined. In the fourth section, the correlations in intensity fluctuations are determined on the basis of both classical and quantum optics. Conclusions are presented in the final section.

TWO-STATE DENSITY MATRIX AND SYSTEM DISORDER

An ensemble of two-state atoms can be described by a density matrix, p, with elements, p_{ij}. For a pure state, the elements can be parametrized by a polar angle, θ, and a phase angle, Φ, as follows:

$$p_{11} = \cos^2 \theta, \qquad p_{22} = \sin^2 \theta, \tag{4a}$$

$$p_{12} = p_{21}{}^* = \sin 2\theta \exp{(-i\Phi)}/2. \tag{4b}$$

The probability conservation condition, $\text{Tr}(p) = 1$, for a closed system is reflected in equation 4a. For a mixture of states with no quantum correlations in a designated representation, the off-diagonal elements vanish. The magnitude of the off-diagonal elements can range from 0 to $\frac{1}{2}$.

The disorder or information content of a system can be specified by the entropic function, S:[11]

$$S = -\text{Tr}(p \ln p) = -\sum_i p_i \ln(p_i), \tag{5}$$

where p_i ($i = 1, 2$) are the eigenvalues of p given by

$$p_{1,2} = \{(p_{11} + p_{22}) \pm [(p_{11} - p_{22})^2 + 4|p_{12}|^2]^{1/2}\}/2. \tag{6}$$

The density matrix, p, can also be represented in terms of the mean population, P_o, and the elements of a polarization vector, P:

$$p = P_o [1 + P \cdot s], \qquad (7)$$

where s is a vector whose components are the Pauli spin matrices; P_o (which would be $\frac{1}{2}$ for a closed system) and the components, P_i, of P, given by

$$P_o = (p_{11} + p_{22})/2, \qquad (8a)$$

$$P_o P_1 = (p_{12} + p_{21})/2, \qquad (8b)$$

$$P_o P_2 = (p_{21} - p_{12})/2i, \qquad (8c)$$

$$P_o P_3 = (p_{11} - p_{22})/2, \qquad (8d)$$

constitute the Stokes parameters.[12] The eigenvalues of p can therefore also be expressed as

$$p_{1,2} = P_o(1 \pm |P|), \qquad (9A)$$

$$|P| = [(p_{11} - p_{22})^2 + 4|p_{12}|^2]^{1/2}/(p_{11} + p_{22}). \qquad (9b)$$

From equations 5, 9a, and 9b, the disorder and polarization are related as follows:

$$S = -2P_o \ln P_o - P_o[(1 + |P|) \ln(1 + |P|) + (1 - |P|) \ln(1 - |P|)]. \qquad (10a)$$

For a completely polarized ensemble, $|P| = 1$ and $S = -2P_o \ln 2P_o$, which yields $S = 0$ for $P_o = \frac{1}{2}$. For a weakly polarized ensemble ($|P| \ll 1$), equation 10a reduces to

$$S \sim -2P_o \ln P_o - P_o|P|^2, \qquad (10b)$$

which yields $S = \ln 2$ for a completely unpolarized ensemble with $P_o = \frac{1}{2}$.

In the system under consideration, each atom, prepared in a linear superposition of excited states, is presumed to decay radiatively to a lower state; one therefore does not have a true two-state system. The decay can be included in the equation of motion of the excited state density matrix through a suitable relaxation term. The system is in effect an open one, and after the initial excitation, $\mathrm{Tr}(p) = 2P_o \neq 1$.

The time-evolution of the two-state system is governed by the internal Hamiltonian, H, with eigenvalues, w_1, w_2, and a decay operator, G, with eigenvalue, g, for both states. (In natural units with $\hbar = c = 1$, the eigenvalues are expressed as frequencies.) The density matrix equation of motion is

$$dp/dt = -i[H, p] - \{G, p\}/2, \qquad (11a)$$

where the square brackets and curly brackets designate, respectively, the commutator and anticommutator. The phenomenological relaxation term leads to the exponential decay of the excited state populations, as expressed by

$$d\mathrm{Tr}(p)/dt = -\mathrm{Tr}(p\,G) = -g\mathrm{Tr}(p). \qquad (11b)$$

From equations 5, 11a, and 11b, the time-evolution of the system disorder is

$$dS/dt = \mathrm{Tr}(p\,G) + \mathrm{Tr}\{G\,p \ln p\} \qquad (12a)$$

for general G, and

$$dS/dt + gS = \{g\text{Tr}(p^o)\}\exp(-gt) \tag{12b}$$

for $G = g1$, where 1 is the unit two-dimensional matrix; p^o is the initial density matrix. The time-evolution of S is independent of H. Integration of equation 12b gives

$$S(t) = (S_o + gt)\exp(-gt), \tag{13}$$

where S_o is the initial measure of disorder. In the absence of decay, the disorder remains constant, $S(t) = S_o$.

QUANTUM CORRELATIONS IN A TWO-STATE SYSTEM WITH VARYING DEGREES OF ORDER

An ensemble of two-state atoms is subjected to an impulsive interaction at time, t_o, that produces a pure state described by density matrix, p^o, with elements given in equation 2; the phase, Φ, is assumed common to all atoms of the ensemble. Experimentally, state preparation of this kind can be achieved in a variety of ways, as, for example, through electron bombardment,[13] fast ion-beam passage through thin foils,[14] optical excitation through shuttered spectral lamps,[15] and pulsed laser excitation.[16] From equation 11a, it follows that

$$p_{ij}(t, t_o) = p_{ij}^o\exp[-iw_{ij}(t - t_o)]\exp[-g(t - t_o)]. \tag{14}$$

The initial polarization is $|P| = 1$; the initial measure of disorder is $S_o = 0$. From equations 9b and 13, the polarization and disorder as functions of time are given by

$$|P(t, t_o)| = \exp[-g(t - t_o)], \tag{15a}$$

$$S(t, t_o) = g(t - t_o)\exp[-g(t - t_o)]. \tag{15b}$$

The disorder within the system begins to increase as the two excited states are depopulated; maximum disorder is reached at a time, $1/g$, after excitation. There is, again, total order at an infinite time after excitation when all atoms have returned to the ground state.

The time-dependence of the spontaneous emission intensity, $I(t, t_o)$, is given by the expectation value of a detection operator, X,

$$I(t, t_o) = \text{Tr}(p\,X), \tag{16}$$

where

$$X = e \cdot D|0\rangle\langle 0|e \cdot D. \tag{17}$$

Here, e is the light polarization vector, D is the electric dipole operator, and $|0\rangle$ is the lower state to which the excited states decay. It is assumed, for simplicity, that the matrix elements of $e \cdot D$ are real. From equations 16 and 17, it follows that

$$I(t, t_o) = [A + B\cos\{w_{21}(t - t_o) - \Phi\}]\exp[-g(t - t_o)], \tag{18a}$$

where

$$A = D_{10}^2 p_{11}^o + D_{20}^2 p_{22}^o,$$ (18b)

$$B = 2 D_{10} D_{20} |p_{12}^o|.$$ (18c)

The exponentially damped fluorescence from the ensemble of atoms is modulated at the Bohr frequency, w_{21}, with a modulation depth of B/A. If the transition matrix elements from states $|1\rangle$ and $|2\rangle$ to $|0\rangle$ are equal, and the excitation parameter in equation 4 is $\theta = 45°$, the contrast $B/A = 100\%$. The total unpolarized fluorescent emission in a given direction is not modulated; oscillations in intensity are observable only on a polarized component. This can be demonstrated by the Wigner-Eckart theorem. There is no Doppler spread in the beat frequency (to first order in v/c) because the interference effect is produced by coherence in individual atoms, not between different atoms.

For an incoherently prepared state, $B = 0$. The fluorescent emission follows the simple exponential damping,

$$I(t, t_o) = A \exp\left[-g(t - t_o)\right],$$ (19)

which is characteristic of incoherent decay.

If the atomic ensemble is subjected to impulsive excitations occurring over an indefinitely long period of time at a rate, $r(t_o)$, given by

$$r(t_o) = W[1 + m \cos (Ft_o)],$$ (20)

the density matrix, $p(t)$, is obtained by averaging $p(t, t_o)$ over the excitation time, t_o, as follows

$$p(t) = \int_{-\infty}^{t} p(t, t_o)\, r(t_o)\, dt_o$$ (21a)

to yield the elements,

$$p_{ij}(t) = (W/g)[g/(g + iw_{ij}) + 0.5\left\{mg/[g + i(w_{ij} + F)]\right\} \exp (iFt)$$
$$+ 0.5\left\{mg/[g + i(w_{ij} - F)]\right\} \exp (-iFt)]\, p_{ij}^o.$$ (21b)

The optical emission to which this system gives rise is

$$I(t) = (W/g)[A\{1 + mg(g^2 + F^2)^{-1}(g \cos Ft + F \sin Ft)\}$$
$$+ B\{g(g^2 + w_{21}^2)^{-1}(g \cos \Phi + w_{21} \sin \Phi) + 0.5\, mg[g^2 + (w_{21} + F)^2]^{-1}$$
$$\cdot [g \cos (Ft + \Phi) + (w_{21} + F) \sin (Ft + \Phi)] + 0.5\, mg[g^2 + (w_{21} - F)^2]^{-1}$$
$$\cdot [g \cos (Ft - \Phi) - (w_{21} - F) \sin (Ft - \Phi)]\}].$$ (22)

The rate parameter, W, is assumed small compared to the atomic decay rate, g; one may then neglect the occurrence of cycles of stimulated emission and absorption over the period of the excitation pulse.[17]

In the case of incoherent excitation leading to an ensemble of mixed definite states, the populations oscillate in time simply as a trivial consequence of turning the excitation on and off at frequency, F. For $F \gg g$, the populations respond sluggishly to the time-variation of the excitation; the modulated components of p_{ii} fall off as F^{-1}. In effect, one has

$$p_{ij} = (W/g)\, p_{ii}^{o}\, \delta_{ij} \quad (F \gg g). \tag{23a}$$

The polarization of the ensemble is

$$|P| = |p_{11}^{o} - p_{22}^{o}|; \tag{23b}$$

the measure of disorder is

$$S = S_1 + (W/g)[-p_{11}^{o} \ln p_{11}^{o} - p_{22}^{o} \ln p_{22}^{o}], \tag{23c}$$

where

$$S_1 = -(W/g) \ln(W/g) \tag{23d}$$

is the minimum disorder engendered by the excitation and decay processes. The fluorescent intensity is

$$I(t) = WA/g. \tag{24}$$

For excitation into nondegenerate states ($w_{21} > g$) at a resonant frequency ($F = w_{21}$), the element, p_{12}, is

$$p_{12} = (Wm/2g)\, p_{12}^{o} \exp\,[+iFt] \qquad (F = w_{21}); \tag{25a}$$

the elements, p_{ii}, are again given by equation 23a. The polarization of the ensemble takes the form,

$$|P| = [(p_{11}^{o} - p_{22}^{o})^2 + m^2 |p_{12}^{o}|^2]^{1/2}, \tag{25b}$$

which, for $m = 2$, leads to the maximum value, $|P| = 1$, and the minimum extent of disorder, $S_{[res;m=2]} = S_1$. The resonant emission intensity is

$$I(t) = (W/g)[A + 0.5\, mB \cos (Ft - \Phi)] \qquad (F = w_{21}); \tag{25c}$$

under the condition of minimum disorder, $m = 2$, the contrast is B/A, which is the same as in the case of quantum beats from a pure state. Equation 25c, unlike equation 18a, characterizes a steady-state, not transient, optical emission.

Far from resonance, $F \gg (w_{21}, g)$, one can effectively ignore the modulation and consider the ensemble prepared by a random excitation occurring at a constant rate, W. The density matrix element, p_{12}, is

$$p_{12} = W\,(g + iw_{12})^{-1}\, p_{12}^{o}. \tag{26a}$$

The polarization and fluorescent intensity of the ensemble depend on the relative size of g and w_{21}:

$$|P| = [(p_{11}^{o} - p_{22}^{o})^2 + 4\{g^2/(g^2 + w_{21}^2)^2\}\, |p_{12}^{o}|^2]^{1/2}, \tag{26b}$$

$$I(t) = (W/g)[A + B\,g(g^2 + w_{21}^2)^{-1}\,(g\cos\Phi + w_{21}\sin\Phi)] \tag{26c}$$

For degenerate states, $w_{21} = 0$, $|P|$ reduces to the maximal value of 1; the disorder of the system is again S_1, which is the same result as in the case of resonant excitation of nondegenerate states. In both cases, the quantum coherence in the excitation of single atoms is maximally preserved in the entire ensemble. For resonant excitation of nondegenerate states, the source of excitation forces the entire ensemble into phased emission. In the case of degenerate excited states, the quantum oscillations occur at zero frequency for each atom, and the emissions from different atoms consequently do not become dephased in time. The fluorescent emission is

$$I(t) = (W/g)[A + B\cos\Phi] \qquad (w_{21} = 0), \tag{27b}$$

and depends on the atomic coherence.

If the states are nondegenerate ($w_{21} > g$), the polarization is not very sensitive to $|p_{12}^o|$ unless the state populations are equal. The dependence of the fluorescence on the coherence factor, B, is scaled by g/w_{21}:

$$I(t) = (W/g)\,[A + B\,(g/w_{21})\sin\Phi]. \tag{28}$$

INTENSITY FLUCTUATIONS IN THE EMISSION
FROM COHERENTLY EXCITED ATOMS

If a source of excitation produces linear superpositions of states with randomly distributed phase, Φ, the phase average of the density matrix (equations 21a and 21b) is indistinguishable from the density matrix of a mixture of definite energy states (equation 23a). The intensity (equation 22) shows no quantum interference.

From the perspective of classical optics, the instantaneous intensity can be represented by

$$I(t) = \langle I(t)\rangle + \Delta I(t), \tag{29}$$

where the first term is the phase-averaged intensity and the second term is the fluctuation about the average. A measure of the intensity correlations is provided by the degree of second-order coherence, $G(t)$, defined by the relation,

$$G(t) = \langle I(0)I(t)\rangle/\langle I(0)\rangle\langle I(t)\rangle = 1 + \langle\Delta I(0)\Delta I(t)\rangle/\langle I(0)\rangle\langle I(t)\rangle. \tag{30}$$

Only the time delay, t, and not the origin of time, is of consequence for the fields under consideration.

From equations 18 and 30, it follows that

$$G(t) = 1 + 0.5\,(B/A)^2\cos(w_{21}t) \tag{31a}$$

for free radiative decay from a mixture of superposition states impulsively generated by the same excitation event. For excitations occurring at constant rate, $W \ll g$, over an indefinitely long time, it follows from equations 22 and 30 (with modulation amplitude,

$m = 0$) that

$$G(t) = 1 + 0.5 \, (B/A)^2 \, g^2 (g^2 + w_{21}^2)^{-1}. \tag{31b}$$

The second term in equations 31a and 31b represents the correlation within the light field from individual coherently excited atoms. That $G(t)$ contains a term dependent upon $|p_{12}^o|$ might seem reasonable because the atomic polarization (equation 9b) of each subgroup of atoms of given phase depends only on the magnitude, not on the phase, of the off-diagonal matrix elements.

The classical result is not sustained by a quantum optical determination of the degree of second-order coherence defined by the relation,[18]

$$G(t) = \langle E^-(0)E^-(t)E^+(t)E^+(0)\rangle / \langle E^-(0)E^+(0)\rangle \langle E^-(t)E^+(t)\rangle, \tag{32}$$

where the negative and positive frequency contributions to the field under consideration are (to within irrelevant constant factors) given by

$$E^-(t) \sim -i[w_1 a_1{}^+ \exp(iw_1 t) + w_2 a_2{}^+ \exp(iw_2 t)], \tag{33a}$$

$$E^+(t) \sim +i[w_1 a_1 \exp(-iw_1 t) + w_2 a_2 \exp(-iw_2 t)]. \tag{33b}$$

Spatial retardation plays no role in what follows; for simplicity, therefore, photon basis states are not distinguished by momentum vectors. The slight dispersion in frequency resulting from the finite lifetime of the atomic states has been ignored; optical frequencies, w_1, w_2, may be assumed equal where their product appears. The field products appearing in equation 32 lead to the following sequences of creation (a^+) and annihilation (a^-) operators:

$$E^-(t)\,E^+(t) \sim n_1 + n_2 + a_1{}^+ a_2 \exp(-iw_{21}t) + a_1 a_2{}^+ \exp(iw_{21}t) \tag{34a}$$

$$E^-(0)E^-(t)E^+(t)E^+(0) \sim (n_1^2 - n_1) + (n_2^2 - n_2) + 2\,n_1 n_2 (1 + \cos w_{21} t)$$

$$+ [a_1{}^{+2} a_2^2 \exp(-iw_{21}t) + a_1^2 a_2{}^{+2} \exp(iw_{21}t)]$$

$$+ [a_1{}^+ n_1 a_2\{1 + \exp(-iw_{21}t)\} + n_1 a_1 a_2{}^+\{1 + \exp(iw_{21}t)\}]$$

$$+ [a_1 a_2{}^+ n_2\{1 + \exp(iw_{21}t)\} + a_1{}^+ n_2 a_2\{1 + \exp(-iw_{21}t)\}]; \tag{34b}$$

$n_i = a_i{}^+ a_i$ is the number operator. Square brackets enclose Hermitian conjugate pairs.

The state vector of the atom-radiation field system is readily obtained from the Wigner-Weisskopf theory of spontaneous emission[19] as applied to a two-state atom decaying to a single ground state.[20] This state vector (derived on the basis of single-photon electric dipole processes only) consists, in essence, of a linear superposition of the quantum electrodynamic vacuum, $100\rangle$, and the single photon states, $|10\rangle$, $|01\rangle$, where $|n_1 n_2\rangle$ designates a state with n_i photons of frequency, w_i ($i = 1,2$).

I consider the more general state,

$$|\Psi\rangle = A_o|n_1 n_2\rangle + A_1|n_1 + 1\, n_2\rangle + A_2|n_1\, n_2 + 1\rangle$$

$$+ B_1|n_1 - 1\, n_2\rangle + B_2|n_1\, n_2 - 1\rangle, \tag{35}$$

which allows for single-photon stimulated absorption and emission processes, as well as spontaneous emission. The amplitudes, A_i, B_i, can be related to atomic dipole transition and density matrix elements; of particular interest, ultimately, are the relative phases between the amplitudes. Upon taking the expectation values of equations 34a and 34b on the state, $|\Psi\rangle$, given by equation 35, one obtains

$$
\begin{aligned}
\langle E^-(0)E^-(t)E^+(t)E^+(0)\rangle = & \ |A_o|^2 (n_1 + n_2)(n_1 + n_2 - 1) \\
& + (|A_1|^2 + |A_2|^2)(n_1 + n_2)(n_1 + n_2 + 1) \\
& + (|B_1|^2 + |B_2|^2)(n_1 + n_2 - 1)(n_1 + n_2 - 2) \\
& + 2[|A_o|^2 n_1 n_2 + |A_1|^2(n_1 + 1)n_2 \\
& + |A_2|^2 n_1(n_2 + 1) + |B_1|^2(n_1 - 1)n_2 \\
& + |B_2|^2 n_1(n_2 - 1)] \cos w_{21}t \\
& + 2[(n_1 + 1)(n_2 + 1)]^{1/2}|A_1 A_2|[(n_1 + n_2) \cos \phi_A \\
& + n_1 \cos (w_{21}t - \phi_A) + n_2 \cos (w_{21}t + \phi_A)] \\
& + 2[n_1 n_2]^{1/2}|B_1 B_2|[(n_1 + n_2 - 2) \cos \phi_B \\
& + (n_1 - 1) \cos (w_{21}t + \phi_B) \\
& + (n_2 - 1) \cos (w_{21}t - \phi_B)], \quad (36)
\end{aligned}
$$

$$
\begin{aligned}
\langle E^-(t)E^+(t)\rangle = & \ |A_o|^2(n_1 + n_2) + (|A_1|^2 + |A_2|^2)(n_1 + n_2 + 1) \\
& + (|B_1|^2 + |B_2|^2)(n_1 + n_2 - 1) \\
& + 2[\{(n_1 + 1)(n_2 + 1)\}^{1/2}|A_1 A_2| \cos (w_{21}t - \phi_A) \\
& + \{n_1 n_2\}^{1/2}|B_1 B_2| \cos (w_{21}t + \phi_B)], \quad (37)
\end{aligned}
$$

where

$$
\phi_A = \arg (A_2) - \arg (A_1); \quad \phi_B = \arg (B_2) - \arg (B_1). \quad (38)
$$

For the case of spontaneous emission into the vacuum (in essence, the Wigner-Weisskopf state), $n_1 = n_2 = 0$, $b_1 = b_2 = 0$. Equation 37 leads to a modulated intensity; the modulation vanishes for random phase, ϕ_A. Equation 36 leads to an intensity correlation that is identically null independent of relative phase. There is no contribution from the coherent excitation and decay of individual atoms. The distinction between the classical and quantum optical results may be understood as follows: In the classical picture, the light field produced by an atom consists of a superpositon of two waves of frequencies, w_1, w_2, that may interfere at the detector. In the quantum picture, the emission of one photon of energy w_1 or w_2 precludes the emission of the other by the same atom for a given excitation event; there can be no correlation between two photons from the same atom under the above circumstances.

If the atoms are immersed in a sea of photons with $(n_1, n_2) \gg 1$ and $|A_0| \sim 1 \gg |A_1|$,

$|A_2|, |B_1|, |B_2|$, the intensity correlation and intensity are

$$\langle E^-(0)E^-(t)E^+(t)E^+(0) \rangle \sim |A_o|^2 \, [(n_1 + n_2)^2 + 2n_1 n_2 \cos w_{21} t)]$$

$$+ 2(n_1 n_2)^{1/2} |A_1 A_2| \, [(n_1 + n_2) \cos \phi_A + n_1 \cos (w_{21} t - \phi_A)$$

$$+ n_2 \cos (w_{21} t + \phi_A)] + 2(n_1 n_2)^{1/2} |B_1 B_2| \, [(n_1 + n_2) \cos \phi_B$$

$$+ n_1 \cos (w_{21} t + \phi_B) + n_2 \cos (w_{21} t - \phi_B)], \quad \text{(39a)}$$

$$\langle E^-(t)E^+(t) \rangle \sim |A_o|^2(n_1 + n_2)$$

$$+ 2(n_1 n_2)^{1/2} \, [|A_1 A_2| \cos (w_{21} t - \phi_A) + |B_1 B_2| \cos (w_{21} t + \phi_B)]. \quad \text{(39b)}$$

For fixed relative phases, the intensity shows quantum interference in both the absorption and emission; the intensity correlation likewise manifests quantum interference in analogy to that observed in reference 8. A random distribution of phases results in an unmodulated intensity. The intensity correlation, however, has a modulated term, $2n_1 n_2 \cos (w_{21} t)$, independent of phase. This is the classical wave noise of the Hanbury Brown–Twiss experiment;[21] it represents correlations in the light field from different atoms. In the quantum description of light, it characterizes the bosonic nature of the photon. The resulting coherence function is

$$G(t) = 1 + [2n_1 n_2/(n_1 + n_2)^2] \cos (w_{21} t). \quad \text{(40)}$$

A derivation based on a classical light field leads to the same result with photon number, n_i, replaced by intensity, I_i. If, as is usually the case, the atoms are moving relative to the observer, the above result must be averaged over the Doppler profile. Assumption of a Gaussian spectral distribution,

$$J(w) = (q^2/\pi)^{1/2} \exp [-q^2(w - w_o)^2], \quad \text{(41)}$$

of width, $1/q$, for each central frequency, $w_o = w_1, w_2$, leads to

$$\langle G(t) \rangle = 1 + [2n_1 n_2/(n_1 + n_2)^2 \exp [-t^2/2q^2] \cos (w_{21} t). \quad \text{(42)}$$

The degree of second-order coherence, although it does not distinguish ensembles of mixed definite states and mixed superposition states with random phases, does in this case contain information on atomic fine structure that is not provided by direct measurement of the intensity.

CONCLUSIONS

The quantum interference that distinguishes an ensemble of atoms coherently excited into a linear superposition of energy eigenstates from an ensemble of atoms in definite energy states persists in the spontaneous emission intensity. This persists even if the excitation occurs over an indefinite period of time, provided that the relative quantum phases are well defined within the ensemble. Under conditions where the observer has access to the atoms and source of excitation, ensembles with maximum polarization, $|P| = 1$, and minimum disorder, $S_1 = -(W/g) \ln(W/g)$, can be produced by resonant amplitude modulation of the rate of excitation of nondegenerate states or by external field-induced degeneracy of states excited at a constant rate. Quantum interference in stimulated absorption or emission contributes to the correlation of intensity fluctuations of the light field. It also might serve to indicate coherent excitation of individual atoms under conditions where the observer has access only to the radiation and not to the atoms or source of excitation.

If the quantum phases are random variables, quantum interference effects do not appear directly in the fluorescent intensity. The classically computed degree of second-order coherence contains an anomalous contribution to correlations in intensity fluctuations from coherent excitation of individual atoms. The quantum description of light does not lead to this contribution. Nevertheless, in both classical and quantum optics, interference terms may occur in the second-order coherence resulting from correlations between the light from different atoms. Unlike the "quantum beats" from coherently excited individual atoms, the latter beats are affected by the distribution of atomic velocities.

REFERENCES

1. FEYNMAN, R. P., R. B. LEIGHTON & M. SANDS. 1965. The Feynman Lectures on Physics, vol. 3, p. 1–1. Addison–Wesley. Reading, Massachusetts.
2. BREIT, G. 1933. Rev. Mod. Phys. **5**: 117–125.
3. BASHKIN, S. & G. BEAUCHEMIN. 1966. Can. J. Phys. **44**: 1603.
4. MACEK, J. 1969. Phys. Rev. Lett. **23**: 1–2.
5. RUZMAIKIN, A. A. 1976. Sov. Astron. **19**: 702–705.
6. DICKE, R. H. & J. P. WITTKE. 1960. Introduction to Quantum Mechanics, p. 331–355. Addison–Wesley. Reading, Massachusetts.
7. ALEKSANDROV, E. B. 1973. Sov. Phys. Usp. **15**: 436–451 (especially p. 447).
8. ALEKSANDROV, E. B., O. V. KONSTANTINOV, V. N. KULYASOV, A. B. MAMYRIN & V. I. PEREL. 1972. Sov. Phys. JETP **34**: 1210–1215.
9. SILVERMAN, M. P. 1985. Nuovo Cimento **6D**: 283.
10. HANBURY BROWN, R. 1974. The Intensity Interferometer, p. 22–31. Taylor & Francis. London. (See also references contained therein.)
11. FANO, U. 1957. Rev. Mod. Phys. **29**: 84–85.
12. STONE, J. M. 1963. Radiation and Optics, p. 313. McGraw–Hill. New York.
13. HADEISHI, T. & W. A. NIERENBERG. 1965. Phys. Rev. Lett. **14**: 891.
14. SELLIN, I. A., C. D. MOAK, P. M. GRIFFIN & J. A. BIGGERSTAFF. 1969. Phys. Rev. **184**: 56–63.
15. DODD, J. N., W. J. SANDLE & D. ZISSERMANN. 1967. Proc. Phys. Soc. London **92**: 497.
16. HAROCHE, S., M. GROSS & M. P. SILVERMAN. 1974. Phys. Rev. Lett. **33**: 1063–1066 (and references therein).
17. SILVERMAN, M. P., S. HAROCHE & M. GROSS. 1978. Phys. Rev. **A18**: 1507–1516.
18. LOUDON, R. 1973. The Quantum Theory of Light, p. 199–231. Oxford Univ. Press. London.
19. WEISSKOPF, V. & E. WIGNER. 1930. Z. Phys. **63**: 54; **65**: 18.
20. HAROCHE, S. 1976. Quantum beats and time-resolved fluorescence spectroscopy. *In* Topics in Applied Physics, vol. 13. K. Shimoda, Ed.: 253–313. Springer-Verlag. New York.
21. HANBURY BROWN, R. & R. Q. TWISS. 1957. Proc. R. Soc. London **242**: 300–324.

How Come the Quantum?[a]

JOHN ARCHIBALD WHEELER

Center for Theoretical Physics
University of Texas at Austin
Austin, Texas 78712

WHENCE THE NECESSITY OF THE QUANTUM?

The quantum, foundation principle of twentieth century physics, and indispensible working tool for anyone who would make reliable predictions in the world of the small, still comes to many as strange, unwelcome, forced on man from outside against his will. The necessity of the quantum in the construction of existence: out of what deeper requirement does it arise? Behind it all is surely an idea so simple, so beautiful, so compelling that when—in a decade, a century, or a millennium—we grasp it, we will all say to each other, how could it have been otherwise? How could we have been so stupid for so long?

It was not by asking always small questions that physics has achieved its astounding advances. It will surely not be by asking always small questions that the community will some day find the answer to the great question, "How come the quantum?" To ask the right question, however, one must have, as is well known, some glimmer of the answer. It is also old experience that in order to break out of blank puzzlement and into the right question-and-answer circuit, one must try and try again. One must, if necessary, make a fool of oneself many times over, thus following the example of the engine inventor, John Kris, with his familiar words about each new model—"Start her up and see why she don't work."

What are the features and difficulties of a recent model, "existence as meaning circuit"?[1-3] First, let us look at the model, then at the problems.

THE MEANING MODEL: A PARTICIPATORY UNIVERSE

Physics gives rise, as depicted in FIGURE 1, to light, pressure, and sound. They provide means of communication, of the importance of which Niels Bohr notes, "...every analysis of the conditions of human knowledge must rest on considerations of the character and scope of our means of communication."[4] Physics is also the foundation of chemistry and biology, out of which arise communicators. Communicators plus means of communication permit the development of meaning in the sense elucidated by leading English and American schools of philosophy in recent decades, as summarized, for example, by D. Føllesdal: "Meaning is the joint product of all the evidence available to those who communicate."[5]

From meaning back to physics, the circuit under examination makes its way by a less apparent or underground sequence of linkages. Meaning rests on action. Action

[a]This work was assisted by NSF Grant No. PHY-8503890 and by the Center for Theoretical Physics.

forces the choosing between complementary questions and the distinguishing of answers. Distinguishability, in the realm of complementary possibilities, demands for its measurement complex probability amplitudes. The change in the phase of a complex probability amplitude around a closed circuit not only measures the flux of field through that circuit, but can even be regarded as the definition and very essence of that field. Fields, in turn, can be viewed as the building stuff of particles; and fields plus particles generate the world of physics with which the hypothesized meaning circuit began.

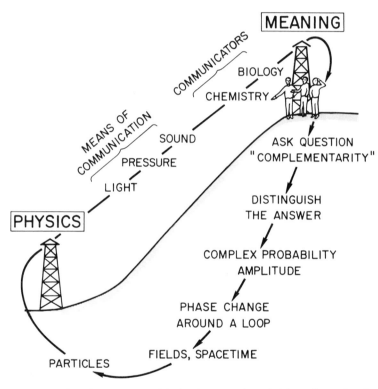

FIGURE 1. Meaning circuit as a model of existence; a loop tied into closure by observer-participancy.

The start of the underground portion of the meaning circuit demands now a closer look.

THE QUESTION-AND-ANSWER FEATURE OF THE ELEMENTARY QUANTUM PHENOMENON

Evidence available to the communicator comes from the asking of a question and the distinguishing of an answer. Do we ask a question about this or that by taking a look at it? Does one glance of the eye take in 10^{10} bits of information? Are we then asked to write a paragraph on what we have seen, or are we required otherwise to display the evidence upon which we act? Do we find that out of a melange so great, the brain has squeezed an amount of information—even at best—that is so small as 10^3 or 10^2 bits?[6] Then, in everyday affairs, we are evidently very far away from the level of the elementary quantum phenomenon. In spite of all the mystery about how the brain accomplishes this action-oriented miracle, though, we know that every bit of information, every item of sight or touch or sound, goes back in the last analysis for its transmission to elementary quantum phenomena.

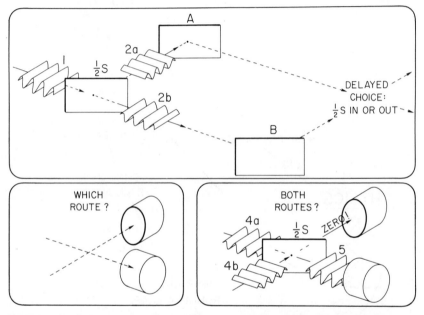

FIGURE 2. Split-beam experiment (above) and the two versions (below) of what happens at the point of crossing when the second half-silvered mirror is omitted (left) or inserted (right) at this crossing point. Not until just before the luminous energy reaches this point is the choice made between "in" and "out" in the delayed-choice version of the experiment.

The elementary quantum phenomenon displays two characteristic features: (1) complementarity in the choice of the question and (2) statistics in the distinguishing of the answer. The split-beam experiment[7] of FIGURE 2 illustrates both. Light arriving from the left is split at the first half-silvered mirror. It is then reflected at the upper or lower totally silvered mirror, and is detected on a photon-by-photon basis by the two counters at the right. We can ask which path does an arriving photon follow—the high road or the low road? That is one choice of question, and the photon detectors stand ready to answer it. To ask for the phase relation between the two beams is a complementary choice of question. To pose this question, we install a second half-silvered mirror at the point of crossing of the two beams and determine the relative counting rate of the two photon detectors.

Shall we install the second half-silvered mirror or shall we leave it out? We cannot do both. Not until we make that decision have we chosen what question to ask. To ask both phase and route at the same time and in the same experiment is impossible.

The choice can be delayed[8] until the photon has passed through the first half-silvered mirror, has undergone reflection at the next mirror, and has arrived almost at the point of crossing of the two beams. This circumstance shows how wrong it is to say that we are finding out in the one case "which route" and in the other case the relation of phases in a "two-route mode of travel." The world is built in such a way that it denies us the possibility to speak in any well-defined way of "what the photon is doing" in its travel from point of entry to point of reception.

No elementary quantum phenomenon[9] *is* a phenomenon until it is a registered phenomenon, brought to a close by an irreversible act of amplification. Definite as are the point of entry and point of detection of the photon, what it is doing in between is totally smoky.[10] Equally smoky is any concept of the path of an electron through an atom. Termination of the smokiness by an act of detection is as close as we can get to establishing reality at the microscopic level. In that answering of a question—in that registration—is always implicit a choice, whether tacit or explicit, between complementary alternatives of what to ask. Complementarity? Choice.

DISTINGUISHABILITY

Distinguishing of the answer is the other half of establishing evidence out of elementary quantum phenomena. What is the phase difference between the two beams that fly off from the second half-silvered mirror to the counter on the upper right, one of these beams being reflected, the other, transmitted? Zero? Then all the photons go that way. One hundred eighty degrees? Then there are no counts in that photodetector. Are the two counting rates in the detector equal? Then the phase difference is 90° or equivalent. However, what if the experiment terminates with 8 yes counts and 6 no counts (a "no" count in the upper photodetector being an abbreviated way of speaking of a "yes" count in the other photodetector)? Or 80 yes counts and 60 no counts? Or 800 yes and 600 no? Those three outcomes are progressively more distinct from the on-average identical-number outcome that goes with a 90° phase difference. Distinguishability, in brief, depends on two features of the yes and no counts: their total and their ratio.

Distinguish from what? "There is no such thing as a fact," it has been said; "there is only a fact for a purpose."[11] Exaggerated as this statement may be, it nevertheless points to the why of distinguishability: action. Answer A advises one action; a distinct answer, B, advises a very different action. Sometimes the statistics do not suffice to distinguish with the requisite certainty which is the answer. Then more measurements, more statistics, and more certainty. Sometimes there is not enough time to secure those extra counts. Then the upcoming decision of how to act has to be taken with an unacceptable risk. In brief, it is difficult to see how distinguishability can have any possible point except against a background of action.

A PROBABILITY AMPLITUDE AND ONE THAT IS COMPLEX: HOW COME?

For the quantitative determination of distinguishability, the statistician and geneticist, R. A. Fisher, taught us[12] as long ago as 1922 that the wrong number is the probability of a yes or a no in an example like ours, or the probability of blue eyes, grey eyes, or brown eyes in a population-characterizing example like his. The right number, he showed, is the square root of the probability of this, that, or the other outcome, or is, in today's words, the probability amplitude of the specified answer. As descriptor of a run of counts, Fisher thus gave us a point (with all its Cartesian coordinates positive) on the surface of the unit sphere in the space of real numbers—a point in a real Hilbert space. The dimensionality of this space is equal to the number of distinct outcomes for the individual count: two for the split-beam experiment, and three for the illustrative example of the eye colors.

According to a 1980 extension of Fisher's results by the quantum physicist, William K. Wootters, the potential distinguishability of two nearly identical sets of experimental results, or between one set of results and a nearly identical ideal set of results that might serve as a signal to action, is measured by the angle, θ, in Hilbert space between the two probability-amplitude vectors.[13] Here, the "potential distinguishability" is the quantity that has to be divided by the familiar factor, the square root, $N^{1/2}$, of the total counts, N, so as to obtain the actual distinguishability parameter, $\delta = \theta/N^{1/2}$. This parameter (by way of the Gauss function) tells us, for example, that we run odds of 1,680,675 to 1 of being wrong if, when having observed 800 yes counts and 600 no counts in the split-beam experiment, we nevertheless proceed to bet on a phase-shift between the two beams of 90 degrees rather than 81.79 degrees.

How come is it that quantum mechanics, reaching as it does beyond Fisher's genetic concerns, gives us probability amplitudes that are not real, but complex? No one put his finger earlier on the decisive point than E. C. G. Stueckelberg.[14] Probability amplitudes that are exclusively real are incompatible, he showed, with Heisenberg's principle of indeterminism,[15] or, in our translation, with Bohr's principle of complementarity:[16] namely, the freedom to choose, and the necessity to choose, which question we will put to nature.

So much for the sense in which the double demand of complementarity and distinguishability leads to the heart of quantum theory, the complex probability amplitude.

THE CHANGE IN THE PHASE OF A PROBABILITY AMPLITUDE AROUND A CLOSED CIRCUIT AS THE ULTIMATE DEFINER AND ESSENCE OF FIELDS AND SPACE-TIME GEOMETRY

The difference in phase of an electron's probability amplitude around a closed circuit (brought about by a flux of magnetic field through the area bounded by that circuit) shows up in the shift in the pattern of double-slit interference fringes. The idea and the experiment were proposed in 1959 by Y. Aharonov and D. Bohm.[17] This AB effect is by now observationally well established. Likewise, for gravity and for every other gauge field, we have reason to believe[18] that the phase difference in the relevant probability amplitude around a closed circuit provides a way to define and measure that field. The meaning-circuit model translates this conclusion to a new and stronger proposition: Neither field nor geometry has any existence or significance except insofar as it is defined, directly or indirectly, by such phase differences.

THE CLOSURE OF THE MEANING CIRCUIT

With particles owing their definition and existence to fields, with fields owing their definition and existence to phases, with phases owing their definition and existence to distinguishability and complementarity, and with these features of nature going back for their origin to the demand for meaning, we have exposed to view (at least in broad outline) the main features of the underground portion of the model of existence as a meaning circuit closed by observer-participancy.

Before this would-be model can ever rise to the status of a proper model and be subject to quantitative analysis, some questions and difficulties require clarification: (1) What reality does the model ascribe to the physical world before the advent of any meaning-making community? (2) In what respect does it differ totally from the familiar anthropic principle on the issue of why the dimensionless constants of nature have the values they do? (3) What are we to understand by such a term as the community character of meaning? (4) What is the status of an elementary quantum phenomenon that is not put to use in the establishment of meaning? (5) How are we to reconcile the continuum of the world of physics with the discrete yes-or-no character of elementary quantum phenomena? (6) How can we ever hope to quantify meaning? Finally, (7) why a meaning circuit? Why any closed loop at all?

It is appropriate now to take a closer look at these seven questions, of which every one has been suggested by our original query, "How come the quantum?"

Millennia without Meaning before the Advent of the Meaning Makers?

Question one: If life and mind and meaning are so important in the scheme of things, then what is the status of the past? Do the early revolutions of the Milky Way, the building of the elements, and the formation of the elementary particles—all before the advent of life—rank lower in reality than today's wind, snow, and shiver? No. Through the photons that reach the telescope, we see more clearly a quasar event of six billion years ago (before there was any life anywhere) than we can perceive the three-encyclopedia-long sequence of bits in our own DNA, in the here and now.

Does the past exist (and exist only) in the records of the present? If so, then the past ranks no lower and no higher than the rest of what we call existence. In the words of Torgny Segerstedt, "reality is theory."

The quantum brings a new insight, however, to this old conclusion. What is the polarization of that photon that reaches the eye today from a quasar flash of six billion years ago? Is it north-south? Or is it NE-SW? Not until we have set the analyzer to the one orientation or the other have we asked the question. Not until the one or the other of the appropriately paired photodetectors (the yes-counter and the no-counter) clicks have we distinguished an answer. Not until then do we have the right to attribute a polarization to the received photon. This is the respect in which what we ask, or do, in the present has an inescapable consequence for what we have the right to say about the past—even a past long before life. This is the sense in which (through the quantum-level questions we put to nature) we are participators in the making of what we call reality.

To turn from the past to the future is to encounter deeper issues. What is the status of a quantum event so far away that the asking of a question about it and the distinguishing of an answer take place only one hundred million years from now when man has been supplanted by, or has evolved into, intelligent life of quite another form? To attribute a reality to that event now would seem to be premature.

Shall we compare space-time to a great sheet of sandpaper? Shall each glittering glued-down grain represent an event deterministically fixed in space, fixed in time, and fixed in character? What a misleading model of existence! How contradictory to everything the quantum teaches.

Why Are the Dimensionless Constants of Nature Such as to Permit Life?

Question two: How does it come about that the universe ever makes a home for life, mind, and meaning? Many upholders of the anthropic principle[19] propose one answer, which is based on selection. The concept of observer-participancy suggests quite another, which is founded on construction. Both analyses note that life as we know it (not only human life, but any carbon-based life) would be forever impossible in a universe (if such a universe can be imagined) in which one or another of the basic dimensionless constants of physics differs by a few percent either way from its value here. Both take as a starting point the 1957 postulate of Robert H. Dicke[20] that the Weyl-Eddington-Dirac coincidences between the large dimensionless constants of physics [cf. reference 19, chapter 4] "were not random, but conditioned by biological factors." The one account envisages an infinite ensemble of universes, one differing from another in the dimensionless constants of physics, with life totally impossible in the overwhelming majority of these systems. Life, mind, and meaning have only a peripheral and accidental place in the scheme of things in this view. In the other view, they are central. Only by their agency is it even possible to construct the universe or existence, or what we call reality. Those make-believe universes totally devoid of life are (according to this view) totally devoid of physical sense not merely because they cannot be observed, but because there is no way to make them.

The Community Character of Knowledge

Question three: Are there then as many pasts, as many presents, and as many futures as there are observer-participators? A proposal so extravagant overlooks the community character of everything we call knowledge. Already at the quantum level, Niels Bohr warns us of the folly of trying to construct a "quantum language." He emphasizes that no measurement is truly a measurement unless the result can be communicated from one person to another "in plain language." In a wider context, we know that meaning itself would be impossible without communication. There is not a word we speak, a concept we possess, or an idea we conceive that is not rooted in the larger community.

In one of her many wonderful writings, Marie Sklodowska Curie tells us that physics deals with things only—not people. Today, the quantum forces on us a different outlook. It tells us that existence is not a deterministic machine grinding away out there. It is senseless for the uninvolved to try to speak *in abstracto* of what is happening out there at the microscopic level. Involvement is essential: observer-participancy. Not until a choice has been made and not until one or another complementary question has been posed can there be an answer.

The Elementary Quantum Phenomenon That Is Not Put to Use: Does It Count?

Question four: What significance, if any, are we to attribute to an elementary quantum phenomenon that is not put to use to establish evidence and meaning? Despite all that we know about measurement theory in the realm of the quantum, nothing is more puzzling than the linkage between the counter's click and the community that makes meaning. An example will illustrate the problem. A detector, by its irreversible act of amplification, its pulse of current, and the registration of that pulse, brings to a close an elementary quantum phenomenon. However, the apparatus is mounted on a space probe traversing the rings of Saturn. A moment later, before the equipment can beam its message back to earth, a boulder smashes it to atoms. All opportunity vanishes for the quantum process to contribute to the establishment of meaning. An event has taken place, but not an event that is put to use.

As a second example, consider a crystal of zinc sulfide thrown up by nature on the back side of the moon. It stops a cosmic-ray proton. Ten million photons emerge, which is an irreversible act of amplification if there ever was one. The signal, however, dissipates out into space. No use is made of it.

In both examples of quantum events not put to use, the amplifying device consists of some 10^{22}–10^{25} particles coupled by a complex of electromagnetic interactions. Why should we attribute to those unused elementary quantum phenomena any special significance whatsoever? Surely all over the universe, in regions out of sight, interactions are going on all the time and between particles that are stupendous in number compared to the count in our two examples. Amidst that tumult, there is many a concatenation that on anyone's bookkeeping must count as an elementary quantum phenomenon that was brought to a close by an irreversible act of amplification. Not one of these collective electromagnetic twitches is deprived of the status of "phenomenon" through its lack of all of the credentials of today's laboratory equipment: no copper wire, no manufacturer's trademark, no silicon chip.

There is no irreversible act of amplification that may not later be erased. Not unless it is put to use in the establishment of meaning does the elementary quantum phenomenon win any special status. To attribute a unique importance to those elementary quantum phenomena that happen to be observed appears, however, unbelievably anthropomorphic, totally anti-Copernican, and utterly in contradiction to the spirit of physics. Does it diminish the objection to recall that the population of Africa increases by a million every three weeks? Or to reflect that the number of observer-participants a millennium from now may well be orders of magnitude greater than it is today? Or to count on numbers of intercommunicating observer-participants billions of years in the future still greater by many orders of magnitude? Or to recognize the role of the elementary quantum phenomena that they observe in establishing what we call the reality of the here and now?

To say that this concept of a participatory universe, built on a meaning circuit, is anti-Copernican is not of much help in arriving at a rational judgement of it. It is more to the point to recognize its difficulties and incompleteness. To speak of difficulty is to come to the problem of the continuum.

The Continuum as an Elaborate Construction of Imagination and Theory That We Build by Surfacing-Over the World of Elementary Quantum Phenomena

Question five: How can we possibly imagine building the continuous world of physics on the yes-or-no of quantum phenomena, no matter how numerous they are?[21] Physics, after all, presents to us a continuous infinity of locations for particles, a continuous infinity of field strengths, and a continuous infinity of degrees of freedom of dynamic space geometry. To construct all that out of the discrete is totally impossible.

It is one of the great achievements of the mathematics (and mathematical logic) of recent decades to destroy belief in the existential character of the continuum of natural numbers. It is an illusion. It is an idealization. It is a dream. With numbers of ever increasing mathematical sophistication, we can approach that limit ever more closely; however, we commit a folly if we think we can ever get there. This lesson of the mathematics of our time carries for physics an inescapable consequence. What we think of at the bottom as a world of the continuous simply is not there.

The concept of the participatory universe replaces the continuum. For the "R" of what we call reality, it gives us a few iron posts of observation, built on elementary quantum phenomena, between which we ourselves trowel in a continuum of papier-mâché and of plaster of Paris, an elaborate construction compounded of imagination and theory. In no other way do we know how to reconcile the continuum of everyday impressions (and of long-established physics) with the discreteness of the means by which alone, in the last analysis, we acquire our knowledge. How else can the appearance of a continuum arise except by our own surfacing-over the discrete?

How Are We to Quantify Meaning?

Question six: How can we possibly use the concept of "meaning" in any well-defined way in the world of physics when the world of philosophy gives us for that term a definition totally deprived of any quantitative handle? Bit? We know what that is. Information capacity of a communication channel? That, too, we know how to define and measure. But meaning? Neither a physics-minded definition nor a way of measurement is available.

If the motto is correct that every difficulty is an opportunity, then there is no better place to apply it than "meaning." Happily for such an enterprise, we know that the view of science that used to say, "define your terms before you proceed," is totally out of date. Nowadays, we recognize that all the laws and theories of physics have this deep and subtle character, that they both define for us the needful concepts, and that they make statements about these concepts. Contrariwise, the absence of some body of theory, law, and principle deprives us of a means properly to use or even to define concepts. In any forward step in human knowledge, the theory, concept, law, and method of measurement—forever inseparable—are born into the world in union. That forward step has yet to be taken in the realm of meaning. Until it is, we will not have grasped the why of the quantum.

Why a Circuit Rather than a Foundation?

Question seven: Why speak of a circuit? Why not seek instead for a foundation?

There is an old legend about the foundation that supports the world: Our globe rests on the back of a great elephant. The elephant stands on the back of a giant tortoise. A lady in the audience, listening to the speaker's account of this idea, asks, "On what does the tortoise stand?" "On the back of a still larger tortoise," she is told. "And what does it stand on," she inquires. The lecturer's reply is famous: "Tortoises, madam; on and on, nothing but tortoises."

How different is the account we give today of the foundation of existence? Matter is built on molecules. The molecule is built on atoms. The atom has a nucleus. The nucleus is built on nucleons. The nucleon is built on quarks. The quark is built on fields. The field is built on geometry of one or another dimension. At each stage of the unfolding story, at each clear view of one turtle, we have had to look for the next turtle. Is there ever to be an end? How can there be an end if we ask always for foundation of foundation of foundation. . .?

No escape is evident from this view of worlds without end—or tortoises without end—except in a line of influence that closes on itself, that forms a loop, that makes a circuit. No model for such a loop is available to us today except one of information-theoretic character, the model of existence as a meaning circuit.

SURVEY OF THE DIFFICULTIES OF THE MEANING-CIRCUIT MODEL

The model under analysis here accepts that the meaning-creating community of observer-participants, past, present, and future, is brought into being by the machinery of the world. However, it goes on to interpret this very world of past, present, and future, and of space, time, and fields, to be (despite all its apparent continuity, immensity, and independence from us) a construction of imagination and theory troweled and plastered in over countably many elementary quantum phenomena, surfaced over the iron posts of discrete acts of observer-participancy, the ant-like but magnificent labor of a community stretching from far in the past to even farther in the future.

The worst model of existence that we possess today is surely one so oriented as this to observer-participancy, information, and meaning. It is the worst, except we possess no other model that puts in central place the quantum and the question of "how come the quantum?".

Is spacetime an illusion? Time itself not primordial, precise, and supplied from outside physics, but secondary, approximate, and derived (as elasticity is in today's bookkeeping)? Repelled we may be in the beginning by the thought of giving up the concept of a spacetime existing out there, but in the end by one decisive circumstance attracted. No feature of the 4-geometry of physics is more impressive than the existence of far-distant events separated by a zero interval, and none has more to do with the structure of all the laws of physics. This intimacy of connection between the apparently disconnected: how does it come about? Are we not well advised to look for the connection in the quantum, in the elementary quantum phenomenon, in the great smoky dragon whose tail is sharply defined, whose bite is also well marked, but which in between cannot be followed? What better reason is there to say that something cannot be followed than to recognize that there is nothing there to follow? And thus to ascribe to multitudes of elementary quantum phenomena those null intervals that tie existence together so tightly?

No continuum (and mathematical logic denies the concept of the continuum) means no dimensionality; neither four nor ten nor any higher number. Moreover, the only feature of a description of nature that could be worse than no dimensionality at all would be a dimensionality.[22] To confront a number, to ask why this number rather than another number, is to be forced to seek a foundation, after which comes another foundation question, and then yet another, and so on and on: nothing but turtles.

Can we formulate the laws of physics without recourse to the continuum? We do not know how. That is perhaps the most conspicuous difficulty of the meaning model. Is the problem soluble? There is one favorable indication. The laws of electrodynamics, of geometrodynamics, of chromodynamics, and of string theory all are structured[23] on the central principle of algebraic geometry, that identity which states that the boundary of a boundary automatically vanishes. This identity comes into all these theories twice over: once at the 1-2-3 dimensional level, and again at the 2-3-4 level in the case of the three older theories (and at the corresponding higher-dimensional levels in the case of string theory). The identity itself is not tied to any particular dimensionality. It even leaps across dimensionality in the sense that it applies to a complex put together out of manifolds of varied dimension. Could this circumstance indicate that the laws of physics will in the end let themselves be formulated in dimension-free language?

Every law of physics, to the extent that it is not pure tautology or mathematical identity, must be at bottom statistical and approximate in its predictions, according to the view of existence under consideration here. By that forecast, the meaning-circuit model exposes itself to destruction, that decisive requirement, according to Karl Popper,[24] for any previously untested way of looking at things.

Charles Darwin, in replying[25] to a letter from his friend Joseph Dalton Hooker, wrote, "It is mere rubbish, thinking at present of the origin of life; one might as well think of the origin of matter." Today, thanks not least to Darwin himself, we do understand (at least in broad outline) the origin and mechanism of life. Large numbers are absolutely central to that explanation, as we see nowhere more spectacularly than in the functioning of the "life machine" of Manfred Eigen.[26]

Numbers of still more stupendous exponent we will hardly be able to escape if, following the guidelines of the meaning model, we are ever to quantify meaning, translate continuum physics into the language of the discrete, bridge the chasm between life and universe, account for the structure of existence, and explain how come the quantum. In confronting that challenge, we can perhaps gain a little courage from the famous adage of Philip W. Anderson: "More is different."

NOTES AND REFERENCES

1. WHEELER, J. A. 1977. Genesis and observership. *In* Foundational Problems in the Special Sciences. R. Butts & J. Hintikka, Eds.: 1–33. Reidel. Dordrecht; 1979. Frontiers of time. *In* Problems in the Foundations of Physics. Proceedings of the International School of Physics "Enrico Fermi" (course 72). N. Toraldo di Francia, Ed.: 395–497. North-Holland. Amsterdam.

2. WHEELER, J. A. 1980. Beyond the black hole. *In* Some Strangeness in the Proportion: A Centennial Symposium to Celebrate the Achievements of Albert Einstein. H. Woolf, Ed.: 341–375. Addison–Wesley. Reading, Massachusetts.

3. WHEELER, J. A. 1984. Bits, quanta, meaning. *In* Problems in Theoretical Physics. A. Giovannini, F. Mancini & M. Marinaro, Eds.: 121–141. Univ. of Salerno Press. Salerno, Italy; 1986. Physics as meaning circuit: three problems. *In* Frontiers of Non-Equilibrium Statistical Physics. G. T. Moore & M. O. Scully, Eds.: 25–32. Plenum. New York.

4. BOHR, N. 1958. Atomic Physics and Human Knowledge. Wiley. New York; 1963. Essays 1958–1962 on Atomic Physics and Human Knowledge. Wiley. New York.

5. FØLLESDAL, D. 1975. Meaning and experience. *In* Mind and Language. S. Guttenplan, Ed.: 254. Oxford Univ. Press (Clarendon). Oxford.

6. To John J. Hopfield go the author's thanks for his explanation of these bit counts.

7. WHEELER, J. A. 1980. Delayed-choice experiments and the Bohr-Einstein dialog. *In* The American Philosophical Society and the Royal Society: Papers read at a meeting, June 5, 1980, pp. 9–40. Amer. Phil. Soc. Philadelphia.

8. WHEELER, J. A. 1978. The "past" and the "delayed-choice" double-slit experiment. *In* Mathematical Foundations of Quantum Theory. A. R. Marlow, Ed.: 9–48. Academic Press. New York. The concept of a delayed-choice experiment is foreshadowed by a passing commentary by K. F. von Weizsäcker in his "Ortbestimmung eines electrons durch ein mikroskop" (1931. Z. Phys. **70:** 114–130) and in an early and solitary sentence of Niels Bohr: "... it ... can make no difference, as regards observable effects obtainable by a definite experimental arrangement, whether our plans for constructing and handling the instruments are fixed beforehand or whether we prefer to postpone the completion of our planning until a later moment when the particle is already on its way from one instrument to another." (1949. Discussion with Einstein on epistemological problems in atomic physics. *In* Albert Einstein: Philosopher-Scientist. P. A. Schilpp, Ed.: 230. Library of Living Philosophers. Evanston. Illinois.)

9. BOHR, N., 1958, emphasizes in reference 4 on p. 88 the "irreversible act of amplification" and on p. 73 the importance of this act in bringing to a "close" what we call here (references 1–3, 7, 8, and 10) "the elementary quantum phenomenon."

10. MILLER, W. A. & J. A. WHEELER. 1984. Delayed-choice experiments and Bohr's elementary quantum phenomenon. *In* Proceedings of International Symposium on Foundations of Quantum Mechanics in the Light of New Technology. S. Kamefuchi *et al.*, Eds.: 140–151. Physical Society of Japan. Kyoto. Via a picture of Field Gilbert, they symbolize this entity as a smoky dragon, and also illustrate nine different delayed-choice experiments.

11. Statement attributed to Friedrich Engels (1820–1895), but shortened and reworded here.

12. FISHER, R. A. 1922. Proc. R. Soc. Edinburgh **42:** 321. This and two related references are discussed by W. K. Wootters in reference 13: CAVALLI-SFORZA, L. L. & F. CONTERIO. 1960. Atti Assoc. Genet. Ital. **5:** 333; KIMURA, M. 1962. Diffusion Models in Population Genetics, pp. 23–25. Methuen. London.

13. WOOTTERS, W. K. 1980. Doctoral thesis: The acquisition of information from quantum measurements. University of Texas at Austin (May 1980). Available from University Microfilms, Inc., Ann Arbor, Michigan.

14. STUECKELBERG, E. C. G. 1960. Helv. Phys. Acta **33:** 727–752; STUECKELBERG, E. C. G. & M. GUENIN. 1961. Helv. Phys. Acta **34:** 621–628.

15. HEISENBERG, W. 1927. Über den anschaulichen Inhalt der quantentheoretischen Kinematik und Mechanik. Z. Phys. **43:** 172–198. (English translation. 1983. *In* Quantum Theory and Measurement. J. A. Wheeler & W. H. Zurek, Eds.: 62–84. Princeton Univ. Press.

Princeton, New Jersey. This book also contains several of the other items cited in the present bibliography.)

16. BOHR, N. 1928. The quantum postulate and the recent development of atomic theory. Nature **121:** 580–590.

17. AHARONOV, Y. & D. BOHM. 1959. Phys. Rev. **115:** 485.

18. See, for example: ANANDAN, J. 1977. Phys. Rev. **D15:** 1448–1457; 1980. Int. J. Theor. Phys. **19:** 537–556; 1980. *In* Quantum Theory and Gravitation. A. R. Marlow, Ed.: 157–176. Academic Press. New York.

19. BARROW, J. D. & F. J. TIPLER. 1986. The Anthropic Cosmological Principle. Oxford Univ. Press (Clarendon). Oxford.

20. DICKE, R. H. 1957. Rev. Mod. Phys. **29:** 375; 1961. Nature **192:** 440.

21. For a further discussion of the problem of the continuum, see: WHEELER, J. A. 1986. Hermann Weyl and the unity of knowledge. Am. Sci. **74:** 366–375.

22. To Frank Tangherlini, Physics Department, Holy Cross College, Worchester, Massachusetts, the author is indebted for a look at the extensive bibliography he has collected on the changing views over the years as to why the world has $3 (+1)$ dimensions.

23. For a survey, recent new results, and a bibliography, see: KHEYFETS, A. 1986. The boundary of a boundary principle: a unified approach. Found. Phys. **16:** 483–497.

24. POPPER, K. 1963. Conjectures and Refutations. Routledge & Kegan Paul. London.

25. DARWIN, C. 1919. March 29, 1863 letter to Joseph Dalton Hooker. *In* The Life and Letters of Charles Darwin, Including an Autobiographical Chapter. F. Darwin, Ed.: 203. Appleton. New York/London. The author thanks Frederick Burckhardt for locating this passage.

26. EIGEN, M. 1976. Das Spiel. Piper. München; also in subsequent publications.

Causality as Identified with Conditional Probability and the Quantal Nonseparability

O. COSTA DE BEAUREGARD

Laboratoire de Physique Théorique
Institut Henri Poincaré
75005 Paris, France

To begin with, let us have a look at Boltzmann's colliding molecules. The (unnormalized) collision probability, $|A)(C|$, for two molecules is the product of three independent probabilities: their mutual cross section, $(A|C)$, endowed with the symmetry property,

$$(A|C) = (C|A), \tag{1}$$

and the occupation numbers, $|A) \equiv (A|$ and $|C) \equiv (C|$, of their initial states. It is thus expressed as

$$|A)(C| = |A)(A|C)(C| = |C)(C|A)(A|. \tag{2}$$

This is for prediction. Retrodictively, the same formula holds, with $|A)$ and $(C|$ denoting the final occupation numbers of the final states. In this, we have an instance of Loschmidt's reversibility. Considering the shape of the ABC zigzag, where B denotes the collision, either in space-time or in the momentum-energy space, we can say that equation 2 is the same for Λ and V shapes of the zigzag.

Equation 2 also holds if A denotes the initial state and C denotes the final state of a molecule; then $(A|C)$ denotes the intrinsic transition probability, $|A)$ denotes the initial occupation number of the initial state, $(C|$ denotes the final occupation number of the final state, and $|A)(C|$ denotes the overall transition probability. The classics, including Boltzmann, multiplied $(A|C)$ by $|A)$, but not by $(C|$. This, however, was "intrinsically illogical" because multiplication by $|A)$ implies "statistical indistinguishability," and, if so, there are $(C|$ ways in which a transiting molecule can reach the C state. Physics, of course, vindicates equation 2, thus revealing that there are two sorts of particles: bosons, which are such that $|A) = (C| = 0, 1, 2, \ldots$, and fermions, which are such that $|A) = (C| = 0, 1$. Let us say that in this case, the ABC zigzag has a $\langle$ or a C shape. What has been shown is that, in statistical mechanics, equation 2 for an overall collision or transition probability has a topological invariance with respect to distortions of the ABC zigzag into V, Λ, or C shapes in either space-time or the momentum-energy space.

LAPLACEAN ALGEBRA OF CONDITIONAL PROBABILITIES

Equation 2, together with equation 1, has a validity far exceeding the case of colliding molecules. For example, $(A|C)$ can denote the joint probability that a male

United States citizen has a weight, A, and a height, C, that is also, in the absence of prior probabilities of A and C, the reversible intrinsic conditional probability of "A if C" or "C if A." Of course, there are cases where the prior probabilities, $|A)$ and $(C|$, should be considered; for example, the joint probability (equation 2) may be estimated in the subclass of basketball players or in the subclass of weight lifters.

The point, here, is that these various probabilities are thought of irrespective of any time connotation; in other words, probabilities can be defined in a timeless fashion. If timing is implied for some other reason, it does not show up in the formulas; thus, we get the topological invariance previously mentioned. For example, in a United States national park, we may ask what is the (intrinsic) conditional probability, $(A|C)$, that there is at A, the male bear, and at C, the female bear of a couple, with the A-C vector being spacelike, or future timelike, or past timelike. Speaking of a couple of bears implies that a connection exists between them—for instance, that they meet at some unknown intermediate place called B. This can be in the common past or future of A and C if the A-C vector is spacelike, or it can be after A and before C if it is future timelike. From the standpoint of logic, this makes absolutely no difference. Therefore, in the conceptualization of the Poincaré-Minkowski four-dimensional geometry, we can say that the prior numbers of chances, or occupation numbers, $|A)$ and $(C|$, of the initial and/or final states are "actually there." Thus, we end up with the (at first sight surprising) conclusion that the relativistic four-dimensional geometry is not committed to a deterministic view, but instead can quite easily accommodate a probabilistic view of physics. With this conclusion, an (intrinsic) conditional probability, $(A|C)$, has the timeless interpretation of an (intrinsic) transition probability between two "representations of a system"—for example, the weight representation and the height representation of a United States citizen, or the male representation and the female representation of a couple of bears.

An intrinsic conditional or transition probability, $(A|C) = (C|A)$, can be expressed with a summation over "hidden intermediate states," namely, $|B) = (B|$; and this, if timing is implied, can be done in all three cases of a V-, or a Λ-, or a C-shaped ABC zigzag. The corresponding formula,

$$(A|C) = \Sigma (A|B) (B|C), \tag{3}$$

is known as the generating formula of Markov chains. Due to the symmetry property of equation 1 (which I call Laplacean because it is the basic assumption in Laplace's[1] 1774 "Memoir on the Probabilities of Causes"), a Markov chain consisting of links, A, B, etc...., articulated at vertexes, A, etc...., can zigzag arbitrarily throughout either space-time or the momentum-energy space, regardless of the macroscopic time or energy arrow. The intermediate summations, $|B) (B|$, are over mutually exclusive hidden states such that

$$(B|B') = \delta(B, B'); \tag{4}$$

the "end states" of $|A)$ and $(C|$ are also assumed to belong to such orthocomplemented representations of the system.

In summary, the intrinsic timelessness of the transition or conditional probability concept, together with its intrinsic Laplacean symmetry property, yields a scheme where the correlation between two chance occurrences, A and C, is discussed "*sub specie aeternitatis,"* and, if there is timing, in a manner that is topologically invariant with respect to V, Λ, or C shapes of an *ABC* zigzag.

The title of Laplace's "memoir," essentially dealing with the conditional probability concept, mentioned "probabilities of causes." Now, although Laplace's discourse is much time-laden (the idea being that "cause precedes effect"), his formulas are not; thus, cause and effect can be exchanged in them. It is, therefore, only natural to conclude that there is nothing specific in the causality concept, which can, and should, merely be identified with the conditional or transition probability concept—this being a timeless definition (or, if there is timing, an arrowless definition). After all, logical implication is a form of causality, and it is timeless. Basically, the calculus of probabilities has to do with logic, not with timing.

THE 1926 REVOLUTION: A WAVELIKE PROBABILITY CALCULUS

In 1926, Born[2] initiated and Jordan[3] systematized a radically new "wavelike probability calculus" where partial amplitudes rather than probabilities are added, and where independent amplitudes rather than probabilities are multiplied. This was for clarifying the wave-particle dualism, and it was not the first time that probability acted as a mediator between the continuous and the discrete.

The cornerstone of the correspondence between the classical and the quantal probability calculus is the expression of a transition or conditional probability, $(A|C)$, in terms of a conditional or transition amplitude, $\langle A|C \rangle$, endowed with the Hermitian symmetry,

$$\langle A|C \rangle = \langle C|A \rangle^*, \tag{5}$$

via the formula,

$$(A|C) = |\langle A|C \rangle|^2, \tag{6}$$

entailing the Laplacean symmetry of equation 1.

The expression in equation 6 contains diagonal and off-diagonal terms. If alone, the former would reproduce the classical rules. The latter (which are interference or beating terms), however, entail 1001 paradoxical traits in quantum mechanics, with the 1001th showing up in the EPR correlations to be discussed.

A quantal transition probability connects two "representations" of a system (the basic definition of which is timeless) given inside a Hilbert space. In many (but not all) cases, one is led, so to speak, to draw it down from there into either space-time or the 4-frequency space by means of those specialized transition amplitudes termed propagators. State vectors such as $|B\rangle$, which make up a representation of the system, are submitted to the orthonormality condition,

$$\langle B|B' \rangle = \delta(B,B'). \tag{7}$$

Corresponding to the expression (equation 2) of a joint probability, there is that of a joint amplitude,

$$|A\rangle \langle C| = |A\rangle \langle A|C \rangle \langle C|, \tag{8}$$

implying prior amplitudes, $|A\rangle$ and $\langle C|$, the absolute squares of which are occupation numbers. Furthermore, corresponding to the generating formula (equation 3) of Markov chains, there is that of Landé chains:

$$\langle A|C\rangle = \Sigma\,\langle A|B\rangle\,\langle B|C\rangle. \qquad (9)$$

Due to the basic timelessness of these concepts and due to the Hermitian symmetry property (equation 5), a Landé chain can zigzag arbitrarily throughout either space-time or the 4-frequency space, regardless of the macroscopic time or energy arrow. In it, any ABC zigzag has topological invariance with respect to V, Λ, or C shapes of the zigzag. An important generalization of Landé chains consists of the Feynman graphs, where more than two links, $\langle A|B\rangle$, can be attached to any vertex, A. Topological invariance is a well-known property of Feynman graphs.

Speaking of correlations, the generic difference between the classical (equation 3) and the quantal (equation 9) expressions is that, while the classical summation, $|B\rangle$ $(B|$, is over "real hidden states," the quantal summation, $|B\rangle\,\langle B|$, is over virtual states, which is a necessary consequence of the off-diagonal terms in equation 6.

In this mathematical fact consists what is termed quantal nonseparability, or, whenever a space-time connotation is attached to the chance occurrences, $|A\rangle$ and $|C\rangle$, quantal nonlocality. Also in this consists what is specifically paradoxical (that is, alien to classical thinking) in the EPR correlations.

EPR CORRELATIONS, PROPER AND REVERSED; WHEELER'S "SMOKY DRAGON" METAPHOR

EPR correlations proper are visualized by a V-shaped ABC zigzag. Equation 9 then expresses the conditional amplitude that will, when measurements are performed at two distant places, A and C, upon subsystems originating from a common source, B, respectively yield state vectors, $|A\rangle$ and $|C\rangle$. The summation, $|B\rangle\,\langle B|$, is over virtual states of the source, B, insofar as these are expressed as products of state vectors of the two partial subsystems. However, in the product Hilbert space of the overall system, $A \otimes C$, the state is a pure state, for example, a spin-zero state in the well-known cascade experiments. In addition, the Hermitian scalar product, $\langle A|C\rangle$, can also be thought of as the transition amplitude between two representations of the overall system, namely, the "A representation" and the "C representation."

A Λ-shaped ABC zigzag visualizes a reversed EPR correlation in which preparations performed at two distant places, A and C, converge into a common sink, B. Of course, only those $|A\rangle$ and $|C\rangle$ pairs having the right phase relation are absorbed in the sink; thus, we have an aspect of "lawlike reversibility versus factlike irreversibility" (which is discussed in APPENDIX 1).

What then of C-shaped ABC zigzags? They do visualize the concept that Wheeler[5] terms metaphorically as the "smoky dragon." What is the state vector, $|B\rangle$, of a quantal evolving system between its preparation as $|A\rangle$ and its measurement as $|C\rangle$? Is it the retarded state generated by $|A\rangle$, or is it the advanced state going into $|C\rangle$? It cannot be both if there is a transition; and why should it be the one rather than the other, given the Hermitian symmetry property in equation 5? Truly, the evolving system is neither in the retarded nor in the advanced state because it is actually transiting from the one to the other. Therefore, it is in a virtual state that can be expressed as a sum of products of state vectors belonging to the $|A\rangle$ and the $|C\rangle$ Hilbert spaces. However, in the product Hilbert space, it is a pure state; that is, the pure state of the virtual particle that, in the S-matrix scheme, would wash out the difference between the $|A\rangle$ and the $|C\rangle$ states.

Thus, of the quantal system evolving between its preparation, $|A\rangle$, and its measurement, $|C\rangle$, Wheeler[5] can say that it is a "smoky dragon," where only the tail, $|A\rangle$, and the biting mouth, $|C\rangle$, are down inside our familiar space-time. Wheeler also says that "no quantum phenomenon is a phenomenon until it is registered", and, indeed, intrinsic symmetry between the retarded wave generated by $|A\rangle$ and the advanced wave going into $|C\rangle$ (much reminiscent of the symmetry in the Fermat or the Maupertuis-Hamilton extremum integrals) is one more ghostly aspect of the dragon living "up there."

All this means is that the familiar concept of an "evolving state vector," $|\psi(t)\rangle$ (here labeled $|B\rangle$), is nothing more than a worthless spook, as was the late "luminiferous ether." Only the transition amplitude, $\langle A|C\rangle$, makes sense.

Let us illustrate all this by an example. The well-known expression of the conditional amplitude, $\langle A|C\rangle$, for correlated linear polarizations of a spin-zero photon pair issuing from an atomic cascade is (with $\alpha \equiv C - A$ denoting the angle between the polarizers)

$$\langle A|C\rangle = 2^{-1/2}\begin{cases} \cos\alpha = \cos A \cos C + \sin A \sin C \\ \sin\alpha = \cos A \sin C - \sin A \cos C \end{cases} \tag{10}$$

(for type 1 and type 2 cascades, respectively). This is also the transition amplitude between the $|A\rangle$ representation and the $|C\rangle$ representation of the pair. As expressed in terms of $|A\rangle$ and $|C\rangle$, it is a superposition; specifically, a superposition of virtual states of the source, B. This is because the angles, A and C, are referred to a two-dimensional Cartesian frame, defined up to an arbitrary rotation, where the frame can be termed B.

Using the smoky dragon metaphor, we say that we have at A and C two mouths biting, but, at B, only a smoky dragon; therein consists the EPR paradox. However, of course, we can also say that at B we have the spin-zero state of the pair.

So much for a V-shaped ABC zigzag. As for a Λ-shaped one, figuring a reversed EPR correlation, the comment mirrors in time the preceding one.

Now, let us consider a C-shaped ABC zigzag. The formulas in equation 10 are valid for a beam of photons prepared in a linear polarization state, $|A\rangle$, and measured in a linear polarization state. $|C\rangle$. We can think of the preparing and measuring devices as birefringent crystals so that both lines in equation 10 make sense.

It is quite easy to actualize the intermediate virtual state, $|B\rangle$. One just has to insert between A and C a third birefringent crystal, B, with its length being such that a zero phase-shift (modulo $2n\pi$) is introduced between the two beams. The conditional or transition amplitude, $\langle A|C\rangle$, is not changed, and the crystal B can be arbitrarily rotated. Of each photon going through B, nothing definite can be known (nor even should be thought) because there is no means to decide "upon which beam it is traveling." Thus, it is a smoky dragon. However, crystal B is in a pure state; it is a sort of virtual particle attached to vertex B.

SUMMARY

Therefore, on the whole, the space-time or the momentum-energy phenomenologies of the classical and the quantal correlations are very much the same, including intrinsic reversibility and topological invariance vis-à-vis the V, Λ, and C shapes of an *ABC* zigzag. Thus, the essential difference between them consists of the substitution of the wavelike Born-Jordan probability calculus for the classical, Laplacean one, which entails that intermediate summations are over "virtual" instead of "real hidden" states. It is this that renders "dramatic" (instead of merely "interesting") the arrowlessness of microcausality.

If causality has any operational meaning at all, it implies that something can be arbitrarily adjusted at some place; then, it belongs to physics (not to philosophical apriorities) to decide where "consequences" are observed. In the EPR correlations, either proper or reversed, adjustable parameters exist at *A* and *C*, and not at *B*, so that these correlations directly display, respectively, an advanced and a retarded aspect of the reversible microcausality.

In straight accordance, I believe, with Laplace's thinking, but including the import of Jordan's revolution, I submit that, at the basic level, physical causality can be merely identified with the transition or conditional amplitude concept (which, of course, is a basic idea in the relativistic S-matrix scheme).

The S-matrix scheme, together with the EPR correlations that are inherent in it,[6,7] displays direct, long-range, Fokker-like[8] interactions, insensitive to "cause-effect" exchange, where the topologically invariant Feynman zigzags are the links displaying quantal nonseparability in its nonlocality aspect. It goes without saying that great experimental care is needed for exhibiting over macroscopic distances these aspects of the quantal microreversibility because they are easily blurred by loss of phase coherence. They are specific of a *sui generis* space-time telegraph using waves as channels and a wavelike cybernetical coding. It is then simply reasonable to envisage that there should exist low-level neurophysiological manifestations of this peculiar sort of nonlocality.

REFERENCES

1. LAPLACE, P. S. 1891. Mémoire sur les probabilités des causes par les évènements. *In* Oeuvres Complètes, Vol. 8, pp. 27–65. Gauthier-Villars. Paris.
2. BORN, M. 1926. Z. Phys. **38**: 803.
3. JORDAN, P. 1926. Z. Phys. **40**: 809.
4. LANDÉ A. 1965. New Foundations of Quantum Mechanics, pp. 76–89. Cambridge Univ. Press. London/New York.
5. MILLER, W. A. & J. A. WHEELER. 1984. Delayed choice experiments and Bohr's elementary phenomenon. *In* Foundations of Quantum Mechanics in the Light of New Technology. S. Kamefuchi *et al.*, Eds.: 233–241. Physical Society of Japan. Tokyo.
6. COSTA DE BEAUREGARD, O. 1983. Phys. Rev. Lett. **50**: 867–870.
7. COSTA DE BEAUREGARD, O. 1985. Found. Phys. **15**: 871–887.
8. FOKKER, A. D. 1965. Time and Space, Weight and Inertia. Pergamon. Oxford.
9. BOLTZMANN, L. 1964. Lectures on Gas Theory, pp. 446–448 (S. G. Brush, translator). Univ. of California Press. Berkeley.
10. EINSTEIN, A. 1928. *In* Electrons et Photons, Rapports et Discussions du Cinquième Conseil Solvay, pp. 253–256. Gauthier-Villars. Paris.
11. LÜDERS, G. 1952. Z. Phys. **133**: 325–339.

12. HEISENBERG, W. 1927. Z. Phys. **43**: 621–646.
13. VON WEISZÄCKER, C. 1931. Z. Phys. **70**: 114–130.

APPENDIX 1

Lawlike Reversibility and Factlike Irreversibility

The conditional probability concept, T $(A|B)$, traditionally used since the days of Bayes and of Laplace, differs from the reversible, intrinsic conditional probability, $(A|B) = (B|A)$, that we have used. Namely,

$$|A|B) = |A) (A|B), \qquad |B|A) = |B) (B|A), \tag{11}$$

so that

$$|A) (B| = |A|B)(B| = |B|A)(A|. \tag{12}$$

Clearly,

$$|A|B) \neq |B|A) \, if \, (A| \neq (B|, \tag{13}$$

and this is the basis of both Laplace's[1] and Boltzmann's[9] discussions of "lawlike reversibility versus factlike irreversibility." (Laplace's discussion, though, is far more general in that it is conducted inside the calculus of probabilities per se.)

Maximal irreversibility is obtained if, say, all $|B)$'s are equal to each other, so they need not be mentioned. This is what both Laplace and Boltzmann assumed for the prior probabilities of the final states. Laplace's motivation was that "one has no sufficient reason for ascribing different $(B|$ values," which amounts to stating that prior probabilities of future chance events cannot be known. Boltzmann's motivation was that, physically speaking, blind statistical prediction is operational, while blind statistical retrodiction is not, which amounts to stating that the time arrow points to increasing, not decreasing, probabilities.

However, counterexamples can definitely be given. For example, in the Darwinian line of the horse, if we are given the "eohippus," can we predict the horse? Certainly not. However, we can retrodict correctly the "primeval molecular soup" by merely using the Laplace and Boltzmann prescription in reverse and disregarding the prior probabilities, $|A)$, of "causes."

This argument shows well that, as we have said, it is logic, not timing, that is basic in the probability calculus.

APPENDIX 2

CPT Invariance

In 1927, at the Fifth Solvay Council, Einstein[10] very rightly stated that there is a conflict between the EPR style correlations and his 1905 relativity theory, which can be called the "macrorelativity theory", because it assumes invariance of physical laws under the orthochronous Lorentz group, including invariance of the thermodynamical "second law," invariance of the law of wave retardation, and invariance of the concept of a retarded causality.

However, as shown by Lüders[11] in 1952, quantal physics is endowed with a stronger invariance, which can be termed the "microrelativistic invariance": invariance under rotations and reversals of the Poincaré-Minkowski tetrapod. He emphasizes that "strong reflection" is the appropriate generalization of Loschmidt's 1876 motion reversal.

Geometrical reversal, $\Pi\Theta$, of all four space-time or momentum-energy axes has two effects. One is the reversal of the network of collisions in the manner of Loschmidt, which implies exchange of emission and absorption processes, and, in quantum mechanics, of preparations and measurements; this we call covariant motion reversal and denote as PT. The second effect is the reversal of the arrows of 4-vectors, which is where, according to the Stückelberg-Feynman description, we get particle-antiparticle exchange (denoted by C).

Therefore,

$$\Pi\Theta = CPT = 1,$$

meaning that covariant motion reversal and particle-antiparticle exchange are two "relative images" of essentially the same process.

T-reversal in nonrelativistic quantum mechanics and CPT-reversal in relativistic quantum mechanics induce, between preparations and measurements, the Hermitian symmetry (equation 5) and the Laplacean symmetry (equation 1). This is exactly how the Laplacean, timeless, lawlike symmetry and (possible) factlike asymmetry are turned into their time-laden counterparts.

APPENDIX 3

Operational Discussion of the EPR Thought-Experiment Proper

We imagine that at B, a positronium atom disintegrates into two photons, each of which is received in one of two microscopes pointing straight at each other along the x-axis. One of these, A, is a "Heisenberg microscope,"[12] the "object plane" of which contains B; the other, C, is a "von Weiszäcker microscope,"[13] the focal plane of which contains B. Thus, A measures (that is, retrodicts) the position, r, of the positronium atom inside the yz-plane just before it disintegrates, while C similarly measures (that is, retrodicts) its momentum, $p = \hbar k$.

The intrinsic conditional amplitude, $\langle A|C \rangle$, is here the Fourier nucleus, $\langle r|k \rangle$, so the reciprocal "dressed" conditional amplitudes, $|r\rangle \langle r|k \rangle$ and $|k\rangle \langle k|r \rangle$, are Fourier-associated, and thus endowed with mutual Heisenberg uncertainties. Therefore, a joint use of the two microscopes does not yield exact values for the position, r, and the momentum, $\hbar k$, of the decaying positronium atom.

However, the impacts of the two photons in the "image planes" of the microscopes, A and C, can be measured quite accurately. What happens is that inside the yz-plane, there are two diffraction patterns associated with them. If the angular apertures of the microscopes are equal, the optimal Heisenberg limitation is obtained.

This discussion clearly shows that:

(1) results of the measurements performed by A and C do not preexist when the photons leave the source, B;
(2) measurements performed upon two subsystems issuing from a common source need not fit each other.

Taken together, these statements summarize the "EPR paradox." They emphasize the existence of a retroactive causality much more strongly than would the discussion of a classical correlation.

APPENDIX 4

Additional Remarks

The reader may have noticed that the new formalization I have introduced for the Laplacean algebra of conditional probabilities exactly "corresponds" to the one that is now standard for the Born-Jordan algebra of transition amplitudes.

Setting $C = A$ in equation 2, we get

$$|A)(A| = |A)(A|A)(A|,$$

showing that $|A)(A|$ is a projector, and that $(A|A) = 1$: "The intrinsic conditional probability of A if A equals unity." Then, setting $C = A$ in equation 12, we get $|A|A) = |A)$: "The extrinsic, Laplacean probability of A if A equals the prior probability of A."

In the Bayesian approach to probability, $|A)$ is shorthand for a "background conditional probability," $(E|A)$. Similarly, the quantal $|A\rangle$ is shorthand for a "background transition ampltiude," $\langle E|A \rangle$, which Dirac denotes as $\langle x|A \rangle$ or as $\langle k|A \rangle$ in, respectively, the space-time or the 4-frequency pictures of an evolving system.

Gauge-Fields and Integrated Quantum-Classical Theory[a]

HENRY P. STAPP

Lawrence Berkeley Laboratory
University of California
Berkeley, California 94720

INTRODUCTION

This paper responds to a number of issues raised by previous speakers. It responds in particular to the challenge by J. A. Wheeler to use quantum theory to construct not only devices and machines, but also the universe itself.[1] It also responds to the reminder by Wigner[2] of the limited scope of contemporary quantum theory and to his concerns pertaining to space-time points. It adds depth to the remarks of Wigner,[2] Zurek,[3] and Joos[4] about the importance of the interplay between the whole and its parts. Furthermore, it also addresses the crucial question of where experimentalists should look to find phenomena that may shed light on the nature of the connection between the classical and quantum aspects of nature.

To set the problem, it is useful to distinguish between the "strict" and "informal" levels of the Copenhagen interpretation. Both levels adhere to the basic precept of the Copenhagen interpretation, which is that the quantum formalism "merely offers rules of calculation for the deduction of expectations pertaining to phenomena obtained under well-defined experimental conditions specified by classical physical concepts."[5] Thus, both levels recognize and insist that the quantum formalism should be regarded merely as a "tool" for making predictions about observations, and that the "realities" with which the formalism deals are the observations and knowledge of the community of communicating observers.[6]

However, this pragmatic character of the Copenhagen interpretation does not mean Copenhagenists deny the existence of external reality. There is certainly a tacit acceptance throughout the writings of Bohr that "our observations" are observations of (macroscopic) qualities that exist independently of their being observed by anybody. Heisenberg goes still further. In his 1958 book, *Physics and Philosophy,* in the chapter on the Copenhagen interpretation, he speaks of "possibilities" and "actualities," and says:

> If we want to describe what happens in an atomic event, we have to realize that the word "happens" can apply only to the observations, not to the state of affairs between two observations. It applies to the physical, not the psychical act of observation, and we may say that the transition from the "possible" to the "actual" takes place as soon as the interaction of the object with the measuring device, and thereby the rest of the world, has come into play; it is not connected with the act of registration of the result in the mind of

[a]This work was supported by the Director, Office of Research, Office of High Energy and Nuclear Physics, Division of High Energy Physics of the U.S. Department of Energy under Contract No. DE-AC03-76SF00098.

the observer. The discontinuous change of the probability function, however, takes place with the act of registration because it is the discontinuous change in our knowledge of the instant of recognition that has its image in the discontinuous change of the probability function.[7]

The passage just quoted distinguishes nicely between the two levels of description. At the "strict" level, one deals only with observations, knowledge, and the formalism (as indicated in the final sentence). However, at the "informal" level, one speaks of what actually happens.

The description provided at the informal level is imprecise: it is not spelled out in detail. This imprecision is acceptable because the informal description does not enter into the calculations, which are the core of the strict interpretation. This gratuitous character of the informal level of description is acknowledged in the opening phrase: "*If* we want to describe what happens. . . ."

The tension between the strict and informal levels of the Copenhagen interpretation can be viewed as the motive force behind this conference: If there is some as yet imprecisely spelled out transition from possible to actual, or from quantum to classical, occurring at the level of the macroscopic devices, then not every physicist can suppress his curiosity about the nature of this basic mechanism.

MODEL UNIVERSE

A model universe that accords generally with Heisenberg's conception of external reality consists of an alternating sequence of density matrices and projection operators,

$$\ldots, \rho_{i-1}, P_i, \rho_i, P_{i+1}, \ldots,$$

where the ρ's are density matrices corresponding to Heisenberg states, and

$$\rho_i = P_i \rho_{i-1} P_i / \text{tr } P_i \rho_{i-1}.$$

Here, P_i is an element of some specified set $\{P_z\}_i$ of projection operators, z labels the elements of this set, and

$$\Sigma P_z = I.$$

This sum is over the elements of $\{P_z\}_i$. The probability that P_z will be selected by nature from the set $\{P_z\}_i$ is

$$\text{Prob } (P_z) = \text{tr } P_z \rho_{i-1}.$$

As an example, consider a measurement in which a pointer with center mass, x, swings perceptibly either to the right, $x > a > 0$, or to the left, $x < b < 0$. In this case, $\{P_z\}_i$ can be the set consisting of P_1 and P_2, where (at any one of an appropriate continuum of times after the measurement) $P_1 |x\rangle = \theta(x)|x\rangle$, $P_2 = I - P_1$, and $\theta(x)$ is the Heaviside function.

More generally, we can define a "measurement" to be a situation in which some quantity well described by classical physics (e.g., the center of mass of the pointer) ends up in one of a set of well-separated "bins." Then $\{P_z\}_i$ is the set of projection operators onto the set of distinct "bins."

CONTINUUM PROBLEM

This simple model encounters difficulties if one considers the continuum problem raised by Einstein.[8] The situation involves a radioactive source, a detector, a mechanism, and a macroscopic object. The object is given a kick by the mechanism when a decay is detected. After a while, the position, x, of the center of mass of the *macroscopic* object will be spread continuously over a macroscopic interval; there is no natural evolution into well-separated "bins." Hence, we can say that no "measurement" has taken place. However, in an objective description of nature itself, one must specify whether, in this continuum case, some "reduction of the wave packet" occurs, and if so, what the corresponding set $\{P_z\}_i$ is.

THE PROBLEM

Fundamentally, our problem is that contemporary quantum theory applies only under special conditions of "separation":[9] some part of the universe separates from the rest for an interlude and then later rejoins the whole. The process of separation is the preparation, and the process of rejoining is the detection. During the interlude between the preparation and detection, the "quantum system" must be separated (or isolated) from the rest of the universe. What this means is that it does not act significantly upon the rest. For if the quantum system acts significantly upon some other part of the universe, and hence phase correlations are established, then that other part must be included in the quantum system in order for the quantum laws to hold. The observer and his devices must remain outside the quantum system, in the rest of the universe.[9,10]

This separation condition is well satisfied in the domain of atomic physics. However, both Bohr[11] and Heisenberg[12] have emphasized the problematic character of the applicability of the quantum theory conceived in this way to, for example, biological systems. If we want to provide a foundation for all of the sciences, then we must consider not only isolated systems, but also systems that exist in close liaison with their environments and act significantly upon their environments. Measuring devices are special cases of such systems.

The specific problem posed by these considerations is to construct a theory for the emergence of a distinct classically describable form from an amorphous quantum potentiality in systems that exist in close liaison with their environment. Contemporary quantum theory should emerge in the limiting cases, where the system does not act significantly upon its environment. The theory would then subsume measurement theory, which deals with the special case in which certain "classical" variables become effectively confined in well-separated "bins" by the natural evolution of the system.

TWO PRINCIPLES

The problem just posed involves passing from a limiting case to a more general case. In order to pass from a special case to a general case, some principles are needed.

I shall accept here two principles:

(1) The first principle is that the solution should be tight-knit. There should be no arbitrariness: no accidents. The entire scheme of things should fit together into a tight-knit unity.[13] This nonarbitrariness includes even the Lagrangian. Normally, the theory of measurement is approached from a very general point of view in which the specific nature of the interactions occurring is regarded as irrelevant. I shall assume just the opposite: that the specific nature of the interactions is of crucial importance.

(2) The second principle is that the form that emerges from the actualization of quantum potentialities should be *strictly describable* in terms of the concepts of classical physics. Bohr's phrase "specified by classical physical concepts" is often interpreted as merely entailing that the classical concepts be appropriate in some fuzzy, imprecise kind of way. To eliminate fuzziness from our conception of the quantum-classical connection, and thereby introduce a very restrictive condition, I interpret Bohr's words in a strict way, and demand that the qualities actualized by Heisenberg's measurements be *strictly describable* in terms of the concepts of classical physics. In this case, the collection of Heisenberg's transitions from "possible" to "actual" will actualize a world that is strictly describable in terms of the variables and concepts of classical physics.

TWO NONACCIDENTS

I shall take the following two features of the world in which we live to be nonaccidential:

(1) Light (electromagnetism) produces the form of the macroscopic world in which we live. It provides the forms of objects and devices, the forms of our bodies and brains, and the form of our principal means of communication. (Gravity should perhaps ultimately be included, but for the present, I consider only light.)

(2) Gauge-fields play a central role in nature. Hence, structures arising from gauge invariance are likely to be important in the structure of nature.

THE TECHNICAL BASIS

The gauge-invariance property of electromagnetism plays an essential role in preserving the correspondence between quantum theory and classical physics in macroscopic limits. The infrared divergences associated with the masslessness of the photon appear to disrupt this correspondence by altering the character of physical-region singularities. However, the correspondence is rescued by gauge invariance, which leads to the following expression for the S matrix:[14]

$$S = \sum_P U(P_h)\, \tilde{S}(P_{hq}) \tag{1}$$

$$\simeq \sum_P U(P_h)\, \tilde{S}(P_h). \tag{2}$$

In equation 1, there is a sum over all Feynman paths, P. There is an arbitrary separation of the photon interaction into hard and soft parts, and then a further separation of the soft part into its "classical" and "quantum" parts. The "hard path" P_h arises from P by omitting all soft vertices, and P_{hq} arises from P by omitting all "classical vertices" at which the classical part of the photon interaction couples.

Equation 1 has a rather amazing form that is very useful for the consideration of infrared problems. The expression, $\tilde{S}(P_{hq})$, involves only the hard and quantum parts of the interaction, and is expressible in terms of Feynman rules with a modified photon interaction term. It gives no infrared problems. The quantum coupling vanishes in the limit, $|k|_{\text{Eucl}} \to 0$. This leads to equation 2 if the separation between hard and soft photons is made at small $|k|_{\text{Eucl}}$.

All of the contributions from the "classical" interactions are collected into the factor, $U(P_h)$. This, however, involves only the path P_h, which contains none of the soft photon vertices of P. In fact, all of the "classical" interactions are shifted to the hard-interaction vertices. An arbitrary number of identical classically coupled photons are emitted from each hard-interaction vertex. They constitute the bremsstrahlung radiation from that vertex.

This occurrence of arbitrary numbers of identical photons that do not depend upon the presence or absence of other soft photons allows the sum over all numbers of classically coupled photons to be expressed in closed form. The result, $U(P_h)$, is a (pseudo) unitary operator that, in acting upon the photon vacuum state, gives precisely the coherent photon state that corresponds to the (soft-mode part of the) classical electromagnetic field radiated by a classical particle of charge e moving on the space-time path P_h.

The close connection between coherent states and classical physics is well known.[15,16] For each single mode, i, the radiation field from the classical charge moving on P_h can be described asymptotically by an amplitude, $a_i(P_h)$, and its time derivative, $\dot{a}_i(P_h)$. This pair of numbers is equivalent to a complex number, $z_i(P_h)$. The properties of the coherent state, $|z_i(P_h)\rangle$, that correspond to this classical radiation field are defined by the single complex number, $z_i(P_h)$, together with the identification of the mode function, $\emptyset_i(x,t)$.

This coherent state of the quantum formalism has many properties that are similar to the properties of the corresponding classical state.[15,16] Thus, we have in equation 1 the automatic emergence from gauge invariance of quantum mechanical structures that correspond closely to classical physics. They are naturally described in terms of the variables of classical physics and have only the classical degrees of freedom.

The central idea of the following proposal is to give special ontological status to these naturally occurring quantum-classical structures of light.

THE PROPOSAL

To give definite form to the objective model described in the second section of this paper, we must specify the sets $\{P_z\}_i$. The proposal is to give special status to the coherent states of light by taking each set $\{P_z\}_i$ to be the set of projection operators

$P_z = |z\rangle\langle z|$ (where $z \in \mathbb{C}^n$ and $|z\rangle = |z_1\rangle_1 \otimes \ldots |z_n\rangle_n$) onto the coherent states built on a set of modes $\{\emptyset_1, \ldots, \emptyset_n\}_i$ of the electromagnetic field. The specified set $\{\emptyset_1, \ldots, \emptyset_n\}_i$, which depends on i, consists of modes with "large" numbers of photons. The definition of "large" will be discussed later.

APPLICATION TO THE CONTINUUM PROBLEM

Consider again the Einstein continuum problem. Focus attention on the detection device and on the soft photons emitted during the transition from the initial to the final state of this device. Then suppose that the set of modes, $\{\emptyset_1, \ldots, \emptyset_n\}_i$, with "large" numbers of photons is given. Also suppose, for simplicity, that there are initially no photons in these modes, and that the photons are sufficiently soft so that equation 2 can be used. Then the probability density for nature to choose the projector P_z from $\{P_z\}_i$ is

$$\text{Prob}(P_z) = \text{tr } P_z S \rho_{i-1} S^\dagger = \sum_{P_h} \sum_{P_h'} \langle z|z(P_h)\rangle\langle z(P_h')|z\rangle \times \text{tr } \tilde{S}(P_h)\rho_{i-1}\tilde{S}^\dagger(P_h').$$

The coherent-state matrix element is[15]

$$\langle z|z(P_n)\rangle = \exp \sum_i \left[-\frac{1}{2}|z_i - z_i(P_h)|^2 + i \text{ Im } z_i^* z_i(P_h) \right],$$

where the scale of the exponential falloff factor is a change of photon number by one unit. Thus the selected z will be close to the $z(P_h)$ for some set of important contributions, P_h, to the transition under consideration. Conversely, once the $P_z = P_i$ is selected (by nature), the same matrix element in

$$\rho_i = P_i\rho_{i-1}P_i/\text{tr } P_i\rho_{i-1}$$

will damp out the contributions from the Feynman paths P_h for which

$$|z(P_h) - z| > \sim 1.$$

The well-known relationship[15]

$$\pi^{-n} \int dz\, P_z = 1,$$

where

$$dz = dz_1 \ldots dz_n$$

and

$$dz_i = dx_i dy_i,$$

with

$$z_i = x_i + iy_i,$$

replaces

$$\Sigma\, P_z = I.$$

It guarantees that the results will conform to the demands of probability theory. It also guarantees that they will conform to the demands of ordinary measurement theory in the measurement-theory cases where z space can be divided into well-separated "bins," with the contributing domain of the variable $z(P_h)$ effectively confined to the interiors of these "bins."[16]

SELECTIONS OF MODES

To complete the theory, the rule must be given for selecting, for each i, that set of modes $\{\emptyset_1, \ldots, \emptyset_n\}_i$ having "large" numbers of photons. Certain self-consistency conditions (which have not previously been mentioned) will, it is hoped, fix these sets of modes. These conditions should also shape the detailed form of the theory in various other ways.

Though I had expected these aspects of the theory to be worked out in time for this conference, the theory is, at present, still in a developmental stage: the self-consistency conditions are, fortunately, rather severe.

BASIC FEATURES OF THE MODEL

In spite of its incomplete character, I believe that the model described above has some features that are worth mentioning. It would account for the emergence of distinct forms from the amorphous quantum potentialities and would account for them even in continuum situations, which occur ubiquitously in nature. I believe that most of the competing models, including the many-worlds interpretation, fail to account for the emergence of distinct forms in continuum situations, and they fail to specify, in continuum situations, the precise character of the distinct forms that can emerge.

The forms that emerge, according to this model, are completely quantum mechanical in character, yet describable in terms of the concepts of classical electromagnetic theory. These special quantum-classical forms of light play a role similar to that ascribed by the Copenhagen interpretation to the human observer—namely, the role of specifying the special aspects of nature that characterize the distinctive features of actual situations. Light, rather than knowledge, becomes, in this theory, the substance of actual being.

Notice that the classical electromagnetic field is described in ordinary three-dimensional space and not in $3n$-dimensional configuration space. On the other hand, only certain components of this field associated with soft photons are actualized. Thus, space-time points do not occur at the level of the actual.

WHERE SHOULD EXPERIMENTALISTS LOOK?

The distinction between quantum systems and classical systems is often confused with the distinction between microscopic and macroscopic. Thus, we have seen at this conference many experimental contributions, ostensibly pertaining to the problem of the quantum-classical connection, showing the high degree of conformity of phenomena to the predictions of quantum theory both for large systems and for systems involving large numbers of elementary excitations (e.g., Cooper pairs). It must be stressed, however, that the condition for a system to be a quantum system, according to the Copenhagen view, is not a condition of smallness, or of smallness of the number of degrees of freedom. The condition is rather that the quantum system be unable to communicate to the rest of the world during the interlude between its preparation and detection.

In this connection, it is of course understood that the "system" involved here refers to a set of degrees of freedom. The degrees of freedom of a macroscopic object can be parameterized in an infinitude of ways. Any set of degrees of freedom that does not act significantly upon the remaining ones, or upon the rest of the world, is a "quantum system," to which quantum theory should apply. Phenomena related to the quantum-classical connection should occur only in systems that are communicating, but not too strongly, to the rest of the world.

The interplay between quantum systems and their environments has been the focal point of many contributions to this conference (Zurek, Joos, Glauber, and Namiki). It has also been the subject of a host of recent theoretical papers.[17] In these studies, the environment is generally regarded as part of the whole quantum mechanical system. This is justified only to the extent that the environment is not communicating information about itself to the rest of the world.

This raises the question of what can be said in situations where the system is interacting significantly upon its environment, and the environment is acting significantly on the rest of the world; that is, in situations where there is no separation of the kind mandated by contemporary quantum theory.

One conceivable possibility (diametrically opposed to the Copenhagen interpretation) is to consider the entire universe as a quantum system. This immediately pushes the problem of the distinctness of our perceptions (and their describability in terms of the concepts of classical physics) onto the mind-body problem. Quantum theory then becomes useless in a practical sense, both because of the need to bring the whole universe, including human brains, into our calculations, and because of the fundamental problem of understanding how distinct perceptions can ever emerge from amorphous potentialities without introducing some fundamental element of distinctness.

The present model shifts the quantum-classical transition away from the level of the mind-body interaction down to the level where a limited system is sending signals to its environment via soft-photon coherent-state radiation. This shifts the calculations from a realm where they are essentially intractable, to the realm of soft-photon interactions with limited systems. These interactions are perhaps the best understood and most tractable in all of physics.

Space does not permit sample calculations (which will be given elsewhere). Roughly speaking, systems copiously emitting coherent-state soft photons should behave more classically than would be predicted by naive quantum mechanical calculations that do not fully account for the coupling of the quantum system to the classically described part of nature.

ACKNOWLEDGMENT

It is a pleasure to thank Geoffery Chew for a long series of stimulating and encouraging conversations related to this work.

REFERENCES

1. ALLEY, C.O. 1986. Contribution to this conference.
2. WIGNER, E. 1986. Opening contribution to this conference.
3. ZUREK, W. 1986. Contribution to this conference.
4. JOOS, E. 1986. Contribution to this conference.
5. BOHR, N. 1963. Essays 1958–1962 on Atomic Physics and Human Knowledge, p. 60. Wiley. New York.
6. STAPP, H. 1972. Am. J. Phys. **40:** 1098.
7. HEISENBERG, W. 1958. Physics and Philosophy, p. 54. Harper & Row. New York.
8. EINSTEIN, A. 1949. In Albert Einstein, Philosopher-Scientist. P. A. Schilpp, Ed.: 670. Tudor. New York.
9. BOHR, N. 1934. Atomic Theory and the Description of Nature, p. 53. Cambridge Univ. Press. Cambridge, England.
10. STAPP, H. 1986. On the unification of quantum theory and classical physics. In Symposium on the Foundations of Modern Physics—50 Years of the Einstein-Podolsky-Rosen Gedanken Experiment. P. Lahti & P. M. Mittelstaedt, Eds. World Scientific. Singapore; and Lawrence Berkeley Laboratory report no. LBL 20039.
11. BOHR, N. 1934. See reference 9, p. 21.
12. HEISENBERG, W. See reference 6, appendix B.
13. CHEW, G. 1968. Science **161:** 762.
14. STAPP, H. 1983. Phys. Rev. **28D:** 1386.
15. KIBBLE, T. & R. GLAUBER. 1970. In Quantum Optics. S. M. Kay & A. Maitland, Eds. Academic Press. London/New York.
16. STAPP, H. 1986. In Quantum Theory and Beyond (Tentative Title of Festschrift Honoring David Bohm). Routledge & Kegan Paul. Oxfordshire, England; and Lawrence Berkeley Laboratory report no. LBL 19144.
17. CHAKRAVARTY, S. & A. LEGGETT. 1985. Phys. Rev. Lett. **52:** 5 and references cited therein.

APPENDIX

The Preferred Basis

The problem of the preferred basis has been discussed at this conference, but not resolved. Suppose, for example, that the interaction between the system and its environment is governed by

$$H_{SE} = g\left[\frac{1}{2}(1 + \sigma_z)\,(a_1 + a_1^*) + \frac{1}{2}(1 - \sigma_z)\,(a_2 + a_2^*) + \frac{1}{2}(1 + \sigma_x)\,(a_3 + a_3^*)\right],$$

where the Pauli matrices σ_i act in the system space, and a_i^* creates a quantum in mode i of the environment. No nontrivial operator in the system space commutes with H_{SE}. This is the normal situation: different oscillators of the environment generally couple to different projection operators in the system space. Thus, if one asks whether photons couple to position or momentum, the answer is neither: each photon mode is coupled in a different way.

In the theory discussed here, the preferred basis vectors are the coherent states. The expectation value of an operator, P, in a state with initial density matrix, ρ, is typically

$$\langle P \rangle_\rho = \int \frac{dz_1}{\pi} \cdots \frac{dz_m}{\pi} \, \text{tr} \, P P_{z_m} P_{z_{m-1}} \cdots P_{z_1} \rho P_{z_1} \cdots P_{z_m},$$

where, for each i, the set,

$$z_i = [z_{i1}, z_{i2}, \ldots, z_{in(i)}],$$

specifies some set of modes that generally depend on i. Taking, for simplicity, the case where $m = 1$, we have

$$\langle P \rangle_\rho = \int \frac{dz}{\pi} \, \mathrm{tr} \, PP_z \rho P_z$$

$$= \int \frac{dz}{\pi} \, \mathrm{tr} \, P_z P \rho P_z$$

$$+ \int \frac{dz}{\pi} \, \mathrm{tr}[P, P_z] \rho P_z$$

$$= \mathrm{tr} \, P\rho + \int \frac{dz}{\pi} [P, P_z] \rho P_z.$$

The second term is the effect of the collapses of the wave function.

Amplifiers, Attenuators, and Schrödinger's Cat[a]

ROY J. GLAUBER

Lyman Laboratory of Physics
Harvard University
Cambridge, Massachusetts 02138

INTRODUCTION: TWO PARADOXES

When we describe measurements made in the quantum domain, we usually imagine them to be registered by large-scale classical instruments. A deep problem then besets us. Where in the account of those measurements is the transition to be made from the quantum mechanical to the classical description? Furthermore, how can any transition between two descriptions so different in principle be carried out in a mathematically consistent way?

Some work on the theory of quantum mechanical amplifying devices has persuaded me to believe that at least part of that question can be answered in largely physical terms. Arbitrary states of the electromagnetic field, for example, can be used as inputs for the amplification process, and the amplified output fields can be so intense that they qualify as fully classical—that is to say, accurately measurable without any significant disturbance of the field. Such amplification processes are, in fact, actually used in many experiments to render quantum phenomena observable, but even where they are not used in practice, it is interesting to imagine the effect their use would have. They suggest, in other words, an interesting class of *gedanken* experiments, and I shall try presently to illustrate a few of them.

There was a time, well over a century ago, when clever schemes to construct perpetual motion machines enjoyed considerable attention. None of course succeeded, but the effort spent on them was not all wasted; they did help teach us two important principles of thermodynamics. We are not so deeply concerned with that venerable subject any more, but we do seem still to be learning about two more recent areas of interest: relativity theory and quantum mechanics. Therefore, it should not be too surprising that the same infernal ingenuity that once went into devising perpetual motion machines is now suggesting means for communicating faster than light, and for confounding the principle of complementarity. Some of these are interesting schemes; they too might just be capable of teaching us something.

One interesting proposal amounts to using the Einstein-Podolsky-Rosen (EPR) paradox[1] as a means of communication. To be able to do that would mean, in fact,

[a]Partial support for this work was provided by the Department of Energy under Contract No. DE-AC02-76ER03064 and by the Office of Naval Research under Contract No. N0014-85-K-0724. A preliminary version of this paper was presented at the Conference on Frontiers of Quantum Optics held at the Royal Signals and Radar Establishment, Malvern, England, December 18, 1985.

336

being able to communicate faster than light, and that is not a possibility to be altogether ignored. Such a thought must indeed have occurred to many of us as soon as we began reading of the EPR paradox and of the species of nonlocality it imposes on quantum mechanics.

Let us recall, therefore, the most elementary kind of proposal for superluminal communication that we might try to base on the EPR paradox. We begin with a light source that gives out photons in pairs. An ordinary atom that does that will give them off in random directions, but if we do not mind using the gamma rays of annihilation radiation, those photons can, in fact, be given off back-to-back—and with zero total angular momentum. That, of course, is an essential point. The two photons must have closely correlated angular momenta so that any statement made about the angular

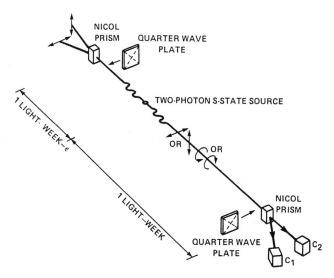

FIGURE 1. Projected setup for using pairs of photons with correlated polarizations for superluminal communication by means of the EPR paradox.

momentum of one of them, or any observation, conveys a unique implication about the other.

Now, what must we do to communicate by this strange medium? We may begin by setting up our own equipment at a certain distance from the source. We do not want it too far because we do not want to lose sight of the source, but let us just say it is one light-week away or perhaps a bit less. Our equipment is represented in the upper left of FIGURE 1. The friend with whom we want to communicate may be at a comparable distance from the source; let us say down in the right foreground of FIGURE 1. Now all we have to do is to make polarization measurements upon the photons that come our way. It is a bit wasteful in practice, though, if we do that with polarizing filters; they just absorb half the photons and there is no point in letting that happen. It is a much better idea to use a Nicol prism or, better still, a Wollaston prism, which will send vertically plane polarized photons in one direction, and the others, with horizontal polarization, in another direction, so that none at all are lost. Then, of course, we can add to the equipment a quarter-wave plate, if we like, with its two axes at 45 degree angles with respect to the polarization directions that are separated by the prism. Putting the quarter-wave plate in front of the prism makes of it, in effect, a circular polarization detector for the two possible circular polarizations.

How do we send the message? We have no control whatsoever over the polarization of the photons being produced by our source. However, what we can do, of course, is to exercise our choice either to leave things as they stand in FIGURE 1, and observe one or the other of two plane polarizations, or alternatively, to slide the quarter-wave plate into the beam we are detecting, and then we will inevitably observe one or the other of two circulation polarizations.

The correlation that exists between the polarizations of the photons going off in opposite directions then assures us that we, even at this great distance, have a certain control over the photons that are appearing virtually instantaneously at our friend's position. We are able to determine, simply by sliding the quarter-wave plate in or out, whether the individual photons our friend receives are going to be plane polarized or circularly polarized. If they are plane polarized, we cannot control which of the two plane polarizations they have. However, we can send him circularly polarized photons whenever we please and they are presumably distinguishable, in principle, from plane polarized ones. We can let photons polarized in those ways represent the dots and dashes, respectively, of Morse code, or the binary digits, and repeat our messages as often as our friend needs in order to overcome any statistical problems he may have.

The drawback of this communication scheme, of course, is that it does not work at all. Its failing lies in the very essence of what is necessary to send a message. Our friend has no idea, to begin with, whether any given photon he receives is polarized circularly or linearly. His ability to detect the message depends on his ability to determine the polarizations of those individual photons. Unfortunately, there is only a limited amount of measurement that he can make on any one photon before it is absorbed, or he otherwise loses track of its initial state. He can, for example, pass it through a plane-polarization filter. However, the fact that it has passed through the filter does not tell him whether its initial polarization was plane or one of the two circular varieties; that remains really quite undetermined. Let us say, for example, that a photon has passed through our own prism arrangement and has been revealed to have plane polarization. Our distant friend then receives a plane polarized photon, but he still cannot say with better than 50/50 likelihood that the arriving photon is either plane polarized or circularly polarized. Thus, there is no information transmitted at all, and the scheme collapses. That much has probably occurred to most of us as students of the EPR paradox.

A new and interesting suggestion has been added to this picture, however, by N. Herbert,[2] who proposes to improve our friend's polarization measurements greatly by adding, in effect, an amplifier to his system. He calls it a "laser gain tube," which you will recognize as a characteristically innocent and passive sounding name, and he uses another well-chosen term for its action; it "clones" the photons. Once the "gain tube," which is shown in place in FIGURE 2, has "cloned" for our friend lots of photons identical to the original one, he should no longer find it difficult to determine their state of polarization. What he can do, for example, is to install one or more beam-splitters in order to send most of those cloned photons into another laboratory where he has all sorts of equipment available and where he can make measurements on as many of the identical photons as he likes; in that way, he can get an excellent idea of their polarization. He thereby determines precisely what the polarization was (whether plane or circular) of the photon that first entered his laser gain tube.

If we have found, at last, the means for him to do that (as the argument indicates), then we can indeed communicate outside the light cone and create miracles of all sorts. Well, does the scheme work? Let me postpone telling you the answer until we have developed the means of describing a bit better the role played by the quantum amplifier. Then we will be able to say what the insertion of an amplifier really does in that scheme, along with what it does in several other sorts of experiments as well.

In the meantime, I should like to tell you another story. This one is much older and

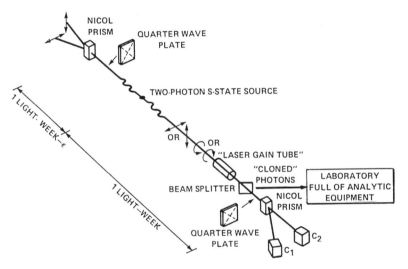

FIGURE 2. Improved version of the setup for superluminal communication via the EPR paradox. The addition of the "laser gain tube" is intended to facilitate polarization measurements.

much better known. It deals with one of the fundamental dilemmas of the quantum theory of measurement. Schrödinger,[3] responding to questions about the completeness of quantum mechanics in 1935, indicated quite some dissatisfaction with the field he had pioneered. He was troubled by the fact that one never sees in our everyday world anything that looks like a superposition of grossly different quantum mechanical states. The microscopic world, on the other hand, is full of them.

You can easily imagine experimental arrangements in which events in the microscopic world would seem to imply the creation of such superpositions in our everyday world. Let us suppose that the quantum state, $|a\rangle$, of something in the microworld implies, by some kind of rigorous dynamics, that the state of something else that we can actually observe in the laboratory goes to a particular state, $|A\rangle$, and suppose too that the alternative microstate, $|b\rangle$, whatever it may be, leads to a large-scale state that we can label $|B\rangle$. Now, let us imagine a third microstate, $|c\rangle$, which is physically quite distinguishable from both $|a\rangle$ and $|b\rangle$, but can be expressed as a superposition of those two states with nonvanishing coefficients, α and β:

$$|c\rangle = \alpha|a\rangle + \beta|b\rangle.$$

That state should obviously lead to a similar linear combination,

$$|C\rangle = \alpha|A\rangle + \beta|B\rangle,$$

as a final state of whatever it is we observe. That looks like no more than the postulate of the linearity of quantum mechanics, and it is hardly anything you could disagree with.

However, Schrödinger did indeed have some trouble with that idea, and he described a gedanken experiment that has become the definitive illustration of his dilemma. He imagined a diabolic arrangement in which a cat is confined to a box containing a lethal device that may be either triggered or left passive according to whether a radioactive nucleus decays or fails to decay. If the radioactive decay takes place, which he assumed would happen half the time, a hammer would strike a vial of cyanide, and the cat would be dispatched. It is not immediately clear, of course, how a radioactive nuclear decay process trips a hammer. Schrödinger evidently did not consider that a problem, but we may. The hammer will not budge unless the quantum signal is amplified greatly, and that amplification is what we want to discuss.

We can simplify Schrödinger's example a bit by thinking, not of radioactive decay processes, but of photons that can be polarized either horizontally or vertically. We can let the state of horizontal polarization for a single photon, $|h\rangle$, be the state $|a\rangle$, and let the state of vertical polarization, $|v\rangle$, be the state $|b\rangle$:

$$|a\rangle = |h\rangle, \tag{1}$$

$$|b\rangle = |v\rangle. \tag{2}$$

In addition, for our two states in the macroscopic world, let us take as state $|A\rangle$, the cat, alive and healthy,

$$|A\rangle = \left|\, \begin{array}{c}\text{(cat, alive)}\end{array} \right\rangle, \tag{3}$$

and as the state $|B\rangle$, the cat, not so alive and not so healthy,

$$|B\rangle = \left|\, \begin{array}{c}\text{(cat, dead)}\end{array} \right\rangle. \tag{4}$$

Now, let us take our two coefficients, alpha and beta, both to be $1/\sqrt{2}$. The state,

$$|c\rangle = \frac{1}{\sqrt{2}}\,(|h\rangle + |v\rangle), \tag{5}$$

the superposition of the two polarizations, is a state that is quite meaningful to us in the microworld. Such a superposition of the horizontal and the vertical polarizations is just another linear polarization inclined at 45 degrees to the two axes.

That gives us a simple way of carrying out Schrödinger's experiment. We can send a single photon polarized at 45 degrees (relative to the axes of a Wollaston prism) through the prism and let it go off in either of the two emergent polarized beams. In one of those two beams, we can place a photodetector that, when it registers, does something awful to the cat, and we can leave the other beam free, so that if the photon goes there, nothing happens to the cat. According to Schrödinger's analysis then, and according to our earlier argument, the cat is left finally in a linear superposition of two states,

$$| c \rangle = \frac{1}{\sqrt{2}} \left\{ \left| \text{🐱} \right\rangle + \left| \text{😿} \right\rangle \right\}. \tag{6}$$

It has, to be precise, an amplitude of 0.7071 for being alive and an amplitude of 0.7071 for being dead. That is a very strange state of affairs because we do not recognize the existence of any such superposition in the everyday world. While we encounter superposition states of all sorts in the microscopic world, we certainly do not encounter states like $| C \rangle$ in the large-scale world. We shall have to examine the argument for their generation much more carefully.

The cat paradox may not seem too closely related to superluminal communication, but let us recall its requirement that the polarization of a single photon induce the tripping of a hammer. Clearly, it can only do that if some process of amplification intervenes. Thus, we are back once more to talking about amplifiers, and once more I would like to postpone further consideration of the problem until we have managed to discuss how they work.

A QUANTUM MECHANICAL ATTENUATOR: THE DAMPED OSCILLATOR

It may be a good idea, before discussing amplification, to say a few words about dissipation or attenuation, which is a much more natural state of affairs. Amplification, we will then show, can be described by making only a few small (but highly significant) changes in the basic mechanism. The model of the damped harmonic oscillator[4] I want to recall to you gives about the simplest description you can have of the attenuation process.

The damped oscillator is something that can easily be constructed from an assembly of simple harmonic oscillators in the following way: one oscillator, the central oscillator, which is described by the amplitude operators, a and $a^\dagger$, is coupled to a whole heat bath full of oscillators, described by the amplitude operators, b_k and $b_k^\dagger$, for $k = 1, \ldots, N$, where N is quite large, or perhaps even infinite. The Hamiltonian for the system need only couple the central oscillator to the heat bath oscillators through the familiar "rotating wave" terms. We write

$$H = \hbar \omega a^\dagger a + \sum_k \hbar \omega_k b_k^\dagger b_k + \hbar \sum_k (\lambda_k a^\dagger b_k + \lambda_k^* b_k^\dagger a), \tag{7}$$

in which the frequencies, ω_k, cover a range in the neighborhood of ω fairly densely, and where the λ_k are a set of coupling parameters. This Hamiltonian remains invariant when we make the phase transformation,

$$a \rightarrow ae^{i\theta},$$

$$b \rightarrow be^{i\theta},$$

on all of the operators it contains. That invariance means that there is a corresponding conservation law. In the present case, the coupling obviously conserves the total number of quanta in the system. That property helps to make of it a highly soluble model.

The equations of motion, of course, are linear:

$$\dot{a} = -i\omega a - i \sum_k \lambda_k b_k,$$

$$\dot{b}_k = -i\omega_k b_k - i\lambda_k^* a. \tag{8}$$

Furthermore, for this simple coupling, the Schrödinger states have the wonderful property that an initially coherent state remains coherent at all later times.[5] Therefore, in fact, the equations of motion could every bit as well have been written as equations for a set of c-number amplitudes $\alpha(t)$ and $\beta_k(t)$ for the coherent states of all the oscillators. The Schrödinger state of the oscillators, in other words, apart from a time-dependent phase factor of no interest, is just given by

$$|t\rangle = |\alpha(t)\rangle \prod_k |\beta_k(t)\rangle, \tag{9}$$

which is a product of coherent states in which the amplitudes, $\alpha(t)$ and $\beta_k(t)$, obey the equations of motion (equation 8). There is a sense, then, in which this fully quantum mechanical system behaves as if it were classical. The fact that it is quantum mechanical even becomes a bit of a joke. The evolution of the system just carries its zero-point uncertainty cloud around the classical trajectory without altering it in any way. That is all that ever happens in such a system.

If the entire system is initially in a pure coherent state, its density operator in the Schrödinger picture at time t will be just

$$\rho(t) = |\alpha(t), \{\beta_k(t)\}\rangle\langle\alpha(t), \{\beta_k(t)\}|, \tag{10}$$

which is still a pure coherent state for all of the individual oscillators. Note that the phase factor left undetermined in the state vector has now canceled out.

It will be useful now to write the solutions to the equations of motion for the time-dependent amplitudes in an abbreviated form. The functions $\alpha(t)$ and $\beta_k(t)$ can be expressed always as linear combinations of their initial values, which we can write as α and β_k, respectively. The coefficients will be time-dependent functions, which we can write as $u(t)$ and $v_k(t)$, so that we have, for example,

$$\alpha(t) = \alpha u(t) + \sum_k \beta_k v_k(t), \tag{11}$$

and the initial conditions,

$$u(0) = 1, \qquad v_k(0) = 0. \tag{12}$$

We shall presently determine the functions, $u(t)$ and $v_k(t)$, explicitly, but there is a good deal we can say before doing that.

The only one of the oscillators that really interests us is the central one. We can find the reduced density operator for that one by taking the trace over all of the variables for the heat bath oscillators. What we have left then is just

$$\rho_A = \text{Trace}_B \rho(t) = |\alpha(t)\rangle\langle\alpha(t)|, \tag{13}$$

which still represents a pure state for the central oscillator.

Of course, if the heat bath begins in a mixed state rather than a pure coherent state, then we must mix together coherent states of this sort that correspond to different values of the initial amplitudes, β_k. The amplitudes, $\alpha(t)$, according to equation 11, depend linearly on the β_k, and so the appropriate reduced density operator should take the form,

$$\rho_A(t) = \int |\alpha(t)\rangle\langle\alpha(t)| P(\{\beta_k\}) \prod_k d^2\beta_k. \tag{14}$$

When the heat bath is not at zero temperature, the amplitudes, β_k, have a characteristically chaotic distribution.

It is most convenient to express the reduced density operator for the central oscillator in terms of what I have called the P-representation;[6] that is to say, a mixture of pure coherent states, $|\gamma\rangle\langle\gamma|$, with a weight function $P(\gamma)$, that is, strictly speaking, a quasi-probability distribution.

If we assume that the central oscillator is indeed initially in a coherent state with amplitude, α, then its reduced density operator can be written in the general form,

$$\rho_A(t) = \int P(\gamma, t | \alpha, 0) |\gamma\rangle\langle\gamma| d^2\gamma. \tag{15}$$

The weight function, $P(\gamma, t | \alpha, 0)$, in this expression can be thought of as a conditioned quasi-probability density for the occurrence of a coherent state amplitude γ, at time t, given the amplitude α, at time zero. If we then take the heat bath oscillators to be initially in chaotic states (i.e., Gaussian mixture states), with mean occupation numbers, $\langle n_k \rangle$, finding the function P is simply a matter of carrying out some Gaussian integrations. The result, we find, is always Gaussian in form:

$$P(\gamma, t | \alpha, 0) = \frac{1}{\pi D(t)} \exp\left\{ -\frac{|\gamma - \alpha u(t)|^2}{D(t)} \right\}. \tag{16}$$

The dispersion of this Gaussian function is given by

$$D(t) = \sum_k \langle n_k \rangle |v_k(t)|^2, \tag{17}$$

and its mean value is given by $\alpha u(t)$. To evaluate the dispersion and the mean value of the Gaussian function, we must, of course, solve the equations of motion to find the functions, $u(t)$ and $v_k(t)$.

According to the initial condition (equation 12), the functions $v_k(t)$ must all vanish at $t = 0$, so the dispersion, $D(t)$, is zero initially and the function P begins life as a delta-function. That, of course, is no surprise because the central oscillator starts out in a pure coherent state, $|\alpha\rangle$. What is more interesting is that if we take the heat bath to be at zero temperature, that is, take all of the $\langle n_k \rangle$ to vanish, the dispersion, $D(t)$, remains zero at all times and the function P always remains a two-dimensional delta-function,

$$P(\gamma, t | \alpha, 0) = \delta^{(2)}[\gamma - \alpha u(t)]. \tag{18}$$

In this case, in other words, the central oscillator always remains in a pure coherent state. It will typically lose its initial excitation to the heat bath oscillators or, to express that somewhat differently, we should expect the function $u(t)$ to decrease in modulus as the time t increases. That, at least, is the behavior we should anticipate in a dissipative system.

It is worth stressing two points, therefore, at this stage of the calculation. Firstly, the results we have reached at this point are exact; we have made no approximations. Secondly, because the result given by equation 18 is exact, it still reflects the intrinsic reversibility of the equations of motion. It is entirely possible for the heat bath oscillators to reexcite the central oscillator, and such Poincaré recurrences, though they may be enormously delayed, are in fact inevitable. The function, $u(t)$, then, when solved for exactly, will not in general decrease monotonically in modulus forever. However, the Poincaré recurrence times go rapidly to infinity as the number, N, of heat bath oscillators increases. In practice, N need not be very large before it becomes an excellent approximation (over lengths of time exceeding the age of the universe) to ignore the Poincaré recurrences altogether and use approximations in which the modulus of $u(t)$ does decrease steadily. Those are the approximate ways of approaching the equations of motion that also introduce the notion of irreversibility.

The equations of motion (equation 8) have essentially the same structure as a set of coupled equations derived after a number of approximations by Weisskopf and Wigner[7] in order to describe the process of radiation damping. If the coupling constants, λ_k, are not too large in modulus and there are enough heat bath oscillators with frequencies, ω_k, near ω, then the function $u(t)$ can be approximated quite well by a complex exponential function,

$$u(t) = e^{-[\kappa + i(\omega + \delta)]t} = e^{-(\kappa + i\omega')t}. \tag{19}$$

This function has a certain frequency shift, $\delta\omega$, in it, and it has a certain damping constant, κ, as well. Those constants are given by the relation,

$$\delta\omega - i\kappa = \lim_{\epsilon \to 0} \sum_k \frac{|\lambda_k|^2}{\omega - \omega_k + i\epsilon}, \tag{20}$$

which is characteristic of second-order perturbation theory, although the overall approximation retains terms of all orders in the coupling strengths.

With the heat bath at temperature zero then, the conditional quasi-probability density is given, according to equations 18 and 19, by

$$P(\gamma, t | \alpha, 0) = \delta^{(2)}(\gamma - \alpha e^{-(\kappa + i\omega')t}). \tag{21}$$

Because the state of the central oscillator, in this case, remains at all times a pure coherent state, it always has minimal uncertainty. This model for the dissipation process, in other words, is completely noise-free.

The randomness we refer to as noise only enters the dissipation process when the heat bath possesses initial excitations that exert random driving forces on the central oscillator. For those cases, which correspond to $\langle n_k \rangle \neq 0$ in our model, the noise is described by the dispersion, $D(t)$. We can evaluate that expression approximately by noting that the functions $v_k(t)$ have a resonant character; they are only large in modulus for modes with frequencies, ω_k, within an interval of width κ, about the frequency $\omega' = \omega + \delta\omega$. If the mean occupation numbers, $\langle n_k \rangle$, take on the constant value $\langle n'_\omega \rangle$ within this narrow band, we can write equation 17 as

$$D(t) = \langle n_{\omega'} \rangle \sum_k |v_k(t)|^2. \tag{22}$$

To evaluate the sum in this expression, we can note that the functions, u and v_k, obey an identity equivalent to the conservation law,

$$|u(t)|^2 + \sum_k |v_k(t)|^2 = 1, \tag{23}$$

which follows from the equations of motion (equation 8) and the initial conditions (equation 12). The dispersion can then be written as

$$D(t) = \langle n_{\omega'} \rangle (1 - |u(t)|^2), \tag{24}$$

which in the Weisskopf-Wigner approximation reduces to

$$D(t) = \langle n_{\omega'} \rangle (1 - e^{-2\kappa t}). \tag{25}$$

The dispersion, $D(t)$, then increases from the initial value zero, while the center of the Gaussian distribution given by equation 16 circles about on the exponential spiral given by equation 19. A three-dimensional portrait of the quasi-probability density as a function of the complex amplitude γ is shown in FIGURE 3. For times t much greater than the damping time, κ^{-1}, the central oscillator comes to equilibrium with the heat bath oscillators. The dispersion then reaches the limiting value $\langle n_{\omega'} \rangle$ and the Gaussian distribution settles down into the stationary form shown at the center of FIGURE 4.

A QUANTUM MECHANICAL AMPLIFIER

How can we build a device that amplifies signals at the quantum level? In fact, we can do that too with harmonic oscillators, but at least one of them must be rather special[8] in nature. The energy levels and the potential of the special oscillator are illustrated in FIGURE 5. As you can see, there is something a bit unusual about that harmonic oscillator. Its Hamiltonian is just the negative of the familiar one; both the potential and kinetic energies go down instead of up. That simple change of sign does not change the algebraic properties of the amplitude operators, a and $a^\dagger$, however. They obey the same commutation relation they did before. In fact, only one thing changes: reversing the sign of the Hamiltonian implies reversing the sign of the frequency ω in the equation of motion. Thus, $a(t)$ varies as $a(0)e^{i\omega t}$ instead of $a(0)e^{-i\omega t}$.

Our inverted oscillator, strictly speaking, no longer has a ground state; it has a state of maximum energy that we must inevitably associate with quantum number $n = 0$. That leads to a certain dilemma of terminology. We need a name for the highest lying state and, lacking a better one, shall call it the ground state, as we usually do the $n = 0$ state. However, we must remember that we are describing a system in which everything that happens goes on underground.

The inverted oscillator still has a discrete succession of eigenstates that can be generated by applying powers of $a^\dagger$ to the "ground state":

$$|n\rangle = \frac{1}{\sqrt{n!}} (a^\dagger)^n |0\rangle. \tag{26}$$

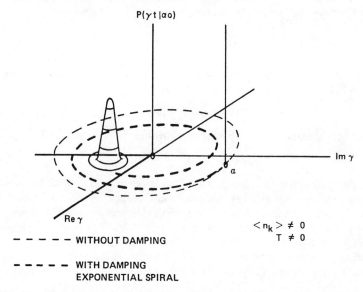

FIGURE 3. Conditioned quasi-probability density for the complex amplitude of the damped harmonic oscillator. The oscillator has begun at $t = 0$ in a pure coherent state of amplitude α. The mean value of the amplitude moves on an exponential spiral, decreasing steadily in modulus, while its dispersion increases.

One must remember, however, that the energies of these states have the negative sign in them, $E_n = -(n + \frac{1}{2})\hbar\omega$, so the creation operator, $a^\dagger$, really creates de-excitations, rather than positive energy quanta. Furthermore, the annihilation operator, a, actually raises the energy of the oscillator by decreasing the quantum number, n, by one unit.

Once we have absorbed those trifling changes, we are prepared to let the inverted oscillator take over the role of the central oscillator in the scheme we used earlier to discuss dissipation. The heat bath can remain precisely the same as we had it before, but when we couple the inverted oscillator to it, we must interchange the roles of a and $a^\dagger$ in the coupling terms in order to retain the "rotating wave" form. The coupling terms that tend to conserve energy, in other words, take the forms, ab_k and $b_k^\dagger a^\dagger$ rather than $ab_k^\dagger$ and $b_k a^\dagger$. When we make this interchange, the Hamiltonian for the coupled

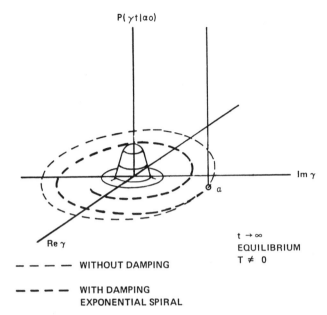

P($\gamma t | a_0$)

Im γ

Re γ

a

$t \to \infty$
EQUILIBRIUM
$T \neq 0$

— — — — WITHOUT DAMPING

— — — — WITH DAMPING
EXPONENTIAL SPIRAL

FIGURE 4. Limit for $\kappa t \to \infty$ of the quasi-probability distribution for the complex amplitude of the damped oscillator. The oscillator has come to equilibrium with its "heat bath".

system becomes

$$H = -\hbar \omega a^\dagger a + \Sigma_k \hbar \omega_k b_k^\dagger b_k + \hbar \Sigma_k (\lambda_k a b_k + \lambda_k^* b_k^\dagger a^\dagger). \tag{27}$$

This Hamiltonian has a certain invariance in it, which is a bit different from the one we saw earlier. If we alter the phase of a, then the b_k's must all undergo the complex conjugate transformation.

$$a \to a e^{i\theta}, \qquad b_k \to b_k e^{-i\theta}. \tag{28}$$

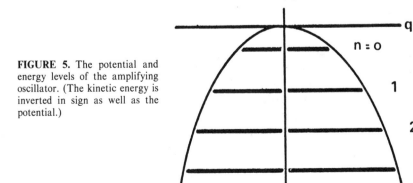

V(q)

q

n = 0

1

2

3

FIGURE 5. The potential and energy levels of the amplifying oscillator. (The kinetic energy is inverted in sign as well as the potential.)

That gives us a different sort of conservation law. The quantity conserved is the difference of the number of quanta in the central oscillator and the number in the heat bath,

$$a^\dagger a - \sum_k b_k^\dagger b_k = \text{constant.} \tag{29}$$

The equations of motion, of course, are still linear,

$$a = i\omega a - i \sum_k \lambda_k^* b_k^\dagger$$
$$\tag{30}$$
$$b_k = -i\omega_k b_k - i\lambda_k^* a^\dagger,$$

but they mix the adjoint operators in with the nonadjoints and that changes the character of the solutions.

Before undertaking the explicit solution of those equations, however, it is useful once more to go as far as we can with the generic forms the solutions must take. Let us thus write the solution to the equations of motion for $a(t)$ in the form,

$$a(t) = a(0)U(t) + \sum_k b_k^\dagger(0)V_k(t), \tag{31}$$

and define thereby a set of functions, $U(t)$ and $V_k(t)$, that obey the initial conditions,

$$U(0) = 1, \quad V_k(0) = 0. \tag{32}$$

We shall eventually have to solve for those functions, but, as before, we can gain a number of insights before having to do that.

We can no longer use the trick of saying that a coherent state remains always a coherent state. In fact, for this model, a coherent state does not remain a coherent state; its intrinsic uncertainty cloud grows explosively. That is unavoidable as we will see in quantum mechanical linear amplifiers. Thus, if we are to evaluate the reduced density operator for the inverted oscillator, we must fall back on some more general analytic technique than we have used earlier.

It is sufficient for this purpose to introduce the characteristic function for the unknown density operator, in fact, it is sufficient to use the specific form in which the a and $a^\dagger$ operators are normally ordered,

$$\chi_N(\mu, t) = \text{Trace } \{\rho(0)e^{\mu a^\dagger(t)}e^{-\mu a(t)}\} \tag{33}$$

$$= \text{Trace } \{\rho(t)e^{\mu a^\dagger(0)}e^{-\mu a(0)}\}. \tag{34}$$

The trace that defines this characteristic function is written on the upper line in the Heisenberg picture and on the lower line in the Schrödinger picture. Let us again take the initial state of the system to be one in which the central (inverted) oscillator is in the coherent state $|\alpha\rangle$, while the heat bath oscillators are in chaotic states with occupation numbers $\langle n_k \rangle$:

$$\rho(0) = |\alpha\rangle\langle\alpha| \prod_k \int e^{-|\beta_k|^2/\langle n_k \rangle}|\beta_k\rangle\langle\beta_k| \frac{d^2\beta_k}{\pi\langle n_k \rangle}. \tag{35}$$

We can use this form for the density operator then, and we can use the expression for

$a(t)$, given by equation 31, to evaluate the Heisenberg form for the characteristic function.

If we now write the reduced density operator in the Schrödinger picture in precisely the same form as we used in equation 15, that is to say, the P-representation form, we find that the characteristic function, $\chi_N(\mu, t)$, is just a two-dimensional Fourier transform[9] of the unknown weight function, $P(\gamma, t|\alpha, 0)$. That transform is easily inverted and we then find a Gaussian form for the conditioned quasi-probability density,

$$P(\gamma, t|\alpha, 0) = \frac{1}{\pi \mathcal{N}(t)} \exp\left\{ -\frac{|\gamma - \alpha U(t)|^2}{\mathcal{N}(t)} \right\}, \tag{36}$$

in which the dispersion, $\mathcal{N}(t)$, is given by

$$\mathcal{N}(t) = |U(t)|^2 - 1 + \sum_k \langle n_k \rangle |V_k(t)|^2. \tag{37}$$

The functions, $U(t)$ and $V_k(t)$, obey an identity in this case too—one that is equivalent to the conservation law of equation 29 and states

$$|U(t)|^2 - \sum_k |V_k(t)|^2 = 1. \tag{38}$$

We can use this relation to write the dispersion as

$$\mathcal{N}(t) = \sum_k (1 + \langle n_k \rangle) |V_k(t)|^2. \tag{39}$$

This dispersion must vanish initially when we assume the central oscillator begins in a pure coherent state. However, at later times, the dispersion takes on positive values in general, and it does that even when the heat bath has no initial excitation, that is, when all $\langle n_k \rangle$ are zero.

The dispersion, $\mathcal{N}(t)$, is a measure of the noise present in the excitation of the central oscillator. There is no avoiding the occurrence of such noise. It results, for example, from the spontaneous emission of quanta from the inverted oscillator into the heat bath, even when the latter is at zero temperature, and also when the initial amplitude vanishes as well.

The functions $U(t)$ and $V_k(t)$ can be approximated by the same sort of approximation we used earlier. This time, though, it should perhaps be called the anti–Weisskopf-Wigner approximation because the function $U(t)$ now blows up exponentially instead of decreasing. We find we can write $U(t)$ as

$$U(t) = e^{[\kappa + i(\omega - \delta\omega)]t} = e^{[\kappa + i\omega'']t}, \tag{40}$$

where the amplification constant, κ, and the line shift $\delta\omega$ are given once again in terms of the coupling strengths and the frequencies ω_k by equation 20.

The functions $V_k(t)$ have a resonant character for the case of amplification as well as dissipation. They are largest in modulus for frequencies ω_k close to ω. We can use

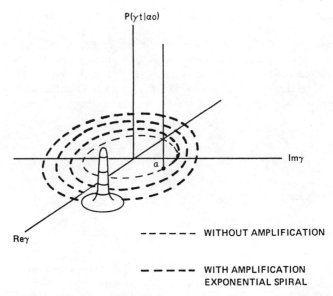

– – – – – – WITHOUT AMPLIFICATION

– – – – – WITH AMPLIFICATION
EXPONENTIAL SPIRAL

FIGURE 6. Conditioned quasi-probability density for the complex amplitude of the amplifying oscillator. The amplifier has begun at $t = 0$ in a pure coherent state of amplitude α. The mean value of the amplitude moves on a spiral, increasing exponentially in modulus, while its dispersion also increases exponentially.

that fact once more to approximate the dispersion function given by equation 38 as

$$\mathcal{N}(t) = (1 + \langle n''_\omega \rangle) \sum_k |V_k(t)|^2$$

$$= (1 + \langle n''_\omega \rangle)(|U(t)|^2 - 1) = (1 + \langle n''_\omega \rangle)(e^{2kt} - 1). \tag{41}$$

The initial amplitude α may be regarded, in a sense, as an input signal for our amplifier. Then it is clear from the general form of the quasi-probability function (equation 36) that the mean value of the distribution circles about the complex γ-plane in an exponentially increasing spiral. That is to say, the amplified signal, $\alpha U(t)$, blows up exponentially in modulus. At the same time, furthermore, the dispersion $\mathcal{N}(t)$ or the noise present blows up just as dramatically. A somewhat subdued picture of the way the function, $P(\gamma, t \,|\, \alpha, 0)$, changes with time is given in FIGURE 6. The dispersion tends to increase more rapidly than the figure indicates, but flattened-out Gaussian functions are very difficult to portray in three dimensions.

Now that we know what happens when the amplifier begins in a pure coherent state, $|\alpha\rangle$, it is easy to find out what happens for a great variety of other initial states. To see what the amplifier does when it begins in the $n = 0$ state, for example, we just substitute $\alpha = 0$ in equation 36 to find the quasi-probability distribution,

$$P_0(\gamma, t) = \frac{1}{\pi \mathcal{N}(t)} \exp\left\{-\frac{|\gamma|^2}{\mathcal{N}(t)}\right\}. \tag{42}$$

This simple Gaussian function represents the purest sort of noise. A large part of it comes from the amplification of zero-point fluctuations or, equivalently, from amplified spontaneous emission. The remainder comes (when the $\langle n_k \rangle$ are not equal to zero) from random forcing of the central oscillator by the heat bath.

It is not much more work to find the P-distribution that corresponds to any initial n-quantum state. To do that, we simply observe that the density operator for the pure coherent state $|\alpha\rangle$ can be written as

$$|\alpha\rangle \langle \alpha| = e^{-|\alpha|^2} \sum_{n,m} \frac{\alpha^n \alpha^{*m}}{\sqrt{n!\, m!}} |n\rangle \langle m|. \tag{43}$$

It is, in other words, a species of generating function for the operators $|n\rangle \langle m|$. Included among these are the alternative initial density operators,

$$\rho_A(0) = |n\rangle \langle n|. \tag{44}$$

We can find the quasi-probability distributions that evolve from the entire set of these initial states just by expanding the function $P(\gamma, t\,|\,\alpha, 0)$, given by equation 36 in a power series analogous to equation 43, and then evaluating the appropriate coefficients. The function $P(\gamma, t\,|\,\alpha, 0)$ given by equation 36 is, in fact, a species of generating function[10] for the Laguerre polynomials, L_n, and so we easily find that an n-quantum initial state leads to

$$P_n(\gamma, t) = \frac{(-1)^n}{\pi \mathcal{N}^{n+1}(t)} L_n\left[\left(1 + \frac{1}{\mathcal{N}(t)}\right)|\gamma|^2\right] e^{-|\gamma|^2/\mathcal{N}(t)}. \tag{45}$$

Some inkling of the appearance of these functions at a time, t, of the order of κ^{-1} is given in FIGURE 7. We may note that the function P_1, for example, takes on negative values for $|\gamma| < 1$, and then the higher order functions P_n do as well for values of $|\gamma|$ that are of the order of unity. The mean value of $|\gamma|$, on the other hand, increases exponentially as $e^{\kappa t}$, and for values of $|\gamma|$ large compared to unity, all of the functions P_n assume positive values and vary quite smoothly. While the quasi-probability

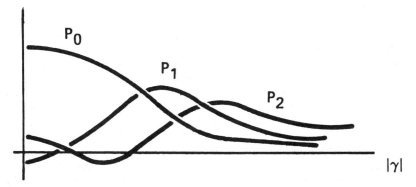

FIGURE 7. General appearance of the quasi-probability densities for the oscillator amplitude γ that evolves from amplification of initial n-quantum states.

densities, P_n, do not behave like ordinary probability densities within the quantum domain (for which $|\gamma|$ is of the order of unity), they do indeed behave like probability densities in the classical domain, $|\gamma| \gg 1$, to which the amplification process inevitably brings the excitation. When the amplification has taken place over a period several times κ^{-1} in duration, almost the entire normalization integral of P_n comes from the classical domain of $|\gamma| \gg 1$, and it becomes quite correct asymptotically to interpret P_n as a classical probability distribution for the oscillator amplitude. When the heat bath is initially at zero temperature, for example, the functions $P_n(\gamma, t)$ become asymptotically

$$P_n(\gamma, t) = \frac{1}{\pi n!} \frac{|\gamma|^{2n}}{(|U(t)|^2 - 1)^{n+1}} e^{-|\gamma|^2/|U(t)|^2 - 1}. \qquad (46)$$

Sometimes, we may be interested in finding the behavior of the amplifier for initial states that are superpositions of different n-quantum states. In fact, the examples we shall discuss involve some uncertainty in whether the amplifier begins in an $n = 0$ or an $n = 1$ state, so we need to know what the effect is of adding nondiagonal terms like $|0\rangle \langle 1|$ and $|1\rangle \langle 0|$ to the initial density operator. The density operator (equation 43) for a pure coherent state is evidently a generating function for these operators too, and so their contribution to the time-dependent density operator can also be found from the appropriate terms of the same expansion of the function P.

Sometimes, we are also interested in knowing the matrix elements of the density operator in the n-quantum state basis. We can find those as well by using the generating function device. For an initially pure coherent state, $|\alpha\rangle$, for example, we thus find the matrix element for $\rho_A(t)$:

$$\langle n | \rho_A(t) | m \rangle$$

$$= \sqrt{\frac{n!}{m!}} \frac{\mathcal{N}^m}{(1 + \mathcal{N})^{n+1}} \left(\frac{\alpha U(t)}{1 + \mathcal{N}} \right)^{m-n} L_n^{m-n} \left(\frac{-|\alpha|^2 |U|^2}{\mathcal{N}(1 + \mathcal{N})} \right) \exp \left(- \frac{|\alpha|^2 |U|^2}{1 + \mathcal{N}} \right). \qquad (47)$$

It is interesting to examine the ratio of the off-diagonal terms of this matrix to the diagonal ones. For $m > n$ and $\kappa t \gg 1$, we find

$$\frac{\langle n | \rho_A(t) | m \rangle}{\langle n | \rho_A(t) | n \rangle} \to \frac{1}{(m - n)!} \sqrt{\frac{n!}{m!}} \left(\frac{\alpha}{U^*(t)} \right)^{m-n}, \qquad (48)$$

but this ratio goes to zero as $\exp[-(m - n)\kappa t]$. The off-diagonal matrix elements, therefore, tend to become quite small in comparison to the diagonal ones. That is not quite the same thing as saying that the matrix assumes a precisely diagonal or stationary form because there are so very many nonvanishing off-diagonal matrix elements present. It is a kind of asymptotic near-diagonality that the density matrix possesses, and it takes on that property eventually no matter what the initial state of the central oscillator may have been.

This asymptotic descent of the density matrix into quasi-diagonality is even more dramatic in the coordinate-space or momentum-space representations. The coordinate-space representation of the general expression (equation 15) for the density operator is

$$\langle q' | \rho_A(t) | q'' \rangle = \int P(\gamma, t | \alpha, 0) \langle q' | \gamma \rangle \langle \gamma | q'' \rangle d^2\gamma. \qquad (49)$$

The coherent state wave functions, $\langle q'|\gamma\rangle$ and $\langle\gamma|q''\rangle$, are Gaussian in form,[6] and they vanish quite rapidly except for values of q' and q'' that lie close to $(2\hbar/\omega)^{1/2}(\text{Re }\gamma)$. The coordinate values for which the product $\langle q'|\gamma\rangle\langle\gamma|q''\rangle$ is significantly different from zero only allow $|q' - q''|$ to take on values comparable to the range of zero-point fluctuations, $(2\hbar/\omega)^{1/2}$. When this product of wave functions is multiplied by a smooth P-function and integrated over γ, as in equation 49, the constraint becomes even tighter. With the function, P, given by the pure noise distribution of equation 42, for example, we find that the matrix element (equation 49) approaches zero for $|q' - q''|$ larger than

$$\left(\frac{2\hbar(2\mathcal{N} + 1)}{\omega\mathcal{N}(\mathcal{N} + 1)}\right)^{1/2},$$

a distance that shrinks exponentially to zero.

This interesting property of asymptotic or macro-diagonality that the density matrix possesses will have an important consequence when we begin looking at experiments. It will imply that we cannot use our amplifier to generate any of those weird large-scale superposition states that quantum mechanics seems in principle to admit, but that we have never in our lives seen. Those are the states that Schrödinger maintained were intrinsically absurd consequences of quantum mechanics. They are not so much absurd as unrealizable.

How do we define the gain and noise figures for our amplifier? We can define the amplitude gain in an obvious way. It is just the exponential $e^{\kappa t}$. The power gain then is just the square of that:

$$G = |U(t)|^2 = e^{2\kappa t}. \tag{50}$$

The noise figure requires a bit more subtlety. A conventional way of defining the noise figure of an amplifier is to imagine a noiseless amplifier with the same gain and ask how much noise you would have had to put in initially in order for the noiseless amplification process to produce the same final noise that the real amplifier produces. That figure then offers a fair measure of how strong your input signal ought to be if it is to be detectable above the final noise.

The amount of Gaussian noise you must add to an initially coherent state $|\alpha\rangle$ in order for this hypothetically noiseless amplification process to lead to the P-distribution of equation 36 is

$$N_{\text{noise}} = \frac{\mathcal{N}(t)}{|U(t)|^2} = (1 + \langle n_{\omega''}\rangle)\,[1 - (1/G)]. \tag{51}$$

In a recent paper on amplifiers, Caves[11] has established a lower bound for this noise figure by invoking general principles rather than any specific model. His result for the noise figure was $N_{\text{noise}} > 1 - (1/G)$, which is entirely consistent with equation 51.

There is an interesting game that you can play with this sort of amplifier and with the attenuator that you can construct by turning the inverted oscillator back into a normal one. Let us say we put a microscopic signal of some sort into our amplifer and amplify it considerably. Then we stop the process and reinvert the central oscillator so that the signal is attenuated back down to its original strength. The question we now ask is, will we get the oscillator back to the quantum state in which it began? The attenuation process, we have noted, is completely noiseless as long as the heat bath is at temperature zero. Let us assume, therefore, that the heat bath always starts at temperature zero, even for the amplification process as well.

There would be some strange consequences if, in fact, it were possible to get back to the original state. The amplification process we are discussing is irreversible and this may be one of the better illustrations of that fact. The analysis is quite elementary, so we need not go through it in detail. Let us just note that by changing the sign of the frequency parameter, we can indeed turn the amplifier into an attenuator with a decay period equal to the prior amplification period. We can then decrease the oscillator excitation noiselessly, but we can never get its state back to the form in which it began. What happens is that the cycle of amplification and attenuation superposes on that state a certain amount of Gaussian noise. If the initial state of the amplifer is described by the coherent-state amplitude distribution $P(\alpha)$, and the amplifying and attenuating halves of the cycle each last for a length of time t, then the final state reached will have the reduced density operator,

$$\rho_A = \frac{1}{\pi M(t)} \int e^{-|\gamma - \alpha|^2/M(t)} P(\alpha) |\gamma\rangle \langle\gamma| d^2\alpha d^2\gamma.$$

This operator describes a superposition of an average number of quanta $M(t)$ of Gaussian noise upon the original state. If the heat bath modes have an average occupation number $\langle n_\omega \rangle$ at the amplifier frequency ω, the average number of noise quanta may be shown to be

$$M(t) = (1 + 2 \langle n_\omega \rangle) (1 - e^{-2\kappa t}). \tag{52}$$

For a heat bath at zero temperature then, the number of noise quanta added is just $1 - e^{-2\kappa t}$, and for $\kappa t \gg 1$, each of our cycles adds, on the average, just a single quantum of noise.

Suppose it were true that we could carry out the cycle of amplification and attenuation and still return the system to precisely the state from which it began. We could put the central oscillator into some interesting quantum state and amplify it until all its variables assumed classical strength. We could then measure them all, including the complementary ones, without disturbing any of them significantly, and finally, we could attenuate the signal noiselessly to reestablish exactly the initial state. We would then find ourselves in possession of all sorts of information about the state that contradicts the uncertainty principle. It is the quantum mechanical nature of the amplification process ultimately that makes it both noisy and irreversible, and thus prevents the occurrence of any such miracle.

Our model for the amplifier may seem a bit unrealistic. It depends, after all, quite explicitly on the use of an inverted oscillator, and oscillators of that kind are not available "off-the-shelf." In fact, if we were in possession of just one such oscillator, it could solve the world's energy problems, so that does not sound too likely. However, there is no need, in fact, for us to find an inverted oscillator in the literal sense. All we need is something that behaves like one over the limited range of variables in which it is actually used. Many systems are available that do behave in essentially that way.

Let us consider, for example, a system (say, an atom) with a large total angular momentum, $j \gg 1$. If the atom has a magnetic moment in the direction of the angular momentum, J, and we place it in a uniform magnetic field, it will have $2j + 1$ equally spaced Zeeman levels. As long as the atom is in any of the states with J_z not too far from j, that is, near the state of maximum energy, its behavior will quite closely approximate that of an inverted oscillator. The operator, $(J_x + iJ_y)/\sqrt{2j}$, that raises the magnetic quantum number J_z by one unit then plays the role of the annihilation operator, a. Its commutator with its Hermitian adjoint has eigenvalues appropriately close to unity for the states with J_z near j. We can then identify the angular momentum states $|J_z = j - n\rangle$ with the states $|n\rangle$ of the inverted oscillator (see FIGURE 8).

When this atom is in any state of small n and is coupled to the radiation field in the usual way, it will begin to emit quanta and descend to states of larger n in just the way that we have described for the inverted oscillator. Of course, the acceleration of the radiation rate will not continue indefinitely. When the quantum number, n, becomes comparable to j, it will no longer increase as rapidly. The rate of radiation reaches maximum for $n = j$ and then begins to decrease. All of this is only to say that a magnetic moment associated with a large value of j is not really a linear amplifier. It is a nonlinear one. However, there is a regime for large values of J_z in which it duplicates quite accurately the behavior of a linear amplifier.

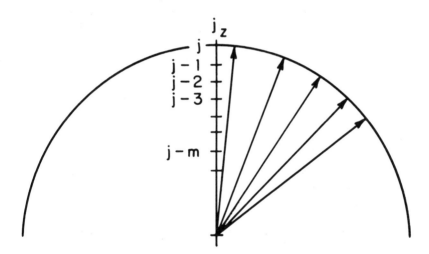

FIGURE 8. The succession of magnetic substates for large j and m near j in value. These are the states for which radiative transitions are amplified exponentially.

The example of an atom with a huge angular momentum, j, may seem a bit farfetched, but there is a context in which we often deal with such systems these days. A single two-level atom is equivalent algebraically to a system of spin $\frac{1}{2}$ in a magnetic field. A system of N such atoms with identical couplings to the radiation field is therefore precisely equivalent to the angular momentum model we have just discussed with $j = N/2$. When all or nearly all of the N atoms are initially in their excited states, the emission process that ensues is superfluorescent in character. The initial phase of superfluorescence is one of linear amplification.[12] It continues long enough in practice to generate fields of essentially classical strength that are easily observed with large-scale laboratory equipment. The inverted oscillator model, in fact, is just an idealization of the way in which the superfluorescent radiation process begins.

Of course, the quanta that are being amplified in the inverted central oscillator are not the usual sorts of excitations of positive energy. They are, strictly speaking, de-excitations or, in effect, quanta of negative energy. We can easily alter that feature of the model without significantly changing its mathematical analysis by turning all of the oscillators upside down once more. We let the central oscillator, in other words, be a normal one with quanta of positive energy, and let the heat bath oscillators all be inverted. Any quanta initially present in the central oscillator will then be amplified to large positive energies. It is easy to verify that the only significant changes in our earlier results are inversions of the signs of the frequency parameters, ω and ω_k.

SPECIFICATION OF PHOTON POLARIZATION STATES

One of the subjects we mentioned initially is a scheme for superluminal communication involving photon polarizations. That proposal gave a special role to states of plane and circular polarization, but any two distinguishable pairs of orthogonal polarization states would do equally well. It will be of some help, therefore, to have in hand a general procedure for dealing with photon polarization states of all sorts.

For a light wave that propagates in a fixed direction, the polarization vectors are defined in a two-dimensional space transverse to that direction. Complex vectors of unit length in that two-dimensional space define a two-parameter family of elliptical polarization states; any two orthogonal vectors of that sort are eligible to be a pair of basis states. Transformations from one pair of basis states to another must then be unitary matrix transformations in two dimensions. They are, thus, a two-parameter subgroup of the group SU(2), which is the special unitary group in two dimensions.

There is a well-known correspondence between the transformation of SU(2) and real rotations in three dimensions that gives us a simple way of picturing the various polarization states. They can be put in one-to-one correspondence with the points on a unit sphere, so the transformations of SU(2) simply rotate them into one another. This way of dealing with all of the polarizations at once was invented by Poincaré[13] in 1892, well before the discovery of spinors by Cartan.

FIGURE 9 then is a picture of the Poincaré sphere. We have taken the north and south poles of the sphere to represent the two orthogonal states of circular polarization, and we have accordingly labeled them for the state $| + \rangle$, of helicity one, and for the state $| - \rangle$, of helicity minus one. Of course, you can equally well label them L and R for left and right circular polarizations (if you can remember which is which). An arbitrary polarization state, which we can call $|\theta, \varphi\rangle$, can then be written as

$$|\theta, \varphi\rangle = e^{i\varphi/2} \cos \frac{\theta}{2} | + \rangle + e^{-i\varphi/2} \sin \frac{\theta}{2} | - \rangle, \tag{53}$$

where the angles θ and φ are limited by

$$0 \le \theta \le \pi, \qquad -\pi \le \varphi < \pi. \tag{54}$$

Each point on the surface of the sphere thus defines a unique state of elliptical polarization. Antipodal points on the sphere always represent orthogonal polarization states.

Let us take $|h\rangle$ and $|v\rangle$ to represent the usual horizontal and vertical states of plane polarization; thus, the circular polarization states can be written as

$$| \pm \rangle = \frac{1}{\sqrt{2}}(|h\rangle \pm i|v\rangle). \tag{55}$$

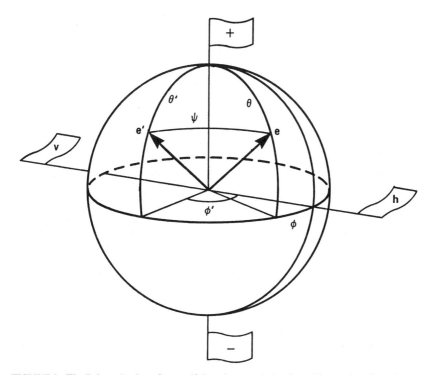

FIGURE 9. The Poincaré sphere for specifying photon polarizations. The north and south poles represent the two circular polarizations. All equatorial points represent linear polarizations. Antipodal points represent orthogonal elliptical polarizations, more generally.

Then we find that in the $|\theta, \varphi\rangle$ scheme, these states are

$$|h\rangle = \left| \frac{\pi}{2}, 0 \right\rangle, \qquad |v\rangle = \left| \frac{\pi}{2}, -\pi \right\rangle. \tag{56}$$

We have also indicated their locations on the Poincaré sphere in FIGURE 9. They lie on the equator, which consists exclusively of plane polarizations.

One of the conveniences of the Poincaré sphere is that it gives a simple way of dealing with the scalar products of polarization vectors. The probability that a photon with polarization $|\theta, \varphi\rangle$, for example, is transmitted by a filter that selects polarizations $|\theta', \varphi'\rangle$ is the squared scalar product $|\langle\theta', \varphi'|\theta, \varphi\rangle|^2$. According to equation 55, the scalar product is

$$\langle\theta', \varphi'|\theta, \varphi\rangle = e^{(i/2)(\varphi-\varphi')} \cos\frac{\theta'}{2}\cos\frac{\theta}{2} + e^{-(i/2)(\varphi-\varphi')} \sin\frac{\theta'}{2}\sin\frac{\theta}{2}. \qquad (57)$$

The squared modulus of this expression depends only on the angle between the radii to the points (θ, φ) and (θ', φ') on the sphere. If we call that angle, ψ, as in FIGURE 9, and recall the spherical law of cosines,

$$\cos\psi = \cos\theta\cos\theta' + \sin\theta\sin\theta'\cos(\varphi - \varphi'), \qquad (58)$$

then we find that the transmission probability of our photon is just

$$|\langle\theta', \varphi'|\theta, \varphi\rangle|^2 = \frac{1}{2}(1 + \cos\psi) = \cos^2\frac{1}{2}\psi. \qquad (59)$$

MEASURING PHOTON POLARIZATIONS

If we are to communicate by means of photon polarizations, we must be prepared to answer questions like this: A photon goes through a filter that transmits with 100% efficiency the polarization $|\theta', \varphi'\rangle$; what is the probability that such a transmitted photon really had the initial polarization $|\theta, \varphi\rangle$? That is a question that can only be posed probabilistically because you cannot go back and verify what the state was. The possibility of communication, on the other hand, depends critically on the determination of those probabilities. How do we find them? We will presently show that Bayes' theorem gives a convenient way of determining such *a posteriori* probabilities, but we do not need all of that generality quite yet.

Let us assume we have some arbitrary beam of photons. We place in the beam a filter that transmits only the polarization $|\theta', \varphi'\rangle$. When a photon is transmitted, we can obviously say that the probability that its initial polarization was $|\theta, \varphi\rangle$ is proportional to the probability that a photon of polarization $|\theta, \varphi\rangle$ is transmitted by a filter that transmits polarizations $|\theta', \varphi'\rangle$. That probability, in other words, is proportional to the squared scalar product in equation 59, and has the angular dependence of $\cos^2(\psi/2)$. The $\cos^2(\psi/2)$ distribution is spread out quite smoothly all over the sphere, but it does convey some information. When you make a measurement on one photon, what you find is a new way of weighting whatever information you had initially about where its polarization vector might have been pointing. The new weighting multiplies whatever distribution you knew of before by the factor $\cos^2(\psi/2)$; if you knew nothing at all beforehand, if the *a priori* distribution were uniform, for example, then the final distribution over the surface of the sphere would just be a constant times $\cos^2(\psi/2)$.

If you were to attempt to perform the Einstein-Podolsky-Rosen experiment we described initially, and to use it to communicate via measurements made on individual photon polarizations, you would quickly find that you cannot distinguish between circular polarizations and linear polarizations. In fact, you cannot distinguish between any one pair of antipodal points on the Poincaré sphere and any other. The angles ψ for any pair of antipodal points are naturally supplementary, so the sum of the two probabilities is proportional to

$$\cos^2(\psi/2) + \cos^2\left(\frac{\pi - \psi}{2}\right) = \cos^2(\psi/2) + \sin^2(\psi/2) = 1,$$

and that is constant and quite independent of which pair of orthogonal polarization states was chosen. Thus, the task is hopeless. One polarization measurement on a single photon cannot ever provide the information desired.

We have the alternative suggestion, however, that we use a "laser gain tube" to multiply the number of photons to be processed. What such a laser gain tube does, presumably, is just to amplify in similar ways photons that are in any of the possible polarization states. Those polarization states can all be considered to be superpositions of one pair of basis states. Then everything the laser gain tube does can be represented by the action of two identical amplifiers, each of which is fed by the appropriate polarization component. Because we want to amplify normal positive energy photons, we should use as amplifiers normal positive energy oscillators that are coupled, as noted earlier, to heat baths consisting of inverted oscillators.

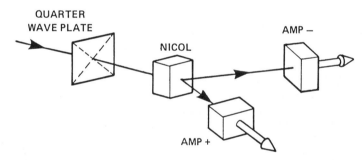

FIGURE 10. A setup illustrating the use of a pair of amplifiers as a photon polarization detector.

An appropriate sort of amplifier-detector arrangement is shown in FIGURE 10. The quarter-wave plate converts circular polarizations into plane polarizations and the Nicol or Wollaston prism separates the latter into two beams, each of which is sent into its own amplifier and emerges in considerably strengthened form. In effect, then, one of those amplifiers amplifies the right-handed circularly polarized component of the incident beam and the other amplifies the left-handed component. The two output beams are so strong that we may describe them classically, and we can measure them to our heart's content without disturbing them in any way.

Let us agree, however arbitrarily, to carry out our calculations by using circularly polarized basis states. Let $a_+^\dagger$ be a creation operator for the state of helicity one and let $a_-^\dagger$ be a creation operator for the state of helicity minus one. Then a state with n_+ photons of the first variety and n_- of the second can be generated from the vacuum state, $|n_+ = 0, n_- = 0\rangle \equiv |0, 0\rangle$, by applying the appropriate creation operators,

$$|n_+, n_-\rangle = \frac{(a_+^\dagger)^{n_+}}{\sqrt{n_+!}} \frac{(a_-^\dagger)^{n_-}}{\sqrt{n_-!}} |0, 0\rangle. \tag{60}$$

We want still to be able to deal with photons in arbitrary polarization states. For a photon in a polarization state, $|\theta, \varphi\rangle$, we can define the creation and annihilation operators as

$$a_{\theta\varphi}^\dagger = e^{i\varphi/2} \cos\frac{\theta}{2} a_+^\dagger + e^{-i\varphi/2} \sin\frac{\theta}{2} a_-^\dagger, \tag{61}$$

$$a_{\theta\varphi} = e^{-i\varphi/2} \cos\frac{\theta}{2} a_+ + e^{i\varphi/2} \sin\frac{\theta}{2} a_-, \tag{62}$$

so that a single-photon state, $|\theta, \varphi\rangle$, can be written as

$$|\theta, \varphi\rangle = a_{\theta\varphi}^\dagger |0, 0\rangle. \tag{63}$$

The initial density operator that represents this state is just this vector multiplied by its dual,

$$\rho(0) = a_{\theta\varphi}^\dagger |0, 0\rangle \langle 0, 0| a_{\theta\varphi}. \tag{64}$$

The amplifiers we are discussing are, of course, transient amplifiers. It would be nicer in some ways to imagine this experiment as carried out with continuously operating linear amplifiers. However, it is somewhat more complicated to construct models of CW amplifiers, and it is not really very essential for conceptual purposes. The time-dependent scheme we are discussing, in fact, suits the practical needs of a *gedanken* experiment quite well. One can adjust the various initial times and amplification times so that one secures an appropriately strong output signal from a single photon arriving at time zero. That does, however, require a somewhat delicate adjustment because these amplifiers are devices that provide an output signal even if there is no photon present at time zero. One must be careful about the coordination of such equipment, but there is nothing difficult about that, at least, in principle.

USE OF THE COMPOUND AMPLIFIER

We can deal with our pair of amplifiers very much as we dealt with a single one before. If the photon incident upon our detector is in the state $|\theta, \varphi\rangle$, the initial density operator for the two amplifiers is given by equation 64. The final reduced density operator for the two amplifiers can then be written as a two-mode P-representation that has the general form,

$$\rho(t) = \int P(\gamma_+, \gamma_-, t|\theta, \varphi)|\gamma_+\rangle\langle\gamma_+||\gamma_-\rangle\langle\gamma_-|d^2\gamma_+ d^2\gamma_-. \tag{65}$$

Evaluating the function P precisely is now, for the most part, a repetition of the calculation described earlier for the single-mode case. The only new points to be observed are that the function depends on two variables, $\gamma_\pm$, and that the initial density operator given by equation 64 contains off-diagonal terms in the quantum numbers $n_\pm$. The effect of such terms as we have noted can easily be found by the same generating function devices that we used for the diagonal ones.

The function P that we find in this way is

$$P(\gamma_+, \gamma_-, t | \theta, \varphi) = \frac{1}{\pi^2 \mathcal{N}^2} \left\{ 1 - \frac{|U|^2}{\mathcal{N}} + \frac{|U|^2}{\mathcal{N}^2} \left| \gamma_+ e^{-i\varphi/2} \cos \frac{\theta}{2} + \gamma_- e^{i\varphi/2} \sin \frac{\theta}{2} \right|^2 \right\}$$

$$\cdot \exp \left\{ -\frac{|\gamma_+|^2 + |\gamma_-|^2}{\mathcal{N}} \right\}, \quad (66)$$

where the functions U and $\mathcal{N}$ for the amplifier are those defined earlier and approximated by equations 40 and 41, respectively. We can express this result a bit more simply by imagining the two amplified output fields to be superposed and then defining a polarization vector for the superposed fields. An appropriate unit polarization vector is

$$|\hat{e}_{\gamma_+\gamma_-}\rangle = \frac{1}{\sqrt{|\gamma_+|^2 + |\gamma_-|^2}} \{\gamma_+ | + \rangle + \gamma_- | - \rangle\}. \quad (67)$$

We can define the intensity associated with any polarization state, $|\theta', \phi'\rangle$, of the superposed output fields as

$$I(\theta', \varphi') = \text{Trace} \{\rho(t) a_{\theta'\varphi'}^\dagger a_{\theta'\varphi'}\} \quad (68)$$

$$= \int P(\gamma_+, \gamma_-, t | \theta, \varphi) |\gamma_+ e^{-i\varphi'/2} \cos \frac{\theta'}{2} + \gamma_- e^{i\varphi'/2} \sin \frac{\theta'}{2}|^2 \, d^2\gamma_+ d^2\gamma_-$$

$$= \int |\langle \theta', \varphi' | \hat{e}_{\gamma_+\gamma_-} \rangle|^2 (|\gamma_+|^2 + |\gamma_-|^2) P(\gamma_+, \gamma_-, t | \theta, \varphi) \, d^2\gamma_+ d^2\gamma_-. \quad (69)$$

We can use the vector $|\hat{e}_{\gamma_+\gamma_-}\rangle$ furthermore to write the expression for the function P a bit more compactly as

$$P(\gamma_+, \gamma_-, t | \theta, \varphi) = \frac{1}{\pi^2 \mathcal{N}^2} \left\{ \frac{|U|^2}{\mathcal{N}^2} | \langle \hat{e}_{\gamma_+\gamma_-} | \theta\varphi \rangle|^2 (|\gamma_+|^2 + |\gamma_-|^2) - \frac{1}{\mathcal{N}} \right\}$$

$$\cdot \exp \left\{ -\frac{|\gamma_+|^2 + |\gamma_-|^2}{\mathcal{N}} \right\}. \quad (70)$$

The Gaussian integral for the polarization dependence of the amplified intensity leads to the simple zero-temperature result

$$I(\theta', \varphi') = |U(t)|^2 \{1 + |\langle \theta', \varphi' | \theta, \varphi \rangle|^2\} - 1 \quad (71)$$

$$= e^{2\kappa t} \{1 + |\langle \theta', \varphi' | \theta, \varphi \rangle|^2\} - 1. \quad (72)$$

The compound amplifier, we see, does indeed "remember" the initial polarization state of the photon in the classical output it generates. While the output field follows the distribution of equation 70 and is therefore highly random, it is indeed polarized, on the average, in the direction, $|\theta, \varphi\rangle$. The fact that we can measure the polarization of a classical field as precisely as we like may seem to favor the EPR communication scheme, so we had better say a bit more about polarizations.

To define the (θ, φ) polarization of the amplified beam, we must compare the intensity, $I(\theta, \varphi)$, with the intensity for the orthogonal polarization state. Let $\bar{\theta} = \pi - \theta$ and $\bar{\varphi} = \varphi \pm \pi$ be the polar coordinates of the antipodal point on the Poincaré sphere. Then, the polarization in the (θ, φ) direction is

$$p(\theta, \varphi) = \frac{I(\theta, \phi) - I(\bar{\theta}, \bar{\phi})}{I(\theta, \phi) + I(\bar{\theta}, \bar{\phi})} \tag{73}$$

$$= \frac{|U(t)|^2}{3|U(t)|^2 - 2}, \tag{74}$$

$$= \frac{1}{3 - 2e^{-2\kappa t}}. \tag{75}$$

The last of these expressions shows that though the compound amplifier does remember the initial photon polarization, it does not have the clearest of memories. The strong field that emerges for $\kappa t \gg 1$ only has polarization $\frac{1}{3}$. That happens because of the amplified noise output that both amplifiers generate even with no initial photon present.

The amplified intensity given by equation 71 has a fully polarized component, $|U(t)|^2|\langle\theta', \varphi'|\theta, \varphi\rangle|^2$, which we may consider as the amplified signal due to the incident photon. However, it also contains an unpolarized component, $|U(t)|^2 - 1$, which represents the noise output contributed equally by the two amplifiers. The amplification of the noise keeps pace with the signal, and in the long run, there is usually even somewhat more noise present than signal.

The compound amplifier that is part of our detector scheme duplicates precisely the action of a "laser gain tube" on the incident photons. However, it is not at all clear that such action deserves to be called "cloning." Both the compound amplifier and the laser gain tube are bound to generate more or less random numbers of photons in two orthogonal polarization states. There is no alternative, clearly, to suffering the presence of two varieties of photons. The description of polarization states requires two basis states, and spontaneous emission alone assures us that both varieties of photons will be present in general.

In a note inspired by the EPR communication scheme, Wootters and Zurek[14] have shown that it is not possible, by using a single amplifier, to clone photons of arbitrary polarization. Their analysis takes the definition of cloning quite literally, requiring all photons to be identical, and places the further restriction that the initially pure one-photon state has to always remain pure. It is not related, therefore, to the action of any real amplifier, let alone the pair of them that is necessary for the measurement of arbitrary polarizations. That a pair of analyzing systems is sufficient for the unbiased analysis of polarizations has been pointed out by Mandel,[15] who discussed a detector consisting of two atoms.

SUPERLUMINAL COMMUNICATION?

Let me now return to our superluminal communication problem. Having introduced the quantum optical means one might use to make the measurements, I would like to persuade you that we can, in fact, dismiss the "laser gain tube" scheme very quickly. I will nonetheless go on to analyze it a bit further as it is interesting to see in somewhat more detail how and why it does not work; there are also some more practical uses for the analysis as well.

Let us try to describe some devices that boil the communication problem down to its barest essentials. Let us say we have two devices, which could even be different states of the same device producing two varieties of signal. These are wave packets being sent off to a distant receiver. You can see them in FIGURE 11. One variety I will call a dot, and the other one, a dash (Morse code). Our distant observer listens with whatever equipment he has and measures some property, X, of those wave packets. He hopes, on the basis of a measurement of X, to determine which variety of wave packet it is that he has received; that is, whether it is a dot or a dash. He must choose X to be a quantity that makes the clearest distinction between the two. Yet, he must inevitably face the problem, given the observation $X = x$, what is the probability that the signal is a dot? And given the observation $X = x$, what is the probability that it is a dash? Now,

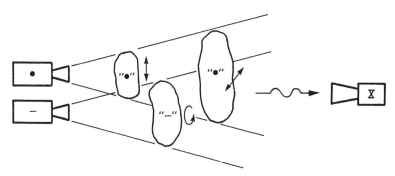

FIGURE 11. Schematic picture of the use of polarized photon wave packets for communication purposes. One signal generator produces linearly polarized packets that are represent by "dots." The other produces circularly polarized packets that are represent by "dashes."

here, I do not know of any alternative to the use of Bayes' theorem or more sophisticated decision theoretical notions.

What are the dashes and dots in our communication model? The dashes might be represented by circularly polarized photon packets and the dots by linearly polarized packets. We want, if possible, to distinguish clearly between them. However, we must carefully note one thing more. In the class of linearly polarized packets that represent dots, we have no control over which of two polarizations is sent. Some of those dots are going to be vertically polarized, and an equal number, on the average, are going to be horizontally polarized. In the class of dashes, some of the packets are going to be right-handed circularly polarized, and some are going to be left-handed circularly polarized.

To phrase the decision problem more formally, our signaling devices have to be described statistically. Each of our signal generators puts the field into a state described by a particular density operator. The detection problem is to make measurements that offer a clear distinction between those two density operators. By measuring X, or whatever it is, in each wave packet, the detector device asks, in effect: do you represent the density operator for a dot, or the density operator for a dash?

We can phrase the mathematical part of the problem as follows: Let the probability that a given packet represents a dash or a dot be $p(-)$ and $p(\cdot)$, respectively. Let the probability that the detector observes the value x, if the input is a dash, be $P(x|-)$. Then, the joint probability that a packet represents a dash and the detector observes x is

$$P(x, -) = P(x|-)p(-). \tag{76}$$

Bayes' theorem asserts that this joint probability can be also be written as the product,

$$P(x, -) = P(-|x)p(x), \tag{77}$$

in which $p(x)$ is the probability that the detector registers x no matter which sort of packet arrives, and $P(-|x)$ is the probability, given the measurement of x, that the incident packet represents a dash. The probability $p(x)$ is evidently given by

$$p(x) = P(x|-)p(-) + P(x|\cdot)p(\cdot), \tag{78}$$

while the probability we seek, namely the probability that the incident packet represents a dash, is evidently

$$P(-|x) = \frac{P(x|-)p(-)}{P(x|-)p(-) + P(x|\cdot)p(\cdot)}. \tag{79}$$

An analogous expression of course holds for $P(\cdot|x)$.

However, now that we have created all this machinery, we have to face the fundamental difficulty that if we look at the ensemble of wave packets that represent dots, we will find them unpolarized. What is the density matrix that represents an unpolarized beam? It is one-half of the unit matrix; the density operator is just one-half of the unit operator. Now, let us consider the ensemble that represents dashes. We have said they are circularly polarized, but in fact they are circularly unpolarized; they have no net polarization either. What is the density matrix that the dash generator turns out? That is once again one-half of the unit matrix. Therefore, we are asking our distant friend, whatever detection device he may be using, to make a distinction between things that are absolutely identical. The two density operators he must recognize individually are identical twins. This is a classic example of a distinction without a difference. The probabilities that result must satisfy the identity,

$$P(x|-) = P(x|\cdot), \tag{80}$$

and thus,

$$P(-|x) = p(-). \tag{81}$$

The *a posteriori* probability, in other words, is equal to the raw *a priori* probability. Measuring x, whatever it may be, does not add to our knowledge of the message at all.

That difficulty is bound to frustrate our distant friend. It cannot be too encouraging either to the theorists who insist on examining the detection problem microscopically rather than surveying it from this more global viewpoint. Our argument assures us that whatever useful possibilities we seem to see present from a microscopic standpoint are going to cancel out before the calculation is finished, and that it is just not possible to use the polarization scheme as a means of communication. Having said that, I want nevertheless to look a bit further at the scheme because it is an interesting one; most particularly, it is interesting as an illustration of what amplifiers do. We will find that our calculations do indeed have practical applications, but only in other experimental contexts.

Let us go back to the pair of amplifiers we are using to amplify each photon that is received and see what additional information we can elicit from them. What we do is let the amplifiers amplify for several gain periods, so that the field intensity is increased substantially. We are then talking about classical outputs. We need have no embarrassment about measuring those field amplitudes because they can be just as strong as we like; we can measure them without disturbing anything.

In this strong-field limit, we have

$$\frac{1}{\mathcal{N}(t)} = \frac{1}{e^{2\kappa t} - 1} \rightarrow 0$$

and

$$\frac{|U(t)|^2}{\mathcal{N}(t)} = \frac{e^{2\kappa t}}{e^{2\kappa t} - 1} \rightarrow 1.$$

When the output fields are that strong, the P-distribution for their amplitudes becomes, in effect, a classical probability density; equation 70 then reduces to the form,

$$P(\gamma_+, \gamma_-, t \,|\, \theta, \varphi) = \frac{1}{\pi^2 \mathcal{N}^2} \,|\langle \hat{e}_{\gamma_+ \gamma_-} | \theta \varphi \rangle|^2 (|\gamma_+|^2 + |\gamma_-|^2) \exp\left\{ -\frac{|\gamma_+|^2 + |\gamma_-|^2}{\mathcal{N}} \right\}. \quad \text{(82)}$$

We can use this expression now to determine what classical measurements made on the amplified fields can tell us about the original polarization state of any incident photon.

In any given detection process, we insert a photon in the compound system and let the two amplifiers amplify their initial fields. Then, we observe a pair of classical output field amplitudes, γ_+ and γ_-, that are governed by the probability distribution of equation 82. Once we have measured any such pair of amplitudes, we can ask the question: what is the probability that the initial photon had a polarization $|\theta, \varphi\rangle$? The answer is, in fact, staring at us in equation 82. It is the very same weighting that we would have arrived at by making a measurement on a single photon with a single polarizer. We are now no longer talking simply about the superposition of different polarization states. The amplification process, combined with the corruption of the information by noise, has brought us back, however, to exactly the same position we were in before. The compound amplifier, as far as polarization is concerned, has contrived to tell us nothing at all new because of the noise it has added. We can only make the same inferences about initial polarization states that we made without it. In fact, from that standpoint, the compound amplifier is no better than a single polarizer.

INTERFERENCE EXPERIMENTS AND SCHRÖDINGER'S CAT

Since we have some experience now at using amplifiers in pairs, there are all kinds of interesting games we can play. One is to perform Young's classic double-pinhole interference experiment with an amplifier placed behind each of the pinholes, as in FIGURE 12.

Conceivably, we could use such a scheme to determine which pinhole any given photon has really passed through. Let us agree that we are going to look only at cases in which a single photon packet falls symmetrically on the two pinholes. That means that we are starting our amplifiers out in an initially pure state that is a superposition of the two states in which a photon enters one, while the other remains in its empty or

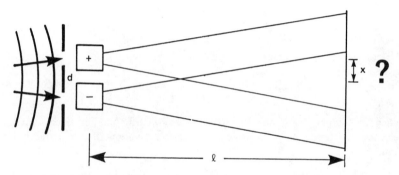

FIGURE 12. Young's double-pinhole interference experiment carried out with a single incident photon and an amplifier behind each pinhole. What sort of pattern appears where the emergent beams are superposed on the distant screen?

"ground" state. We can use the plus and minus signs now just to label the two amplifiers. Those signs then no longer refer to polarizations. With that one change, we can make use of the same calculations we carried out earlier.

Now, what shall we expect to see when the amplified fields are superposed by projecting them onto the distant screen? Let me, for the sake of argument, list three bad guesses. Bad guess number one: A classical physicist who just believes in probability theory and no more will say that the photon is bound to go through one hole or the other. It will have a probability of ½ for going through the upper hole, and if it does that, the upper amplifier will produce a strong output field, while the lower one will produce nothing. Of course, it may happen the other way around, but we will never see interference fringes. That is what this person would say, however, benightedly.

Bad guess number two might be made by somebody who has studied Young's experiment as it is usually described, and takes the classical view of it. He will note that the photon wave enters those two holes coherently and is strengthened symmetrically by passage through both amplifiers. The fields projected by the two amplifiers, he will say, should simply show Young's interference fringes on the screen. In saying that, he too is of course overlooking something quite important.

This may not be an exhaustive list of bad guesses; naiveté can take many forms. However, a naively sophisticated view we should not overlook would be this: The photon begins in a well-defined initial quantum state. You may remember the Schrödinger cat example; the situation is not unlike that. Here, we have a well-defined initial superposition state. The photon may alternatively, but coherently, enter either of the two amplifiers. If their action has the elegant simplicity Schrödinger assumed his diabolical cat-killing machine to have, we should then find, as their output, a quantum mechanical superposition of two amplified fields.

What is the meaning of such a quantum mechanical superposition of two quantum states containing highly amplified fields? The two output states involved are orthogonal and quite dissimilar. They can easily be distinguished from one another classically. A quantum mechanical superposition of those states regards the two amplified outputs as alternatives. That feature is quite characteristic of superpositions of states in quantum mechanical Hilbert space. When you superpose two orthogonal states, $|A\rangle$ and $|B\rangle$, in Hilbert space, you are saying in a certain sense, "either $|A\rangle$ or $|B\rangle$, but not both." Therefore, you may just see in this third, slightly more sophisticated view of the amplification problem, the ghost of Schrödinger's cat.

Here, we indeed have a device in which we can trace what happens all the way from the quantum to the classical domain. It permits us, at last, to answer the question of whether we will see the quantum mechanical superposition of two macroscopic states as envisioned by Schrödinger. That pure state, if it were to occur, would be characterized again by a strong output from either one amplifier or the other, but not both. The product of the two classical output field strengths would always be zero, and thus there would be no interference fringes.

What is the correct way to treat the interference problem? When the photon impinges on the two pinholes, we can think of the two amplifiers, labeled $+$ and $-$, as beginning in the pure state,

$$|\psi\rangle = \frac{1}{\sqrt{2}}\{|1\rangle_+|0\rangle_- + |0\rangle_+|1\rangle_-\}, \qquad (83)$$

in which $|0\rangle_\pm$ and $|1\rangle_\pm$ are the $n_\pm = 0$ and $n_\pm = 1$ states, respectively. This state corresponds precisely to the plane-polarization state, $|h\rangle = |\pi/2, 0\rangle$, for a single photon in the analysis we have just described, and so the results of that calculation may be taken over directly. If $\gamma_\pm$ are the complex amplitudes of the classical fields generated by the two amplifiers, we can write the probability distribution for those amplitudes, according to equation 82, as

$$P(\gamma_+, \gamma_-, t|\psi) = P\left(\gamma_+, \gamma_-, t\left|\frac{\pi}{2}, 0\right.\right)$$

$$= \frac{1}{2\pi \mathcal{N}^3}|\gamma_+ + \gamma_-|^2 \exp\left\{-\frac{|\gamma_+|^2 + |\gamma_-|^2}{\mathcal{N}}\right\}. \qquad (84)$$

This result shows us immediately that the two amplifiers will have positively correlated outputs; they will, to some degree, tend to radiate coherently, and thus to create fringe patterns on the screen.

How do we calculate the intensity of the light on the screen? We can assume that the fields emitted by the two amplifiers are nearly parallel plane waves, and then try to recall the geometric approximations that we used so often as students. When the pinholes are a distance d apart, the screen is at a distance ℓ, and we observe at a point x on the screen, as opposed to the central point (see FIGURE 12), we find that the waves arriving from the two amplifiers undergo shifts of phase by $\pm\pi dx/\lambda\ell$.

When a single photon enters the system and the output fields of the amplifiers have amplitudes γ_+ and γ_-, the intensity on the screen will be proportional to

$$I(x, \gamma_+, \gamma_-) = |\gamma_+ \exp(i\pi dx/\lambda\ell) + \gamma_- \exp(-i\pi dx/\lambda\ell)|^2. \tag{85}$$

We should emphasize that this is an intensity distribution for an entire interference pattern, and not a probability distribution for the appearance of a single photon on the screen. A single photon arriving at the front end of our system produces an intense, classical interference pattern on the distant screen. (In fact, we would even find an interference pattern there, in general, when no photon arrives.)

To the extent that the amplitudes γ_+ and γ_- are more or less random variables, the interference pattern of equation 85 will also have some random features. It will always contain parallel intensity fringes, unless one or the other of $\gamma_\pm$ happens to vanish, but the fringes will shift in position from one repetition of the experiment to another. The fringes, furthermore, will usually not have the strong contrast typical of Young's experiment. The intensity has no zeroes unless $|\gamma_+| = |\gamma_-|$.

When we repeat the experiment many times, the random fringe system will have the average intensity,

$$I(x) = \int |\gamma_+ e^{i\pi dx/\lambda\ell} + \gamma_- e^{-i\pi dx/\lambda\ell}|^2 P(\gamma_+, \gamma_-, t|\psi) \, d^2\gamma_+ d^2\gamma_-$$

$$= 2\left(1 + \cos^2 \frac{\pi dx}{\lambda\ell}\right). \tag{86}$$

Taking the average, in other words, leaves us with Young's fringe pattern set against a constant background intensity. That constant background, of course, is the intensity due to spontaneous emission noise. It is just the average intensity we would find for the random fringes generated when no photon enters the system. The average visibility of the fringes when a photon does enter is

$$\mathcal{V}(x) = \frac{I_{max} - I_{min}}{I_{max} + I_{min}} = \frac{1}{3}. \tag{87}$$

This result corresponds, loosely speaking, to a mixture of all three of the wrong guesses we listed earlier, and probably some others as well. In any case, it does not correspond at all closely to the guess Schrödinger would have made by means of the same reasoning he used for his cat. The final state with an amplified wave coming from the upper amplifier and none from the lower one could correspond, according to Schrödinger's picture, to finding the cat alive, and the opposite configuration to finding the cat dead. The actual state of the amplified fields, however, is far from being Schrödinger's superposition of those two states. It is not any pure state at all; in the coherent state representation, it is a Gaussian mixture with an enormous variance. In the n-quantum state representation, it is a quasi-diagonal mixture with a vast dispersion too. The error in this projection of Schrödinger's argument is its omission of the effects of noise, and the noise in unavoidable; it is there for intrinsically quantum mechanical reasons.

It is occasionally said that quantum mechanics deals only with averages taken over ensembles of experiments, but here we have an explicit counterexample. The outputs of our amplifiers and the appearance of the fringes on the screen vary greatly from one repetition of the experiment to another, but they are all observable individually. In addition, we have no trouble measuring them without disturbing them in any way. In any one repetition, for example, the amplifiers may give us the two amplitudes, γ_+ and γ_-. The visibility of the set of fringes that results is then

$$\mathcal{V}(\gamma_+, \gamma_-) = \frac{2|\gamma_+||\gamma_-|}{|\gamma_+|^2 + |\gamma_-|^2}. \tag{88}$$

This expression only takes on the value one, which expresses strong fringe contrast, when the two amplitudes $\gamma_\pm$ are equal in modulus.

The question that always fascinates us about Young's experiment is: Which pinhole did the photon really go through? We can, in fact, say something about that in the present version of the experiment. If it should turn out in one repetition of the experiment that $|\gamma_+|$ is far larger than $|\gamma_-|$, we would have a certain indication that the photon went through the upper pinhole and amplifier rather than the lower ones. Of course, we can only make such a statement on a probabilistic basis. The way to make it is to use Bayes' theorem again to define the probability $P(+|\gamma_+, \gamma_-)$ that the photon passed through the upper pinhole, given that the two field amplitudes are $\gamma_\pm$. The result, you can easily see, is

$$P(+|\gamma_+, \gamma_-) = \frac{|\gamma_+|^2}{|\gamma_+|^2 + |\gamma_-|^2}. \tag{89}$$

Let us abbreviate the two probabilities $P(\pm|\gamma_+, \gamma_-)$ as $p_\pm$ so that we have

$$p_\pm = \frac{|\gamma_\pm|^2}{|\gamma_+|^2 + |\gamma_-|^2}. \tag{90}$$

The product of these probabilities, according to equation 89, is proportional to the square of the fringe visibility:

$$p_+ p_- = (\tfrac{1}{4})\mathcal{V}^2. \tag{91}$$

An alternative way of phrasing the same relation is to write

$$(p_+ - p_-)^2 = \left\{ \frac{|\gamma_+|^2 - |\gamma_-|^2}{|\gamma_+|^2 + |\gamma_-|^2} \right\}^2 = 1 - \mathcal{V}^2. \tag{92}$$

Both of these relations show that when we have any degree of certainty about which way the photon went (i.e., $p_\pm = 1$), the fringe contrast, $\mathcal{V}$, goes to zero. It is only when we have no inkling of which way the photon went (i.e., $p_+ = p_- = \tfrac{1}{2}$) that we can see fringes with strong contrast, $\mathcal{V} = 1$. Complementarity, in short, has won again. The incident photon can behave either as a particle or a wave, but it never exhibits both extremes of behavior at once. What one usually sees is neither the one behavior nor the other, and equations 91 and 92 describe a whole continuum of possible compromises.

Young's experiment could be a bit difficult, in practice, to carry out with two amplifiers. The pinholes, after all, must be quite close together and the space available for the amplifiers is rather cramped. There are other interference experiments, however, in which the geometry is less constraining. Plenty of room would be available for the amplifiers in the two arms of an interferometer, for example, and one might entertain the hope of using their outputs to determine which arm a photon actually entered. A suggestion of just such an experiment, using a single amplifier in one arm of

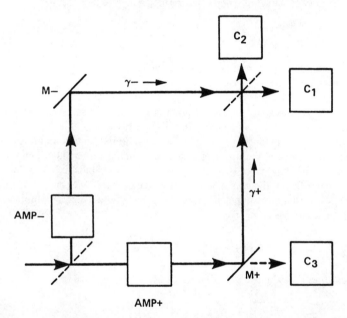

FIGURE 13. Proposed setup for the inclusion of an amplifier in each arm of a Mach-Zehnder interferometer. When the mirror M_+ is made partially transparent, detection of photons by counter C_3 and measurement of C_1-C_3 and C_2-C_3 coincidences furnish information on the path chosen by the incident photon.

a Mach-Zehnder interferometer, has been made recently by Gozzini.[16] That arrangement, with a second amplifier added in the other arm, is shown in FIGURE 13. Placing the photodetectors, C_1, C_2, and C_3, in the positions shown and letting the mirror M_+ be slightly transparent make it possible to carry out several interesting experiments.

If the geometry is such that the two interferometer paths are precisely symmetric, and if the amplifiers were absent, then the detector C_1 would register photons, while C_2 would detect none. The two waves reaching the latter would interfere destructively.

When the amplifiers are present, we may assume that their outputs are described in precisely the same way as in Young's experiment. In other words, the two output fields have random amplitudes, γ_+ and γ_-, that are governed by the probability distribution in equation 84.

The total field amplitude at the counter C_1, we may assume, is proportional to the symmetric sum $(1/\sqrt{2})\,(\gamma_1 + \gamma_2)$, while that at the counter C_2 is the antisymmetric sum $(1/\sqrt{2})\,(\gamma_1 - \gamma_2)$. Then, the average counting rates at the two counters will be

$$I_{C_1} = \{\tfrac{1}{2}|\gamma_+ + \gamma_-|^2\}_{\text{av.}} = 2\mathcal{N}(t), \tag{93}$$

$$I_{C_2} = \{\tfrac{1}{2}|\gamma_+ - \gamma_-|^2\}_{\text{av.}} = \mathcal{N}(t). \tag{94}$$

The effects of spontaneous emission noise are again evident in these results; they provide a nonvanishing intensity for C_2 and contribute two-thirds of the total intensity recorded by the two detectors.

Making the mirror M_+ slightly transparent and placing the detector C_3 behind it offers an interesting, if somewhat sneaky, way of trying to determine which of the two interferometer paths the incident photon actually took. If the amplifiers were noiseless, the detection of any light by C_3 would mean the initial photon penetrated the first beam-splitter and set out on the route we have labeled $+$. The amplitude γ_- would then be zero, and the counters C_1 and C_2 would receive equal amplitudes $(1/\sqrt{2})\,\gamma_+$. The coincidence rate of C_1 and C_3, in other words, would be equal to the coincidence rate of C_2 and C_3. Deviations from that prediction, it has been suggested, might then mean that there was still some interference involving a pilot wave or other mysterious goings-on in the half of the interferometer that the photon avoided.

We do expect the prediction of equal coincidence rates to prove false, but that is because the amplifiers are anything but noiseless. A signal recorded by C_3 does not tell us uniquely which path the original photon took. The actual C_1-C_3 coincidence rate is proportional to

$$\{\tfrac{1}{2}|\gamma_+ + \gamma_-|^2\,|\gamma_+|^2\}_{\text{av.}} = 4\mathcal{N}^2, \tag{95}$$

while the C_2-C_3 rate is proportional to

$$\{\tfrac{1}{2}|\gamma_+ - \gamma_-|^2\,|\gamma_+|^2\}_{\text{av.}} = 2\mathcal{N}^2. \tag{96}$$

The two rates are not equal; the C_1-C_3 rate is twice the C_2-C_3 rate. That should not be too difficult a result to verify experimentally.

ACKNOWLEDGMENTS

I would like to thank Philip Pearle for bringing the superluminal communication problem to my attention, and E. R. Pike and his staff for considerable editorial help.

REFERENCES

1. EINSTEIN, A., B. PODOLSKY & N. ROSEN. 1935. Phys. Rev. **47:** 777.
2. HERBERT, N. 1982. Found. Phys. **12:** 1171.
3. SCHRÖDINGER, E. 1935. Naturwissenschaften **23:** 807, 823, 844.
4. GLAUBER, R. J. 1969. *In* Quantum Optics. Proceedings of the Enrico Fermi International School of Physics, Course 42. R. J. Glauber, Ed.: 32. Academic Press. New York.

5. GLAUBER, R. J. 1966. Phys. Lett. **21:** 650.
6. GLAUBER, R. J. 1963. Phys. Rev. **131:** 2766.
7. WEISSKOPF, V. & E. WIGNER. 1930. Z. Phys. **63:** 54.
8. I have presented descriptions of this model for an amplifier at several conferences: University of Texas Workshop on Irreversible Processes in Quantum Mechanics and Quantum Optics, San Antonio, March 14–18, 1982; GLAUBER, R. J. 1983. *In* Group Theoretical Methods in Physics. Proceedings of the International Seminar, Zvenigorod, November, 24–26, 1982. Vol. II, p. 165. Nauka. Moscow; 1985. *In* Group Theoretical Methods in Physics. Vol. I, p. 137. Harwood Academic Publishers; 1986. *In* Proceedings of the VIth International School on Coherent Optics, Ustron, Poland, September 19–26, 1985. In press. The inverted oscillator has also been used in connection with a laser model and with a different coupling by: SCHWABL, F. & W. THIRRING. 1964. Ergeb. Exakten Naturwiss. **36:** 219.
9. CAHILL, K. E. & R. J. GLAUBER. 1969. Phys. Rev. **177:** 1882 (in particular, equations 3.21 and 3.22 on p. 1887).
10. See, for example: MOLLOW, B. R. & R. J. GLAUBER. 1967. Phys. Rev. **160:** 1076 (in particular, the appendix, p. 1096).
11. CAVES, C. 1981. Phys. Rev. **D23:** 1693.
12. GLAUBER, R. & F. HAAKE. 1978. Phys. Lett. **68A:** 29.
13. BORN, M. & E. WOLF. 1980. Principles of Optics, 6th ed., p. 31. Pergamon. Oxford/New York.
14. WOOTTERS, W. K. & W. H. ZUREK. 1982. Nature **299:** 802.
15. MANDEL, L. 1983. Nature **304:** 188.
16. GOZZINI, A. 1984. *In* The Wave-Particle Dualism. S. Diner *et al.,* Eds.: 129. Reidel. Dordrecht.

Reality and Quantum Mechanics

FRITZ ROHRLICH

Department of Physics
Syracuse University
Syracuse, New York 13244

THE PROBLEM OF REALITY

Why should we physicists worry about reality? We do not even know exactly what it means, and in any case, it does not belong in science. This is a problem for philosophers.

These words may be a common response to the title of the present paper. At the same time, particle physicists would strongly protest the assertion that electrons or protons may not really exist and may be only a fiction of the imagination of theoretical physicists. Like most scientists, they would rather embrace Einstein's statement that "the belief in an external world independent of the perceiving subject is the basis of all natural science."

Therefore, for the present purpose, let us adopt this as our definition of "real": an object is real if it actually and objectively exists independent of our attempt to observe it. Physics then deals with a real world and theoretical physics searches for the laws underlying this real world. What else would physical theory be about?

All this is quite noncontroversial as long as we deal with classical physics. However, in quantum physics we are usually taught otherwise. Here, the interpretation varies from more extreme to less extreme forms. A typical opposition to the realistic view just expressed is most dramatically portrayed by the frequently quoted assertion that "reality is created by the observer." There are also weaker statements that contradict our notion of reality. For example, Bohr often emphasized that the quantum system and the measuring apparatus form an epistemologically irreducible whole: the properties of a quantum system can be described meaningfully only in relation to the apparatus that is used to measure it. The object that is measured and the measuring apparatus thus merge into an indivisible whole that makes it impossible to ascribe independent existence to the object.

As a result, most physicists, especially those not particularly concerned with such issues, develop a somewhat schizophrenic view. On the one hand, they accept all of the Copenhagen interpretation, including the epistemological irreducibility of system and observer. On the other hand, they insist on the reality of quantum systems even when these are not observed.

Some people have expressed the hope that an interpretation of quantum mechanics along essentially classical lines might be possible, and they have suggested alternatives to the Copenhagen interpretation. Such expectations have largely been shattered[1] in recent years by the series of EPR-Bohm experiments culminating in the ones by Aspect and collaborators.[2] Thus, an interpretation along the notion of classical reality is pretty well excluded.

Can one, then, modify the Copenhagen interpretation so that it becomes consistent with a realist (though nonclassical) view of nature? This is the problem that we want to address: we do not wish to argue here that a realist interpretation is preferable to the Copenhagen interpretation; rather, we wish to show that such a realist interpretation is possible and is not excluded by empirical evidence or by the mathematical formalism of quantum mechanics, which is well established. As already indicated, however, to this end one must abandon classical realism in the quantum domain and adopt instead a new view of reality that I shall call "quantum reality." Both classical and quantum reality are consistent with the definition of reality that was adopted earlier.

I suspect that what I shall have to say in the following pages has all been said before. However, in view of the considerable divergence of opinions on this subject, I believe that it is desirable to present the argument in this way.[3]

BLURRED VARIABLES

When one compares quantum mechanics with classical mechanics in their canonical forms, one difference is immediately apparent. A classical system with n degrees of freedom in configuration space has $2n$ variables in phase-space and is dynamically characterized by $2n$ first-order differential equations. Completeness requires the exact specification of all $2n$ variables at some initial time. The analogous system in quantum mechanics also involves these $2n$ "variables" (although they are now represented by operators). These "variables" are all observables. However, their canonical commutator algebra now contains n noncommuting pairs among them so that, at most, n of them can have (sharp) values simultaneously. The other half of the observables are "blurred." Nevertheless, the system is specified completely by only those that commute with one another, that is, by only half the number of variables that are needed in the classical case. The dynamics preserves this number.

Many of the problems of interpretation have their origin in this situation: the complete commuting set of observables (CCSO) characterizing a state prevents a large number of observables (those that do not commute with them) from being sharp. What are we to make of all those blurred observables?

Blurring of an observable does not mean that we just do not know what its value is while the actual state of the system is in a definite value of that observable. Rather, blurring means that there is a probability distribution of values for that observable so that if it is measured in a large number of identical systems, different values are obtained according to the predictable distribution; it also means, furthermore, that the system is not in any one of these values prior to the measurement, but attains one of them as it interacts with the apparatus during the measuring process. This has been established experimentally.[4]

The simplest example is a spin-½ system in a pure state with spin in the $+z$-direction. The spin in the x-direction is then blurred so that its measurement will yield either $+\frac{1}{2}$ or $-\frac{1}{2}$ with equal probabilities. However, it is not correct to surmise that if one had an ensemble, half of it would have x-component $+\frac{1}{2}$ and the other half $-\frac{1}{2}$. The state is not a mixture; instead, it is a pure state. There is no (definite) value for that observable until the measurement interaction takes place.

We deduce from this that blurring is a new irreducible notion that does not exist in the classical domain of physics. It is an *ontic* characteristic of quantum systems; it is not just a matter of incomplete knowledge on our part.

This being so, one wonders what this implies for the actual existence of quantum systems. Are they therefore not real? Is their existence in doubt because of this novel feature of blurred properties? The answer is clearly "no" once blurring is accepted as ontic. Thus, we have here the first difference between classical and quantum reality.

QUANTUM SYSTEMS

Bohr was very much aware of the linguistic problem posed by the fact that the denotative use of words brings with it their connotative meaning. Thus, words such as "particles" and "waves" have connotative meanings that are deduced from our classical experience and that do not fit quantum objects. Perhaps the most obvious difference is the one just mentioned: quantum objects lack definite values for all those observables that do not commute with the CCSO characterizing the system. For that reason, some people made up special words for the objects of quantum physics.[5] We shall use the term "quantum particles" in contradistinction to "classical particles."

The question concerning the actual existence of systems in which half or more of the classically sharp properties are blurred is aggravated by the fact that the state of a given quantum system can be changed (that is, prepared to be in a state associated with a CCSO different from the earlier one). In that case, some or all of the previously sharp observables will become blurred and previously blurred observables will become sharp. One can transform a state from one characterized by one CCSO to one characterized by a different CCSO. It seems that one cannot count on observables to be sharp all the time. However, in that case, one cannot use observables to specify a physical system such as a quantum particle. What, then, can be used for an unambiguous identification?

Let us examine this question a little further. First, we note that we do not use the position or velocity of a particle for identification purposes even in classical physics. These properties are incidental and not characteristic of the particle. Rather, we usually identify a particle by its mass and by its charge. However, mass and charge are phenomenological parameters in both classical mechanics and quantum mechanics.[6] They are not represented by observables that are operators in quantum mechanics, and they always have the same parametric values. There is therefore no difficulty in those cases.

However, more sophisticated situations exist. Spin is one of the important identifying properties and that observable is surely represented by an operator, $\hat{s}$, say. Again, we know that for a particle of spin s, the operator $\hat{s}^2$ is always a member of any CCSO. A spin s particle remains a spin s particle until its annihilation.

This is, in fact, a special case of a much more general situation. The Hilbert space of quantum mechanics is broken up into incoherent subspaces that do not allow transitions between them (superselection rules). The quantum numbers characterizing each subspace of this nature are also the quantum numbers that identify quantum systems. All the other observable properties are incidental. Most importantly, only these incidental properties may be blurred; the observables governed by superselection rules are always sharp. This then is exactly what matters for the unambiguous identification of quantum systems. The reality of these systems can therefore be based on the superselected observables.

On a more sophisticated level than nonrelativistic quantum mechanics (for example, in quantum field theory), mass and charge are also represented by operators. In that case, their eigenvalues are part of the set that characterizes the incoherent subspaces. On this higher level, the incoherent subspaces continue to identify quantum particles, while those properties that can blur continue to be irrelevant in this respect.

Equally important is the fact that the mass and charge operators commute with the Hamiltonian, and the fact that these three operators are part of every physical CCSO. It follows that the sharp properties of mass and charge are preserved throughout the motion of the quantum particle. We can thus conclude that blurring does not prevent one from identifying quantum systems unambiguously.[7] In that respect, blurring does not stand in the way of a realistic interpretation.

NONSEPARABILITY

While the absence of certain properties due to quantum mechanical blurring is sufficient reason to distinguish between classical and quantum systems, nonseparability is even more so. This is the characteristically quantum mechanical phenomenon in which our notion of two or more noninteracting and seemingly spatially separated systems can be seriously in error. This can arise, for example, as a consequence of the indistinguishability of quantum particles and the associated symmetric or antisymmetric property of the wave function. In these and other cases, the superposition principle results in phase relations between seemingly separated particles, thereby producing one single spread-out (nonlocal) system. The integrity of that system as a nonseparable entity (in fact, its holistic character) is well established experimentally, for example, by statistical correlations that cannot be accounted for in any classical way. I shall cite three very different experiments indicative of this holistic character:

(a) The well-known EPR-Bohm experiments.[2] In these, one probes two simultaneously created quantum particles that are in a singlet state (usually two photons or two electrons). However, these two particles are also in a holistic two-particle state: observation of either one of them destroys the holistic character of that system by breaking the phase relation between the particles; it transforms that single two-particle system into two actually separate particles.

(b) Experiments with the neutral K system.[8] The creation of a K° and a $\overline{K}^\circ$ provides a correlation in the lifetimes of these particles. The regeneration experiments demonstrate how a K° beam is gradually transformed into a K_L beam and back to a K° beam. K° is the holistic system of a K_s and a K_L, and a K_L is the holistic system of a K° and a $\overline{K}^\circ$. The 2π decay of the K_s turns K° into K_L, and the absorption of the $\overline{K}^\circ$ turns K_L into K°.

(c) The Hanbury Brown–Twiss experiment.[9] It probes the correlations of the intensity fluctuations at two different points of a plane wave front. The quantum mechanical nature of these correlations is introduced through the photoelectric effect in the two photodetectors located at these two points.

These correlations are of great practical value in astronomy; however, they are also equally valuable for the fundamental conceptual understanding of quantum mechanics: they provide a measure of the degree of coherence of the photons. The correlation appears in terms of a diffraction pattern when the output of the photodetectors are combined. It is, in this sense, similar to the double-slit experiment. The epistemic fact of coherence goes hand in hand with ontic nonseparability.

The counterintuitive nature of the results of these experiments is quite striking. Is it, therefore, not reasonable to object to an interpretation that insists on an ontic nature of nonseparability? Is it not preposterous to expect one to believe that our change in knowledge about a system goes hand in hand with a change in its actual being? Could there not be a more detailed structure that has so far escaped our observation?

There is no doubt that the logical possibility for such a detailed structure exists. Postulating its existence is very much in the spirit of Einstein's view on quantum mechanics also expressed in the EPR paper:[10] conventional quantum mechanics is incomplete and would be amended by a future development of the theory. Thus, it is in this spirit that David Bohm suggested a hidden variables theory. Of course, in view of the experimental evidence we now have, such a theory must be necessarily nonlocal. Most physicists today, however, find such a theory unconvincing in the face of its complete lack of empirical support. In fact, no experiment has to my knowledge even been suggested that would provide empirical evidence of such a detailed structure.

On the other extreme, one can maintain the view that one should believe only the actually observed phenomena and one should accept the theoretical mechanism explaining it only as a logical bridge relating experimental results. There is no necessity to attach credence to those mechanisms: the theoretical entities associated with them should not be required to refer to actually existing objects (empiricist-instrumentalist view). An extreme consequence of such a view is the denial of reality, or at least the suspension of the belief in quantum particles such as photons or electrons.

If one rejects both the hidden variables and the empiricist-instrumentalist view, the empirical evidence forces one into the realist view of an ontic nonseparability concomitant with a nonlocal, spread-out quantum system.

MEASUREMENTS

Every observation requires an interaction between the system observed, S, and the apparatus, A, that does the observing. For physicists, this is a trivial remark because they are all aware that even seeing involves the reception of photons by A, the eye, that were either created or reflected by S, the object. The essential difference in that respect between classical and quantum physics lies in the way in which this interaction is taken into account. In the classical case, it is a one-way process only—S affects A; in the quantum case, it is a two way process—S affects A and A affects S—thus doing justice to the actual situation rather than ignoring the effect of A on S, which is a good approximation only classically. This has the dire consequence of changing the system whenever an observation is made; the quantum system S is, in general, not left in its initial state just as A is not.

As a result of this situation, we seem to find that the measurement outcome depends on the entire experimental setup. That is what is meant by the epistemological irreducibility of the *S-A* interaction. As Bohr emphasized repeatedly, it is the entire setup that determines the CCSO of the final state. Today, after we have lost some of the fear of analyzing the very complex *S-A* interaction, we are not willing to settle for only irreducibility and would demand that a full account of that interaction is necessary. Realism rejects a muddling of subject and object.

As if irreducibility were not enough of a jolt to the classical epistemology of the measurement process, the most severe shock has come with the realization that the interaction between *S*, a quantum system, and *A*, a classical system, apparently also involves a process that is irreversible, discontinuous, and noncausal. This "projection postulate" (von Neumann's type I process) or "collapse of the wave function" seems to exacerbate greatly the difficulties encountered by a realistic interpretation.

According to some interpretations, the observer as a person (with a mind and a consciousness) plays a key role. I wish to oppose this view emphatically. A measurement is not a measurement unless and until it has produced an irreversible record in the measuring apparatus (which is assumed to be a classical object). The reading of that change by the human observer is quite a separate process. It occurs at a different point in both space and time and is in no way directly linked to the *A-S* interaction. Furthermore, it occurs only after the quantum-classical link in which the particular quantity that is being measured has been "amplified" to a classical scale. The observer as a person can therefore certainly not be a part of the measuring process.

The presumed "epistemological irreducibility" of the *S-A* interaction is at least in large part due to the mistaken belief that the "cut" between the quantum system and the classical apparatus is quite arbitrary. In fact, the cut between the first permanent record and whatever happens thereafter in the measuring process can be localized quite accurately. That cut is certainly not arbitrary. The famous example of Schrödinger's cat may serve as a demonstration.

The spontaneous decay of an unstable nucleus is recorded and this recording device triggers a relay that through further gadgetry eventually kills the cat. While the death of the cat can certainly be used as evidence of that decay, and in that sense, the cat serves as a measuring apparatus, the transition from quantum mechanical interactions to classical interactions takes place in the recording device. Beyond that point, all interactions take place between classical objects. The description of a cat as a quantum mechanical pure state (a superposition of live and dead cat) is therefore nonsensical.

It is thus perfectly possible to distinguish the quantum system from the (classical) apparatus and to associate to both of them real existence. Quantum systems also interact with classical systems when we do not make observations, and the corresponding changes of state still take place. There is no reason whatever to deny real existence to quantum systems when they are not being observed. The observer does not create reality and nor does the apparatus. The change of the quantum system *S* as a result of the *S-A* interaction is not a "creation of reality."

The key process underlying the "collapse" is a breaking of quantum mechanical phase relations (and in general, the formation of other phase relations). For the quantum system, that break is necessary in order to change from one CCSO to another. The parts of a classical object are not phase-related; nonseparability does not exist in the classical world. How this breaking of phase relations takes place is not fully understood, but it has been proven to be a development that is not unitary.[11] It can therefore not be produced by the Schrödinger equation with a self-adjoint Hamiltonian. However, a Hamiltonian that is not self-adjoint is only an attempt to describe the actual interactions in an effective way in the presence of external influences (open systems). If they could have been described completely in terms of a closed system, the development would have to be unitary.

The collapse also involves a loss of information about the system and therefore increases its entropy. In this respect, the situation resembles statistical mechanics where "coarse-graining" also leads to irreversibility.

What is essential for the present argument, however, is that none of this prevents one at present from maintaining a realist interpretation of the measurement process. In fact, the localization of the "collapse" in the chain of events in a measurement process helps to demystify that process and to eliminate the subject-object confusion. Of course, pending a full clarification of the "collapse," we cannot rule out that future developments could prevent a realist interpretation.

In addition, the indeterministic nature of the measurement outcome does not affect realism. A clear distinction then must be made here between realism and determinism. We certainly do not question reality in deterministic chaotic classical systems where predictability fails because of the extreme sensitivity to the initial conditions. While physicists know that a detailed classical mechanics exists for dice or roulette wheels, that knowledge does not play a decisive role for everyone's belief in the reality of these objects even during their unpredictable motions. Thus, determinism is not essential for a belief in reality.

Einstein was much less concerned with the lack of determinism in quantum mechanics than he was with its violation of realism in the conventional interpretation. It is clear, however, that his form of realism, a form of classical realism, cannot be maintained in quantum mechanics.

QUANTUM REALITY

Scientific realism can be characterized by the general assertion that scientific theory is about nature and not only about our knowledge about nature. When applied specifically to quantum mechanics, I call it quantum realism. This interpretation of quantum mechanics rejects statements such as: there is no quantum world; there is only an abstract quantum physical description.[12] Quantum realism claims that quantum mechanics is more than a theoretical formalism that serves as a pragmatic computational tool permitting correct predictions of experimental outcomes.[13] Rather, it claims that quantum mechanics refers to actually existing objects in nature and describes their behavior. The fact that this behavior is different from that of classical objects in essential ways should not be surprising; we have no experience in that world far removed from our senses. In any case, this "weird" behavior cannot be sufficient grounds for arguing the quantum world out of existence.

We thus conclude that a realist interpretation of quantum mechanics is at least at present not excluded either by experiments or by its mathematical structure. However, there is a price to pay for it.

Realism as the belief in the existence of an external world independent of an observer can be maintained in the quantum domain as well as in the classical domain.

However, what real objects are like is quite different in these two areas. In particular, the classical world involves localizability of objects and provides, in general, sharp values of all variables. Any blurring in classical physics is statistical and can be accounted for, in principle, because it is associated with sharp substructures. In contradistinction, in the quantum world we are forced to accept blurring as a fundamental ontic feature that, in principle, cannot be accounted for by averaging over sharp substructures. Quantum objects with blurred features therefore really exist.

Another difference lies in the property of nonseparability. Two or more dynamically independent (noninteracting) parts of a quantum system (particles as constituents of that system) can occur in an entangled way that is linked statistically as expressed by phase relations. This linkage is a direct consequence of the superposition principle that is thus responsible for one of the most important distinctions between quantum and classical physics. Its absence in classical physics insures the absence of nonseparability.

Classical physics therefore permits a characterization of reality such as the one given in the EPR paper, whereas quantum reality, with its blurring and nonseparability, requires a different characterization. There is no way of getting around that. We learned this lesson most recently from the Paris experiments.

This concludes the argument of the present paper; I sketched, within the limited space available, that a properly understood realism can be maintained consistently for the interpretation of quantum mechanics. That this realism requires an unintuitive picture of quantum objects may be deplorable, but can hardly be a sound reason for its rejection. That quantum realism is actually preferable over other interpretations of quantum mechanics must be left to discussions elsewhere.

ACKNOWLEDGMENT

I want to thank Abner Shimony for helpful comments to an earlier version of this paper.

NOTES AND REFERENCES

1. We exclude (nonlocal) hidden variables theories.
2. The papers on the Paris experiments (ASPECT, A. *et al.* 1982. Phys. Rev. Lett. **49:** 91 and 1804) provide references to earlier experiments.
3. The extensive literature on scientific realism can be reached through two recent publications: LEPLIN, J., Ed. 1984. Scientific Realism. Univ. of California Press. Berkeley, California; BUNGE, M. 1985. Treatise on Basic Philosophy, vol. 7. Reidel. Dordrecht. See also: ROHRLICH, F. 1985 (June). Schrödinger's criticism of quantum mechanics—fifty years later. Symposium on Foundations of Modern Physics: Fifty Years of the Einstein-Podolsky-Rosen Gedankenexperiment. Joensuu, Finland, 1985. P. Lahti & P. Mittelstaedt, Eds.: 555–572. World Scientific. Singapore.
4. WU, C. S. & I. SHAKOV. 1950. Phys. Rev. **77:** 136.
5. For example, "quanton."
6. We consider here only nonrelativistic theories.
7. The indistinguishability of quantum particles is, of course, to be taken into account.
8. A similar discussion was first given by: DAY, T. B. 1961. Phys. Rev. **121:** 1204.

9. HANBURY BROWN, R. & R. Q. TWISS. 1957. Proc. R. Soc. London Ser. **A242:** 300 and
    A243: 291; MANDEL, L. 1963. Prog. in Optics II. North-Holland. Amsterdam.
10. EINSTEIN, A., B. PODOLSKY & N. ROSEN. 1935. Phys. Rev. **47:** 777.
11. SHIMONY, A. 1974. Phys. Rev. **D9:** 2321.
12. PETERSON, A. 1963. Bull. At. Sci. **19:** 8; 1968. Quantum Physics and the Philosophical
    Tradition. MIT Press. Cambridge, Massachusetts. Both sources claim that Niels Bohr
    has expressed this view.
13. STAPP, H. P. 1972. Am. J. Phys. **40:** 1098.

Probability in Quantum Mechanics

L. E. BALLENTINE

Department of Physics
Simon Fraser University
Burnaby, British Columbia V5A 1S6, Canada

INTRODUCTION

Probability plays a fundamental role in the interpretation of quantum mechanics, yet the concept and theory of probability are usually treated rather loosely and superficially. The textbooks on quantum mechanics do not demonstrate just how the axioms of probability theory are satisfied by the formalism of quantum mechanics. Moreover, it has sometimes been claimed that "classical" probability theory does not apply to quantum mechanics. In this paper, I shall review the axiomatic theory of probability, and show that quantum mechanics does satisfy those axioms. I shall examine some of the alleged contradictions between quantum mechanics and probability theory, which turn out to be based on misinterpretations of probability theory. Finally, I shall discuss the need for experimental tests of the probability postulates in quantum mechanics.

AXIOMATIC PROBABILITY THEORY

The mathematical content of the theory of probability concerns the properties of a function, $P(A|B)$, which may be read as "the probability of A conditional on B." A and B may be "events," in which case $P(A|B)$ is "the probability that event A will happen under the conditions specified by the occurrence of event B." Alternatively, A and B may be propositions, in which case $P(A|B)$ is "the probability that A is true given that B is true." For the sake of definiteness, I will use the language of events in this section.

It is desirable to treat sets of events as well as elementary events. Therefore, we introduce notations for certain composite events: $\sim A$ ("not A") denotes the nonoccurrence of A; $A \cdot B$ ("A and B") denotes the occurrence of both A and B; $A \vee B$ ("A or B") denotes the occurrence of at least one of the events, either A or B. For brevity, these sets of events will also be referred to as "events." The three operators ($\sim$, $\cdot$, $\vee$) are called negation, conjunction, and disjunction, respectively. In evaluation of complex expressions, the negation operator has the highest precedence. Thus, $\sim A \cdot B = (\sim A) \cdot B$, and $\sim A \vee B = (\sim A) \vee B$.

Several different, but mathematically equivalent forms of the axioms can be given.[1] The particular choice used here is influenced by the work of R. T. Cox,[2] who derives these quantitative axioms from more fundamental qualitative postulates:

$$0 \leq P(A|B) \leq 1, \tag{1}$$

$$P(A|A) = 1, \tag{2}$$

$$P(\sim A|B) = 1 - P(A|B), \tag{3a}$$

$$P(A \cdot B | C) = P(B | A \cdot C) P(A | C). \tag{4}$$

As will soon be shown, an alternative to axiom 3a is the rule of addition of probabilities for mutually exclusive events:

$$P(A \vee B | C) = P(A | C) + P(B | C). \tag{3b}$$

We say that A and B are mutully exclusive on condition C if $P(A \cdot B | C) = 0$.

Axiom 2 states the convention that the probability of a certainty (the occurrence of A given the occurrence of A) is one, and axiom 1 says that no probabilities are greater than the probability of a certainty. Axiom 3a expresses the intuitive notion that the probability of nonoccurrence of an event increases as the probability of its occurrence decreases. It also implies $P(\sim A | A) = 0$, which is to say, an impossible event (the nonoccurrence of A given that A occurs) has zero probability. Axiom 4 states that the probability that two events both occur (under some condition C) is equal to the probability of occurrence of one of the events multiplied by the probability of the second event given that the first event has occurred.

The probabilities of negation $(\sim A)$ and conjunction $(A \cdot B)$ of events each required an axiom. However, no further axioms are required to treat disjunction because $A \vee B = \sim(\sim A \cdot \sim B)$; in words, "$A$ or B" is equivalent to the negation of "neither A nor B." Thus, from axiom 3a, we have

$$P(A \vee B | C) = 1 - P(\sim A \cdot \sim B | C). \tag{5}$$

This can be evaluated from the existing axioms to yield (see APPENDIX A)

$$P(A \vee B | C) = P(A | C) + P(B | C) - P(A \cdot B | C), \tag{6}$$

of which axiom 3b is a special case. It is also possible to derive axiom 3a from axiom 3b (see APPENDIX B). We thus have two equivalent sets of axioms depending upon whether we use axiom 3a or 3b. The former is more elegant because it applies to all events, whereas axiom 3b applies only if A and B are mutually exclusive. Nevertheless, the latter is often used, and we shall see that it has certain advantages.

A very important concept in probability and its applications is that of independence of events. If $P(B | A \cdot C) = P(B | C)$, that is to say, if the occurrence of A has no influence on the probability of B, then we say that B is independent of A (under condition C). From axiom 4, we then obtain

$$P(A \cdot B | C) = P(B | C) P(A | C). \tag{7}$$

The symmetry of this formula implies that independence is a mutual relationship; if B is independent of A, then also A is independent of B. This notion is called statistical or stochastic independence in order to distinguish it from other notions such as causal independence.

INTERPRETATION OF PROBABILITY CONCEPTS

The abstract probability theory consisting of axioms, definitions, and theorems must be supplemented by an interpretation of the term, "probability." This provides the correspondence rule by means of which the abstract theory can be applied to practical problems. There are many different interpretations of probability because anything that satisfies the axioms may be regarded as a kind of probability. The various interpretations should not be viewed as rivals, but rather as being appropriate to different classes of problems.

For application to quantum mechanics, the propensity interpretation[3] is most appropriate. The probability, $P(A|C)$, is interpreted as a measure of the tendency, or propensity, of the physical conditions described by C to produce the result A. In this interpretation, probability is regarded as a characteristic of the physical situation C that may potentially give rise to a sequence of events, rather than as a property (frequency) of an actual sequence of events. This fact is emphasized by always writing probability in the conditional form, $P(A|C)$, and never merely as $P(A)$. Its relationship to frequency emerges, suitably qualified, in a theorem (the law of large numbers).

In addition to the probability, P, one must choose an interpretation of the arguments, A and C, of the function, $P(A|C)$. So far, we have spoken of them as being events, but one can also treat them as propositions. In many cases, the difference between the two interpretations is merely verbal. Corresponding to the event A is the proposition stating "event A has occurred."

Let A be the proposition stating "the position of the particle lies between q_1 and q_2." Let B be the proposition stating "the momentum of the particle lies between p_1 and p_2." Quantum mechanics provides a means of computing the probability that A is true, and also for computing the probability that B is true. However, it does not provide any formula for the probability that the compound proposition, $A \cdot B$ ("A and B"), is true. Whether or not it is a defect of the present formulation of quantum mechanics, this limitation can be reasonably accommodated when A and C are interpreted as events. In computing the probability, $P(A|C)$, of an event A, one must specify all the physical conditions C that are relevant. This may reasonably be held to include the configuration of any measuring apparatus because it can influence the outcome of an event. Because the apparatuses used to measure position are different from those used to measure momentum, one will be dealing with $P(A|C_q)$ and $P(B|C_p)$, where C_q includes the configuration of the position measuring device and C_p includes the configuration of the momentum measuring device. However, one has no occasion to consider events A (detection of position within a certain range) and B (detection of momentum within a certain range) under a common condition C, and so one does not need to compute $P(A \cdot B|C)$ in this case.

PROBABILITY AND FREQUENCY

Although no direct connection between frequency and probability is postulated in the propensity interpretation, a close connection emerges through a theorem known as the law of large numbers. The simplest form of this theorem (called the "weak law of large numbers") is as follows.

Consider an experiment E that may have outcome A, with probability, $P(A|E) = $ p. In a sequence of n identical independent repetitions of E (denoted E^n), the event A may occur m times ($0 \le m \le n$). We refer to $f = m/n$ as the frequency of outcome A in a realization of the experimental sequence, E^n. One expects, intuitively, that f should be close to p as n becomes large. In fact, the weak law of large numbers asserts that for any $\epsilon > 0$, $P(|f - p| \geq \epsilon \,|E^n)$ converges to zero as n tends to infinity. Thus, the probability that the frequency of A is more than ϵ away from p approaches zero as n becomes arbitrarily large. From the practical point of view, this is the most important theorem in probability theory because it establishes the connection between abstract probabilities and frequencies in observable data.

The full proof[4] of this theorem requires axioms 1, 2, and 3b, and the notion of independence (equation 7), but it does not need axiom 4. If, however, axiom 3a is used as an axiom, then axiom 4 will be needed in order to derive axiom 3b. This is one reason why axiom 3b may sometimes be a more convenient axiom that axiom 3a.

PROBABILITY IN QUANTUM MECHANICS

In quantum mechanics, a dynamical variable, R, is represented by a self-adjoint operator, **R**, whose eigenvalues are the possible values of R:

$$\mathbf{R}|r_n\rangle = r_n|r_n\rangle \tag{8}$$

According to a standard postulate of quantum mechanics, the probability of obtaining the particular value of R $= r_n$ is given by

$$P(\mathrm{R} = r_n|\Psi) = |\langle r_n|\Psi\rangle|^2, \tag{9}$$

which is for the simplest case of a discrete nondegenerate eigenvalue spectrum and a pure state represented by the vector Ψ. (All vectors here are assumed to have unit norms.) However, it is not sufficient to merely assert that certain mathematical expressions are probabilities unless it can be shown that they satisfy the mathematical theory of probability. In particular, we must verify that such expressions obey the four axioms of probability theory and, in appropriate circumstances, the independence property (equation 7).

The expression on the left-hand side of equation 9 can be read as "the probability that the dynamical variable, R, has the value, r_n, conditional on Ψ." The latter portion of this statement requires some comment because the state vector, Ψ, is not a physical object. Its significance is twofold. First, it is an abstract mathematical object from which the probability distributions of observable quantities can be calculated. Secondly, to assert that the state vector is Ψ can be regarded as implying that the system has undergone a corresponding state preparation procedure; this could be described in more detail, but all of the relevant information is contained in the specification of Ψ.

It is clear that equation 9 satisfies axiom 1 because this is a direct consequence of the Schwartz inequality. If the state vector is the eigenvector, $|\Psi\rangle = |r_n\rangle$, then equation 9 becomes $P(\mathrm{R} = r_n|r_n) = 1$, which is the equivalent of axiom 2. Axiom 3a follows from the additivity rule (axiom 3b). The events described by R $= r_1$, R $= r_2$, etc., are mutually exclusive, and the additivity rule, $P\{(\mathrm{R} = r_1) \vee (\mathrm{R} = r_2)|\Psi\} = |\langle r_1|\Psi\rangle|^2 + |\langle r_2|\Psi\rangle|^2$, holds almost by definition. We shall defer consideration of axiom 4 because it can be better treated by a more general formalism. If the system consists of two independent noninteracting components (which are only formally regarded as a single system), then the state vector can be written in the form, $|\Psi\rangle = |\Psi\rangle^{(a)} \otimes |\Psi\rangle^{(b)}$, where the superscripts refer to the two components. The joint probability distribution for the dynamical variables, $\mathrm{R}^{(a)}$ and $\mathrm{R}^{(b)}$, belonging to components, a and b, respectively, is

$$P(R^{(a)} = r_m, R^{(b)} = r_n | \Psi) = |\langle r_m | \Psi \rangle^{(a)}|^2 |\langle r_n | \Psi \rangle^{(b)}|^2, \qquad (10)$$

which is in full agreement with equation 7. We have now verified that the quantum mechanical postulate (equation 9) satisfies all the ingredients of probability theory that are needed to derive the law of large numbers. Indeed, if we interpreted the components, a and b, above as systems in the sequence of independent measurements, E^n (described in the previous section), we could recapitulate the derivation of the law of large numbers in the language of quantum mechanics.

The most general state description in quantum mechanics is by means of the state operator, ρ, which has unit trace, is self-adjoint, and is nonnegative definite:

$$\text{Tr } \rho = 1, \qquad (11)$$

$$\rho = \rho\dagger, \qquad (12)$$

$$\langle u | \rho | u \rangle \geq 0 \text{ for all vectors } u. \qquad (13)$$

In the special case of a pure state (represented above by the vector $|\Psi\rangle$), the state operator is $\rho = |\Psi\rangle \langle\Psi|$. Associated with any dynamical variable, R, is a family of projection operators, $M_R(\Delta)$, that are related to the eigenvalues and eigenvectors of equation 8 as follows:

$$M_R(\Delta) = \Sigma_{r_n \in \Delta} |r_n\rangle \langle r_n|, \qquad (14)$$

where the sum is over all eigenvectors (possibly degenerate) whose eigenvalues lie in the subset, Δ. The probability that the value of R will lie within Δ is postulated to be

$$P(R \in \Delta | \rho) = \text{Tr}\{\rho\, M_R(\Delta)\}. \qquad (15)$$

It is easily verified that the general form (equation 15) reduces to equation 9 in the appropriate special case.

We must now verify that equation 15 satisfies the axioms of probability theory. Axiom 1 follows directly from equation 11 and from the fact that $M_R(\Delta)$ is a projection operator. The analogue of axiom 2 is obtained if we chose a state prepared in such a manner that the value of R is guaranteed to lie within Δ. This will be so for those states that satisfy $\rho = M_R(\Delta)\rho M_R(\Delta)$, for which equation 15 is identically equal to the value of 1. Axiom 3a follows from the additivity rule (axiom 3b). To verify it, we consider two disjoint sets, Δ_1, and Δ_2, the union of which is denoted $\Delta_1 \cup \Delta_2$. Now, $(R \in \Delta_1) \vee (R \in \Delta_2)$ is equivalent to $R \in (\Delta_1 \cup \Delta_2)$. Because the two sets, Δ_1 and Δ_2, are disjoint, it follows that $M_R(\Delta_1)M_R(\Delta_2) = 0$, and the projection operator corresponding to the union of the sets is just the sum of the separate projection operators: $M_R(\Delta_1 \cup \Delta_2) = M_R(\Delta_1) + M_R(\Delta_2)$. Hence, it is clear that axiom 3b is satisfied. The factorization property (equation 7) follows, as did equation 10, from the factorization of the state function for two independent uncorrelated systems, $\rho = \rho^{(a)} \otimes \rho^{(b)}$. We have now verified that the general statistical postulate (equation 15) satisfies all of those parts of probability theory that are needed to derive the key theorem, namely, the law of large numbers.

The remaining axiom (no. 4) is not essential for most of the applications of probability in quantum mechanics (provided that axiom 3b replaces axiom 3a as an axiom), but it must be considered for completeness. Let R and S be two dynamical variables represented by the operators, $\mathbf{R}$ and $\mathbf{S}$, whose eigenvalues and eigenvectors are given by $\mathbf{R}|r_n\rangle = r_n|r_n\rangle$ and $\mathbf{S}|s_n\rangle = s_n|s_n\rangle$. The corresponding projection operators are denoted $\mathbf{M}_R(\Delta_a)$ and $\mathbf{M}_S(\Delta_b)$. Finally, let A denote the event of R taking on a value within the set Δ_a, and let B denote the event of S taking on a value within the set Δ_b. We must now evaluate each of the three probabilities in axiom 4 with the conditional event C being the preparation of a general state represented by ρ.

The joint probability on the left-hand side of axiom 4, $P(A \cdot B|\rho)$, can be evaluated from the formalism of quantum mechanics only if the operators, $\mathbf{R}$ and $\mathbf{S}$, are commutative (the corresponding projection operators, $\mathbf{M}_R$ and $\mathbf{M}_S$, then also being commutative). In that case, the product, $\mathbf{M}_R(\Delta_a)\mathbf{M}_S(\Delta_b)$, is also a projection operator, and the desired joint probability is given by equation 15 to be $P(A \cdot B|\rho) = \mathrm{Tr}\{\rho\mathbf{M}_R(\Delta_a)\mathbf{M}_S(\Delta b)\}$. However, there is no accepted formula in quantum mechanics for a joint probability distribution for dynamical variables whose operators do not commute.

On the right-hand side of axiom 4, the second factor, $P(A|\rho)$, is given directly by equation 15 with $\Delta = \Delta_a$. However, the first factor, $P(B|A \cdot \rho)$, requires careful interpretation. The second argument of the probability function, which we have called "the conditional event," must describe the actual physical conditions to which the probability (or "propensity") refers. It does not denote mere subjective information or personal belief. Therefore, just as ρ signifies that the system has undergone a certain state preparation, so $A \cdot \rho$ implies that the system has been subjected to additional filtering interactions that ensure that the value of R lies within Δ_a. In principle, one should analyze the dynamics of this process in detail in order to compute the resulting state function. However, if this filtering process does nothing but remove unacceptable values of R, then it is reasonable to represent its result by the projected and renormalized state operator,

$$\rho' = \mathbf{M}_R(\Delta_a)\rho\mathbf{M}_R(\Delta_a)/\mathrm{Tr}\{\mathbf{M}_R(\Delta_a)\rho\mathbf{M}_R(\Delta_a)\}.$$

One then obtains the following result for the right-hand side of equation 4:

$$P(B|A \cdot \rho)\,P(A|\rho) = \mathrm{Tr}\{\rho'\mathbf{M}_S(\Delta_b)\}\,\mathrm{Tr}\{\rho\mathbf{M}_R(\Delta_a)\}$$
$$= \mathrm{Tr}\{\mathbf{M}_R(\Delta_a)\rho\mathbf{M}_R(\Delta_a)\mathbf{M}_S(\Delta_b)\}.$$

If $\mathbf{M}_R$ commutes with $\mathbf{M}_S$, then this expression further reduces to

$$P(B|A \cdot \rho)\,P(A|\rho) = \mathrm{Tr}\{\rho\mathbf{M}_R(\Delta_a)\mathbf{M}_S(\Delta_b)\} = P(A \cdot B|\rho),$$

which is in agreement with axiom 4. Thus, we see that this last axiom of probability theory is obeyed by the formalism of quantum mechanics provided that the probability of the joint event, $A \cdot B$, is defined in the formalism. The restriction, in this case, to dynamical variables whose operators commute is not a restriction on the applicability of "classical" probability theory to quantum mechanics. It is rather a limitation of the formalism of quantum mechanics in that it does not assign meaning to the conjunction of arbitrary events. (See the discussion at the end of the third section of this paper.)

ERRONEOUS APPLICATIONS OF PROBABILITY THEORY IN QM

The Double Slit

This example has been repeated many times in slightly differing versions—the first of which may be that due to Feynman.[5] The experiment consists of a particle source, a screen with two slits (labeled #1 and #2) in it, and a detector. By moving the detector and measuring the particle count rate at various positions, one can measure the probability of a particle passing through the slit system and arriving at the point, X. If only slit #1 is open, the probability of detection at X is $P_1(X)$. If only slit #2 is open, the probability of detection at X is $P_2(X)$. If both slits are open, the probability of detection is $P_{12}(X)$. Now, passage through slit #1 and passage through slit #2 are certainly exclusive events, so one might expect, from axiom 3b, that $P_{12}(X)$ should be equal to $P_1(X) + P_2(X)$. However, experiment clearly shows that this is not true; hence, it might be concluded that rule 3b of probability theory does not hold in quantum mechanics.

In fact, the above argument draws its radical conclusion from an incorrect application of probability theory. One is well advised to beware of probability statements expressed in the form, $P(X)$, instead of $P(X|C)$. The second argument may be safely omitted only if the conditional event or information is clear from the context, and only if it is constant throughout the problem. This is not the case in the double slit example. The probability of detection at X in the first case (only slit #1 open) should be written as $P(X|C_1)$, where the conditional information, C_1, includes (at least) the state function, Ψ_1, for the particle beam and the screen state, S_1 (only slit #1 open). In the second case (only slit #2 open), the probability should be written as $P(X|C_2)$, where C_2 includes the state function, Ψ_2, for the particle beam and the screen state, S_2 (only slit #2 open). In the third case (both slits open), the probability is of the form $P(X|C_3)$, where C_3 includes the state function, Ψ_{12} (approximately equal to $\Psi_1 + \Psi_2$, but this fact plays no role in our argument), and the screen state, S_3 (both slits open). We observe from experiment that $P(X|C_3) \neq P(X|C_1) + P(X|C_2)$. This fact, however, has no bearing on the validity of rule 3b of probability theory. Essentially, this counter argument to Feynman was given by Koopman.[6]

The Superposition Fallacy

The following argument is taken from section 2.2 of the textbook by Trigg,[7] although other versions of it exist: "Classical probabilities are compounded according to the relation

$$P(B'|A') = \sum_{C'} P(B'|C') \, P(C'|A') \tag{16?}$$

where the summation is over all members C' of a set of non-overlapping states connecting A' and B'." It is then noted that in quantum mechanics, this relation is satisfied by amplitudes, $\langle B'|A'\rangle = \Sigma_{C'} \langle B'|C'\rangle \langle C'|A'\rangle$. Because the probabilities are the squares of the amplitudes, $P(B'|A') = |\langle B'|A'\rangle|^2$, it follows that equation 16? of the "classical theory" can hold only if the quantum interference terms are negligible.

There is no doubt that equation 16? fails to hold as written, but we must examine more closely its status with respect to probability theory. We may presume from the context that A', B', and C' denote events that can be characterized by unique values for certain corresponding dynamical variables. Moreover, we can presume that the set of possible values of C', say, is a mutually exclusive and exhaustive set. That is to say, no more than one such value can occur at a time (exclusive), and there are no possible outcomes in the relevant class of events other than one of the values from this set (exhaustive). Put yet another way, if the set $\{C_1, C_2, C_3, \cdots\}$ contains all possible values of C', then the disjunction of all those possibilities, $C_1 \vee C_2 \vee C_3 \vee \cdots$, is a certainty. In attempting to derive equation 16?, we make use of axiom 4 to obtain $P(B' \cdot C' | A') = P(B' | C' \cdot A') P(C' | A')$, and then sum over all possible values of C'. Because each of $B' \cdot C_1$, $B' \cdot C_2$, $\cdots$, are exclusive, it follows from axiom 3b that $\Sigma_{C'} P(B' \cdot C' | A') = P\{B' \cdot (C_1 \vee C_2 \vee C_3 \vee \cdots) | A'\} = P(B' | A')$. Therefore, the correct deduction from "classical" probability theory is

$$P(B' | A') = \sum_{C'} P(B' | C' \cdot A') P(C' | A'), \qquad (17)$$

rather than the questionable equation 16?

It is now apparent that the quantum mechanical superposition principle for amplitudes is not incompatible with the formalism of probability theory. It is also apparent that the contrary claim was based on an incorrect application of probability theory. The error in this example is very similar to that in the subsection entitled THE DOUBLE SLIT. In the former case, the conditional argument of the probability function was omitted, leading to an erroneous conclusion. In this case, only a part of the relevant conditional information was included by writing $P(B' | C')$ instead of $P(B' | C' \cdot A')$ in equation 16? That would be permissible only if it could be shown that the additional information was not relevant, which is evidently not the case.

Another example of an erroneous application of probability theory in quantum mechanics is discussed in reference 4, but the above examples are sufficient to illustrate the point that the most commonly alleged contradictions between quantum mechanics and probability theory have their origin in misinterpretations of probability theory.

EXPERIMENTAL TESTS

Although there must be thousands of experimental results that have been successfully interpreted by means of quantum theory, it is difficult to find experimental tests of the fundamental probabilistic postulates such as equations 9 and 15. The most familiar of such postulates is that the position probability density is given by $|\langle \vec{r} | \Psi \rangle|^2 = |\Psi(\vec{r})|^2$. Where is the evidence in support of this postulate? If we were to suppose the probability density to be equal to $|\Psi|^n$, then what limits are placed upon n by experiments? I do not know of any paper that addresses this fundamental question.

The situation is much more satisfactory for the momentum probability density, $|\langle \vec{p} | \Psi \rangle|^2$. FIGURE 1 shows the data of Lohmann and Weigold[8] obtained by electron impact ionization of atomic hydrogen. The agreement between theory and experiment is very good.

The probability current density is usually asserted to be

$$\vec{J} = \mathrm{Re}\,\Psi^*(-i\hbar\vec{\nabla}/m - q\vec{A}/mc)\Psi$$

$$=(i\hbar/2m)(\Psi\vec{\nabla}\Psi^* - \Psi^*\vec{\nabla}\Psi) - q\Psi\vec{A}\Psi^*/mc, \tag{18}$$

where q and m are the charge and mass of the particle, respectively, c is the speed of light, and $\vec{A}$ is the electromagnetic vector potential. This expression is justified by showing that the probability density and it satisfy the continuity equation,

$$\mathrm{div}\,(\vec{J}) + \partial|\Psi|^2/\partial t = 0. \tag{19}$$

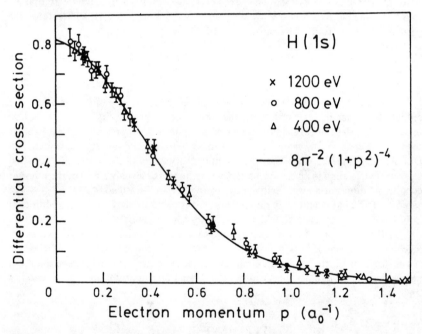

FIGURE 1. Electron momentum distribution in atomic hydrogen as measured by electron impact ionization. (Reprinted from: WEIGOLD, E. 1982. Momentum wave functions–1982. AIP Conf. Proc. no. 86, p. 4.)

However, this derivation permits one to replace $\vec{J}$ by $\vec{J} + \vec{v}$, where $\vec{v}$ is any vector that has zero divergence,

$$\mathrm{div}\,(\vec{v}) = 0. \tag{20}$$

Is there any experimental evidence in support of equation 18 against its infinitely many mathematically acceptable alternatives? This is not merely a pedantic question because Landau and Lifshitz[9] have argued that we should add to equation 18 the additional term,

$$\vec{v} = \text{curl} \ (\Psi^*\vec{s}\Psi) \ \beta c/q, \tag{21}$$

where $\beta\vec{s}$ is the magnetic moment operator for the particle.

If the geometry is such that the flow is essentially one-dimensional, the $\vec{J}$ is determined up to an additive constant by equation 19. Because we can reasonably require $\vec{J}$ to vanish when Ψ vanishes, it follows that the additive constant must be zero. Therefore, a nontrivial test of equation 18 is not possible if the symmetry or geometry reduces the flow to a one-dimensional pattern.

CONCLUSIONS

In this paper, I have demonstrated explicitly that the axioms of probability theory are satisfied by the formalism of quantum mechanics, thereby refuting any and all claims that "classial" probability theory is not valid in quantum mechanics. The only anomaly is the fact that joint probability distributions for two or more dynamical variables are not conventionaly defined unless the corresponding operators are commutative. However, quantum mechanics can hardly be said to contradict (literally, "speak against") probability theory on this point because the accepted formalism of quantum mechanics is simply silent here.

Some examples of erroneous applications of probability theory in quantum mechanics have been exposed and analyzed. In view of the fact that these errors were committed by well-educated physicists, one is led to the conclusion that probability theory needs greater emphasis in the education of physics students.

Finally, I have drawn attention to the need for more experimental tests of the fundamental probabilistic postulates of quantum mechanics.

REFERENCES

1. FINE, T. L. 1973. Theories of Probability, and Examination of Foundations. Academic Press. New York.
2. COX, R. T. 1961. The Algebra of Probable Inference. Johns Hopkins Press. Baltimore.
3. POPPER, K. R. 1957. The propensity interpretation of calculus of probability, and the quantum theory. *In* Observation and Interpretation. S. Korner, Ed.: 65–70. Butterworths. London.
4. BALLENTINE, L. E. 1986. Probability theory in quantum mechanics. Am. J. Phys. To be published.
5. FEYNMAN, R. P. 1951. The concept of probability in quantum mechanics. *In* Proceedings of the Second Berkeley Symposium on Mathematical Statistics and Probability, pp. 553–541. Univ. of California Press. Berkeley, California.
6. KOOPMAN, B. O. 1955. Quantum theory and the foundations of probability. *In* Applied Probability. L. A. MacColl, Ed.: 97–102. McGraw–Hill. New York.
7. TRIGG, G. L. 1964. Quantum Mechanics. Van Nostrand. Princeton, New Jersey.
8. LOHMANN, B. & E. WEIGOLD. 1981. Direct measurement of the electron momentum probability distribution in atomic hydrogen. Phys. Lett. **86A:** 139.
9. LANDAU, L. D. & E. M. LIFSHITZ. 1958. Quantum Mechanics, Non-Relativistic Theory. Section 128. Pergamon Press. London.

APPENDIX A

Derivation of Equation 6

To evaluate equation 5 by means of axioms 1–4, we require a lemma:

$$P(X \cdot Y | C) + P(X \cdot \sim Y | C) = P(X | C)P(Y | X \cdot C) + P(X | C)P(\sim Y | X \cdot C)$$
$$= P(X | C) \{ P(Y | X \cdot C) + P(\sim Y | X \cdot C) \}$$
$$= P(X | C). \tag{A.1}$$

Here we have used axioms 3a and 4. Using equation A.1 with $X = \sim A$ and $Y = \sim B$, we obtain

$$P(\sim A \cdot \sim B | C) = P(\sim A | C) - P(\sim A \cdot B | C).$$

In the first term, we use now axiom 3a, and in the second term, we use equation A.1 with $X = B$ and $Y = A$. This yields

$$P(\sim A \cdot \sim B | C) = 1 - P(A | C) - \{ P(B | C) - P(B \cdot A | C) \}.$$

Upon substitution of this result into equation 5, we obtain equation 6.[a]

APPENDIX B

Derivation of Axiom 3a from Axiom 3b

By noting that A and $\sim A$ are mutually exclusive, and by substituting $B = \sim A$ in axiom 3b, we obtain $P(A \vee \sim A | C) = P(A | C) + P(\sim A | C)$. Now, $A \vee \sim A$ ("A or not A") is intuitively a certainty, and if we set its probability equal to 1, then we immediately obtain axiom 3a. The only gap in this proof lies in the fact that certainty is defined by axiom 2, and we should relate our intuitive notion of certainty to that definition. A formal proof that $P(A \vee \sim A | C) = 1$ is to be found on page 17 of the book by Cox.[2]

---

[a]This derivation of equation 6 is based upon section 5 of reference 2 by R. T. Cox.

Towards a Theory of Single Events in Spin Correlation Experiments

A. O. BARUT

Department of Physics
University of Colorado
Boulder, Colorado 80309-0390

INTRODUCTION AND SUMMARY

Born[1] in his first paper on the statistical interpretation of quantum mechanics has already emphasized the problematic situation between a single event and the probabilistic statements in repeated events. Einstein[2] repeatedly argued for the incompleteness of quantum mechanics because it did not describe single events. If the standard interpretation of quantum theory can only make predictions about repeated events, any assumption, tacit or explicit, that we make on how a single event behaves or looks, must go beyond quantum mechanics. We should repeat the event many times, one after another, or take a collection of similar single events. Only then should we compare the relative frequencies of occurrence of events with theory or with other models.

I shall show that in the EPR-problematic or spin correlation experiments, when one compares quantum theory with realistic hidden variable models, one makes such tacit assumptions about single events. Otherwise, as far as the final probabilities are concerned, there is absolutely no conflict. Specifically, I shall show:

(a) that quantum and classical spin models give the same correlation, $E(\hat{a}, \hat{b})$, in the EPR-Bohm spin correlation experiment; thus, a hidden variable classical model exists as far as this particular experiment is concerned, and as far as we are comparing the final correlations after repeated experiments in both cases;

(b) that the supposed exclusion of a class of hidden variables by Bell's inequalities is based on additional assumptions about single events going beyond quantum theory;

(c) that progress is possible towards a theory of single quantum events encompassing the standard interpretation.

CLASSICAL AND QUANTUM SPIN CORRELATION FUNCTIONS

The classical state of two correlated spins is represented by two spin vectors, $\vec{S}_1$ and $\vec{S}_2$, with $\vec{S} = \vec{S}_1 + \vec{S}_2$. $\vec{S} = 0$ corresponds to the total spin 0 (singlet state), and $\vec{S} = 2\vec{S}$ ($|\vec{S}_1| = |\vec{S}_2|$) corresponds to the triplet state. There are two directions, $\vec{a}$ and $\vec{b}$, and we are interested in the correlation function of the two observables, $A = \vec{S}_1 \cdot \vec{a}$ and $B = \vec{S}_2 \cdot \vec{b}$, defined by

$$E(\hat{a}, \hat{b}) = \frac{\langle AB \rangle - \langle A \rangle \langle B \rangle}{\sqrt{\langle A^2 \rangle \langle B^2 \rangle}}. \tag{1}$$

The experiment is repeated. Assuming the spins are isotropically distributed in all

393

directions and with $\langle \cdot \rangle$ meaning that the integrations are over all angles with measure $1/4\pi \int d\phi d\theta \sin \phi$, we find $\langle A \rangle = 0$, $\langle B \rangle = 0$, and[3]

$$E(\hat{a}, \hat{b}) = \cos v \cos (\theta - u), \tag{2}$$

where $\cos \theta = \hat{a} \cdot \hat{b}$, and u and v are the two angles between $\vec{S}_1$ and $\vec{S}_2$: $\theta_2 = \theta_1 + v$, $\phi_2 = \phi_1 + u$. In particular,

$$u = 0, v = 0 \qquad E(\hat{a}, \hat{b}) = \cos \theta, \tag{3}$$
(parallel spins) \qquad triplet

$$u = 0, v = \pi \qquad E(\hat{a}, \hat{b}) = - \cos \theta, \tag{4}$$
(antiparallel spins)[4] \qquad singlet

$$u = 0, v = \pi/2 \qquad E(\hat{a}, \hat{b}) = 0. \tag{5}$$
(perpendicular spins)

These results are true for any value of the magnitudes, S, of the spins.

If it is difficult to perform the experiment from a state of total spin 0 (singlet), it is equally important to have any other initial state be able to test the correlation function.

The factor, $\cos v$, is a measure for the total spin, S:

$$S^2 = S_1^2 + S_2^2 + 2\vec{S}_1 \cdot \vec{S}_2; \quad \text{for } |S_1| = |S_2|, \quad S = 2S_1^2 + (1 + \cos v).$$

Quantum mechanically, we also use basic equation 1. For a general coherent state of two spin-1/2 particles of the form,

$$\psi = \xi|\uparrow\downarrow \rangle + \eta|\downarrow\uparrow\rangle, \tag{6}$$

we obtain[3]

$$E(\hat{a}, \hat{b}) = \frac{2|\xi||\eta| \cos (\theta + \Delta\psi_{\xi\eta})}{|\xi|^2 + |\eta^2|}, \tag{7}$$

where $\cos \theta = \hat{a} \cdot \hat{b}$ and $\Delta\psi_{\xi\eta}$ is the phase difference between ξ and η. In particular, for the singlet state, we have $E(\hat{a}, \hat{b}) = -\hat{a} \cdot \hat{b}$.

In fact, for any two spins of magnitude, S, in a state of $S_{tot} = 0$, the correlation function is[5]

$$E(\hat{a}, \hat{b}) = -\hat{a} \cdot \hat{b}, \tag{8}$$

which is the same result for any two opposite classical spins, S.[3]

The quantum mechanical result for arbitrary spins, S, in the state, $S_{tot} = 0, \ldots$, $2S$; $S_z = - S_{tot}, \ldots, + S_{tot}$, is apparently not known.

WHERE IS THE PROBLEM?

So far, there is no problem with reconstructing the quantum correlation function by a deterministic realistic hidden variable model. However, one would like to construct (going beyond the premise of standard interpretation of quantum theory) a realistic model that for each individual event gives discrete outcomes. It is tacitly assumed that the whole experiment is divided into a collection of successive individual events that are all counted, rather than waves, for example, which produce discrete clicks on the counters.

Quantum theory does not tell us that in the EPR situation, "a spin zero initial system decays into *two* subspins and each and everyone of them will be detected in repeated experiments, and every event produces a plus or minus result on the polarizer." Instead, quantum theory says that "there is coherent spin-0 two particle state, ψ, and that the expectation value of the product of observables $(\vec{\sigma}_1 \cdot \vec{a}, \vec{\sigma}_2 \cdot \vec{b})$ in that state has the value, $-(\hat{a} \cdot \hat{b})$." Thus, the state, ψ, persists up to the distance of the two detectors. Now, the classical model similarly says that "two correlated spin vectors when their projections are measured along two directions $\vec{a}$ and $\vec{b}$, respectively, give also (after repeated measurements) exactly the same expectation value of the correlation function, $-(\hat{a} \cdot \hat{b})$." Again, the direction of the spins persist up to the distance of the detectors.

Nevertheless, it is possible to arrange our classical spin model in such a way that the discreteness of the counts is reproduced without changing the correlation function.

DISCRETE CLASSICAL SPINS

A Stern-Gerlach device is the prototype of a measurement with discrete outcomes, specifically, a quantum spin measurement according to which the component of the spin-1/2 results in two values. Here again, though, we cannot give a meaning to a single event and we do not know if each event is counted. Only in repeated events do we have two outcomes with certain probabilities.

In order to model such discrete spin values classically, we can choose the spin vector, $\vec{S}_1$, pointing in the upper hemisphere relative to $\vec{a}$ as plus, and in the lower hemisphere as minus. Then, for the projection of spin along $\hat{a}$, we must introduce a factor, $\cos(\phi - \phi_a)$. It is then possible to reproduce again the quantum mechanical correlation function, $E(\hat{a} \cdot \hat{b})$.

We note that there are two other observables,

$$A' = \text{sign}\,(\vec{S}_1 \cdot \vec{a}) \text{ and } B' = \text{sign}\,(\vec{S}_1 \cdot \vec{b}) . \tag{9}$$

These observables differ from A and B of equation 1 by the absence of the cosine factor for the projection of spin along $\vec{a}$ or $\vec{b}$. For the correlation function, we find[6]

$$E'(\hat{a}, \hat{b}) = \frac{2}{\pi}\theta - 1 . \tag{10}$$

The measurement of A' and B' would require a different apparatus than the measurement of A and B. Specifically, it would require a device that responds to the sign of the spin component rather than to the magnitude of the spin projection.

The corresponding quantum mechanical form of the operators, A', B', such that in the singlet state, equation 10 is obtained, that is,

$$\frac{\langle\psi|A'B'|\psi\rangle}{\sqrt{\langle\psi|A^2|\psi\rangle\langle\psi|B^2|\psi\rangle}} = \frac{2}{\pi}\theta - 1 , \tag{11}$$

is unknown to me.

The outcomes of the classical observables, A' and B', are already discrete, with values of ± 1. Going back to the observables, A and B, we want now to calculate the correlation function for the above discretization procedure.

Instead of $E(\hat{a}, \hat{b})$, we can consider the projection operators of the observables,[3]

$$P_\pm^A = \frac{1}{2} \frac{[\sqrt{\langle A^2 \rangle} \pm A]}{\sqrt{\langle A^2 \rangle}},\tag{12}$$

and the following expectation values and joint probabilities,

$$P_\pm(a) = \langle P_\pm^A \rangle, \; P_\pm(b) = \langle P_\pm^B \rangle\tag{13a}$$

and

$$P_{ij}(\hat{a}\hat{b}) = \langle P_i^A P_j^B \rangle \qquad (i, j = \pm 1),\tag{13b}$$

respectively, both in classical and quantum theory. We have identically

$$E(\hat{a}\hat{b}) = P_{++}(\hat{a}\hat{b}) + P_{--}(\hat{a}\hat{b}) - P_{+-}(\hat{a}\hat{b}) - P_{-+}(\hat{a}, \hat{b}).\tag{14}$$

The single and joint probabilities for the discrete classical models for observables, A and B, are then

$$P_i(a) = \frac{1}{4} \int_{\Omega^i(a)} d\phi \cos(\phi - \phi_a) = \frac{1}{2} \qquad (i = f, l);\tag{15a}$$

this is the same for B, and

$$P_{ij}(a, b) = \int_{\Omega_a^i \Omega_b^j} \frac{1}{4} |\cos(\phi - \phi_a)| \, d\phi \qquad (i, j = \pm 1),\tag{15b}$$

where for Ω_a^i, $i = \pm 1$ are the upper and lower hemispheres with respect to $\hat{a}$, and similarly for Ω_b^i.

For the observables, A' and B' (equation 9), we have

$$P_i'(a) = \frac{1}{2\pi} \int_{\Omega^i(a)} d\phi = \frac{1}{2} \quad (i = +, 1),\tag{16a}$$

$$P_{ij}'(\hat{a}, \hat{b}) = \frac{1}{2\pi} \int_{\Omega_a^i \cap \Omega_b^i} d\phi = \begin{cases} \dfrac{1}{2\pi} & \text{for } +-, \, -+ \\[2mm] \dfrac{1}{2} - \dfrac{\theta}{2\pi} & \text{for } ++, \, --. \end{cases}\tag{16b}$$

Equations 16a and 16b are in the form of integrals of densities over the hidden variables, λ, namely,

$$P_i(a) = \int d\lambda \rho(\lambda) \, \chi^i(\lambda, a),$$

$$P_{ij}(\hat{a}, \hat{b}) = \int d\lambda \rho(\lambda) \, \chi^i(\lambda, a) \, \chi^i(\lambda, b),$$

where $\chi^i(\lambda, a)$ are the characteristic functions of the hemispheres, $\Omega^i(a)$.

Equations 15a and 15b, though, are not of this form. However, the evaluation of integrals in these equations gives exactly the same result as the quantum mechanical joint probabilities.[4]

H. P. Seipp[7] has recently shown that equations 15a and 15b can be put in the local probabilistic form if one interprets the projection factor, $\frac{1}{4}\cos(\phi - \phi_a)$, as a kind of detection efficiency.[8] Specifically, the model is

$$P_+(a, \phi) = M\chi(\phi, a)\cos(\phi - a)$$

$$P_-(a, \phi) = M[\chi(\phi, a) - 1]\cos(\phi - a)$$

$$P_0(a, \phi) = 1 - P_+ - P_-$$

$$P_+(b, \phi) = N[1 - \chi(\phi, b)]$$

$$P_-(b, \phi) = N\chi(\phi, b)$$

$$P_0(b, \phi) = 1 - N, \tag{17}$$

where ϕ is the hidden variable, $\chi(\phi, a)$ and $\chi(\phi, b)$ are the characteristic functions of the hemicircles around $\hat{a}$ and $\hat{b}$, respectively, P_0 is the probability that the event is not counted, and M and N are constants where $0 < M \leq 1, 0 < N \leq 1$. Then, one easily finds by integration that

$$P_i(a) = \frac{1}{2\pi}\int d\phi P_i(a, \phi) = \frac{1}{\pi}M, \qquad i = \pm 1,$$

$$P_o(a) = \frac{1}{2\pi}\int d\phi P_o(a, \phi) = 1 - \frac{2}{\pi}M,$$

$$P_i(b) = \frac{1}{2\pi}\int d\phi P_i(b, \phi) = \frac{1}{2}N,$$

$$P_o(b) = \frac{1}{2\pi}\int d\phi P_o(b, \phi) = 1 - N,$$

$$P_{ij}(a, b) = \frac{1}{2\pi}\int d\phi P_i(a, \phi)P_j(b, \phi)$$

$$= \begin{cases} \dfrac{1}{2\pi}MN[1 - \cos(a - b)] & \text{for } ++, -- \\[2ex] \dfrac{1}{2\pi}MN[1 - \cos(a - b)] & \text{for } +-, -+, \end{cases}$$

$$P_{io}(a, b) = \frac{1}{\pi}M(1 - N), \qquad i = +, -,$$

$$P_{oi}(a, b) = \frac{1}{2}N - \frac{1}{\pi}MN, \qquad i = +, -,$$

$$P_{oo}(a, b) = 1 - N - \frac{2}{\pi}M(1 - N). \tag{18}$$

The normalized probabilities on the space of all coincidences, as they are experimentally measured,[9]

$$\bar{P}_{ij}(a, b) = \frac{P_{ij}(a, b)}{P_{++} + P_{+-} + P_{-+} + P_{--}} = \frac{P_{ij}(a, b)}{C},$$ (19)

become exactly the quantum mechanical probabilities,

$$\bar{P}_i(a) = \frac{1}{2}, \qquad \bar{P}_i(b) = \frac{1}{2}; \qquad i = \pm 1,$$

$$\bar{P}_i(a) = \frac{1}{2}, \qquad \bar{P}_i(b) = \frac{1}{2}; \qquad i = \pm 1,$$

$$\bar{P}_{ij}(a, b) = \begin{cases} \frac{1}{4}[1 - \cos(a - b)], & ++, -- \\ \frac{1}{4}[1 + \cos(a - b)], & +-, --, \end{cases}$$ (20)

independent of the choice of M and N. Thus, by equation 14, we have again

$$\overline{E(a,b)} = - \hat{a} \cdot \hat{b}.$$ (21)

The asymmetry in the model can be removed by setting

$$M = \frac{\pi}{2} N, \quad 0 \le N \le \frac{2}{\pi} = 0.64.$$ (22)

Then, the model gives an upper bound for

$$\frac{C}{1 - P_{oo}} = \frac{N}{2 - N} \le \frac{1}{\pi - 1} \simeq 0.47 = \frac{\text{total no. of coincidences}}{\text{total no. of coincidences} + \text{single counts}}$$

or

$$\frac{\text{single count}}{\text{coincidence counts}} \ge \pi - 2.$$

If the process indeed proceeds as we tacitly assume (namely, a collection of discrete events, each producing a click on the detector), it would be important to record the single clicks on each side, as well as the coincidences. For $M = (\pi/2) N$, the single events are symmetric and independent of $\hat{a}$ and $\hat{b}$:

$$P_{io}(a, b) = P_{oi}(a, b) = \frac{N}{2}(1 - N), \quad i = \pm 1.$$ (23)

The probability of events not recorded in both detectors is

$$P_{oo}(a, b) = (1 - N)^2.$$ (24)

Thus, because $N \le 2/\pi$, we get $P_{oo} \ge (1 - 2/\pi)^2 = 0.132$.

DISCUSSION AND CONCLUSIONS

It is interesting that in all three versions of the classical spin correlation model, a different assumption underlying Bell's inequalities is not satisfied. All three versions reproduce the quantum mechanical correlation function. In the continuous spin model (equation 5), the so-called locality assumption is satisfied, but the densities, $|A(a, \lambda)|$, $|B(b, \lambda)|$, in the formula,

$$E(a, b) = \int d\lambda \rho(\lambda) A(a, \lambda) B(b, \lambda) , \tag{25}$$

are not bounded by 1 (or $\frac{1}{2}$). In the discrete spin model (equations 16a and 16b), the densities are bounded, but the locality assumption (equation 25) is not satisfied. Finally, in the probabilistic version (equation 20), both locality and boundedness are satisified, but we have the additional probabilities, $P_{\pm 0}$, $P_{0\pm}$, and P_{00}.

Thus, the discussion about EPR becomes not whether or not classical theory and quantum theory give the same probabilities (they do), but what further assumptions should we make about single events. I find it remarkable and hopeful that quantum theory, which wanted to avoid making statements about single events, finally cannot fully avoid it. It now becomes a task of theoretical physics to build models and theories of single events, and a task of experimental physics to record more of single events. We should ask about the behavior of a single event when it is produced and what of it is recorded at the measuring apparatus. Accepting the realistic existence of all three components of spin as we did in our model (or more generally, starting from realistic models of atomic objects), and from this vantage point of view, the goal is to construct dynamical theories such that at the end of the experiment discrete values of the spin are observed. A more complete theory has to describe the behavior of the hidden variable, λ (in our case, the angles, θ, ψ, of spin), during the measurement. I have discussed elsewhere[10] one such model using nonlinear effects in the equation of motion of spin. The nonlinearities in the equations for the electron exist due to its self-energy or radiative reactions. Unfortunately, little attention has been given to such nonlinear effects as being too small and being treated only perturbatively. They may be crucial to the problem we raised here[11] because it is well known from recent developments in nonlinear equations that chaotic and discrete behavior is not strange to deterministic equations.

REFERENCES

1. BORN, M. 1926. Z. Phys. **37**: 863; **38**: 803.
2. See, for example: EINSTEIN, A. 1953. *In* Scientific Papers Dedicated to Max Born. Hafner. New York.
3. BARUT, A. O. 1985. Classical and Quantum Spin Correlations in 50 Years of EPR, Proc. Joensuu Conference. World Scientific. Singapore.
4. BARUT, A. O. & P. MEYSTRE. 1984. Phys. Lett. **105A**: 458.
5. MERMIN, N. D. 1980. Phys. Rev. **D22**: 356.
6. PERES, A. 1978. Am. J. Phys. **46**: 745.
7. SEIPP, H. P. Found. Phys. To be published.
8. See also: CASER, C. 1982. Phys. Lett. **92A**: 13; 1984. Phys. Lett. **102A**: 152.
9. ASPECT, A., J. DALIBARD & G. ROGER. 1982. Phys. Rev. Lett. **49**: 1804.
10. BARUT, A. O. 1986. *In* Foundations of Quantum Theory, Proc. Albany Conference 1984. Gordon & Breach. New York.
11. BARUT, A. O. 1984. *In* Proc. Intern. Symposium on Foundations of Quantum Mechanics, p. 321. Physical Society of Japan. Kyoto.

Towards a Stochastic Classical Theory of the Particle Behavior of Light

TREVOR MARSHALL[a] AND EMILIO SANTOS[b]

[a]36 Victoria Avenue
Didsbury, Manchester M20 8RA, England

[b]Departamento de Fisica
Universidad de Santander
Santander 39005, Spain

INTRODUCTION

In the last two decades, a number of experiments have been performed to test for "nonclassical effects" in the statistical properties of light.[1-10] The most remarkable ones among these experiments have been those showing anticorrelated counts in the channels of a beam-splitter,[4,5] the atomic cascade tests of the Bell inequalities,[2,3,7-10] and the demonstration of "antibunching" in resonance fluorescence.[6] Though only the second type was specifically designed to test for nonlocality, it has been pointed out[11] that all three bodies of data seem to imply that this highly implausible feature of all existing quantum theories is a real physical phenomenon.

These experiments also add evidence to the old "proofs" of the nonclassical behavior of light. It is well known that the old proofs, based simply on the photoelectric effect, are not conclusive because of the work of Crisp and Jaynes[12,13] in the sixties. However, these authors did not propose a classical alternative to quantum electrodynamics; instead, they proposed a semiclassical one in which the electromagnetic field is described classically, while the particles' motion is quantized.

As a result of the new evidence, the opinion is now widespread that no classical or semiclassical alternative to quantum optics is possible. Our main purpose in this article is to show that this is an incorrect conclusion. We shall propose a unified theory of the electromagnetic field that is completely classical and that fits all of the above new experimental results.

This theory, which we call "stochastic optics" for reasons explained below, is the logical continuation of two lines of research now converging:[14,15] (i) stochastic electrodynamics, and (ii) the Bell inequalities.

PRINCIPLES OF STOCHASTIC OPTICS

Stochastic optics is a part of stochastic electrodynamics just as classical optics is a part of the normal classical electrodynamics; indeed, the latter may be said to include stochastic electrodynamics provided we adjust the boundary conditions at infinity to represent a real zero-point field. Stochastic electrodynamics may be traced back to Planck and Nernst, and even its modern revival is now more than 30 years old. There are several review articles of this subject,[16-19] and there is one excellent popular account.[20]

The basic idea of stochastic optics is to treat the transmission of light (through lenses, mirrors, polarizers, etc.) exactly as in classical optics, but with the inclusion of the existence of a zero-point radiation present everywhere. The assumption is made that the zero-point radiation has the same nature as ordinary light, but, for reasons to be discussed later, it cannot be detected directly. In consequence, we assume for the transmission of light (including the zero-point) the same laws as in classical optics. On the other hand, we shall use ad hoc assumptions for the emission and absorption of radiation. We hope that these rules will one day be derived from more basic (classical, although stochastic) principles.

After this general idea of what stochastic optics is, we must consider two problems before developing it. The first one is how to separate, from the extremely energetic sea of zero-point radiation, the part that is relevant in a given phenomenon. The second problem, which is related, is to explain why the zero-point radiation alone does not activate "photon" detectors.

The zero-point field has a very high energy. Indeed, it is infinite if some high frequency cutoff is not considered. Even with a cutoff, the contribution of the short wavelengths would be very large. Therefore, the question arises: How may a light signal (sometimes, a weak light signal) give rise to observable phenomena while the strong zero-point field is not observed? In order to get an answer, we must first take into account that in stochastic electrodynamics, it is assumed that the zero-point field is one of the causes of the difference between classical and quantum physics; thus, in that sense, it is frequently observed. In the second place, we must remember that the (Maxwell) equations of the electromagnetic field are linear, which means that each part of the radiation evolves independently. This implies that in stochastic optics, we may forget about the zero-point radiation with frequencies outside the visible, the near-infrared, or the ultraviolet.

We may consider many kinds of light (coherent, chaotic, etc.), but in this paper, we shall be mainly concerned with light signals that in quantum optics are said to correspond to "one-photon states." This is because most "nonclassical features" in quantum optics have been shown with this type of light. It is reasonable to assume, in a purely classical theory, that "one-photon states" correspond to wave packets of minimum (or almost minimum) uncertainty. This means that

$$\Delta x \Delta k_x \simeq \Delta y \Delta k_y \simeq \Delta z \Delta k_z \simeq 2\pi. \tag{1}$$

Our idea about the wave packets corresponding to one-photon states is similar to Einstein's original proposal[21] of needle radiation (Nadelstrahlung) interpreted literally as a strongly directed pencil of radiation. Nowadays, we have at least one macroscopic example of such a pencil in synchrotron radiation where the directed character is a consequence of the ultrarelativistic motion of the charged particle in its orbit. We propose that, for reasons not yet understood, light radiation from an atom is of this same character (see, however, reference 22 for a possible mechanism within stochastic optics for needle radiation).

In stochastic optics, we do not assume the existence of photons. In certain cases, we may consider instead needle wave packets carrying an energy of the order, $\hbar\omega$, as said above. Therefore, "photon counters" are simply macroscopic devices that can be activated when some amount of light enters into them. For clarity, we shall consider phototubes, but the analysis of other "photon detectors" (e.g., photographic plates) would be similar. A phototube is constructed so that it can be put in some metastable state (ready to count) that may go to the stable state under the action of light; this process then gives rise to a count. A purely classical theory of the activation of a phototube (or the blackening of a grain in a photographic plate) is not easy. In fact, in normal classical optics, it is assumed that the energy of a light beam is distributed more or less uniformly over the wave front.

The situation is different in stochastic optics. The existence of the background noise (or zero-point field) gives rise to intensity fluctuations of any light beam both in time and space. As a consequence, the power arriving at the relevant part of the phototube may also have fluctuations. The probability of activation of the detector between t and $t + dt$ will depend in a complex form on the power (and its distribution in frequencies) arriving at the detector at times earlier than t. The activation probability, P, cannot be simply proportional to the total power arriving at the detector, including that of the zero-point. In fact, if this were the case, photographic plates would be blackened in the dark by the action of the zero-point radiation alone. This suggests putting

$$P(t)dt = \text{const.} \, [I(t) - I_{\text{th}}]_+ \, dt, \qquad (2)$$

where $I(t)$ is the intensity arriving at the detector at time, t, suitably averaged over space, and I_{th} is a threshold. The notation, $[\ ]_+$, means putting zero in if the bracket is negative. The intensity, $I(t)$, will include the zero-point because we postulated that there is no difference in nature between the signal and the zero-point radiation.

THE STOCHASTIC ACTION OF BEAM-SPLITTERS

From the point of view of stochastic optics, optical devices can be divided into two classes depending on whether or not they divide the light beam incident on them. In class I, we shall include devices not dividing the light intensity associated with each single mode of the radiation; however, they may separate different modes from each other. To this class, belong lenses, ordinary mirrors, and filters. In class II, we consider devices that divide the light intensity of a single mode into two different modes. To this class, belong semitransparent mirrors and polarizers.

We assume that the behavior of devices belonging to class I is the same as in classical optics, except for the fact that the zero-point noise always accompanies the light both in the outgoing and in the incoming beam. The essential point is that the ratio between the intensities "above the sea" (of zero-point radiation) and "below the sea" remains the same before and after the interaction of the light beam with the device.

The behavior of a device of class II is more complex. In order to understand it, we consider the beam-splitter as depicted in FIGURE 1. For a similar treatment of linear polarizing devices, see reference 15. We have an incoming plane wave with an electric vector, $\underline{E}$. The electric vectors, $\underline{E}_t$ and $\underline{E}_r$, of the transmitted and reflected waves, respectively, are obtained by superposing contributions from the incoming signal, $\underline{E}$, and the relevant part of the zero-point field. Of course, there is zero-point radiation going in all directions and with all frequencies, but we may forget about all of it, except for that part able to interfere coherently with E. We represent this relevant part by $\underline{E}_0$.

Then, the amplitudes of the transmitted and reflected beams will depend in a stochastic manner on the phase of $\underline{E}_o$ relative to $\underline{E}$. These outgoing fields will be given by (see also reference 11 for a similar treatment of the beam-splitter in quantum optics)

$$\underline{E}_t = 2^{-1/2}(\underline{E} + \underline{E}_o), \qquad \underline{E}_r = 2^{-1/2}(\underline{E} - \underline{E}_o). \tag{3}$$

The point is that, taking into account the existence of a threshold (see equation 2), it is likely that the reflected beam cannot be detected when the transmitted one can, and vice versa. This gives rise to a corpuscle behavior of light in a beam-splitter ("one photon is either reflected or transmitted, but not divided").

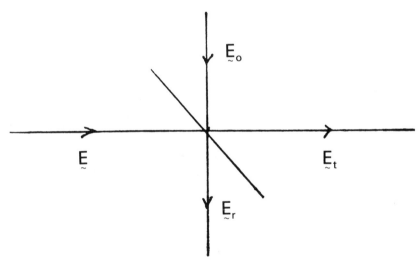

FIGURE 1. The action of a beam-splitter on a signal, $\underline{E}$. The signal is split and mixed with the noise component, $\underline{E}_o$, to give the reflected and transmitted signals, $\underline{E}_r$ and $\underline{E}_t$, respectively.

INTERPRETATION OF THE ANTICORRELATION EXPERIMENTS

Several experiments have been performed[4,23] to illustrate the particle-like behavior of light by measuring the anticorrelation in the two channels of a beam-splitter. Recently, Grangier, Roger, and Aspect[5] measured, as a ratio of counting rates, the quantity,

$$\alpha = p_c/(p_r p_t), \tag{4}$$

where $p_r (p_t)$ is the detection probability of a signal in the reflected (transmitted) beam after the splitter, and p_c is the coincidence probability. Conventional wave theory of light predicts $\alpha \geq 1$, while a value as low as 0.18 ± 0.06 was measured in one of the experimental runs.

Grangier *et al.* used, as a measure of the beam intensity, the product, Nw, where N

is the rate of photon emission by the source and w ($=9$ ns) is a suitable time interval. If we accept the standard estimate of accidental coincidences, we have

$$\alpha = 1 - (1 - \alpha_o)\chi, \tag{5}$$

$$\chi = [1 + Nw/f(w)]^{-2}, \tag{6}$$

where[5] $f(w)$ is very close to one, and α_o is the value of α extrapolated to the zero-value of Nw. In reference 15, we have made a calculation of α_O using a plausible estimate of the signal-to-noise ratio, E^2/E_o^2 (see FIGURE 1), in the stochastic optics model. The best

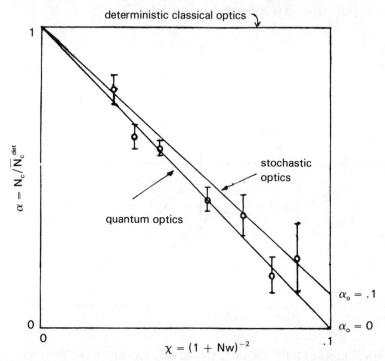

FIGURE 2. Plot of the Grangier parameter, α, as a function of the source intensity, N, for the models of deterministic classical optics, stochastic optics, and quantum optics. The experimental data are obtained from figure 2 of reference 5, and the error bars are one standard deviation.

value seems to lie in the neighborhood of $\alpha_O = 0.1$, while quantum optics predicts $\infty_o = 0$.

In the experiment, seven values of α were measured, each as a ratio, n_i/m_i, between the number of coincidences actually found and the number predicted under the assumption, $\alpha = 1$. The values of n_i, m_i, and N_iw can be found from figure 2 of reference 5, assuming that the statistical error bars come from the error in n_i, which is $\sqrt{n_i}$, and all other errors are negligible. In this way, we found, for instance, for $Nw \simeq 0.065$, $n_7 = 6$ and $m_7 = 24$, and for $Nw \simeq 0.12$, $n_6 = 9$ and $m_6 = 50$. (The values of n_6 and m_6 are quoted in the article referred to above.) The maximum-likelihood estimate[24] obtained from the data is

$$\alpha_o = 0.06. \tag{7}$$

We also obtained a 90% confidence interval,

$$0 \le \alpha_o \le 0.17. \tag{8}$$

In FIGURE 2, we plot n_i/m_i for the values of Nw investigated by Grangier et al.

OTHER RELATED PHENOMENA

Although the theory presented here is based on a purely wavelike description of light, it explains, within experimental error, the phenomenon generally considered to give the most convincing demonstration of particle-like properties. We submit, therefore, that the so-called wave-particle duality of light has not been convincingly established.

Because stochastic optics is a purely wave theory, there is, naturally, no difficulty in explaining the part of reference 5 that deals with "single photon interference." For details on the wave recombination experiment, see reference 15.

Finally, we point out that by using the above description of signal and noise, and with the same ratio between them, our model gives a qualitative explanation of enhancement in linear polarizing devices.[14] This is known[25] to be a necessary feature of any realist explanation of the cascade coincidence data.[2,3,7-10] A detailed calculation[15] of the quantities observed in these experiments shows that a good fit may be obtained. We, therefore, submit that stochastic optics is a challenging competitor to quantum optics over quite a substantial range of phenomena previously considered nonclassical.

REFERENCES

1. MANDEL, L. 1976. Prog. Opt. **13:** 27.
2. CLAUSER, J. F. & A. SHIMONY. 1978. Rep. Prog. Phys. **41:** 1881.
3. SELLERI, F. & G. TAROZZI. 1981. Riv. Nuovo Cimento **4:** 1.
4. CLAUSER, J. F. 1974. Phys. Rev. **D9:** 853.
5. GRANGIER, P., G. ROGER & A. ASPECT. 1986. Europhys. Lett. **1:** 173.
6. DAGENAIS, M. & L. MANDEL. 1978. Phys. Rev. **A18:** 2217.
7. ASPECT, A., P. GRANGIER & G. ROGER. 1981. Phys. Rev. Lett. **47:** 460.
8. ASPECT, A., P. GRANGIER & G. ROGER. 1982. Phys. Rev. Lett. **49:** 91; ASPECT, A. & P. GRANGIER. 1985. Nuovo Cimento Lett. **43:** 345.
9. ASPECT, A., J. DALIBARD & G. ROGER. 1982. Phys. Rev. Lett. **49:** 1804.
10. PERRIE, W., A. J. DUNCAN, H. J. BEYER & H. KLEINPOPPEN. 1985. Phys. Rev. Lett. **54:** 1790.
11. CHUBAROV, M. S. & E. P. NIKOLAYEV. 1985. Phys. Lett. **110A:** 199.
12. CRISP, M. D. & E. T. JAYNES. 1969. Phys. Rev. **179:** 1253.
13. JAYNES, E. T. 1978. Coherence and Quantum Optics IV. L. Mandel & E. Wolf, Eds.: 495. Plenum. New York.
14. MARSHALL, T. W. 1985. Report to the Conference on Microphysical Reality and Quantum Formalism, Urbino, Italy.
15. MARSHALL, T. W. & E. SANTOS. 1986. Stochastic optics: a classical alternative to quantum optics. Preprint. University of Santander, Spain.

16. BOYER, T. H. 1970. Ann. Phys. (N.Y.) **56:** 474.
17. CLAVERIE, P. C. & S. DINER. 1977. Int. J. Quantum Chem. **12**(suppl. 1): 41.
18. BOYER, T. H. 1980. Foundations of Radiation Theory and Quantum Electrodynamics. A. O. Barut, Ed.: 49. Plenum. New York.
19. DE LA PEÑA, L. 1983. Stochastic Processes Applied to Physics and Other Related Fields. B. Gomez, S. M. Moore, A. M. Rodriguez-Vargas & A. Rueda, Eds.: 428. World Scientific. Singapore.
20. BOYER, T. H. 1985. The classical vacuum. Sci. Am. (August 1985).
21. EINSTEIN, A. 1917. Phys. Z. **18:** 121.
22. MARSHALL, T. W. 1986. Report to the Conference on Quantum Violations, Bridgeport, Connecticut.
23. ADAM, A., L. JANOSSY & P. VARGA. 1955. Acta Phys. Hung. **4:** 301; Ann. Phys. **16:** 408.
24. MARSHALL, T. W. & E. SANTOS. 1986. Statistical analysis of the experimental evidence for a photon anticorrelation effect in a beam splitter. Preprint. University of Santander, Spain.
25. CLAUSER, J. F. & M. A. HORNE. 1974. Phys. Rev. **D10:** 326.

Quantum Theory of Measurement

WILLIS E. LAMB, Jr.

*Department of Physics
University of Arizona
Tucson, Arizona 85721*

Quantum mechanics was discovered sixty-one years ago in 1925. It began with Heisenberg's introduction of matrix mechanics, which was followed by Schrödinger finding his wave equation. Then Dirac gave a formulation of quantum mechanics that contained the two earlier theories as special cases and was much more general. The interpretation of the wave function as a probability amplitude was added by Born in 1926. The following discussion of the problem of measurement in quantum mechanics is limited to the nonrelativistic theory. Hence, there will be no mention of photons or spin. No doubt I will be taking other things for granted and I hope you will be able to infer them from the context.

The Born probability interpretation was very well suited for discussing the blackening of a photographic plate exposed to a beam of electrons scattered by an atomic system. It was necessary to decide whether the wave function represented a beam of many electrons or only a single electron. One knows now that for the analysis of most such experiments, the theory is applied in a probabilistic way for a single electron, and the blackening of the plate by a beam of many electrons is worked out by plausible nonquantum mechanical considerations. The absolute square of the wave function at a point of the plate gives the probability for finding the electron there.

If we had only to deal with that kind of problem in wave mechanics, there might not have been need for this conference. However, quantum mechanics lent itself very naturally to an enormous generalization of the theory of measurement. Dirac had introduced the two ideas of states and observables. The state was a generalization of the wave function, but without the emphasis on space coordinates associated with the Schrödinger wave function. Observables were physical quantities that could be represented by Hermitian operators that were often, but not always, taken over from classical mechanics. Rules were given for calculation of real numbers (called expectation values) for any observable of a system in any of its states. The operator observables had eigenstates and eigenvalues. For the Hamiltonian observable, $H(q,p)$, of a conservative dynamical system, the eigenstates were in close correspondence with the stationary states of the corresponding wave mechanical problem, and the eigenvalues were the stationary state energies known from the earlier quantum theory of Bohr.

The structure of quantum mechanics makes it very natural to pretend that some (if not all) of the observables that characterize a dynamical system can be "measured" experimentally at least in principle. The following assumptions are made: If the state, Ψ, is one of the eigenstates, Ψ_n, of the observable, Ω, a measurement of Ω should give the corresponding eigenvalue, Ω_n. A measurement of observable Ω for a system in any state, Ψ, should give one of the eigenvalues, Ω_n, of Ω. If this state, Ψ, is a linear combination of eigenstates of the form,

$$\Psi = \Sigma\, c_n \Psi_n,$$

407

then the absolute square, $|c_n|^2$, of the expansion coefficient, c_n, gives the probability that the system would be found in state, Ψ_n, by a suitable measurement. The expectation value, $\langle \Psi | \Omega | \Psi \rangle$, of the observable, Ω, for the state, Ψ, is given by the weighted average of eigenvalues,

$$\langle \Psi | \Omega | \Psi \rangle = \Sigma \, |c_n|^2 \, \Omega_n.$$

Unfortunately, the founders of the theory did not tell us much about how such measurements could be made. Heisenberg started his development of matrix mechanics with the belief that the theory should only deal with experimentally measurable quantities. In 1927, he considered a gamma ray microscope for position measurement, but he never gave a quantum mechanical analysis of the operation of such a device. In his Chicago lectures[1] of 1929, he considered momentum measurements. To measure the distribution of momentum values for an electron in a certain state of an atom, he suggested that the electrostatic binding force between the electron and the nucleus should be suddenly turned off, with a time-of-flight study made on the then free electron to determine its velocity. Repeated observations would give the desired momentum distribution for an ensemble of atoms in the same state.

In the first chapter of his 1930 book, Dirac[2] introduced the ideas of preparation of a state, and measurement of an observable. Most of what he wrote there dealt with photons and not electrons, but I will carry out a translation into language appropriate for a spinless massive particle in order to keep the discussion nonrelativistic. Dirac did not indicate how either preparation of a state or measurement of an observable was to be carried out. He did introduce the postulate (stated here for systems of one degree of freedom) that if a measurement of an observable, Ω, was made, the state of the system just afterwards would be the eigenstate, Ψ_n, corresponding to the result, Ω_n, obtained in the measurement. A very similar idea appears in the 1932 book of von Neumann,[3] and is often called the "hypothesis of wave packet reduction."

An enormous number of papers have been written on quantum mechanical measurement theory. Among the books on the subject are those of Jammer,[4] D'Espagnat,[5] and Wheeler and Zurek.[6] It is not much of an exaggeration to state that very few of these works deal with the preparation of a state or the measurement of an observable except in a formal and schematic way. For most authorities, it is sufficient to say "let a measurement be made," and it is made. Ever since I learned some quantum mechanics (about 1934), I have wondered about such questions. In 1968, I gave a lecture at Lindau, which was afterwards published[7] in *Physics Today,* under the title, "An Operational Interpretation of Non-Relativistic Quantum Mechanics." This paper considers some theoretically possible, but highly impractical, ways of preparing states and making measurements. I was a little disappointed with the small amount of attention that the measurement-theoretic community paid to this paper. I was therefore very pleased when Wheeler requested permission to make use of my article in his forthcoming book with Zurek. This book is an admirable collection of papers on measurement theory in quantum mechanics. It turned out, however, that Wheeler only felt the need for a joke on the subject of measurement for his preface, and was able to find one in the first paragraph of my paper. Except for that, nothing in the paper was mentioned in the book. However, you can imagine my pleasure when a recent paper[8] described my 1969 article as "classic."

My treatment of the problem of measurement of an observable operator function of

x and p was patterned after Heisenberg's method for measuring momentum. For this kind of measurement, the process was so very invasive of the dynamical system being studied that one could learn nothing about the original state of the system by making more than one such measurement on it. This meant that one could not deal with a series of successive measurements of the sort needed in *Star Wars* for tracking an incoming missile. My feeling at the time was that the object of a quantum mechanical measurement was to enable a test to be made of the quantum theory. An ensemble of identical systems were prepared. They were each allowed to evolve in time with the same Hamiltonian. After some time, an observable would be measured by subjecting the system to certain specified external forces, which would be followed by something like a Stern-Gerlach analysis. The result from an ensemble of such measurements was statistical information about the observable. Any single system under study would be so disturbed by the measurement process that only one such measurement could meaningfully be made without starting the whole procedure over again.

Naturally, we all have a human desire and need to be able to follow the motions of large-scale systems as a function of time. However, there is no reason why we should be able to do so for systems that have to be described by the laws of quantum mechanics. To treat a problem in quantum mechanics, we have to know what the system is and we need to have an accurate knowledge of its Hamiltonian or Lagrangian operator at all times. There are systems, such as a reasonably well isolated hydrogen atom, where these conditions are met in a sufficiently good approximation. They are not met, however, in a large-scale system like a gravity wave detector. In principle, they could be, but they are not in practice. The location of the border between categories of large and small systems is not rigidly fixed, but depends somewhat on the amount of time, trouble, and expense that one can tolerate.

Having said this, I will proceed to discuss the problem of repeated measurements on a quantum system. For simplicity, I will consider the position measurement of the Cartesian coordinate, x, of a particle of mass, m, that is confined to move along the x-axis. Let its normalized wave function be $\psi(x)$ at the time, $t = 0$, of measurement. Taking the Dirac and von Neumann hypotheses literally, if the result of measurement is x', the wave function of the particle becomes the eigenfunction of the operator, x, corresponding to the eigenvalue, x'. This eigenfunction is a singular function, namely, a square root of the Dirac delta function, $\delta(x - x')$. The future time evolution of the singular function can be easily calculated, but it has nothing to do with things we wanted to know about the system before the measurement. It is, of course, possible to try to make a "bad" measurement of x that smears out the singularity, but then we would need to develop a theory of bad measurements that should not have too many arbitrary and nonquantum mechanical features. A theory of bad measurements is not as easy to find as a bad theory of measurements.

Instead, I turn to the well-trodden path of considering the use of a "meter" system. I take this to have a Cartesian coordinate, X, and a (very large) mass, M. Initially, the meter system has been put in a state with a normalized wave function, $\chi(X)$. The wave function of the combined x, X system is then initially a simple product, $\psi(x) \cdot \chi(X)$, which is normalized in the two-dimensional configuration space. The two parts of the system are then allowed to interact for a short time and the combined system wave function becomes a nonproduct wave function, $\Phi(x, X)$. One then turns off the interaction between the x and X parts of the system and makes a measurement of X, thereby hoping to learn something worth knowing about the x system. Presumably, the nature of the interaction between x and X has been such that there is a meterlike quality in the wave function, $\Phi(x, X)$. There is a certain circularity in this plan, because if we knew how to measure something for the X system, we could use the method directly for the x system. To get around this difficulty, we can try to say that the X system has such a large mass that we can treat it classically, and that then we can measure X by merely saying that we measure X. We could, of course, introduce another still more massive meter system with coordinate, Y, which we could use to study the X system in order to learn something about the x system, etc., etc.

Actually, in the last two pages of his 1932 book, von Neumann did give an example of a specific model for the kind of meter mentioned above. The interaction potential was taken to be pulselike in time,

$$V = x \, P \, \delta(t),$$

and was dependent on a product of the coordinate, x, of the particle and the momentum, P, associated with the meter coordinate, X. To get an idea what this interaction might do for us, consider the fully classical problem of the effect of the pulsed interaction potential described by Hamilton's equations of motion,

$$\frac{\partial X}{\partial t} = x\delta(t) \qquad \frac{\partial P}{\partial t} = 0$$

$$\frac{\partial x}{\partial t} = 0 \qquad \frac{\partial p}{\partial t} = -P\delta(t).$$

After the pulse interaction, the dynamical variables, x, p, X, and P, have become $x = x_0$, $p = p_0 - P_0$, $X = X_0 + x_0$, and $P = P_0$, instead of their initial values, x_0, p_0, X_0, and P_0. We could learn the value of the initial coordinate, x_0, by measuring the displacement of the meter pointer, X. Something like this same feature is found in the quantum treatment: After the interaction, the wave function of the combined system becomes

$$\Phi(x, X) = \psi(x) \, \chi(X - x),$$

so that if $\chi(X)$ is a very sharply peaked function, a measurement of X will give the value of x.

There are quite a few things about this model that spoil our pleasure. The delta function of time will have to be realized physically by use of a pulse of short, but not zero time duration. That will complicate the problem because the forces internal to the system will contribute to the time evolution during the pulse. We have to have a good supply of measuring systems in a prepared quantum state. The interaction potential is very unphysical in all respects. It reminds us of a part of the Larmor interaction Hamiltonian for a charged particle in a magnetic field. I regard it as unacceptable. I am working on some models with more physically reasonable forms of interaction (which will be reported elsewhere). However, the von Neumann model is computationally simple, along with being easy and convenient to work with. It does serve to illustrate some important features of the measurement process. Hence, the remainder of this paper will be devoted to working out the numerical consequences of it in a situation that might be met in gravity wave detection.

In order to give an accurate measurement of x, the wave function, $\chi(X)$, has to be very sharply peaked. Then, as we will see, the x system after the measurement will have been very strongly disturbed.

A very serious difficulty is that after the interaction, we no longer have the original x system, but only the coupled x, X system. The X part of the system can be ignored dynamically, but not kinematically. We would have to say that the x system no longer has a wave function, but only a statistical distribution of wave functions that can be described by a density matrix, which, in the coordinate representation, is given by

$$\rho(x', x'') = \int dX\, \Phi(x'', X)^*\, \Phi(x', X).$$

Therefore, what do we do now? It seems pretty clear that to make measurements one will have to add some new postulate to the theory. Having rejected the Dirac–von Neumann reduction hypothesis as applied to the x system, we might still apply a variation of it to the x, X system. We will assume that when the combined wave function is $\Phi(x, X)$ in the x, X configuration space, and we have measured X, obtaining a particular result, that from then on the X system can be completely forgotten. The x system again gets a pure case wave function, which is just equal to

$$\psi(x) = \Phi[x, (X)],$$

where (X) is no longer a dynamical variable, but merely a parameter with the value, X, obtained in the measurement of X. The wave function, $\psi(x)$, will have to be renormalized as a single degree of freedom system.

Clearly, if one thought that the above assumption was too invasive of the x system, it would be possible to introduce another system with coordinate, Y, for measurement of X. In that case, after measuring Y, the x, X system would be assumed to have a wave function, say, $\Xi[x, X, (Y)]$, and the x system would be described by a density matrix. The system described by the density matrix would have to be followed by consideration of an ensemble of calculations with wave functions randomly selected from the distribution of wave functions of the mixture appropriate to the density matrix. If this complication was bearable, one might introduce a further system, Z, etc., etc.

I first saw something like the above modified Dirac–von Neumann hypothesis in another unsung, but classic paper[9] by Arthurs and Kelley of 1965, who applied it to "simultaneous" measurement of x and p.

For the calculations of the present paper, I have combined the von Neumann meter model and the modified Dirac–von Neumann reduction hypothesis. I will contemplate a one-dimensional system of a particle, either free, or moving in a force field described by a potential function of x with, at most, linear and quadratic terms. This potential can have any desired time dependence in order to allow for external perturbations of the system. Time will be divided up into a multilayer sandwich made of "lucid" intervals of causal evolution under the (possible time-dependent) Hamiltonian, with each separated by the short "mad" burst of a measurement process of the von Neumann type. The time dependence of the wave function during the causal periods can be dealt with easily, either analytically or with a computer. The measurement processes produce discrete changes in the wave function as outlined above, and they are described in more detail in the following discussion. Such changes depend on the result of the measurement. The result of measurement is chosen at random using the appropriate probability distribution for getting that result.

One feature of this model is that the system is described by a wave function at all times. However, each measurement involves a random process, so that if the calculations are repeated from the beginning, a different history of the time evolution will be obtained. One must decide whether a complete ensemble of histories has to be calculated, or whether one or a few histories will suffice for the purposes at hand.

It is very convenient to use wave functions in Gaussian exponential form. Thus, we will take the meter wave function to be

$$\exp\left(-\beta X^2\right),$$

where β is a real constant that measures the inverse square width of the Gaussian. It will not be necessary to supply normalization factors in the following discussion. This function could be regarded as the ground-state wave function for a simple harmonic oscillator problem for the X system. When the meter is applied to the system, the spring exerting forces on X is thrown away. Only the mass, M, with exponential wave function is needed. I do not explain how this system was put into the harmonic oscillator ground state.

The wave function for the x system, also apart from normalization, can be taken to be a complex Gaussian,

$$\psi(x) = \exp\left[-\alpha(x - a)^2\right],$$

where a and α are complex functions of time. This form of the wave function can provide solutions of Schrödinger's wave equation for an x-dependent potential depending linearly and quadratically on x, with the provision that the quantities, α and a, are properly chosen functions of time. The case of an infinite free particle plane wave function can be approached in a limiting case, where α is real and small, and a is large and purely imaginary.

The wave equation giving the time evolution of ψ during the lucid intervals will be the Schrödinger equation with a Hamiltonian that contains the usual kinetic energy operator—possibly a harmonic oscillator potential and possibly a term representing the effect of a time-dependent uniform force field, $F(t)$, applied to the system,

$$H = \frac{P^2}{2m} + \frac{1}{2}\, m\omega^2 x^2 - F(t)x.$$

Substitution of ψ into the time-dependent wave equation gives two coupled ordinary differential equations for the complex functions, $\alpha(t)$ and $a(t)$. [It is possible to append a normalization factor, $N(t)$, to $\psi(x, t)$, but we do not need to do this because the normalization factor can be calculated easily in terms of $\alpha(t)$ and $a(t)$ whenever we want it.] These differential equations are

$$\frac{da}{dt} = \frac{i}{2\alpha\hbar}\,(F - m\omega^2 a),$$

$$\frac{d\alpha}{dt} = \frac{i}{\hbar}\left[-\frac{2\alpha^2\hbar^2}{m} + \frac{1}{2}\,m\omega^2\right].$$

In some cases, these equations can be solved analytically, but even when F and possibly ω depend on time, they are easily solved on a computer.

Having indicated how the causal dynamics are to be treated, we turn to the effect of a measurement. Let the wave function of the x system at the end of one of its lucid intervals be

$$\psi(x) = \exp\left[-\alpha1(x - a1)^2\right].$$

The coupling with a meter system X produces a wave function,

$$\Phi(x, X) = \exp\left[-\alpha1(x - a1)^2\right] \exp\left[-\beta(X - x)^2\right].$$

Then with the modified reduction hypothesis, when the result of the measurement of X gives the value, $X = b$, we assume that the state of the x system becomes

$$\psi(x) = \exp\left[-\alpha1(x - a1)^2\right] \exp\left[-\beta(x - b)^2\right].$$

By completing the square, we find that this wave function is equivalent to

$$\psi(x) = \exp\left[-\alpha2(x - a2)^2\right],$$

which has the same form as the wave function just before the measurement, except that the parameters, $\alpha1$ and $a1$, have changed to $\alpha2$ and $a2$ given by

$$\alpha2 = \alpha1 + \beta$$

and

$$a2 = \frac{\alpha1 a1 + \beta b}{\alpha1 + \beta}.$$

The next stage in the calculation is to obtain from the wave function, $\Phi(x, X)$, the probability density that a value, X, is obtained in the measurement. This is given by

$$W(X) = \int dx \, \Phi(x, X)^* \, \Phi(x, X),$$

which is a Gaussian distribution in X with a peak at $X = X_p$ with

$$X_p = \frac{\text{Real}(\alpha1 \, a1)}{\text{Real}(\alpha1)}.$$

The probability distribution for the value of b is proportional to

$$\exp\left[-\frac{1}{2}\left(\frac{b - X_p}{\sigma}\right)^2\right],$$

where the standard deviation, σ, is given by

$$\sigma^2 = \frac{1}{4}\left(\frac{1}{\text{Real}(\alpha1)} + \frac{1}{\beta}\right).$$

Each time a measurement is to be made, the computer uses its random number generator to select a value for b. The system wave function is changed according to the above rules, and the next stage of causal evolution occurs. At the end of the run, the whole history of the wave function has been recorded, together with the results of the sequence of measurements. For gravity wave detection, one would not know the force, $F(t)$, and one would have to solve the inverse problem of getting $F(t)$ from the sequences of the b values. Reasonable prescriptions can be given for approximate solutions of such a problem.

Because we have no data to analyze yet, I will show results for calculations made on a massive free particle that has been acted on by a force given by a pulse rectangular in time. The elapsed time is shown horizontally. The centroid of the wave packet is plotted vertically. Th following parameters are taken: $m = 10^6$ gm and $\omega = 0$ sec^{-1}, with the initial $\alpha = 10^{32}$ cm^{-2}. There is a pulse force of $F = 2.5 \times 10^{-12}$ dynes, lasting for 100 sec, applied at the midpoint of the total elapsed time of 10,000 sec. Two cases are considered: (a) FIGURE 1 has $\beta = 10^{32}$ cm^{-2} and (b) FIGURE 2 has $\beta = 10^{30}$ cm^{-2}. In each case, five histories of the centroid of the wave packet are shown. One of the five shows the simpler history obtained when no disturbing measurements are made. In the other four runs, a von Neumann measurement of x is made once every 100 seconds. The four runs differ because of the random number feature in the computational algorithm.

I conclude this paper with some remarks about the uncertainty principle. Most papers[10] dealing with gravity detectors make extensive use of the uncertainty principle. This seems to me to be very unsatisfactory. There are at least three forms of the uncertainty relationship. The first involves the application of Fourier expansion theory to derive a relation like $\Delta \nu \, \Delta t \geq 1$. The second was the Heisenberg[11] 1927 application of

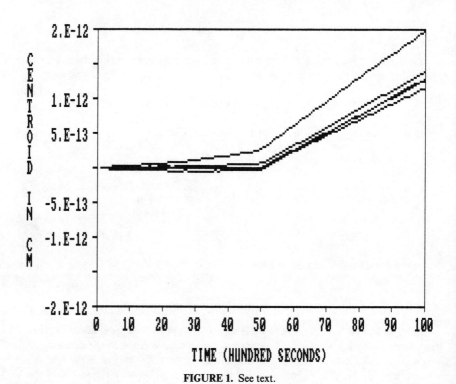

TIME (HUNDRED SECONDS)

FIGURE 1. See text.

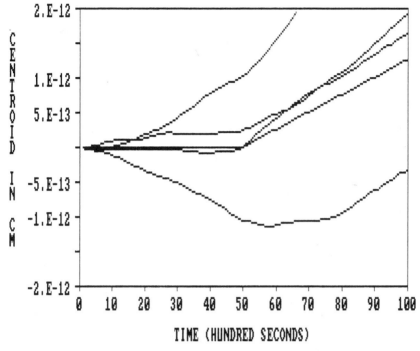

FIGURE 2. See text.

this kind of analysis, along with simple physical ideas taken from the Compton effect, to derive $\Delta x \, \Delta p \geq \hbar/2$. The third was derived from quantum mechanical expectation values and the use of Schwartz's inequality by Robertson[12] in 1929 and (a little more generally) by Schrödinger[13] in 1930. In the second case, there was no derivation using valid quantum mechanics to deduce the observational consequences for x and p measurement. In the last case, Δx and Δp were distribution widths for x and p, respectively, and had nothing to do with simultaneous measurement of x and p. I draw the conclusion that it is very dangerous to use uncertainty relations to discuss measurements. They do have one merit in that the calculations begin by being dimensionally correct. The kind of treatment outlined in this paper seems to me to be much closer to the physics of the measurement problem. Also, it is entirely based on conventional quantum mechanics, except for the addition of one postulate. As pointed out, an additional assumption has to be made to avoid the circular argument. Obviously, the von Neumann meter will have to be replaced by a more physical (and more complicated) device.

REFERENCES

1. HEISENBERG, W. 1930. The Physical Principles of the Quantum Theory. Chicago Univ. Press. Chicago.

2. DIRAC, P. A. M. 1930. The Principles of Quantum Mechanics (1st edition). Oxford Univ. Press. London/New York.
3. VON NEUMANN, J. 1932. Mathematical Foundations of the Quantum Mechanics. Springer-Verlag. Berlin. (Also reprinted in translation: 1955. Princeton Univ. Press. Princeton, New Jersey.)
4. JAMMER, M. 1966. Conceptual Development of Quantum Mechanics. McGraw–Hill. New York.
5. D'ESPAGNAT, B. 1976. Conceptual Foundations of Quantum Mechanics (2nd edition). Benjamin. New York (now Addison–Wesley. Reading, Massachusetts).
6. WHEELER, J. & W. ZUREK, Eds. 1983. Quantum Theory and Measurement. Princeton Univ. Press. Princeton, New Jersey.
7. LAMB, W. E., JR. 1969. An operational interpretation of non-relativistic quantum mechanics. Phys. Today 22: 23–28. See also: VON NEUMANN'S REDUCTION OF THE WAVE FUNCTION. 1975. In Proceedings of the Fourth International Conference on the Unity of the Sciences, pp. 297–303. International Cultural Foundation, Tarrytown, New York; WU, T-Y. Festschrift. 1979. Remarks on the interpretation of quantum mechanics. In Science of Matter. S. Fujita, Ed.: 1–8. Gordon & Breach. New York; A LETTER TO KIP THORNE. 1983. In CCNY Physics Symposium in Celebration of Melvin Lax's Sixtieth Birthday. H. Falk, Ed.: 40–43. City College of New York. New York; SCHRÖDINGER'S CAT. In Dirac Festschrift. B. Kursunoglu & E. Wigner, Eds. Cambridge Univ. Press. London. To be published.
8. ROYER, A. 1985. Measurement of the Wigner function. Phys. Rev. Lett. 55: 2745–2748.
9. ARTHURS, E. & J. KELLY. 1965. On the simultaneous measurement of a pair of conjugate observables. Bell Syst. Tech. J. 44: 725–729.
10. See, for example: BRAGINSKY, V., Y. VORONTSOV & K. THORNE. 1980. Quantum non-demolition measurements. Science 209: 547–557.
11. HEISENBERG, H. 1927. On the intuitive content of the quantum mechanical kinematics and mechanics. Z. Phys. 43: 172–198.
12. ROBERTSON, H. P. 1929. The uncertainty principle. Phys. Rev. 34: 163–164.
13. SCHRÖDINGER, E. 1930. On Heisenberg's uncertainty principle. Sitzungsber. Preuss. Akad. Wiss., pp. 296–303.

Novel Properties of Preselected and Postselected Ensembles[a]

Y. AHARONOV, D. ALBERT, A. CASHER,
AND L. VAIDMAN

Physics Department
University of South Carolina
Columbia, South Carolina 29208
and
School of Physics and Astronomy
Raymond and Beverly Sackler Faculty of Exact Sciences
Tel Aviv University
Tel Aviv 69978, Israel

The present considerations first arose in the context of an ongoing attempt to think carefully about what quantum mechanics allows us to infer about the past. My collaborators and I had for some time been thinking, more particularly, of ensembles of quantum mechanical systems that are defined by both preselection and postselection. Consider, for example, a spin-$\frac{1}{2}$ system (with zero Hamiltonian) measured on Monday to be in the state, $L_z = +\frac{1}{2}$, and which is measured on Friday to be in the state, $L_x = +\frac{1}{2}$. If it so happens that L_z was measured on that system on Wednesday, then, of course, that measurement finds with certainty that $L_z = +\frac{1}{2}$, and if it happens that L_x was measured on that system on Wednesday, then that measurement finds with certainty that $L_x = +\frac{1}{2}$; thus, these two facts seem to amount to saying that for such a system as this, on Wednesday, $L_x = +\frac{1}{2}$ and $L_z = +\frac{1}{2}$, albeit $(L_x, L_z) \neq 0$. On the other hand, it seems, at first sight, to be impossible to give two such assertions as these any experimental meaning at any single time for any single system, because if both L_z and L_x are measured on Wednesday, those two measurements disrupt one another, and the results, $L_x = +\frac{1}{2}$ and $L_z = =\frac{1}{2}$, will no longer be invariably obtained. We began to wonder at a certain point whether those disruptive effects might somehow be controlled or eliminated by somehow reducing the accuracy with which L_x and L_z are measured. It was this wondering that eventually produced what is to follow. We will begin by briefly reviewing what quantum mechanical measurements are.

Von Neumann's famous account of the operations of quantum mechanical measuring devices runs roughly like this: In order to measure some given observable, A, of a quantum mechanical system, S, what is required is that one produce a Hamiltonian of interaction between S and a measuring device, which has the form,

$$H_{int} = -g(t)qA, \tag{1}$$

where q is some internal variable of the measuring device, and $g(t)$ is a time-dependent coupling function that is nonzero only during some short interval, $t_o < t < t_1$, when the measuring device is "switched on." Then the measurement is accomplished as follows:

[a]This work was supported by NSF Grant No. PHY-8408265.

the Heisenberg equation for π, where π is defined to be the canonical momentum conjugate to the canonical coordinate, q, of the measuring device, reads

$$\frac{\partial \pi}{\partial t} = g(t)A; \qquad (2)$$

therefore, if π is initially set, say, at zero, and if the value of $\int_{t_o}^{t} g(t)dt$ is known, then the value of A at $t \simeq t_o \simeq t_1$ can be read off from the value of π after t_1 (thus π is often referred to as the "pointer variable").

The fact that any precise measurement of A must necessarily and uncontrollably disturb the values of observables that fail to commute with A can be traced, within this account, to the fact that a precise measurement of A requires that the value of π be precisely fixed prior to t_o. Consequently, this also requires that the uncertainty in q during the measurement interaction described in equation 1 (and hence, as well, the possible strength of that interaction) is unbounded.

On the other hand, it emerges quite clearly within this account that if one is willing to accept uncertainties in the initial value of q, along with the resultant inaccuracies in the measurement of A, then the uncertainties in the value of q during the measurement interaction, and hence, the possible strength of that interaction, and the disturbance caused by it to variables of S that fail to commute with A, can be bounded and controlled. We shall refer here to such a trading-off—specifically, to the sacrificing of the accuracy of measurements of A in order to gain some control of the disturbances caused by such measurements to variables that fail to commute with A—as a weakening of the measurement of A; and our present concern shall be to point out a most extraordinary statistical property of such weakened measurements, which we have recently discovered.

Consider a system of N spin-$\frac{1}{2}$ particles (the Hamiltonian of which we shall suppose, for simplicity, to be zero). Suppose that at the time t_i a precise measurement of the total angular momentum of this N-particle system in the x-direction (L_x) is carried out, and that this measurement produces the (largest possible) result $L = \frac{1}{2}N$; furthermore, suppose that at time $t_f (t_f > t_i)$ a precise measurement of L_y is carried out on this system, and that this measurement happens to produce the result $L_y = \frac{1}{2}N$ (such pairs of results, when N is large, will of course be rare, but they are nonetheless always possible; we should like to confine our attention here to a system wherein such a pair of results happens to have emerged). If we are later informed that another precise measurement of L_x, say, was carried out at time t_1 with $t_i < t_1 < t_f$, then (as is well known) we could assert with certainty that the result of that measurement must have been $L_x = \frac{1}{2}N$ (because otherwise the result of the measurement at t_i could not have been what it was); similarly, if we are later informed that a precise measurement of L_y was carried out at t_2 with $t_i < t_2 < t_f$, we would be in a position to assert with certainty that the result of that measurement must have been $L_y = \frac{1}{2}N$. Indeed, it is even the case that if we were later informed that a precise measurement of L_x was carried out at t_1 and a precise measurement of L_y was carried out at t_2, with $t_i < t_1 < t_2 < t_f$, then we should be in a position to say with certainty that the result of the measurement of t_1 was $L_x = \frac{1}{2}N$ and that the result of the measurement of t_2 was $L_y = \frac{1}{2}N$. However, it should be carefully noted that in this last case, the time-order of the two intermediate measurements is vitally important. These two measurements, after all, being precise, will uncontrollably disturb one another; thus, in the event that $t_i < t_2 < t_1 < t_f$, there will in general be no correlation whatsoever between the results of the measurements of t_i and t_1, nor between the results of those at t_f and t_2.

Suppose, however, that we were to weaken these two intermediate measurements in such a way as to gain some considerable control over (or even to eliminate) the disturbances they cause to one another. Suppose, more particularly, that the initial state of the measuring device is arranged in such a way as to bound the possible value of q as follows:

$$|q| < \frac{1}{(N/2)^{1/2+\epsilon}}, \tag{3}$$

where ϵ may be an arbitrarily small positive number. In that case, the resulting uncertainty in π will be of the order of $\sqrt{N/2}$, which, if N is taken to be large, is small compared with the maximal possible values of L_x and L_y; therefore, measuring devices prepared in this way can still serve (albeit imperfectly) as reasonably informative indicators of the values of those angular momenta. On the other hand, if we set

$$\int g(t)dt = 1 \tag{4}$$

for each of these devices, then the bound (equation 3) on q will guarantee that measurements of L_x, say, with such devices as these, will change the value of L_y only by amounts of the order of $\sqrt{N/2}$, which is (as we have just seen) within the intrinsic error associated with these measurements. Such weakened measurements of L_x and L_y, then, can be expected, as it were, to "commute"; it can be expected, that is, that two such measurements will verifiably leave one another's results essentially undisturbed.

Reconsider, now, the system of N spins described above, which was measured, precisely, at time t_i to be in the state $L_x = \frac{1}{2}N$ and at t_f to be in the state $L_y = \frac{1}{2}N$. Suppose that we are informed later on that a weak measurement of L_x, of the kind we have just described, was carried out at t_1 ($t_i < t_1 < t_f$). Then, especially if N is large, it can be asserted with a high degree of confidence that the result of this weakened measurement was $L_x = \frac{1}{2}N$ (more precisely, it will be the case that if $\langle L_x \rangle = 0$ before the interaction begins, then it will invariably be the case that $\langle L_x \rangle = \frac{1}{2}N$ after t_1, where π is the pointer variable of the weakened L_x measuring device; furthermore, if N is large, the uncertainties in q, both before and after the experiment, will be very small compared with this displacement in its expectation value); thus, by virtue of the time-reversal-symmetric character of the statistical predictions of quantum theory, the same argument can be made concerning a weak measurement of L_y that may have been carried out at t_2 within that same interval. Clearly, no additional complications are introduced by supposing that both measurements (first the measurement of L_x and then that of L_y) are carried out within that interval, as we did above; however, in the present case, because of the "commutative" behavior of these weak measurements, we also expect that the order in which they are carried out will make no difference. Indeed, it can easily be confirmed by straightforward calculation that whether $t_1 < t_2$ or $t_2 < t_1$, the expectation values of the pointer variables of both the L_x and the L_y measuring devices will, in the circumstances described above, be displaced by precisely (up to corrections of the order of $\sqrt{N/2}$) $\frac{1}{2}N$.

This produces something of a paradox, which runs as follows: Suppose that instead (as above) of measuring the value of L_x of time t_1 and the value of L_y of time t_2, we measure, with a single device, the sum of those two values. Such a measurement can easily be accomplished by means of an interaction Hamiltonian of the form,

$$H_{int} = g_1(t)q\frac{L_x}{\sqrt{2}} + g_2(t)q\frac{L_y}{\sqrt{2}}, \tag{5}$$

where $g_1(t)$ is nonzero only in the vicinity of t_1, and $g_2(t)$ is nonzero only in the vicinity of t_2 (the factors of $1/\sqrt{2}$, as the reader shall presently see, have been inserted for the sake of convenience). Furthermore, if "weak" bounds of the form of equation 3 are imposed on q, and in cases where L_x is precisely measured to be $\frac{1}{2}N$ at t_i and L_y is precisely measured to be $\frac{1}{2}N$ at t_f, the total displacement of the expectation value of π after both t_1 and t_2 will, by the above arguments, always be (up to corrections of the order of $\sqrt{N/2}$) $N/\sqrt{2}$, whether t_1 precedes t_2 or t_2 precedes t_1, or, indeed, $t_1 = t_2$. However, consider this last possibility. In the event that $t_1 = t_2$ [in the event, that is, that $g_1(t) = g_2(t)$], the interaction Hamiltonian of equation 5 reduces to

$$H_{int} = g_1(t)q\frac{L_x + L_y}{\sqrt{2}}, \tag{6}$$

which is the Hamiltonian required for a measurement of the projection of the total angular momentum along the α-axis (L_α), where α is the ray that bisects the right angle between x and y. Now, we have just argued that this measurement will (within such intervals as we have just described, and so long as q is bounded in accordance with equation 3) almost invariably produce the result $N/\sqrt{2}$; however, this seems a most paradoxical result, because the particular measurement here in question is (looked at in another way) simply a measurement of L_α, the largest possible eigenvalue of which is the vastly smaller number $\frac{1}{2}N$. How can it be that measurements of L_α, under these circumstances, with such regularity, produce impossible results?

The first thing to do, it would seem, is to verify the result of our argument by more rigorous techniques, and this, happily, is not a particularly difficult task. The state of the composite system consisting of the N spins together with the L_α-measuring apparatus after the L_α-interaction is complete, and supposing that L_x was found to have the value, $N/2$, at t_i, will be

$$e^{iq}\frac{L_x + L_y}{\sqrt{2}}|L_x = \frac{N}{2}\rangle|\pi \simeq 0\rangle, \tag{7}$$

wherein we have supposed, for simplicity, that $g_1(t)$ has the value of 1 whenever the measuring device is "switched on," and wherein $|\pi \simeq 0\rangle$ represents the initial state of that device, which (in accordance with equation 3) will be characterized by some Gaussian distribution of π-values, of width, $\sqrt{N/2}$, and peaked, say, about $\pi = 0$. Now, if it subsequently happens that at t_f, L_y is found to have the value, $N/2$, then the final state of the measuring apparatus (modulo an overall constant of normalization) will be

$$\left\langle L_y = \frac{N}{2}|e^{iq}\frac{L_x + L_y}{\sqrt{2}}|L_x = \frac{N}{2}\right\rangle|\pi \simeq 0\rangle; \tag{8}$$

thus, the time-evolution operator for the measuring apparatus through such a sequence of events will be

$$\left\langle L_y = \frac{N}{2} \middle| e^{iq} \frac{L_x + L_y}{\sqrt{2}} \middle| L_x = \frac{N}{2} \right\rangle. \tag{9}$$

Also, it can rigorously be shown (without too much trouble) that if q is taken to obey the bound (equation 3), then

$$\left\langle L_y = \frac{N}{2} \middle| e^{iq} \frac{L_x + L_y}{\sqrt{2}} \middle| L_x = \frac{N}{2} \right\rangle = e^{iqN/\sqrt{2}} + O\left(\frac{1}{N^\epsilon}\right) \tag{10}$$

as N becomes large. The effect of such a sequence of events, then, in this limit, is invariably to translate the initial $|\pi \simeq 0\rangle$ apparatus state by the impossible (or at least, at first sight, unreasonable) distance of $N/\sqrt{2}$, rather than (what would seem more reasonable) a distance equivalent to any of the eigenvalues of L_α, which is precisely as our earlier (and more intuitive) argument had led us to believe.

What is happening here (albeit the demonstration is quite straightforward) is something of a miracle. The measuring apparatus state is translated, in the course of these events, by a superposition of different distances corresponding to the various possible eigenvalues of L_α; the resultant translated states, in the end, will quantum mechanically interfere with one another in such a way as to produce an effective translation that is larger than any of them. In such sequences of events, everything in the final apparatus states, save the outermost limits of the tails (which must necessarily exist given equation 3) of the translated π-distributions, ends up canceling itself out; the central peaks annihilate one another and disappear, and what remains is a new peak, made up of constructive interferences among the many tails, way out in the middle of nowhere at $N/2$. Moreover (and this is what seems genuinely miraculous), the nature of these anomalous interferences is precisely such as to make the L_x and L_y components of the total angular momentum (both of which have the value, $N/2$) appear, as measured by our weak experiments, to add together in L as if they were components of a classical vector. These, strictly speaking, are of course errors of the measuring apparatus, but they are errors of an astonishingly subtle, systematic, and sensible kind; they are errors that (given initial and final conditions on the spins such as we have postulated here) invariably arise, and that conspire to point an internally consistent picture of a classical (rather than a quantum mechanical) system. However, it ought to be kept constantly in mind that such conspiracies among errors as these necessarily feature exceedingly rare sequences of events; indeed, if such were not the case, such conspiracies would constitute a genuine difficulty for quantum theory.

The effect we have just described, needless to say, is one particular example of what is quite clearly a very broad class of physical phenomena. This broad class of physical phenomena will arise in countless varieties of physical systems, wherein it may well take forms that are yet more striking than the one considered here. Our intent in this present paper has been simply to point out that such a class of phenomena exists; however, we shall have much more to say on the scope and the meaning of these phenomena in forthcoming publications.

The EPR Experiment—Thoughts about the "Loophole"[a]

N. DAVID MERMIN

Laboratory of Atomic and Solid State Physics
Cornell University
Ithaca, New York 14853-2501

INTRODUCTION AND CONCLUSIONS

In a recent article in *Physics Today*,[1] I described a very simple version of the Einstein-Podolsky-Rosen gedanken experiment, produced an elementary Bell inequality for that particular case, and discussed the strange metaphysical implications of the violation of that inequality by the quantum theoretic predictions for the gedanken experiment.

I also stated that the recent photon correlation experiments of Aspect and his collaborators[2] confirming the quantum theoretic predictions were a realization of that gedanken experiment. It was pointed out by several readers of my article that the correspondence between the real and gedanken versions of the experiment is less perfect than I suggested.[3] In particular, in the real experiments there is an important and highly relevant connection between the two faraway detectors, made necessary by the fact that the efficiency for detecting individual photons is rather low. Only events in which both detectors actually register a photon are included in the data, and it is only these events, the selection of which requires nontrivial communication between the detectors, that confirm the quantum theoretic predictions.

The real experiment will have the same implications as the gedanken experiment provided the detected photon pairs are a representative sample of all those actually emitted. If, however, one entertains the possibility that the probability of a photon triggering a detector might be correlated through the value of its hidden variable with its prior experience at a polarization analyzer,[4] then the remarkable metaphysical implications of the gedanken experiment for a local realistic description of nature cannot in fact be extracted from the real experiments without appealing to some additional untestable assumptions on the nature of such correlations.

This does not worry most people, nor does it particularly worry me. If local realism is to be saved by a failure of quantum mechanics to describe the entire ensemble of photon pairs, but in such a way that those pairs actually detected nevertheless do agree with the quantum theoretic predictions, then God is considerably less subtle and significantly more malicious than I can bring myself to believe.

On the other hand, because of this loophole, one cannot currently maintain (as some people would like to do) that the strange metaphysical consequences flow entirely from existing experiments without intervening physical assumptions, quantum theo-

[a]This work was supported in part by the National Science Foundation under Grant No. DMR-83-14625.

retic or otherwise. To the extent that I suggested in *Physics Today* that they did, I plead guilty to metaphysical overkill. To atone for this, I have done an elementary but nasty calculation, the results of which bear directly on this question. I shall only describe the nature of the calculation and the results here. I have some confidence that the results are correct because the same calculation has independently been done by Anupam Garg, who emerged with the same conclusion. We will publish the details elsewhere.

Suppose the quantum theoretic description of the Aspect experiments is in fact correct. One can then ask how high the detector efficiencies must be for the experimental confirmation of the quantum theoretic predictions to rule out any representation of the data in terms of a set of local hidden variables, even one that is capable of exploiting the failure of detectors always to record an event. For experiments like those of Aspect *et al.*, which probe correlations in four different pairs of orientations for the polarization analyzers associated with two different settings for each analyzer, the answer is 83% [more precisely, $2(\sqrt{2} - 1)$]. If the detector efficiency is less than 83%, then one can account for the fact that the detected pairs obey the quantum theoretic correlations by local hidden variables; if it exceeds 83%, then the quantum theoretic data violate a Bell inequality that does not require the kinds of subsidiary assumptions that are used in analyzing the Aspect experiments.

A similar, but weaker result was obtained a few years ago by Lo and Shimony,[5] who derived a particular necessary condition for local realism that can be shown to be violated by the quantum theoretic predictions for detector efficiencies of 86% or more. Our result of 83% (which is the critical efficiency for violating the necessary and sufficient condition) shows that one cannot improve significantly on the Lo-Shimony critical efficiency by constructing more powerful Bell inequalities.

Thus, if one wants to infer a violation of local realism directly from the experimental data, unembellished by subsidiary theoretical assumptions, then one requires either a heroic improvement in the efficiency of the detectors, or else (see below) a heroic readiness to perform computations analogous to the one Garg and I have done for more elaborate sets of data (collected from three or more settings at each detector) than those on which current tests of local realism have been based.

In the absence of this additional, rather difficult analysis, performing experiments with detectors that are less than 83% efficient to rule out specific hidden variable models exploiting detector inefficiencies is likely to prove ultimately futile on this metaphysical battleground, because until the efficiencies reach 83% other models can be invented to fill the gap.

THE NECESSARY AND SUFFICIENT CONDITION

In the experiments under consideration, two appropriately correlated entities (photons or spin-$1/2$ particles) fly apart to two analyzers (that separate polarizations or spins) backed up by particle detectors. Each analyzer can be set to measure the polarization or spin along either of two different orientations. We refer to this arrangement as a 2×2 experiment. All of the theoretical inequalities that test local realism have been derived for 2×2 experiments (except for a theorem of Garg[6] showing that if the data is consistent with inversion symmetry, then 3×3 experiments simply test all 2×2 subcases, and an unpublished proof by Kemperman[7] that this is not the case for 4×4 experiments).

The results of such experiments are summarized by four joint distributions, $p_{ij}(m,m')$, where $i = 1,2$ and $j = 3,4$ specify that one analyzer is oriented along directions, a_1 or a_2, and the other along a_3 or a_4, and where m and m' each assume the values 1 or -1 corresponding to the two possible results of the polarization or spin measurement.

The question at issue is whether all four distributions can be represented in the single form,

$$p_{ij}(m,m') = \int d\lambda \, \rho(\lambda) p_i(m,\lambda) q_j(m',\lambda), \tag{1}$$

where λ is some set of hidden variables with distribution, $\rho(\lambda)$, and $p_i(m,\lambda)$ and $q_j(m',\lambda)$ are conditional distributions for m and m', given the value, λ, for the hidden variable. (If the investigation is restricted to a 2×2 experiment, a completely equivalent form of the question is whether there exists a four-variable distribution, $p_{12,34}(m_1,m_2;m_3,m_4)$, that returns the four-pair distribution, p_{13}, p_{14}, p_{23}, p_{24}, as marginals.)

Clauser and Horne[8] showed that the representation in equation 1 implies the inequalities,

$$|E_{13} \pm E_{14}| + |E_{23} \mp E_{24}| \le 2, \tag{2}$$

where E_{ij} is the correlation function,

$$E_{ij} = \Sigma_{m,m'} \, mm'p_{ij}(m,m'). \tag{3}$$

(Fine[9] later showed that these inequalities are necessary *and sufficient* for the existence of the distribution, $p_{12,34}$.) The quantum theory violates these inequalities, and the Aspect experiments demonstrate that correlations of detected photon pairs from the appropriate atomic cascade also violate them.

In view of the less than perfect efficiency of the detectors, however, it is necessary to introduce additional assumptions before the Clauser-Horne inequality (2) becomes relevant to the actual experiments. The simplest such assumption, already mentioned, is that for each value of the hidden variable λ, the pairs actually detected are representative of all emitted pairs; i.e., that for any value of the hidden variable, the behavior of a particle at an analyzer and the orientation of that analyzer are uncorrelated with the subsequent probability of detection at the photomultiplier. Alternatively, one can use a modified form of the inequality (2) based on a "no enhancement" assumption which asserts that for each value of λ, the probability of detecting a particle in one or the other channel with the analyzer in place does not exceed the probability of detecting it when the analyzer is removed.

Although the consequences of assumptions such as these are subject to test for the entire ensemble of particles and are certainly implied on this level by orthodox quantum mechanics, confirmation of such behavior in the mean does not imply that the behavior must hold for each individual value of λ in some hypothetical hidden variable model. By dropping these untestable assumptions, models have been constructed that exploit detector inefficiencies to fit the quantum theoretic predictions for the observed pairs either exactly or to within the accuracy of existing experiments.[10]

How efficient must the detectors be to rule out such models without subsidiary assumptions? Models that exploit detector inefficiency allow the probability of detection to depend on both the hidden variable λ and the orientation a_i of the analyzer. The predictions of such models can be represented by adding to the values of 1 and -1 for m and m' a third value 0 corresponding to nondetection. Such models will be compatible with local realism if the values of the joint distribution p_{ij} in this expanded domain continue to have a representation of the form found in equation 3.

The data from an experiment now consist not only of the frequencies p_{ij} for $|m|$ and $|m'|$ equal to unity, but also the values when one or the other of them is zero; $p_{ij}(0,0)$, being the frequency of events in which neither detector fires, is unobservable. The question is whether the p_{ij} corresponding to the eight observable frequencies can be supplemented by additional nonnegative numbers, $p_{ij}(0,0)$, that will permit the resulting probabilities to be represented in the form (1).

We have found the necessary and sufficient conditions for such a representation in the 2×2 case provided the pair distributions have the following symmetries:

(i) $p_{ij}(m,m') = p_{ij}(-m,-m')$;

(ii) $p_{ij}(0,1) = p_{ij}(1,0) = p(1,0)$, independent of i,j;

(iii) $\Sigma_m p_{ij}(0,m) = \Sigma_m p_{ij}(m,0) = p(0)$, independent of i,j.   (4)

If one assumes (or verifies by some other means) that the source produces pairs at a steady rate, then all these relations can be subject to direct experimental test. They are all satisfied by the quantum theoretic predictions in conjunction with the known facts about photomultiplier efficiencies. A measured departure from symmetry (i) would violate rotation or inversion symmetry. Symmetry (ii) asserts that the probability of registering an event at one detector when the other detector fails to register a count is independent of the settings of the polarizers. Symmetry (iii) asserts that the probability of registering an event at a detector, without regard to what is happening at the other detector, also does not depend on the setting of either polarizer. Assumptions (ii) and (iii) together imply that the probability, $p(0,0)$, of both members of the pair escaping detection is also independent of the orientation of the analyzers.

The problem posed by such a set of distributions is quite similar to the problem of finding the generalization of the Clauser-Horne inequalities from spin-$1/2$ to spin-1. The steps to solve that problem are spelled out explicitly in a paper I wrote a few years ago with Gina Schwarz.[11] There are slight differences in the simplifying symmetries one can impose in the two cases, and the nonobservability of $p(0,0)$ in the case of interest here modifies the interpretation of the final results. Because, however, of the close similarity, the procedure leading to the final set of inequalities in reference 11 can be followed step-by-step to produce the generalization of the Clauser-Horne inequalities we require here. As a result of the second of the three symmetries in (4), the final form of these inequalities is much simpler in the present case than it is for spin-1 and we find simply

$$|E_{13} \pm E_{14}| + |E_{23} \mp E_{24}| \leq 2[1 - p(0,0)].$$ (5)

Here, the correlation functions E_{ij} continue to be defined by (3), but now the sum over m and m' includes the value, 0, corresponding to no detection.

These inequalities can be written in the form,

$$|e_{13} \pm e_{14}| + |e_{23} \mp e_{24}| \leq 2, \tag{6}$$

where

$$e_{ij} = \Sigma_{m,m'} \, mm' \{ p_{ij}(m,m')/[1 - p(0,0)] \}. \tag{7}$$

Because $p_{ij}(m,m')/[1 - p(0,0)]$ is the probability of the outcome m,m' given that at least one particle is detected, e_{ij} can be computed entirely in terms of observed counting rates, independent of the (unknown) value of $p(0,0)$.

The new conditions (6) are thus nothing but the old Clauser-Horne inequalities (2), except that the correlation functions e_{ij} are reduced from the E_{ij} by the ratio of the number of detected pairs to the number of detected pairs and single events.[12] If, as expected, the detection probabilities are entirely determined by the quantum efficiency of the detectors, then that ratio will be $\eta^2/[1-(1 - \eta)^2] = \eta/(2 - \eta)$. Because the maximum value of the quantum theoretic prediction for the left side of the old Clauser-Horne inequalities (2) is $2^{3/2}$, the renormalized inequalities (6) can be violated only if $2^{3/2} \eta/(2 - \eta) > 2$, which requires $\eta > 2(\sqrt{2} - 1) = 82.8\%$.

Therefore if a set of experiments confirms the expected quantum theoretic behavior, the data can only rule out local realism by violating a 2×2 generalized Clauser-Horne inequality if the detector efficiencies are 83% or better.

It therefore seems unlikely that the loophole will be unambiguously closed in the near future by refinements in photomultiplier technology. My advice to those who take the loophole seriously would be to try to think about closing it on theoretical grounds along the following lines:

The Clauser-Horne inequalities are the necessary and sufficient conditions for compatibility with local realism of a set of 2×2 experiments in which data are collected only for two settings of each polarization analyzer. It is known, however, that 2×2 experiments do not provide the most stringent tests.[13] In general, the N^2 sets of data collected in an $N \times N$ experiment in which each analyzer has N different orientations can be incompatible with local realism, even though all 2×2 subsets satisfy the Clauser-Horne inequalities.

It seems very likely that as N increases, there will be a drop in the detector efficiency above which it is impossible to give a local realistic accounting for all data violating the ideal $N \times N$ Clauser-Horne inequalities. Whether the critical efficiency declines enough to be of help is less clear. Unfortunately, it is an intricate task to generalize the spin-1/2 Clauser-Horne inequalities even to the 3×3 case, and as far as I know the analysis has not yet been done in the spin-1/2 4×4 case. The corresponding spin-1 analysis (which is required to incorporate detector inefficiency) has been done only in the 2×2 case, where it is substantially more difficult than the spin-1/2 problem. In principle, conceptually straightforward algorithms exist for the extraction of the appropriate inequalities in all of these cases;[14] in practice, however, executing these algorithms is a nasty problem in linear programming that might well become computationally entirely unwieldy even for relatively small N.

It seems to me, nevertheless, that anybody who takes seriously this loophole in the Aspect experiments has a duty (a) to warn experimentalists that on the basis of our current ability to execute the algorithm leading to Bell inequalities, no experiment will definitively close the loophole with detector efficiencies less than 83%, and (b) to engage in efforts at least as arduous as those being urged on the experimentalists, by attempting to generalize the analysis to the $N \times N$ case for appropriate N greater than 2.

NOTES AND REFERENCES

1. MERMIN, N. D. 1985. Phys. Today **38**(4): 38–47.
2. ASPECT, A. *et al.* 1981. Phys. Rev. Lett. **47**: 460–463; 1982. **49**: 91–94; 1982. **49**: 1804–1807.
3. See the letters from T. W. Marshall and E. Santos, Thomas M. Jordan, and Peder Voetmann Christiansen, and my comments on those letters in *Phys. Today* **38**(11), November 1985.
4. The earliest paper I am aware of that emphatically points this out is by PEARLE, P. M. 1970. Phys. Rev. **D2**: 1418–1425. It seems appropriate to mention at this conference dedicated to Eugene P. Wigner that Pearle cites a private communication from E. P. Wigner about an unpublished result that sounds, from Pearle's description, rather similar in spirit to the one I describe here.
5. SHIMONY, A. & T. K. LO. 1981. Phys. Rev. **A23**: 3003–3012.
6. GARG, A. 1983. Phys. Rev. **D28**: 785–790.
7. KEMPERMAN, J. Private communication.
8. CLAUSER, J. F. & M. A. HORNE. 1974. Phys. Rev. **D10**: 526–535.
9. FINE, A. 1982. Phys. Rev. Lett. **48**: 291–295.
10. Reference 4 above; also see: MARSHALL, T. W. *et al.* 1983. Phys. Lett. **98A**: 5–9; Phys. Lett. **99A**: 163–166; 1984. Phys. Lett. **100A**: 225–227; FINE, A. 1982. Synthese **50**: 279–294.
11. MERMIN, N. D. & G. M. SCHWARZ. 1982. Found. Phys. **12**: 101–135.
12. The close similarity between conditions (2) and (6) suggests that the latter ought to follow from a straightforward generalization of the arguments leading to the former, or that it ought to be possible to map the case with inefficient detectors back onto the ideal case before carrying out the analysis. I have not been able to find such an argument. While there undoubtedly is a simpler way to establish that (6) is a necessary condition for the representation (1), I know of no way to establish the sufficiency (which is the basis for the rather discouraging implications for subsequent experimental tests) other than by going through the appropriate version of the rather elaborate analysis described in reference 11. A simpler argument would certainly be welcome. [**Note added in proof:** J. F. Clauser pointed out to me at the conference that a proof of necessity can be found in reference 8. I still know of no proof of sufficiency other than by the complicated method of reference 11.]
13. GARG, A. & N. D. MERMIN. 1983. Phys. Rev. **D27**: 339–348; 1982. Phys. Rev. Lett. **49**: 1220–1223.
14. GARG, A. & N. D. MERMIN. 1984. Found. Phys. **14**: 1–39.

Does Bell's Theorem Apply to Theories That Admit Time-Dependent States?[a]

JON P. JARRETT

Department of Philosophy
Harvard University
Cambridge, Massachusetts 02138

It is the purpose of this paper to explore the status of a certain general class of local hidden variables theories with respect to the derivation of Bell-type inequalities. It will be maintained that the central premise of the Bell-type arguments is not (or, at least, is not obviously) an appropriate constraint on theories of this class. While further considerations render unlikely the chances of discovering any plausible empirically adequate local hidden variables theory among that class, an interesting question remains: How might the central premise of the Bell-type arguments be reformulated so as to exclude this class of local hidden variables theories?

The premise in question has been called "local causality,"[1] "generalized locality,"[2] "factorizability,"[3] "conditional stochastic independence,"[4] and (the name also to be used in the present paper) "strong locality."[5] (This list is not exhaustive.) Because Bell-type arguments are framed differently in different presentations, the above-named constraints cannot all be regarded as logically equivalent in any strict sense. However, it will be generally acknowledged that, roughly speaking, each "does the same work" and has a similar physical content.

Adopting the widely used notation of Clauser and Horne,[6] the condition of interest, namely, strong locality, may be expressed as follows:

$$p_{12}(\lambda, a, b) = p_1(\lambda, a) \cdot p_2(\lambda, b), \tag{1}$$

where, given the standard Bohm-Bell-EPR experimental arrangement, $p_1(\lambda, a)$ is the probability of a spin-up outcome of a measurement of the a-component of the spin of particle 1, $p_2(\lambda, b)$ is the probability of a spin-up outcome of a measurement of the b-component of the spin of particle 2, and $p_{12}(\lambda, a, b)$ is the probability of joint spin-up outcomes when both measurements are performed; these are all for two-particle systems in the state $\lambda \in \Lambda$. Here and throughout, the obvious universal quantification clauses that belong in the full statement of such conditions are suppressed. Further specification of the states of the measuring devices is also suppressed in this formalism, but whatever additional information is deemed appropriate may be encoded in the parameters a and b, where these parameters are allowed to have however many components as are necessary to fully specify the measuring device states. The remarks to follow apply *mutatis mutandis* to those counterparts to equation 1 that play the role

[a]This paper is based on parts of a doctoral dissertation, "Bell's Theorem, Quantum Mechanics, and Local Realism", written while the author was a Searle Graduate Fellow at the University of Chicago. Support was provided at that time by the Searle Fund of the Chicago Community Trust.

of strong locality in any Bell-type argument. λ is generally taken to be the state into which the two-particle system has been "prepared." It is just that "hidden" state in which the particles have been left by previous interactions. The probabilities in equation 1 are associated with the outcomes of possible future measurements. Let us consider theories for which the state of the two-particle system evolves (perhaps, but not necessarily, stochastically) during the interval between state preparation and measurements. This will be the class of theories of interest.

In the context of such theories, if λ in equation 1 is taken to be the "initial" state of the two-particle system, then it makes sense only to regard the probability functions in equation 1 as expectations of the following kind (where it is assumed for the moment that the subsequent measurement interactions are instantaneous events that are simultaneous in the laboratory frame, and that they always occur at some fixed time τ after the preparation of the initial state):

$$p_1(\lambda, a) = \int_\Lambda \bar{p}_1(\lambda', a) \, dP(\lambda'|\lambda),$$

$$p_2(\lambda, b) = \int_\Lambda \bar{p}_2(\lambda', b) \, dP(\lambda'|\lambda),$$

$$p_{12}(\lambda, a, b) = \int_\Lambda \bar{p}_{12}(\lambda', a, b) \, dP(\lambda'|\lambda). \tag{2}$$

Here, P is a conditional probability measure. $P(S|\lambda)$ is the probability that a system initially in state λ will have evolved into a state that lies in the set S at the end of time τ. $\bar{p}_1$, $\bar{p}_2$, and $\bar{p}_{12}$ represent probabilities (most naturally regarded as propensities of some sort) for measurement outcomes relative to the state of the system at the instant of measurement (i.e., immediately prior to measurement). Then p_1, p_2, and p_{12} represent second-order probabilistic quantities—that is to say, these probabilities have as their origin not only the presumedly irreducible indeterminism of the measurement outcomes that would obtain even if the state at the time of measurement, λ_τ, were known (which is just the indeterminism represented by the probabilities, $\bar{p}_1$, $\bar{p}_2$, and $\bar{p}_{12}$), but also the uncertainty (relative to the initial state λ) associated with the identity of that future state, λ_τ; in general (if λ evolves stochastically), only the probability that any particular state in Λ will actually be the state into which λ evolves after time τ is given. Accordingly, p_1, p_2, and p_{12} are weighted averages of the "true" probabilities, $\bar{p}_1$, $\bar{p}_2$, and $\bar{p}_{12}$, respectively. The conditional probability measure P and the probability functions $\bar{p}_1$, $\bar{p}_2$, and $\bar{p}_{12}$ are to be specified by the theory.

Considerations that have to do with what may be called the "completeness"[7] of the state descriptions suggest that something like equation 1 may appropriately be imposed on the "true" probability functions evaluated at the moment of measurement, that is,

$$\bar{p}_{12}(\lambda_\tau, a, b) = \bar{p}_1(\lambda_\tau, a) \cdot \bar{p}_2(\lambda_\tau, b), \tag{3}$$

but that equation 1 itself, where the probabilities are of the form given by equation 2, is not an appropriate constraint on local hidden variables theories.[8] Consider equation 3 in the following form:

$$\bar{p}_1(\lambda_\tau, a) = \frac{\bar{p}_{12}(\lambda_\tau, a, b)}{\bar{p}_2(\lambda_\tau, b)}, \quad \text{for } \bar{p}_2(\lambda_\tau, b) \neq 0. \tag{3'}$$

The expression on the right-hand side of equation 3' is the conditional probability[9] for the spin-up outcome of an a-component spin measurement on particle 1 given that the outcome of a b-component spin measurement on particle 2 is also spin-up for a pair of particles in the state λ_τ at the time of measurement. Equation 3' asserts the equality of this conditional probability and the unconditioned probability for the spin-up outcome of the measurement on particle 1.

In order to see the intuitive basis for equation 3' as a constraint on local hidden variables theories, consider how, in general, the probability assigned to a particular outcome of a measurement on particle 1 could be influenced by the acquisition of knowledge of the outcome of a measurement on particle 2. Armed with sufficient knowledge of the laws that govern the prior interaction of the particles, one might, on the basis of knowledge of the outcome of a measurement on particle 2, make inferences about some of the properties of particle 1. However, because the probabilities occurring in equation 3' are the "true" probabilities (and not expectations of the sort given by equation 2), and because the state λ_τ occurring in the arguments of the probability functions is the actual state of the two-particle system at the time of measurement, and because relativity forbids any instantaneous casual influence passing between particle 1 (at the time τ) and the (spacelike) measurement on particle 2, any such information about particle 1 gained via knowledge of the outcome of a measurement on particle 2 must be redundant; for if the state description is suitably complete (as is assumed), precisely all such information is already contained in λ_τ. (This is taken to be part of what it means to say of a state description, that it is "complete.") Thus construed, the conditional probability expressed by the right-hand side of equation 3' must, for local hidden variables theories, equal the probability on the left-hand side of equation 3'.

The attempt to present a parallel account in support of equation 1, however, fails. Consider equation 1 in this form:

$$p_1(\lambda, a) = \frac{p_{12}(\lambda, a, b)}{p_2(\lambda, b)}, \quad \text{for } p_2(\lambda, b) \neq 0. \tag{1'}$$

The expression on the right-hand side of equation 1' is the conditional probability, relative to the initial state λ, for the spin-up outcome of an a-component spin measurement on particle 1 at time τ, given that the outcome of a simultaneous b-component spin measurement on particle 2 is also spin-up.[10] Equation 1' asserts the equality of this conditional probability and the unconditioned probability for the spin-up outcome of the measurement on particle 1.

To appreciate why it is that equation 1' need not hold for (what might otherwise be acceptable) hidden variables theories, consider that the outcome of the measurement on particle 2 at time τ might very well yield information about particle 1 at time τ that was not included in the initial state λ. It may, for instance, provide some further clue to the identity of λ_τ. Indeed, that outcome might even be incompatible with certain antecedently possible final states. At any rate, the conditional probability, relative to λ, for some particular outcome of the measurement on particle 1 at time τ, given some particular outcome of the simultaneous measurement on particle 2, certainly may differ from the unconditioned probability, relative to λ, for the specified outcome of the measurement on particle 1.

A simple example will illustrate the point. Let λ be the initial state of the two-particle system. Suppose that only two possible final states, λ_1 and λ_2, are accessible from λ. Suppose also that the theory makes the following probability assignments:

$$\bar{p}_1(\lambda_1, a) = \frac{1}{2} \qquad\qquad \bar{p}_2(\lambda_1, b) = \frac{1}{2}$$

$$\bar{p}_1(\lambda_2, a) = \frac{1}{3} \qquad\qquad \bar{p}_2(\lambda_2, b) = 0$$

$$\bar{p}_{12}(\lambda_1, a, b) = \frac{1}{4}$$

$$\bar{p}_{12}(\lambda_2, a, b) = 0.$$

(These probabilities satisfy the strong locality condition expressed by equation 3.) Finally, suppose that λ evolves stochastically into λ_1 or λ_2 after time τ in accordance with $P(\lambda_1|\lambda) = \frac{1}{4}$ and $P(\lambda_2|\lambda) = \frac{3}{4}$. From equation 2, it follows that

$$p_1(\lambda, a) = \frac{1}{4} \cdot \frac{1}{2} + \frac{3}{4} \cdot \frac{1}{3} = \frac{3}{8},$$

$$p_2(\lambda, b) = \frac{1}{4} \cdot \frac{1}{2} + \frac{3}{4} \cdot 0 = \frac{1}{8},$$

and

$$p_{12}(\lambda, a, b) = \frac{1}{4} \cdot \frac{1}{4} + \frac{3}{4} \cdot 0 = \frac{1}{16} \neq \frac{3}{8} \cdot \frac{1}{8}.$$

This theory therefore violates equation 1. In terms of the previous discussion, it can be seen that knowledge of a spin-up outcome of the measurement on particle 2 reveals predictively relevant information about particle 1 that was not entailed by λ; namely, that $\lambda_\tau = \lambda_1$.[11] The correct conditional probability[12] (relative to λ) for the spin-up outcome of the measurement on particle 1, given that the outcome of the simultaneous measurement on particle 2 is also spin-up, is therefore $\frac{1}{2}$.

$$\left[\text{Note:} \quad \frac{1}{2} = \bar{p}_1(\lambda_1, a) = \frac{p_{12}(\lambda, a, b)}{p_2(\lambda, b)} \neq p_1(\lambda, a). \right]$$

In general, it is plausible to impose on hidden variables theories the requirement that the two measurement outcomes be stochastically independent relative to the final state description λ_τ. This is what equation 3 expresses. Relative to the initial state λ, however, the two measurement outcomes may be correlated in ways that can be traced to the inadequacy (i.e., the "incompleteness") of the initial state λ for making "true" probability assignments to the outcomes of measurements at the future time τ.

If equation 1 need not hold for local hidden variables theories, then the possibility arises that equation 3 may be satisfied by some theory that reproduces the predictions of quantum mechanics. This possibility will now be investigated.

Let ρ be the probability measure on Λ associated with the distribution of initial states. The observable predictions for the theory are obtained by integrating over the set of "hidden" states as follows:

$$p_1(a) = \int_\Lambda d\rho(\lambda) \int_\Lambda dP(\lambda'|\lambda)\bar{p}_1(\lambda', a)$$

$$= \int_\Lambda d\rho'(\lambda')\bar{p}_1(\lambda', a), \tag{4}$$

where the new measure, ρ', is given by

$$\rho'(S) = \int \int_{S \times \Lambda} dP(\lambda'|\lambda) d\rho(\lambda) = \int_{\Lambda} d\rho(\lambda) P(S|\lambda). \tag{4}$$

Similarly,

$$p_2(b) = \int_{\Lambda} d\rho'(\lambda) \bar{p}_2(\lambda, b) \text{ and } p_{12}(a, b) = \int_{\Lambda} d\rho'(\lambda) \bar{p}_{12}(\lambda, a, b). \tag{4}$$

For a hidden variables theory to succeed, it would have to provide probability functions $\bar{p}_1$, $\bar{p}_2$, and $\bar{p}_{12}$, as well as probability measures ρ and P such that the quantities $p_1(a)$, $p_2(b)$, and $p_{12}(a, b)$ given by equation 4 come out to be equal to the corresponding quantum mechanical probabilities. In particular, that would require:[13]

$$p_1(a) = p_2(b) = \tfrac{1}{2}, \ p_{12}(a, b) = \tfrac{1}{2} \sin^2 \frac{\sphericalangle(a, b)}{2}. \tag{5}$$

However, a little reflection reveals that equation 5 cannot be satisfied by any theory that satisfies equations 3 and 4. Any such theory has the same form as a theory with time-independent states distributed in accordance with the probability measure ρ'. Because the foregoing considerations have no relevance for theories that admit only time-independent states, the standard arguments may be followed to derive Bell-type inequalities for theories that satisfy equations 3 and 4.

In retrospect, this result should not be too surprising. Bell-type arguments apply to theories that specify a distribution of "hidden" states and underlying probabilities satisfying equation 1. Whether one regards that distribution as referring to the initial states (the "prepared" states) or to the final states (i.e., after time τ has elapsed) is without significance as far as the structure of the derivation is concerned. The two cases are formally identical.

To summarize, it has been found that considerations concerning local hidden variables theories that admit time-dependent states provide reasons for challenging the general applicability of equation 1, at least as it is applied in standard versions of Bell-type arguments. It has also been found that these considerations nevertheless apparently fail to block the derivation of Bell-type inequalities for theories that admit time-dependent states.

However, this conclusion ought not to be drawn too hastily. Recall the simplifying background assumptions according to which pairs of measurements are taken to be simultaneous in the laboratory frame and to be instantaneous events occurring at a single fixed time τ in that frame. Following the standard Bell-type arguments, then, and by using the distribution of states at the specific time τ, the Bell-type inequalities that emerge should explicitly exhibit this built-in time-dependence; for example,[14]

$$-1 \le p_{12}(a, b; \tau) - p_{12}(a, b'; \tau)$$

$$+ p_{12}(a', b; \tau) + p_{12}(a', b', \tau) - p_1(a', \tau) - p_2(b, \tau) \le 0. \tag{6}$$

While this might be a satisfactory result if the background assumptions were true, it cannot be expected to hold (even as an approximation) if those assumptions are false. The foregoing analysis relied crucially on their holding exactly. However nearly they may hold in actual experiments, their failure to hold exactly would necessitate a complete reexamination of the problem; furthermore, even though it may be true to a very good approximation that pairs of measurements occur simultaneously in the laboratory frame and that they occur at the same fixed time for each trial, these assumptions are undoubtedly false. (One need only consider that real measuring devices must afford the particles a noninfinitesimal interaction region if measurement is to occur at all; therefore, actual experiments will involve measurements on particles that traverse a range of distances from the source, so even particles emerging with a fixed definite velocity every time will not take exactly the same amount of time to pass from the source to the point of measurement. Moreover, there are practical, if not in principle, limits to the precision with which one can position the source and the measuring devices so as to guarantee simultaneity of the measurements. This is also complicated by the fact that actual measurements are not point events in space-time, but take place over some spatiotemporal region.)

The problem, therefore, is this: If it must be allowed that pairs of measurements need neither be simultaneous in the laboratory frame nor occur at the same pair of different times from one trial to the next, from what strong locality condition (i.e., something like equation 3) can Bell-type inequalities that bear on the actual experiments be derived? Under these circumstances, equation 3 does not even make sense. To be sure, the right-hand side of equation 3 could be amended to include, in place of τ in the $\bar{p}_1$ and $\bar{p}_2$ terms, the two different times, τ_1 and τ_2, respectively, at which the measurements on particles 1 and 2 are taken to occur, but if $\tau_1 \neq \tau_2$, what value then belongs in the place occupied by τ in the $\bar{p}_{12}$ term?; that is, how can the results of a sequence of trials be combined to produce ensemble averages of the terms occurring in equation 6 that continue to satisfy inequalities of that form?[15]

If one wishes to proceed by minimally modifying the existing formulation, two possible approaches may come to mind (where it will continue to be assumed for now that measurements may be regarded as instantaneous events): (i) For each trial, the two measurements are simultaneous in some frame or other. Let τ_i be the time at which measurements in the i-th trial occur in the frame of simultaneity for that trial. (It is allowed that the frames of simultaneity for different trials may differ; that is, τ_i need not equal τ_j for $i \neq j$.) The strong locality condition then has this form:

$$\text{(For all } i) \; \bar{p}_{12}(\lambda_{\tau_i}, a, b) = \bar{p}_1(\lambda_{\tau_i}, a) \cdot \bar{p}_2(\lambda_{\tau_i}, b). \tag{7}$$

The problem now consists in getting from equation 7 to a Bell-type inequality. There might be plausible assumptions (presumably restrictions on the structure of the λ_τ's) that could yield ensemble averages that combine quantities associated with different frames of simultaneity, but as the situation stands, it is not obvious that no theory satisfying strong locality in the sense of equation 7 is compatable with the predictions of quantum mechanics.

(ii) Alternatively, one might entertain a strong locality condition of the form:

$$\text{(For each trial) } \bar{p}_{12}(\lambda_{\tau_1}, a; \lambda_{\tau_2}, b) = \bar{p}_1(\lambda_{\tau_1}, a) \cdot \bar{p}_2(\lambda_{\tau_2}, b). \tag{8}$$

Even if the standard procedures for deriving Bell-type inequalities are extended in a suitable way to accommodate distributions of both states at time τ_1 and states at time τ_2, it is not immediately clear how to employ these procedures in a manner that would take into account the variation of τ_1 and τ_2 from one trial to the next. At least it is not obvious that no theory satisfying equation 8 is compatible with the predictions of quantum mechanics.

While no attempt will be made here to provide a definitive treatment of these issues, it may be helpful to look at one strategy for extending the Bell-type arguments in a way that seeks to resolve these difficulties along the lines of approach (ii) above.[16] To do this, let $\pi(S_1, S_2|\lambda)$ be the probability that a two-particle system prepared in state λ evolves into a state in set S_1 at the time of the measurement on particle 1 and into a state in set S_2 at the time of the measurement on particle 2. (No assumption about the order of the measurements is being made here, but this will be taken into account in what follows.) Let $h_1(t_1)$ be the probability density for the occurrence at time t_1 of the measurement on particle 1. Define $h_2(t_2)$ analogously.[17] In addition, let $\lambda(t)$ be the state of the evolving two-particle system at time t, where $\lambda = \lambda(0)$ is the initial state, and let ρ be the probability measure on Λ associated with the (time-dependent) distribution of states.

Any candidate theory must also provide a conditional probability density u that is to be interpreted as follows: $u[\lambda(t')|\lambda(t)]$ is the probability density for the transition from the state $\lambda(t)$ to the state $\lambda(t')$, where $t' > t$.

Using these definitions, $\pi(S_1, S_2|\lambda)$ may be expressed as

$$\int_0^\infty dt_1 h_1(t_1) \int_0^\infty dt_2 h_2(t_2) \int_{S_i} d\rho(\lambda(t_i)) u(\lambda(t_i)|\lambda) \int_{S_j} d\rho(\lambda(t_j)) u(\lambda(t_j)|\lambda(t_i)),$$

$$\text{where } i = \begin{cases} 1, & t_1 \leq t_2 \\ 2, & t_1 > t_2 \end{cases} \quad \text{and} \quad j = \begin{cases} 1, & t_1 > t_2 \\ 2, & t_1 \leq t_2. \end{cases}$$

This expression then becomes

$$\int_0^\infty dt_2 h_2(t_2) \left(\int_0^{t_2} dt_1 h_1(t_1) \int_{S_1} d\rho(\lambda(t_1)) u(\lambda(t_1)|\lambda) \int_{S_2} d\rho(\lambda(t_2)) u(\lambda(t_2)|\lambda(t_1)) \right.$$

$$\left. + \int_{t_2}^\infty dt_1 h_1(t_1) \int_{S_2} d\rho(\lambda(t_2)) u(\lambda(t_2)|\lambda) \int_{S_1} d\rho(\lambda(t_1)) u(\lambda(t_1)|\lambda(t_2)) \right).$$

Now, let $f(S_1, S_2) = \int_\Lambda d\rho(\lambda)\pi(S_1, S_2|\lambda)$. (Note that this measure is defined in terms of quantities that must be provided by the theory.)

Next, adopt the following as the strong locality condition:

$$\bar{p}_{12}(\lambda_1, a; \lambda_2, b) = \bar{p}_1(\lambda_1, a) \cdot \bar{p}_2(\lambda_2, b),$$

where λ_i is the state at the time of the measurement on particle i. This gives

$$p_{12}(a, b) = \iint_{\Lambda \times \Lambda} df(\lambda_1, \lambda_2) \bar{p}_{12}(\lambda_1, a; \lambda_2, b)$$

$$= \iint_{\Lambda \times \Lambda} df(\lambda_1, \lambda_2) \bar{p}_1(\lambda_1, a) \cdot \bar{p}_2(\lambda_2, b)$$

and

$$p_i(c) = \iint_{\Lambda \times \Lambda} df(\lambda_1, \lambda_2) \bar{p}_i(\lambda_i, c), \quad i = 1, 2.$$

Following Clauser and Horne,[6] for example, yields

$$-1 \le \bar{p}_{12}(\lambda_1, a; \lambda_2, b) - \bar{p}_{12}(\lambda_1, a; \lambda_2, b') + \bar{p}_{12}(\lambda_1, a'; \lambda_2, b)$$
$$+ \bar{p}_{12}(\lambda_1, a'; \lambda_2, b') - \bar{p}_1(\lambda_1, a') - \bar{p}_2(\lambda_2, b) \le 0. \quad (9)$$

Finally, integrating equation 9 over $\Lambda \times \Lambda$ with f as the measure gives the Clauser-Horne inequality:

$$-1 \le p_{12}(a, b) - p_{12}(a, b') + p_{12}(a', b) + p_{12}(a', b') - p_1(a') - p_2(b) \le 0. \quad (10)$$

However, there are objections that jeopardize this line of reasoning.[18] In order for this derivation to go through, it is essential that the functions h_1 and h_2 not depend on the component of spin to be measured. (Otherwise, π, and therefore f, could share this dependence, which would block the move from equation 9 to equation 10.) However, h_1 and h_2 cannot be completely insensitive to the particular constitution and configuration of the experimental apparatus. If the distance a particle must travel between the source and the region of measurement varies even minutely, but systematically, with the apparatus configurations associated with measurements of different components of spin, then h_1 and h_2 will not be independent of the component of spin being measured.

One could try to salvage the argument by imposing additional constraints on the theory. For example, if the state of the two-particle system is required to be a sufficiently slowly-varying function of time, then its associated probability assignments will be nearly constant over small enough time intervals. An assumption of this sort might also justify treating measurements as instantaneous events. Slight variations of h_1 and h_2 with the component of spin being measured will then have negligible effect on the theoretical predictions.

It is not clear how such assumptions are to be justified. In any case, even if some mechanism of this sort could account for the violation of Bell-type inequalities in one particular experiment, it would only raise a new question: If the distribution of measurement outcomes is so sensitive to the precise details of the experimental arrangement, why is there such good agreement among the results of different experiments?; that is, how is it to be understood that in a variety of experimental situations, these mechanisms that distort the results of individual experiments all manage to do so in such a way that, within experimental uncertainties, not only are the Bell-type inequalities violated, but the specific numerical predictions of quantum mechanics are confirmed?[19] Under these circumstances, it should be clear that "explanations" of this sort are apt to make it appear that a fantastic coincidence is behind the similarity of the results of different experiments.

A better treatment of these issues—one that gives relativity its due—might characterize λ as a field on space-time satisfying a suitable locality constraint and might try to do justice to actual measurement interactions. This remains a problem for future research, and it is one whose solution, if it helped to further distinguish the nonclassical features of the quantum mechanical measurement process as it applies to Bell-type phenomena, could be of considerable interest.[20] While it might reasonably be hoped to arrive at more clear-cut conclusions from such a treatment, it might also reasonably be suspected that sufficiently highly contrived local hidden variables theories would manage to dodge any such conclusions.

Nevertheless, it would be highly misleading to suppose this situation provides any serious new "loopholes" in the Bell-type arguments through which plausible local hidden variables may escape. In standard Bell-type arguments, one appeals to plausibility considerations as grounds for dismissing the possibility of "conspiracies" in the overlap of the backward light cones of the measurement events.[21] Similar considerations apply here.

Consider that while the strict anticorrelation of outcomes of measurements of the same component on each particle of a given pair is not a premise in the derivations of generalized Bell-type inequalities,[22] that condition must be met, at least to a good approximation, by any adequate theory. Bearing in mind that in the actual experiments (in different experiments) pairs of measurement events must occur over a range of time intervals, it should be apparent that to reconcile this with a theory that admits states that evolve in the interval prior to the time of measurement is apt to require highly ad hoc tactics. In general, one cannot exclude the possibility that somehow, by suitably local processes, the distribution of two-particle states is correlated with the premeasurement states of the measuring devices, nor the possibility that the measuring device states are correlated with each other precisely so as to fit the entire body of observed data; however, in the absence of more positive reasons for entertaining such possibilities, they should not overly concern us. After all, provided one is willing to countenance sufficiently ad hoc hypotheses, surely there is no conceivable data that cannot be "explained."

ACKNOWLEDGMENTS

I wish to thank Arthur Fine, Geoffrey Hellman, David Malament, and Howard Stein for helpful discussions concerning much of the material presented here. This paper incorporates numerous suggestions they have made for improving an earlier draft.

NOTES AND REFERENCES

1. BELL, J. S. 1976. The theory of local beables. Epistemol. Lett. **9:** 11–24.
2. CLAUSER, J. F. & A. SHIMONY. 1978. Bell's theorem: experimental tests and implications. Rep. Prog. Phys. **41:** 1881–1927.
3. FINE, A. 1982. Hidden variables, joint probability, and the Bell inequalities. Phys. Rev. Lett. **48:** 291–295.
4. HELLMAN, G. 1981. Stochastic Einstein-locality and the Bell theorems. Synthese **53:** 461–504.
5. JARRETT, J. P. 1984. On the physical significance of the locality conditions in the Bell arguments. Nous **18:** 569–589.
6. CLAUSER, J. F. & M. A. HORNE. 1974. Experimental consequences of objective local theories. Phys. Rev. **D10:** 526–535.
7. Much of the present discussion is a further development of the analysis presented in Jarrett (see reference 5), in which the conjunction of a suitably defined "completeness" condition and the prohibition of superluminal signals is shown to be essentially equivalent to strong locality.
8. Actually, the proper condition would have to be stronger than equation 3. Because λ_r (it is presumed) must include information about space-time regions that are spacelike with respect to the measurement of particle 1, a fully relativistic locality condition would require that $\bar{p}_1(\lambda_r, a)$ be equal to $\bar{p}_1(\lambda'_r, a)$ for all states λ_r and λ'_r that differ at most on what they say about regions of space-time that lie outside the backward light cone of the measurement event. This requirement (and analogous ones for $\bar{p}_2$ and $\bar{p}_{12}$) would then be

conjoined with equation 3 to form the desired constraint. For present purposes, equation 3 will suffice.

9. If $\bar{p}_1$, $\bar{p}_2$, and $\bar{p}_{12}$ are regarded as propensities, this expression need be regarded as a "conditional propensity" only in a trivial sense. The point under discussion here is that in the context of suitably complete state descriptions, the idea of a genuinely conditional propensity (i.e., one that does not reduce to an ordinary "unconditioned" propensity) cannot be maintained.

10. One might have supposed that instead of the expression on the right-hand side of equation 1′, which is a ratio of weighted averages of certain probabilities (as given by equation 2), the correct expression for the conditional probability expressed (in words) above ought to be an appropriately weighted average of the ratio of the probabilities. In fact, the latter expression reduces to that on the right-hand side of equation 1′.

11. Actually, it could only be inferred that $\lambda_r = \lambda_1$ with unit probability. In the general case, one could not expect to learn (even in this qualified sense) the identity of λ_r from the outcome of the measurement on particle 2. Nevertheless, one could expect the outcome of the measurement on particle 2 to differentially favor the various possible final states (i.e., to alter the probability distribution associated with the final states), and this is sufficient to establish the point.

12. This is the conditional probability that ought to be reflected in the observed relative frequencies of measurement outcomes.

13. One might only require of a local hidden variables theory that its predictions accord with the experimental results, but because the predictions of quantum mechanics are rather well confirmed, this requirement is only slightly weaker than equation 5.

14. This is a modified version of the inequality derived by Clauser and Horne (see reference 6).

15. It might be noted here that although the earlier discussion was motivated by considering states whose temporal evolution is stochastic, the questions raised here apply as well to states that evolve deterministically. Indeed, these questions apply even to states whose only time-dependence is that which results from measurement interactions.

16. Note that the states of the measuring devices may also be time-dependent. This complication will not be treated explicitly here, but it is not hard to see how a parallel attempt to extend the Bell-type arguments to cover theories that admit such measuring device states would proceed.

17. It will be assumed in what follows (without explicitly restricting h_1 and h_2 so as to insure this) that the pair of measurement events that occur in any given trial are spacelike-related.

18. Note that while this discussion is based on approach (ii), approach (i) is vulnerable to similar problems. (In the latter case, however, there would be only one h function.) As previously noted, approach (i) faces other difficulties having to do with carrying out ensemble averages of quantities associated with different frames of reference.

19. See the discussion of the experimental results in Clauser and Shimony (reference 2), especially their remarks on the status of anomalous results in two experiments (p. 1919).

20. It should be mentioned here that Gorden Fleming, in recent (as yet) unpublished work, has made important progress in giving a Lorentz-invariant account of the quantum mechanical measurement process.

21. See, for example: CLAUSER, J. F. & A. SHIMONY. 1978. Reference 2, pp. 1920–1921.

22. This is not to suggest that there is any real evidence that this assumption of strict anticorrelation (which is predicted by quantum mechanics) is actually violated. However, because there are nonvanishing uncertainties in experimental results, only a nonzero upper limit for the anticorrelation can be extracted from experimental data. Thus, Bell-type arguments that do not impose this strict anticorrelation as a constraint on acceptable hidden variables theories are somewhat stronger than those that do.

When Is a Quantum Measurement?[a]

ASHER PERES

Department of Physics
Technion–Israel Institute of Technology
32000 Haifa, Israel

INTRODUCTION

In many textbooks on quantum mechanics, "measurements" appear as a kind of primitive notion and the "projection postulate" is treated as one of the axioms of the theory. For example, Dirac[1] writes:

... a measurement always causes the system to jump into an eigenstate of the dynamical variable that is being measured, [with] the eigenvalue this eigenstate belongs to being equal to the result of the measurement.

Likewise, Bohm[2] writes:

... when the position of the electron was observed, the wave function suffered a collapse from a broad front down to a narrow region. The exact region to which it collapses is not determined by the state of the wave function before the collapse; only the probability of collapse to a given region is determined, and this probability is proportional to the value of $|\psi|^2$ in that region.

More formally, von Neumann[3] makes a distinction between

two fundamentally different types of intervention which can occur in a system. ... First, the arbitrary changes by measurements which are given by the formula

$$\rho \rightarrow \rho' = \sum_{n=1}^{\infty} (\rho u_n, u_n) P_n \tag{1}$$

[$u_1, u_2, \ldots$, a complete orthonormal set; $P_1, P_2, \ldots$, the corresponding projection operators]. Second, the automatic changes which occur with passage of time. These are given by the formula

$$\rho \rightarrow \rho_t = e^{-iHt/\hbar} \rho e^{iHt/\hbar} \tag{2}$$

(H is the energy operator, t, the time; H is independent of t).

While the above recipes give, in most cases, satisfactory results, they are fundamentally unacceptable. A measurement is not a supernatural event. It is a physical process involving ordinary matter, and whatever happens ought to be explained by the ordinary physical laws. Performing a measurement (whether classical or quantal) means the following: Some apparatus is made to interact with the measured object in such a way that a property of the object is replicated in a property of the apparatus. This process ought to yield a definite result, namely, the outcome of the measurement.

[a]This work was supported by the Gerard Swope Fund.

438

This immediately raises a difficulty if quantum theory is used to describe the dynamical evolution of the combined system (that is, the measured object and the apparatus). The Schrödinger equation is linear. Therefore, if the quantum object is prepared in a superposition of orthogonal states,

$$\psi = \Sigma \, c_n u_n, \tag{3}$$

such that each u_n yields (with certainty) a distinct outcome for the measurement, then the final state will involve a superposition of different outcomes. Formally, if the initial state of the apparatus is ϕ, and if that apparatus is built in such a way that its final state is v_n whenever the initial state of the object is $\psi = u_n$, we have the unitary evolution,[4]

$$\psi\phi \longrightarrow \Sigma \, c_n u_n v_n, \tag{4}$$

whereby states of the object are correlated with states of the apparatus. Thus, unless a single c_n is different from zero, the final state does not represent a definite outcome for the measurement.

Then, a miracle occurs. By fiat, the superposition, $\Sigma c_n u_n v_n$, "collapses" into one of the $u_n v_n$. The corresponding c_n jumps to its new value, 1, while the other components disappear. The purpose of this paper is to explain this "miracle." (The Everett interpretation[5] does not involve miraculous events, but is beset by other difficulties.[6] Its meaning will be analyzed later in the third section of this article.)

The plan of this paper is as follows: In the following section, I discuss the meaning of a state vector, ψ, or a density matrix, ρ. These symbols represent information on the preparation of quantum systems.[7,8] That information can evolve because of known dynamical interactions, as in equation 2. It can also get degraded and become ultimately obsolete with the passage of time. If, and only if, the unitary correlation in equation 4 is followed by a degradation of the available information (because of irreversible coupling with additional, uncontrollable, degrees of freedom), the resulting degraded information is compatible with the "collapse" postulate. The latter does not represent a dynamical miracle, but simply the acquisition of fresh information by means of an actual observation. In the third section, I briefly discuss the role of the "conscious observer" in quantum theory, and Everett's interpretation[5] of the wave function. Finally, in the last section, I mention measurements of finite duration. In particular, this section gives a detailed treatment of the case of a radioactive atom continuously monitored by a detector. It is shown that this continuous monitoring is not a measurement.

ON STATE VECTORS AND MEASUREMENTS

A wave function is not something that "exists" in nature.[9] It is only a mathematical expression, invented by physicists, so that they can compute physical properties of matter and, in particular, probabilities of events[10] following specified preparations. (Those readers who adopt a "realistic" attitude will disagree with my approach. However, it is their problem then to explain the miraculous events described in the previous section.)

Schrödinger wave functions represent information on physical systems.[7,8] When we say that $\psi = u_n$, this means that there is a certain physical test (represented by the projection operator, P_n) that will always give a positive result. Moreover, the same test will always give a negative result if $\psi = u_m$ (any state orthogonal to u_n). These notions are readily generalized to statistical mixtures, which are represented by density matrices.

It is sometimes stated that "quantum theory is deterministic" because the Schrödinger equation is a well-behaved differential equation of first order in time derivatives. One could likewise argue that classical statistical mechanics is deterministic because the Liouville equation has exactly the same properties. In both cases, it is the probability distribution that evolves in a deterministic way. Individual events are unpredictable, except statistically.

As a special case, consider a spin-$\frac{1}{2}$ particle prepared in state $\binom{\alpha}{\beta}$. First, though, I ought to explain the meaning of these terms. The meaning of "spin-$\frac{1}{2}$ particle" is the following: The most exhaustive test performed on such an object is of the Stern-Gerlach type. It can yield only two values, which are conventionally called "up" and "down." There are no additional variables. (Here, for simplicity, I ignore the translational degrees of freedom.) The meaning of "state $\binom{\alpha}{\beta}$" is the following: If we submit the particle to a test whereby it passes through a Stern-Gerlach apparatus oriented along a unit vector, $\vec{n}$, then the particle has probability,

$$P(\vec{n}) = n_x(\alpha^*\beta + \alpha\beta^*) - in_y(\alpha^*\beta - \alpha\beta^*) + n_z(\alpha^*\alpha - \beta^*\beta), \qquad (5)$$

to leave in the "up" beam. The meaning of the word "probability" is the following: The physicist who performs that experiment (namely, a spin-$\frac{1}{2}$ particle passing through a Stern-Gerlach apparatus) can imagine that the same experiment, with exactly the same preparation, is repeated many times. This unique experiment thus becomes part of a conceptual ensemble (a Gibbs ensemble). The probability of a given outcome (e.g., "up") is defined as the ratio of the number of outcomes of that type to the total number of outcomes, when the size of the ensemble tends to infinity.

How can we measure that probability? This is done by simulating the conceptual ensemble by a real ensemble (a Maxwell ensemble) of many noninteracting and uncorrelated systems. As emphasized by Ballentine,[11] these are two different concepts: "One must not confuse the [Gibbs] *ensemble,* which is a conceptual set of replicas of one particle in its experimental surroundings, with a *beam* of particles, which is another kind of (many-particle) system." It will be seen below that these two notions are essentially different because it is impossible to exactly duplicate the experimental surroundings.

Once the terminology has been clearly defined, one can proceed and describe the experimental details. For simplicity, it may be assumed that the Stern-Gerlach apparatus has only two states, which are denoted as $[\begin{smallmatrix}1\\0\end{smallmatrix}]$ and $[\begin{smallmatrix}0\\1\end{smallmatrix}]$. (I shall use parentheses and brackets to denote state vectors in the Hilbert spaces of the observed object and the apparatus, respectively.) Initially, the apparatus is in state $[\begin{smallmatrix}1\\0\end{smallmatrix}]$. The interaction with the spin is such that the apparatus stays in state $[\begin{smallmatrix}1\\0\end{smallmatrix}]$ if the spin is in state $\binom{1}{0}$, and it ends up in state $[\begin{smallmatrix}0\\1\end{smallmatrix}]$ if the spin is in state $\binom{0}{1}$. By linearity, we thus have

$$\binom{\alpha}{\beta}\begin{bmatrix}1\\0\end{bmatrix} \rightarrow \alpha\binom{1}{0}\begin{bmatrix}1\\0\end{bmatrix} + \beta\binom{0}{1}\begin{bmatrix}0\\1\end{bmatrix}, \qquad (6)$$

which is a special case of equation 4.

The evolution in equation 6 is unitary and can be generated by the Hamiltonian,[12,13]

$$H = g(t)(1 - \sigma_z)P, \tag{7}$$

where σ_z refers to the spin, P is the projection operator,

$$P = \frac{1}{2} \begin{bmatrix} 1 \\ -1 \end{bmatrix} \begin{bmatrix} 1 \\ -1 \end{bmatrix}^\dagger, \tag{8}$$

and $g(t)$ is a smooth function of time, with compact support, satisfying $\int g(t)dt = \pi\hbar/2$. Indeed, the unitary evolution generated by H is

$$U = e^{-i\int Hdt/\hbar} = I - (1 - \sigma_z)P, \tag{9}$$

and the right-hand side of equation 6 is equal to $U \binom{\alpha}{\beta} \begin{bmatrix} 0 \\ 1 \end{bmatrix}$, which can easily be verified.

This evolution is reversible.[12,13] This is easily seen by noting that in this model, U is not only unitary, but also Hermitian, so that $U = U^{-1}$. Therefore, the same Hamiltonian that generates the correlation in equation 6 also reverses it:

$$U \left\{ \alpha \binom{1}{0} \begin{bmatrix} 1 \\ 0 \end{bmatrix} + \beta \binom{0}{1} \begin{bmatrix} 0 \\ 1 \end{bmatrix} \right\} = \binom{\alpha}{\beta} \begin{bmatrix} 1 \\ 0 \end{bmatrix}. \tag{10}$$

The right-hand side of equation 6 is a pure state. There is no justification in treating it otherwise, nor is there any justification, in particular, in "collapsing" it so that either α or β disappears.[14] For example, the relative phase of α and β can be measured by observing the expectation values of operators such as[15,16]

$$\left\langle \begin{pmatrix} 0 & 1 \\ 1 & 0 \end{pmatrix} \begin{bmatrix} 0 & 1 \\ 1 & 0 \end{bmatrix} \right\rangle = - \left\langle \begin{pmatrix} 0 & -i \\ i & 0 \end{pmatrix} \begin{bmatrix} 0 & -i \\ i & 0 \end{bmatrix} \right\rangle = \alpha^*\beta + \alpha\beta^* \tag{11}$$

and

$$\left\langle \begin{pmatrix} 0 & 1 \\ 1 & 0 \end{pmatrix} \begin{bmatrix} 0 & -i \\ i & 0 \end{bmatrix} \right\rangle = \left\langle \begin{pmatrix} 0 & -i \\ i & 0 \end{pmatrix} \begin{bmatrix} 0 & 1 \\ 1 & 0 \end{bmatrix} \right\rangle = -i(\alpha^*\beta - \alpha\beta^*). \tag{12}$$

The expectation values of equations 11 and 12 are average values, corresponding, as explained above, to a conceptual (Gibbs) ensemble, whereby all the spins and all the apparatuses are identically prepared in identical environments. For example, to obtain the value of the right-hand side of equation 11, we imagine that after many replicas of the object and the apparatus have been correlated as in equation 6, we separately measure in each one of these replicas, $\begin{pmatrix} 0 & 1 \\ 1 & 0 \end{pmatrix}$ and $\begin{bmatrix} 0 & 1 \\ 1 & 0 \end{bmatrix}$, by means of additional apparatuses. Each one of these measurements yields a result of ± 1. The average value of the product of these pairs of results is $\alpha^*\beta + \alpha\beta^*$.

It is now that we encounter the difficulty. If we want to actually measure the expectation values of equations 11 and 12, we must use a real (Maxwell) ensemble with many spins and many apparatuses that can in the best of cases be in almost identical environments. In other words, the Hamiltonian is not truly given by equation 7, but we must add to it some small, unknown, and uncontrollable terms, which differ from sample to sample. Consequently, our knowledge about the behavior of each sample is degraded.

Let us evaluate how bad the situation may be. As a grossly oversimplified example, suppose that $[\begin{smallmatrix}1\\0\end{smallmatrix}]$ and $[\begin{smallmatrix}0\\1\end{smallmatrix}]$ represent two states of a ferromagnet, with 10^{23} electrons aligned in opposite directions. These two states are macroscopically distinguishable, as it behooves for states of a measuring instrument. The corresponding magnetic moments are $\pm 10^{23}e\hbar/2mc$, or about $\pm 5.8 \times 10^8$ MeV/gauss. If the experiments are performed in a region where unknown, stray magnetic fields are reduced to 10^{-9} gauss, the energy difference between the two states of the magnet will be uncertain by about 1 MeV. These states will therefore lose their phase coherence within 10^{-21} sec or so. After that time has elapsed, the only description of our knowledge is a statistical mixture, with probability $|\alpha|^2$ for state $(\begin{smallmatrix}1\\0\end{smallmatrix}) [\begin{smallmatrix}1\\0\end{smallmatrix}]$ and probability $|\beta|^2$ for state $(\begin{smallmatrix}0\\1\end{smallmatrix}) [\begin{smallmatrix}0\\1\end{smallmatrix}]$.

This is true even if there is a single sample. One might be tempted to imagine that each object + apparatus system has a well-defined wave function that, however, is unknown to us. This is the "realistic" attitude. Whoever adopts it is then faced with the problem of explaining the wave function "collapse" as a physical phenomenon without invoking "miracles." This issue was already discussed at the beginning of this section and I shall not return to it.

Before I explain the "collapse," it is important to notice the crucial difference between "microscopic" and "macroscopic" systems. A microscopic object is one that can be perfectly isolated from its environment (or else placed in a perfectly controlled environment) over a period of time that is long compared to the duration of the experiment. A macroscopic object cannot. The distinction between the two depends, of course, on our technical skill,[18] just as the boundary between reversible and irreversible processes may be pushed somewhat by the progress of technology. Thus, from the assumption that the final states of the apparatus are macroscopically distinguishable, it follows that they will be found in different environments[17] if we repeat the experiment (it is not the energy difference between them that is important, but only the fact that the latter is irreproducible).

I finally come to the "collapse." Because of the unavoidable noise that mars the Hamiltonian (equation 7), the final state of the system is not the right-hand side of equation 6, but, to the best of our knowledge, is represented by a statistical mixture,

$$\rho = |\alpha|^2 \begin{pmatrix} 1 & 0 \\ 0 & 0 \end{pmatrix} \begin{bmatrix} 1 & 0 \\ 0 & 0 \end{bmatrix} + |\beta|^2 \begin{pmatrix} 0 & 0 \\ 0 & 1 \end{pmatrix} \begin{bmatrix} 0 & 0 \\ 0 & 1 \end{bmatrix}, \tag{13}$$

as in the right-hand side of equation 1. This means that the expectation values of the operators such as in equations 11 and 12 are zero. They would indeed yield a zero average if we performed many similar experiments with a real ensemble in a noisy environment. There are, however, some dynamical variables having nonvanishing expectation values, such as

$$\left\langle \begin{pmatrix} 1 & 0 \\ 0 & -1 \end{pmatrix} \right\rangle = \left\langle \begin{bmatrix} 1 & 0 \\ 0 & -1 \end{bmatrix} \right\rangle = |\alpha|^2 - |\beta|^2 \tag{14}$$

and

$$\left\langle \begin{pmatrix} 1 & 0 \\ 0 & -1 \end{pmatrix} \begin{bmatrix} 1 & 0 \\ 0 & -1 \end{bmatrix} \right\rangle = 1. \tag{15}$$

These results are exactly the same as if we had an ordinary mixture containing a fraction $|\alpha|^2$ of

$$\begin{pmatrix}1\\0\end{pmatrix}\begin{bmatrix}1\\0\end{bmatrix}$$

and a fraction $|\beta|^2$ of

$$\begin{pmatrix}0\\1\end{pmatrix}\begin{bmatrix}0\\1\end{bmatrix}.$$

This is true if we consider a real (Maxwell) ensemble of many spins and many apparatuses (or with the same spin and/or same apparatus used many times). Therefore, equation 13 is also the correct description of the conceptual (Gibbs) ensemble representing a unique experiment performed with a single system. Everything that we can predict is included in equation 13.

Having made that statistical prediction, we may now actually perform one experiment and observe its result. It must be either

$$\begin{pmatrix}1\\0\end{pmatrix}\begin{bmatrix}1\\0\end{bmatrix} \quad \text{or} \quad \begin{pmatrix}0\\1\end{pmatrix}\begin{bmatrix}0\\1\end{bmatrix}.$$

Any other result would be incompatible with equations 14 and 15 and other similar expressions yielding zero expectation values. Experimentally, this means the following: After that unique observation has been performed, any further tests, as in equation 5, are always compatible with either

$$\begin{pmatrix}1\\0\end{pmatrix}\begin{bmatrix}1\\0\end{bmatrix} \quad \text{or} \quad \begin{pmatrix}0\\1\end{pmatrix}\begin{bmatrix}0\\1\end{bmatrix}.$$

On the other hand, any further tests are never compatible, in the sense of equation 5, with

$$\begin{pmatrix}1\\0\end{pmatrix}\begin{bmatrix}0\\1\end{bmatrix} \quad \text{nor} \quad \frac{1}{2}\begin{pmatrix}1\\1\end{pmatrix}\begin{bmatrix}1\\1\end{bmatrix},$$

etc. This is the meaning of the "collapse of the wave function." It is not a physical process, but simply the acquisition of fresh knowledge about a physical system. It is a change of our description, whereby we return from a Gibbs ensemble to a single object.

I now come to the crucial point: There is nothing inconsistent (nor miraculous) in this "collapse" because the relative phases in the right-hand side of equation 6 have been blurred so that the expression has been replaced by equation 13. If it were not so, the collapse assumption would be inconsistent. For example, collapsing the right-hand side of equation 6 is inconsistent with the possibility of restoring the left-hand side of equation 6 by applying once more the operator, U, as shown in equation 10. It is, therefore, essential that the measuring instrument, together with its environment, have some noise. In other words, their description must involve some degrees of freedom that are not accounted for, except statistically. It does not matter whether these are internal degrees of freedom[16] or whether the noise is due to external agents.

We are naturally free to imagine that some apparatus has all its degrees of freedom perfectly controlled and isolated from the environment—somewhere in intergalactic space—as in Albert's quantum mechanical automaton.[19] However, in that case, there is no measurement.[20] The fact that some variables of the automaton get correlated to some others is not a measurement.[20,21] The two electrons in the ground state of the helium atom are correlated, but no one would say that each electron "measures" its partner. In general, if we have a piece of hardware that can be used as a measuring apparatus, we must choose one of the following alternatives: either let it work in a noisy environment (including its own internal "irrelevant" degrees of freedom), or let it be perfectly prepared and isolated, and described by the Schrödinger equation. In the latter case, that piece of hardware loses its status of "measuring apparatus."[22] This is just a matter of having consistent definitions: A measuring apparatus must have macroscopically distinguishable states, and the word "macroscopic" has just been defined as "incapable of being isolated from the environment." If there is no irreversibility, there are no measurements.

ON OBSERVERS AND CONSCIOUSNESS

The reader may object that my explanations are anthropocentric and, in particular, that the observer's consciousness (see reference 2, p. 587, or reference 3, p. 420) plays a dominant role. I, therefore, expect some sarcastic questions such as: Should the observer be highly qualified (with a Ph.D. in physics), or what happens in inhospitable places such as stellar interiors, let alone black holes?

This sarcasm is not justified. Just as "wave functions" are mathematical expressions invented by physicists, "observers" too are only figments of our imagination that are used to prove theorems. Fictitious observers are not restricted to quantum theory: They are also used in relating thermodynamics to information theory,[23] and, as is well known, in the special theory of relativity. For example, when we say that no information can be transferred faster than by light signals, we imagine a pair of observers, with one actively making decisions and sending information, and the other passively receiving that information. This apparently subjective distinction between cause and effect yields an absolute distinction between the past and future light cones.

Nobody in his right mind would argue that Lorentz invariance (with all its consequences) is valid only in those parts of the universe that are inhabited by human observers. Likewise, quantum theory is valid even if the observers are not there: We can safely compute cross sections (that is, probabilities of events), energy levels, etc., without invoking fictitious observers. It is enough to invoke fictitious "wave functions" that symbolize the "knowledge" of these observers.[7,8] However, once in a while, the derivation of a formula, the proof of a theorem, or the clarification of a result can be made easier by introducing the mythical observers. There is no reason then to apologize for that.

This paper would not be complete without a mention of Everett's valiant attempt to eliminate the wave function collapse.[5] In Everett's formalism, the observer is included in the wave function and all the terms in the right-hand side of equation 6 always exist. This can be understood in different ways, which have been called the "relative-states interpretation" and the "many-worlds interpretation." None is a satisfactory alternative[6] to the standard formalism with the meaning that was assigned to it in the previous section.[8]

However, Everett's work can also be interpreted in a way that is completely compatible with the standard approach. In the latter, each observer imagines that he or she is dealing with a Gibbs ensemble of quantum objects and apparatuses. The wave function represents all the information compatible with that ensemble. The inclusion of the observer in the wave function simply means that one now has to consider a Gibbs ensemble of observers, with each one of them experimenting with a single quantum object and a single apparatus. It is a matter of personal taste which interpretation one prefers.

There is nothing strange or unusual in being a member of a Gibbs ensemble. This is indeed the situation of anyone having a life insurance policy. The officers of the life insurance company only know a wave function (it is the medical report of their physician who examined the customer) and there is a corresponding Schrödinger equation (they call it a mortality table). According to it, the company collects the insurance premium, until some day the beneficiaries will collect the amount of the policy.

CONTINUOUS MONITORING IN QUANTUM THEORY

Until now, we have considered each "measurement" as an instantaneous event. In other words, it was assumed that the interaction of the measuring instrument with the quantum system was so strong that it could be made arbitrarily brief, and thus one could neglect $Ht/\hbar$ during the measurement. This drastic simplification may not always be justified. Coupling constants occurring in nature are finite, and sometimes very small.[24] It may, therefore, be necessary to couple the measured system and the apparatus during a finite, possibly long time.

This problem is not specific to quantum theory. It may arise in everyday life, for example, when a photographer takes a snapshot of a moving object. However, quantum theory introduces some novel features because a measurement is not only a passive observation, but also the preparation of a new state. The detailed dynamical theory of such quantum measurements of finite duration can be worked out explicitly.[25] It turns out that the result of the measurement is not, in general, the time average of the observed quantity. It may not be one of the eigenvalues of the operator representing the dynamical variable being measured. Finally, some outcomes, those which do correspond to the eigenvalues, appear frozen by the "Zeno effect."[26-29] I shall not repeat here the details of the calculations because they can be found in the literature.[25]

As a final example, consider a radioactive atom in the presence of a perfect detector. It should be emphasized that the mere presence of a detector capable of registering the decay is not a measurement (in the technical sense of this term[3,4]). A complete quantum mechanical treatment[30] of the atom + detector system shows that the final state of the detector (that is, after many mean lifetimes of the atom) is a superposition of states corresponding to different decay times that are distributed according to the familiar exponential decay law. Obviously, the final wave function only gives statistical information on what may happen: quantum theory is unable to predict when an individual atom will decay.

The point is that the continuous interaction between the detector and the decay products is not a measurement (let alone the equivalent of a large number of consecutive measurements). A measurement of the type capable of causing the Zeno effect is a very brief and intense interaction between the observed system (the radioactive atom) and a macroscopic apparatus. This interaction causes different states of the atom to be correlated to macroscopically distinguishable states of the apparatus. As explained above, it is essential to the consistency of the von Neumann formalism[3,4] that these final states be macroscopically distinguishable, that is, incoherent.[13] Otherwise, there may be no Zeno effect.[29]

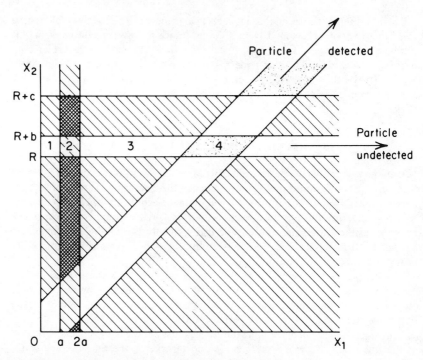

FIGURE 1. Topographic map of the potential energy in equation 19. Blank: $V = 0$; hatched: $V = V_0$; crosshatched: $V = 2V_0$; dotted: $V = -V_0$. See text for details.

To conclude, let me present a very simple one-dimensional model for the radioactive atom and its detector. The "atom" is represented by a particle of mass, m, and position, x_1, in a piecewise constant potential,

$$V_1(x_1) = V_0 \text{ if } a < x_1 < 2a,$$
$$= \infty \text{ if } x_1 < 0,$$
$$= 0 \text{ otherwise.} \tag{16}$$

Here, $V_0 \gg \hbar^2/ma^2$ so that there are long-lived metastable states in the potential well. Likewise, the "detector" is represented by a particle of mass, M, and position, x_2, in a piecewise constant potential,

$$V_2(x_2) = V_0 \text{ if } 0 < x_2 < R \text{ or } R + b < x_2 < R + c,$$
$$= \infty \text{ if } x_2 < 0,$$
$$= 0 \text{ if } R < x_2 < R + b \text{ or } x_2 > R + c. \tag{17}$$

Here, $R \gg a$ is the distance between the atom and the detector, and, for simplicity, I have chosen the same V_0 as before. Moreover, $M(c - b)^2 \gg ma^2$ so that the detector would have a much longer lifetime than the atom if the two did not interact.

Finally, there is an interaction term,

$$V_{int}(x_1 - x_2) = -V_0 \text{ if } |x_1 - x_2| < d,$$
$$= 0 \text{ otherwise.} \tag{18}$$

FIGURE 1 shows a topographic map of the potential,

$$V(x_1, x_2) = V_1(x_1) + V_2(x_2) + V_{int}(x_1 - x_2). \tag{19}$$

Initially, the wave function is localized in region 1, inside both potential wells; that is, the atom is excited and the detector is in its "ready" state. Tunneling then proceeds via region 2 (this is the radioactive decay), and then the ejected particle freely travels through region 3 until it reaches the detector in region 4. It will then continue toward larger x_1, either detected or undetected (the efficiency of the detector depends on the value of $c - b$ versus that of d).

Although this model is grossly oversimplified, it has all the features to describe how the decay of an unstable particle triggers the decay of a detector prepared in a metastable state. Their interaction is continuous and yet it is not subject to any Zeno effect.

ACKNOWLEDGMENTS

Many of the ideas reported here originated during visits at the University of California (Santa Barbara), the University of Texas (Austin), and the Centre International de Sciences Mécaniques (Udine). I am grateful to all of these institutions for their hospitality.

REFERENCES

1. DIRAC, P. A. M. 1947. The Principles of Quantum Mechanics, p. 36. Oxford Univ. Press. Oxford.
2. BOHM, D. 1951. Quantum Theory, p. 120. Prentice–Hall. New York.
3. VON NEUMANN, J. 1955. Mathematical Foundations of Quantum Mechanics. Princeton Univ. Press. Princeton, New Jersey. (Translated from: Mathematische Grundlagen der Quantenmechanik. 1932. Springer-Verlag. Berlin.)
4. WHEELER, J. A. & W. H. ZUREK. 1983. Quantum Theory and Measurement. Princeton Univ. Press. Princeton, New Jersey.
5. EVERETT, H. 1957. Rev. Mod. Phys. **29**: 454.
6. WHITAKER, M. A. B. 1985. J. Phys. A: Math. Gen. **18**: 253.
7. ROTHSTEIN, J. 1951. Science **114**: 171; 1951. Am. J. Phys. **25**: 510.

8. PERES, A. 1984. Am. J. Phys. **52:** 644.
9. FINKELSTEIN, D. 1971. The physics of logic. *In* Paradigms and Paradoxes (vol. V). R. C. Colodry, Ed. Univ. of Pittsburgh Press. Pittsburgh, Pennsylvania. (Reprinted *in* Logico-Algebraic Approach to Quantum Mechanics, vol. II. 1975. C. A. Hooker, Ed.: 141–160. Reidel. Dordrecht.)
10. STAPP, H. P. 1972. Am. J. Phys. **40:** 1098.
11. BALLENTINE, L. E. 1970. Rev. Mod. Phys. **42:** 358.
12. PERES, A. 1974. Am. J. Phys. **42:** 886.
13. PERES, A. 1984. Found. Phys. **14:** 1131.
14. BELL, J. S. 1975. Helv. Phys. Acta **48:** 93.
15. MOLDAUER, P. A. 1972. Phys. Rev. **D5:** 1028.
16. PERES, A. 1980. Phys. Rev. **D22:** 879.
17. ZUREK, W. H. 1981. Phys. Rev. **D24:** 1516; 1982. Phys. Rev. **D26:** 1862.
18. LEGGETT, A. J. 1980. Suppl. Prog. Theor. Phys. **69:** 80.
19. ALBERT, D. Z. 1983. Phys. Lett. **98A:** 249.
20. PERES, A. 1984. Phys. Lett. **101A:** 249.
21. WHEATHER, J. & R. PEIERLS. 1983. Phys. Rev. Lett. **51:** 1601.
22. PERES, A. & W. H. ZUREK. 1982. Am. J. Phys. **50:** 807.
23. SZILARD, L. 1929. Z. Phys. **53:** 840.
24. CAVES, C. M. *et al.* 1980. Rev. Mod. Phys. **52:** 341.
25. PERES, A. & W. K. WOOTTERS. 1985. Phys. Rev. **D32:** 1968.
26. MISRA, B. & E. C. G. SUDARSHAN. 1977. J. Math. Phys. **18:** 756.
27. CHIU, C. B., E. C. G. SUDARSHAN & B. MISRA. 1977. Phys. Rev. **D16:** 520.
28. PERES, A. 1980. Am. J. Phys. **48:** 931.
29. SINGH, I. & M. A. B. WHITAKER. 1982. Am. J. Phys. **50:** 882.
30. PERES, A. 1980. Am. J. Phys. **48:** 552.

The Haunted Measurement in Quantum Theory[a]

DANIEL M. GREENBERGER AND ALLAINE YA'SIN

Department of Physics
City College of the City University of New York
New York, New York 10031

INTRODUCTION

We have been bothered by the problem of trying to decide when a quantum mechanical system that appears to be disordered may actually contain hidden information; namely, information that may in fact be made manifest by a later interaction. We have not been able to say much that is new about this problem as yet, but we do have an example that shows that the problem is important.

An example of this type of behavior occurs in a spin echo experiment. In that case, a spin system is apparently disordered by a magnetic pulse, but a later magnetic pulse reorders the system so that, subsequently, all the spins are coherently aligned for an instant. Our example goes beyond this in that the system is apparently disordered by interacting with a macroscopic object, in which it induces a macroscopic change. All one needs to do is look at the macroscopic object to detect that a measurement has taken place. However, if one does not bother to look, the system subsequently interacts with the object again, thereby undoing the macroscopic effect and completely regaining its coherence.

Thus, there is a window in time within which one can look at the macroscopic object to see that a measurement has been made. After that, it is too late. All traces of the "measurement" have disappeared. It was, alas, merely a ghost. Therefore, the measurement process has been "haunted" by a measurement that was substantial for a while, but then evaporated away.

Quantum mechanical measurements are not supposed to do that. We tend to think of macroscopic effects produced by quantum systems as irreversible traces, such as a count in a detector, accompanied by an incoherent amplification process. However, the point of our opening question is how can we know when an irreversible recording process has taken place? This leads to what we call the "future generations problem." If a particular interaction seems to us to constitute a measurement that appears to destroy the coherence of the quantum system, how do we know that no one will come along at some future time with better experimental techniques? He may then discover that the wave function in this experiment only appeared to be incoherent, and that the interaction merely scrambled up the wave function and did not irreversibly alter it. In that case, he may be able to reconstitute it and show that what we took to be a measurement was in fact only a rearrangement.

[a] This research was supported in part by grants from the National Science Foundation, and the CUNY-FRAP program of the City University of New York.

449

We call such a system, which appears to be incoherent, but in actuality is still coherent, a system with "latent order." Unless latently ordered systems can be distinguished from truly incoherent ones, it would seem that the idea of a quantum mechanical measurement is subjective and subject to the limitations of the state of the art. (The same problem would seem to come up in classical statistics,[1] as in the case of "Gibb's Paradox".)

The possibility of a haunted measurement shows that the concept of measurement within quantum theory is ambiguous and will remain so until the idea of a loosely defined "amplification process" can be rigorously defined within the theory. While we will be describing a purely gedanken-experiment with a neutron interferometer (whose main advantage is that it is exactly calculable), a similar effect has been discussed by M. Scully,[2] which he believes can be actually performed with lasers. We shall only be outlining the general idea here, and the detailed calculation will be published elsewhere.[3]

NEUTRON INTERFEROMETER MODEL

First, we will describe a simple model of the neutron interferometer and then replace it by an even simpler optical analog model. Within this model, we can carry out the necessary calculations exactly. For the purposes of this talk, we will usually describe the limits of coherence relevant to the experiment by a "hand-waving" appeal to the uncertainty principle; however, our claims in this regard can be demonstrated rigorously. We point out in passing that it is rather interesting, from a formal point of view, how these general restrictions manage to actually get mathematically incorporated into the wave function, but we will not concern ourselves with such questions here.

FIGURE 1a shows a top view of a neutron beam entering the interferometer. The beam gets split by Laue scattering at A, gets redirected at B and C, and gets refocused at D. Finally, one can count the neutrons at either of the counters, S1 or S2. The counting rate of these two counters is affected by the relative phase between the two beams. If counter S1 is reading a maximum rate, for example, and the relative phase of the beams is changed by half a wavelength, then counter S1 will read a minimum rate. In addition, because a neutron will pass into one of the two counters, when S1 reads a minimum, then S2 will read a maximum. An experimental apparatus can then be placed into the beam at some point, say E, and its effect on the phase of beam ABD can then be monitored by either of the counters.

In the optical analog (FIGURE 1b), the scattering crystals are replaced by a half-reflecting mirror at A, fully reflecting mirrors at B and C, and a screen at D. The relative phase is then determined by the shifting of the maxima and minima in the diffraction pattern at D. This is all we have to know about the neutron interferometer to describe our experiment.

We shall assume that the neutron wave packet is narrow in momentum space, so that $\delta k \ll k$, and that the group velocity approximation is valid. If the width of the packet is a, so that $\Delta x \sim a$, and $\Delta k \sim 1/a$, then $a \gg \lambda$ and the width is many wavelengths wide. The wave packet, as it travels along, will preserve internal coherence over a distance, $d \sim a^2/\lambda$, which must be much greater than the size of the experiment, L.

FIRST PART OF THE EXPERIMENT

Imagine the following device placed into the neutron beam on one side of the interferometer at E in FIGURE 1. It consists of a double mirror (see FIGURE 2a), where the two parts of which are rigidly connected to each other and separated by a distance, L (which also determines the order of magnitude of the size of the experimental apparatus). The mirror system is mounted so that it is free to slide along the

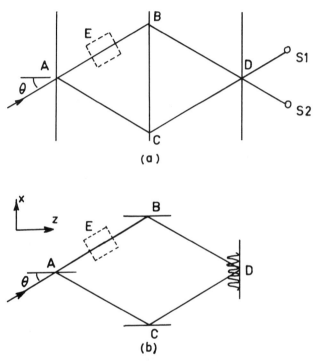

FIGURE 1. The neutron interferometer: (a) Top view of an interferometer. The neutron beam is split at A and recombined at D. The relative counting rates of counters S1 and S2 depend on the relative phases of the beams ABD and ACD. This phase can be changed by an experiment placed into the beam at E. (b) Optical analog of the interferometer, with Bragg scattering crystals replaced by a partially reflecting mirror at A and totally reflecting ones at B and C. A screen at D replaces the counters.

x-direction, which is transverse to the longitudinal direction of the neutron along the interferometer. We assume that the mirror system has a finite mass, m_2, where $m_2 \gg m_1$ (m_1 being the neutron mass). Nonetheless, the mirror system is light enough to be able to recoil when hit by the neutron, and so the neutron slows down slightly on striking the first mirror. The mirror has an uncertainty in momentum, δk_2, which gets transferred to the neutron. However, we would like to keep the neutron momentum uncertainty from growing in order to preserve the group velocity approximation, as

well as to keep the neutron as monochromatic as possible, and so we assume that the
mirror wave packet has been set up with $\delta k_2 \leq \delta k_1$. However, of course, this implies
that

$$\delta x_2 \geq \delta x_1 \sim a \gg \lambda,$$

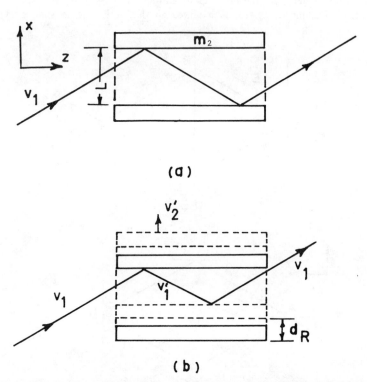

(a)

(b)

FIGURE 2. The double mirror system: (a) A system of two mirrors is inserted into the beam at E.
The two mirrors have a finite mass, m_2, that is much greater than that of the neutron, m_1. If the
mirrors were infinitely heavy, the neutron would stay coherent on rebounding and would take the
path shown with constant speed. (b) For a finite mass mirror system that can recoil only in the
x-direction, the neutron will appear to lose all coherence on rebounding. The mirror recoils a
distance, d_R, that is great enough ($> \Delta x_2$) so that its recoil can be macroscopically detected.
However, the neutron maintains "latent coherence," so after hitting the second mirror, it is again
fully coherent. Nonetheless, it cannot interfere with the wave function on the other path because
the recoil of the mirror allows one to detect which path has been taken. [The mirror wave packet
after recoil (dotted) will be orthogonal to its initial packet (bold).]

so the position of the mirror is not very well known, and, in fact, because of this, the
phase coherence of the neutron is completely "destroyed" on hitting the first mirror.
Nevertheless, there is still a latent order present in the neutron wave function. This is so
because if we measure the neutron wave function after it has collided with the first
mirror, its phase will seem to have been totally washed out. However, it will turn out

that the collision with the second mirror in the system will completely restore the phase.

When the first mirror is hit, we want the recoil of the mirror to be sufficient to be able to tell that it was hit. This means that its recoil velocity, v_2', must be greater than its velocity uncertainty, so

$$v_2' \gg \delta v_2, \quad k_2' \gg \delta k_2.$$

Now, the recoil velocity of the mirror is given by classical physics. Because the neutron is much lighter than the mirror, it merely reverses velocity (approximately) so that $m_2 v_2' \sim 2m_1 v_1$. Therefore, $k_2' \sim 2k_1$, and so

$$\delta k_2' \sim 2\delta k_1' \ll k_1 \sim k_2'.$$

Thus, our above criterion is automatically satisfied by our having chosen the neutron wave packet to be narrow. (This same criterion guarantees us that we could also measure the Doppler recoil of the mirror to see that it has recoiled.) Because the velocity of the mirror is much greater than its uncertainty in velocity, we are guaranteed that it will drift in x-space a distance sufficient to be detected. In other words, x_2 must become greater than Δx_2. This is what we meant by saying that the collision has produced a macroscopic effect. We can detect that the mirror has been hit. Correspondingly, the neutron phase has been severely disrupted.

However, the neutron is now heading toward the second mirror. Furthermore, because relative speed is preserved in an elastic collision, the relative speed between the neutron and the second mirror will be v_1. The time between collisions will, therefore, be $T = L/v_1$, and the distance through which the second mirror has recoiled will be

$$d_R \sim v_2 T \sim 2\frac{m_1}{m_2} v_1 T \sim 2\frac{m_1}{m_2} L,$$

which is independent of v_1. Thus, in the system recoiling with the mirror, the collision is static, regardless of the Fourier distribution of frequencies in the neutron wave packet, and this is why this second collision will reverse all the first-order uncertainties picked up by the neutron wave packet in the first collision.

After the second collision then, the neutron continues with both the momentum and the momentum distribution it originally had, and its wave function, while displaced by the double collision, is once again manifestly coherent with that in the other beam (see FIGURE 2b). After this double recoil, the mirror system (which we will hereafter refer to as MS1) has recoiled an amount, $d_R \sim 2(m_1/m_2)L > \Delta x_2 > a$, where the last restriction is important to guarantee that the recoil of the system is macroscopic, that is, large enough to be able to tell that the system has been displaced, so that one can tell that the system has indeed recoiled. This restriction puts an important experimental upper limit on m_2, which in a real neutron interferometer would limit m_2 to $m_2 < 10^6$ neutron masses. This would certainly limit a practical experiment to Bragg scattering off some macromolecule, and so it would probably be better to use the laser experiment of reference 2, if feasible.

At any rate, even though the neutron has been restored to coherence by the double scattering, nonetheless one still cannot produce an interference pattern—even if one recombines the two beams. This is because the mirror has moved a macroscopic distance, and so its wave function is orthogonal to that in its undisplaced position. Another way to say this is that because the mirror is displaced, one only has to look at it to tell which beam the neutron was in. If the neutron took one path, the mirror will be displaced, while if it took the other path, it will not be. Of course, once one "looks" at the mirror system, by interacting with it, one will destroy any chance of coherently undoing its displacement.

THE HAUNTED MEASUREMENT

As long as one does not observe the mirror system to see if it has been displaced, the system maintains its latent coherence. However, if one wants it to become manifestly

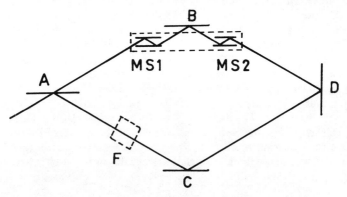

FIGURE 3. The haunted measurement. To undo the displacement of the mirror, a second mirror system (MS2) must be placed into the beam so as to undo the displacement of the first mirror. The two mirror systems are rigidly attached and both are free to slide. Then one only needs to insert a device at F into beam ACD to delay it by the extra distance traveled by the beam ABD. After the neutron has traversed the second mirror system, the entire system will be coherent again, and all traces of which path the neutron took will have been washed away. The measurement performed by the first mirror system will now have disappeared, unless one had looked to see whether a displacement occurred before it was too late.

coherent again, then one must first undo the displacement of the mirror in such a way as to not destroy its latent coherence. The easiest way to do this is by introducing a second mirror system, MS2, which is rigidly attached to the first mirror system, MS1, as in FIGURE 3. Both systems are then free to slide together along the x-direction. After the neutron recoils from mirror B, it will pass through the system MS2, and this will undo the displacement, d_R. Now, the combined mirror systems will be undisplaced from their original positions, and the neutron beam will also be coherent with the one on the other side of the interferometer.

Thus, if one looks at the mirror system after the neutron has passed MS2, there is no way to tell whether the neutron has in fact taken that path, and, in fact, one can produce a diffraction pattern on the screen. However, if one looks at the mirror system before the neutron reaches MS2 (but after it has passed MS1), one finds that the system has either been displaced or not; in either case, it reveals which beam the neutron was in and destroys the possibility of interference. If the system MS2 were not there, one could look at MS1 a week later and see whether the neutron had passed through. Therefore, one has here a macroscopic effect equivalent to a pointer reading in its information content, but with the peculiar property that it is reversible. Here is a macroscopic measurement that disappears if one does not look at it. It is a macroscopic "ghost," and the measurement process is "haunted."

Of course, when we use the above expression, to "look at the mirror," we mean that one performs an observation of the position of the mirror in the accepted macroscopic sense of the word. One can bounce a light ray off the mirror or otherwise make it interact with any device that will subsequently produce a macroscopic record of the motion of the mirror. This will in turn, by its interaction with the mirror, destroy the stored phase information in the mirror and make it impossible to again produce an interference pattern between the two neutron beams. (One could, if one wanted to, make this subsequent measurement subject to our "haunted" process. However, at whatever stage one wishes to say that a macroscopic measurement has indeed been made, at that stage the phase information has been effectively destroyed.)

THE DELAYED CHOICE, SCHRÖDINGER'S CAT, AND EPR EXPERIMENTS

The haunted measurement incorporates several very general features, some of which we would like to point out. First, it is a "delayed choice" experiment. After the neutron has possibly passed through the mirror system, MS1, it is either in beam ABD or ACD. One can ascertain which one by observing the mirror system to see whether it has recoiled. However, it is not until one makes this observation that one can tell which beam the particle is actually in. Yet, from a classical point of view, this decision had to have been made way back at point A, when the beam first split.

Of course, quantum mechanically, not only is the "choice" not made until the mirror system is observed, but in fact the observation need never be made at all. In that case, there will still be an interference pattern at D, so one can say that the particle had to be "in both beams." This points up nicely how alien the concept of a definite trajectory is to the conventional quantum viewpoint.

These same features make the haunted measurement a macroscopic example of "Schrödinger's cat."[4] In that case, a cat is either killed or not by the consequences of a quantum interaction. However, we cannot know whether it is alive or dead until we make an observation on the quantum system. This is a definite result of quantum theory that is very puzzling classically. There are actually two such puzzling features. The first is that the cat should be in a state of suspended animation until we observe it. This feature, though, is exactly like the delayed choice experiment, and the issue of "suspended animation" classically is something that quantum theory has no trouble with because of the superposition principle. In this case, the neutron choosing path ABD or ACD is like the cat being alive or dead. Yet, it is not until the mirror is observed that one can actually tell which state the neutron (or cat) is in. In fact, this case has a nice feature for the neutron that is not present for the cat. For the cat, one can only look to see that it is alive or dead, but one cannot prove that it was in a superposition of the two states before one looked. However, for the neutron, if one does not look, one has an interference pattern that verifies the superposition of states.

Actually, one can go even further because we have here a "haunted" Schrödinger cat. By observing the mirror system, we will see that the neutron has taken path ABD half the time. This corresponds to the cat being dead half the time. The other half of the time, the mirror will not have recoiled; thus, the neutron will be in path ACD or the cat will be alive. However, by not observing the mirror system until after the neutron has passed by system MS2, the mirror will no longer be displaced in any case. This is equivalent to bringing the cat back to life again in half the cases. Therefore, this is indeed a truly "haunted" version of the cat experiment.

The second feature of the cat experiment that we alluded to has to do with the macroscopic nature of a cat. A real cat is a very complicated system, and there are so many irreversible reactions going on in such a living organism as this. Because of this, the coherence time for an actual cat would be incredibly small. Thus, one would never see any quantum interference effects with an actual cat. Our mirror is also a macroscopic system, but a much simpler one, with almost all its degrees of freedom frozen out. Therefore, we have made the theoretical transition to a macroscopic system. However, the question of whether one can actually experimentally produce a macroscopic system that yet produces a sufficiently coherent behavior to detect quantum mechanical superposition effects is an open question, which has been discussed at length at this conference.

Finally, the haunted measurement has a connection to the EPR paradox. EPR gave a "minimal" definition of an element of reality. This definition is minimal in the sense that a "real, objective" property might have further attributes, but EPR felt that any real property would at least pass the test they proposed. This minimal test was that if an object possessed a property that could be determined by performing an experiment elsewhere without in any way disturbing the object, then that property corresponded to an element of reality. They felt that because this property had been established, and because the object had not been disturbed, then this property could not have been affected by the experiment. Therefore, the object must have had this property before the experiment was performed. We may have have been ignorant of the property, but surely it must have been present. Now, as simple and commonsensical as this criterion for reality is, quantum theory of course violates it. It denies the existence of any such property before it has been measured, even if the measurement is remote. Indeed, by now the quantum mechanical picture has been experimentally verified many times.

We shall see that in light of the haunted measurement considerations, the EPR criterion for reality is not so straightforward as it appears to be. First, we note that by the EPR criterion, the property of being in one beam or the other is an element of reality for the neutron. Because one can observe whether or not the mirror system MS1 recoils in beam II, we can use that to tell us whether the particle is located in beam I or not. This is a remote measurement on neutron beam I that we can perform merely by observing the mirror system MS1. This determines uniquely which beam the neutron is in, and thus, this property, being in one beam or the other, is indeed an element of reality. EPR would say that the neutron is in one or the other beam regardless of whether we are aware of it or not.

Now, we do not have to measure which beam the particle is in. The possibility of making such a measurement guarantees for us that the particle is "really" in one beam or the other according to the EPR argument. However, we have seen that after the particle passes through MS2, it again becomes impossible in principle to decide in which beam the particle is. Thus, from this point on, one can no longer perform the measurement just described, and one must conclude that "being in one beam or the other" is no longer an element of reality. We thus have here a time-dependent "element of reality" that no longer seems to possess a solid objectivity. In this case, even though we have never disturbed the particle in beam I, it suddenly acquired an element of reality when beam II reached MS1; it also just as suddenly lost it when beam II reached MS2. Thus, remote measurements cannot only bestow properties on a particle, but they can equally as well remove them. Reality should be made of sterner stuff. We conclude from this that the EPR criterion does not possess the simple qualities it appears to at first sight, and so it becomes less surprising that it does not stand up experimentally.

ACKNOWLEDGMENTS

The first part of this paper was based on a talk given at the Urbino Conference on "Perspectives on the Bohr-Einstein Debate 50 Years After the EPR Argument", September 1985, to be published by Reidel.

NOTES AND REFERENCES

1. We believe that in the classical statistical case, this point has been stressed by N. G. Van Kampen on numerous occasions.
2. See, for example: HILLERY, M. M. & M. O. SCULLY. 1983. On state and reduction and observation in quantum optics: Wigner's friends and their amnesia. *In* Quantum Optics, Experimental Gravity, and Measurement Theory. P. Meystre & M. O. Scully, Eds. Plenum. New York.
3. A general idea similar to a haunted measurement has also been discussed by Asher Peres; however, he only included the first half of our experiment, which will not work as such. Our haunted measurement is similar to his idea of a "premeasurement." See: PERES, A. 1980. Phys. Rev. **D22**: 879.
4. The original papers on Schrödinger's cat, the delayed choice experiments, the EPR argument, and Bohr's answer have all been reprinted in the following book: WHEELER, J. A. & W. ZUREK, Eds. 1983. Quantum Measurement Theory. Princeton Univ. Press. Princeton, New Jersey.

A Discussion of the EPR Contained in Quantum Mechanical Terms without Arguments of Realities or Bell's Relations

ORESTE PICCIONI AND WERNER MEHLHOP

Department of Physics
University of California at San Diego
La Jolla, California 92093

"There is no problem, but it needs a solution"—Bill Cosby, *Fatherhood* (Doubleday).

SOME HISTORY AND SOME REMARKS

It seems to us that the most paradoxical aspect of the Einstein-Podolsky-Rosen (EPR) paradox[1] is the intricacy of the many descriptions of the EPR when we recall the elegant simplicity of the original EPR argument. Their reasoning was as follows: Two particles, A and B, are far and free from each other, and, of course, each is constrained by quantum mechanics (QM) to have uncertainties (Δ) such that $(\Delta x) \cdot (\Delta px) = \hbar$. Yet, QM demands the existence of a state such that if we chose to measure any one of the two quantities, x or px, for A, without disturbing B, we can predict exactly the result of the measurement of the same quantities for B. This, EPR said, is impossible unless we modify QM.

The stringent logic of EPR, when taken as a threat to QM as a whole, triggered a defensive reaction by N. Bohr and others. In retrospect, the strongest defense would have been in pointing out that the words "measuring A without disturbing B" were mistaken for the state described by EPR, which satisfies a stationary Schrödinger equation only if a potential bounds A with B.[2] (No one to our knowledge has shown that a modification of the EPR could work.)

Instead, N. Bohr[3] translated the EPR formula in a highly "gedanken" experiment that has not been shown "in detail" to be a viable proof. Indeed, we believe that it is not viable.

The dialogue between Einstein and Bohr (which went on for more than a decade) went along these lines:

B: There is no paradox because one cannot measure both x and px with the same apparatus nor at the same time.

E: Correct. However, if we can, with certainty, predict the value of px or x for B by measuring A without disturbing B, there must be an element of reality in those values. Both realities will be there whether we measure A or not, and they will exist at the same time.

B: Your definition of reality is wrong. One must add the statement, if they can be observed simultaneously.

E: Then you imply the assumption of an action at a distance.

Discussions based on the concept of reality are still popular even with the lack of any good definition beyond the common meaning as the opposite of "fiction." In their 1935 letter, EPR did not imply that one could reach a truth quasi-independent of human perception.[4] They meant to emphasize that stringent logic compels us to conclude that x and px are both accurately defined despite the impossibility of measuring both at the same time. Trying to transform that strong, but merely intuitive argument into a deep distinction of "what is real" is a frustrating exercise. Sentences like "the singlet state is real, but the unpolarized state of each particle is not," which was heard from a distinguished "scholar of Copenhagen" at the Joensuu Conference,[5] are entirely beyond our comprehension. In the second section of this paper, we will describe the EPR in QM terms using only the concept of eigenstate, without reference to "reality."

Popular writings[5] show even more enthusiasm: "Einstein was wrong. Quantum uncertainty cannot be bypassed. Naive reality—the reality of particles really possessing well-defined qualities in the absence of observation—cannot be sustained. Aspect had put the last nail in the coffin of commonsense physics." Note that a particle prepared in an eigenstate has a defined quality before being observed, and, amusingly enough, in the 1935 description by EPR, the paradox was totally originated by accepting the "quantum uncertainty." Of course, we doubt that Aspect himself would say that he performed his brilliant experiment having in mind that, in physics, common sense is a vice.

Philosophical analyses of "our way of thinking" have not contributed positively, nor have mathematical exercises over the definition of probability[7,8] as involved in the EPR gedanken-experiment. Indeed, the probability of observing a given correlation in mechanical counters, which is all that is involved in the EPR, is the same concept as is commonly used in everyday life.

Unfortunately, such unneeded complications have continued to give the impression that the EPR issue consists of semantics or ill-defined concepts.

A laudable episode has been, of course, the work of J.S. Bell,[9] with his beautiful result of a mathematical relation showing that the invention of classical hidden variables would not solve the problem.

Importantly, however, an unfortunate circumstance has introduced a damaging confusion about the so-called Bell inequalities (BIs). Bell endeavored to prove, in general, that any theory that did not include miraculous actions at a distance (aaad's) could not reproduce the correlations attributed to QM. However, QM is a theory with built-in irremediable uncertainties and cannot be as useful as classical mechanics (CM) to reproduce arbitrarily peculiar correlations. Thus, Bell's arguments, to be valid "in general," could not be tailored only for QM and so had to include the possibility of CM parameters like hidden variables.

As a consequence, the starting premise of Bell (the famous factorization) was phrased in a language and justified with reasonings that were perfectly obvious for two separate objects of CM, but not at all obvious within the domain of QM where "extended states" are all too common. Hence, at that time and even now, distinguished authors[10] state that the domain of BIs is restricted to hidden variables and "deterministic" theories.

Accordingly, the results of the EPR experiments,[11-16] which showed violation of

BIs, were gladly accepted by the "orthodox physicists" as only proving that QM was correct and that deterministic theories (like those of hidden variables) were wrong.

However, this coexistence in separate territories is quite unwarranted because BIs, in fact, must be respected by QM as well as by CM. This is so unless we inject into QM the magic assumption of *aaad*'s (an assumption, which if made for CM, would invalidate BIs for CM as well). This can be shown with a simple accurate reasoning based on the QM concepts and properties of wave packets and eigenstates (see next section).

The reasoning immediately provides a proof of Bell's factorization from which BIs validity for QM follows. However, our presentation, emphasizing the physical meaning of the EPR, shows a natural criterion to test whether the result of an EPR experiment indeed implies *aaad*'s. The criterion is simply whether or not one can invent an analyzer with such properties as to be compatible with the established laws of CM and QM and to give the correlations of the experiment.

Moreover, if we safely assume that QM correctly describes elementary phenomena, then that criterion reduces by a great amount the demand for statistical accuracy of experiments with respect to that required by a BIs test. This is so because the BIs require a test about the shape of the correlation function versus the angle. Such a test requires a costly statistics and accuracy at the intermediate angles, while the value of the function at the extreme angles can show the EPR contradiction with a modest effort.

For example, consider a correlation function represented by a zigzag line[2] that is zero at zero angle, reaches with a straight line the required maximum of 0.5 at 90 degrees, and then, with a discontinuity, reaches again zero at 180 degrees in a straight line. Such a correlation satisfies BIs, but it is unacceptable to QM because it would demand photons with spins much larger than one to account for the sharp discontinuity in the correlation function. This conclusion is reached even more obviously if we try to invent a mechanism to produce a correlation having the extreme values of 0.5 and zero. The best we could do is to assume that the two photons are produced with polarization planes orthogonal to each other, but that are otherwise isotropically distributed. It is then easy to see what sort of analyzer we need so as to obtain the correct extreme values of the correlation. The analyzer efficiency versus the angle between the polarization plane and the plane of the analyzer must be one between zero and 45 degrees and zero (abruptly) between 45 and 90. The correlation will have a triangular shape like the Bell limit described above, but to accept such a dependence for the analyzer response, we will have to upset much of our knowledge about light.

Our point concerning the evaluation of EPR experiments with BIs is also made clear by discussing the data obtained with quarter wave optical plates in the path of the photons from atomic cascades. The first experiment was made by Clauser[17] in 1976, but it was not discussed in any review article that we know[18-20] nor in subsequent experimental reports of the EPR[12,13] until 1985. Even papers proposing hidden-variable models as solutions of the EPR did not mention the data of the quarter wave plates (which also had to be explained) until that year.

Apparently, that result was neglected because it was not accurate enough for conventional BIs.[21] Nevertheless, that experiment was very important because of the following reason: the EPR correlation for atomic photons is described in terms of helicities[2,18] as LL-RR (L,R = left, right helicity), which is a correlation just as strict as that between linear polarizations; however, a hidden-variable model tailored to correlate the linear polarizations would not predict any substantial helicity correlation[22] without appropriate artifices.

Even more to the point is the following: in 1985, the Stirling group[23] experimented again with the quarter wave plates and compared their results with BIs. Other authors also discussed their results in terms of BIs.[21] However, the Stirling's setup could not distinguish between a linear combination and a mixture of states; their results could well be reproduced in a totally classical fashion with a laser, and the BIs test cannot distinguish, for that setup, a local from a nonlocal model. Nevertheless, if our simple criterion had been applied to both the helicity and linear polarization data of Stirling, it could have ruled out most, if not all, hidden-variable schemes.

We also want to emphasize that the annihilation photons data must also be explained. However, the assumptions of enhancements caused by polarizers, which have been tailored to satisfy BIs, have not been shown to work in the context of the Compton scattering of the annihilation photons.

ARGUMENT AGAINST THE EXISTENCE OF THE EPR

We want to show that the EPR state cannot exist because it is in contradiction with QM unless *aaad*'s are postulated. This is still, after fifty years, the cardinal point of the discussion about the EPR because it is obvious that whatever arguments might indicate the need of the EPR state, no argument can predict a transition from any initial state into a nonexisting final one. If the arguments in favor were "inescapable," we should escape them by concluding that the reaction in question is forbidden. Examples of such arguments are the superposition of states and the conservation of angular momentum. The latter will be discussed in the next section.

Our argument has been in essence reported before,[2,5] but because of the importance we attribute to it, we submit it again at this meeting in a somewhat different version that takes into account objections we heard in oral discussions since then.

We follow the tradition of describing the EPR in the context of the singlet state of two fermions despite the fact that the best EPR experiments have been made with photons emitted in cascade by atoms of calcium or mercury. Our justification is that while a discussion of planes of polarization of photons can be interpreted as being done in classical terms, in the case of the fermions, the discussion is clearly in QM terms. The possibility of thinking of the spin state in the fermion's rest frame is also an advantage. At any rate, a perfect correspondence exists between the two cases.

Let us then suppose that indeed a machine (the source) produces pairs of fermions (not necessarily identical) in the well-known state of singlet *ud-du*, and let us assume that the fermions remain in that state even when they are separated by a large distance.

Suppose the source produces pairs at the rate of 100/second, and one of the fermions is directed to a Stern-Gerlach apparatus on the left (LSG) and the other to one on the right (RSG). Both SGs are aligned in a Z-direction that can be arbitrarily chosen because *ud-du* is rotationally invariant. Just for the sake of definition, suppose we measure the left fermion first. The uncontroversial interpretation of $(S) = ud-du$ is that after that measurement, (S) will be projected either in the part *ud* or in *du*.

Accordingly, if the left fermion is found to be in the $-Z$-state, the right one will be projected in the eigenstate $(+Z)$ and will arrrive at RSG in that state. Thus, RSG will confirm the state $+Z$. Moreover, keeping LSG aligned in Z and rotating RSG, we must observe (in accordance with the property of eigenstates) that the results of the measurements when RSG is oriented along X are a random mixture of $+X$ and $-X$.

Importantly, such a randomness is the irremediable QM uncertainty in X for particles in the eigenstate $+Z$. In no sense can the result of the X measurement be predicted for such particles, nor can one think that it is the value that the particle "had before the measurement."

Analogously, we should also observe that every time a fermion on the right is measured first and the result is $+Z$, the one on the left will always be found in the eigenstate $(-Z)$ and will give a random mixture in X. We indicate as $(-ZL, +ZR)$ these types of pairs, remembering that the particle giving $+Z$ was measured first. Given the symmetry of (S), we must also observe pairs that are strictly an eigenstate $(+Z)$ on the left and $(-Z)$ on the right. We indicate as $(+ZL, -ZR)$ this other type of pairs that, like the first type, give correlated results in Z, but no correlation in X when one SG remains along Z. The source produces 50/sec events of each type.

We emphasize that the results described so far are strictly obtained from the assumption of the singlet state and are uncontroversial. We now want to investigate the consistency of our assumption with the fact that the particles are far apart from each other.

To define the words, "far apart," we note that the wavelength of the de Broglie waves of the two fermions can be (in fact, it must be in practical experiments) of the order of fermis. With the inevitable collimations, one can safely assume that the wave packets within which the fermions travel must have dimensions of centimeters in any direction. Thus, we do not deal with "extensive QM states" as often assumed in the literature of EPR.[24]

The above considerations, when made quantitatively for the experiments with atomic photons, are not so obvious, but they become conclusive if we consider that the distances used in the past experiments can be greatly increased.

The recognition that the particles are confined within separate wave packets that are much smaller than the distance between the source and the detectors is a key point in the discussion of the EPR in QM terms. It follows from it that no action can modify in any way the state of a fermion, particularly its spin state, unless the action is exerted within the volume of its own wave packet.

The above affirmation, which we will call the statement of separation, should be obvious. However, it is challenged by some even though it is most often predicated and accepted under the flag of "reality." Indeed, it is manifestly clear also within the domain of QM that the spin of a proton or of an electron (not the orbital angular momentum, of course) is contained, in all senses, to a very small volume around the particle. If the particle is confined to a small wave packet of dimensions of centimeters, there can be nothing connected with the spin outside of that packet.

We could also observe that the Schrödinger equation has, for any sort of spin interaction, a spin operator that cannot produce a change when it operates where the particle does not exist. Therefore, we conclude, on the strength of the Schrödinger equation, that an action on particle 1 cannot produce a consequence of any sort in the spin state of particle 2.

Surely, it is easy to write on the blackboard, $F = (u_1u_2 - u_2d_1)f(r_1, r_2)$, but it would be a mistake to understand F as saying that the spin of 1 depends on the spin of 2 simply because they are correlated when produced. F says that the spins are still connected at any later time.

Thus at this point, we must neither assume that F is true, nor that it is false. We must reason by assuming only the statement of separation. The validity of F has to be decided by the outcome of our analysis.

Another comment is in order at this point. Some readers might object that we should consider only "the whole system" of both fermions and not each particle. Clearly, that would produce the tendency to ignore the distance between the subsystem's fermions. Note that it is this distance that produces the paradox. (We will return to this point in the next section.) Here, we only want to reply that while one can surely choose to apply the Schrödinger equation to the whole system, in no way can one forbid the option of applying QM to any subsystem of our choice, including the subsystems of each particle.

With our choice, we find the answer in the simplest terms: the Hamiltonian of the equation is the free particle Hamiltonian; from this, it follows that the spin states of the particles cannot change in their travel between the source and the detector.

Finally, we note that because the fermions need not be identical in our reasoning (the atomic photons are of different colors), it helps to visualize the phenomenon if we assume that we can tell, without disturbing their spin states, which one goes to the right before they reach their respective detectors.

Therefore, the small dimensions of the wave packets force us to conclude (1) that the fermions leave the source well before any one of them is measured; thus, (2) they are prepared by the source without interference from anything else. In addition, (3) the state in which a fermion is prepared, which establishes the probability of giving $+Z$ or $-Z$, is determined by the source well before the measurements are made. Thus, (4) the source will prepare the fermions exactly as we have observed with the help of the SGs even if we remove the passive SG analyzers. Namely, the source will still produce 50 pairs of eigenstates $(-ZL, +ZR)$ and 50 pairs of eigenstates $(+ZL, -ZR)$ every second, and it is irrelevant which particle is measured first.

This conclusion is inconsistent with the assumption of the singlet state *ud-du* for particles at a distance. This is so because the formula implies that before the first measurement, the particles do not each have a determined state, and, accordingly, their probability of giving $+$ or $-$ in their SG is not determined before that time.

A corollary of our conclusion is that if we align that SGs along X instead of Z, the source cannot notice it and will still produce 50 pairs of eigenstates $(-ZL, +ZR)$ and 50 pairs of eigenstates $(+ZL, -ZR)$ every second. The correlation observed before with the Z alignment must disappear because Z eigenstates will give random results in X. As we have said, this random property is the QM uncertainty principle and cannot be circumvented.

Instead, the assumption of the rotationally invariant singlet state predicts for X the same correlation as predicted for Z. That is, we will be forced to assert that the source produces 50 pairs of eigenstates $(-XL, +XR)$ and 50 pairs of eigenstates $(+XL, -XR)$ every second.

This is the contradiction (unless we invent *aaad*'s). It is impossible to choose between the destruction of QM (for which the properties of an eigenstate are of paramount importance) and the rejection of the primordial rule in physics that states that a piece of machinery (pumps, atoms, beams of light) such as our source cannot in any way change by rotating a gadget placed at an arbitrarily large distance from it. After all, reliance on the combined use of that rule and the properties of eigenstates have produced a wealth of progress in the physics of elementary particles.

Contrary to a popular belief, the inconsistency does not decrease by observing that in the described experiment the source does not produce eigenstates in Z and in X at the same time (because each observation requires a different setting for the SGs). Of course, the paradox would be even brighter in that case. In fact, it would require the total rejection of QM, and not even *aaad*'s could help. However, the more modest, yet unquestionable contradiction at hand cannot be ignored just because it could be worse. Renouncing the assumption that *ud-du* is valid at large distances is the only available option.

With respect to the original EPR reasoning, we have changed both the "concept of reality" and the choice of "what is real." The machine (the source) is surely real in the common sense, and we can keep "looking at it" all the time. Thus, the impossibility of observing the Z and the X spin components at the same time does not vitiate our argument. The Z observation remains entirely valid for the future because distant detectors that passively receive information cannot alter the functioning of a machine.

Another variance between our presentation and that of the EPR is our reference to a large sample of observations that allows the more explicit context based on eigenstates. Moreover, the considerations about the wave packets make it positive that the observations of our gedanken-experiment cannot spoil each other.

Our finding about the wave packets has also an immediate consequence for BIs. The starting point of BIs is[9] that (barring *aaad*'s) the probability of one fermion to be measured as $+Z$ or $-X$, etc., should not depend on how we measure or whether we measure its partner at all. The partner can give us information, of course, but cannot influence the state of the other one.

This premise is exactly what we have been forced to conclude because the small wave packets are prepared only by the source and their probabilities for giving a certain result cannot change until their respective SGs measure them. We emphasize again that our reasoning makes no reference to concepts of reality in QM states.

The subject of *aaad*'s, however, deserves a detailed discussion, one which we have not included here. We have previously discussed[2] the properties of *aaad*'s needed to solve the EPR, and we plan to discuss them more extensively in a contribution to the Urbino conference on "Microphysical Reality and Quantum Formalism."

CONSIDERATIONS ABOUT THE NEED FOR THE EPR STATE

We anticipate that some readers, perhaps inspired by the words of N. Bohr, will observe that we should only consider "the whole system" of both fermions. Then one could reason as follows: (1) the state of the two fermions was the singlet state when initially produced, which would be the case for a spinless molecule disintegrating into two fermion atoms by virtue of an interaction that is spin-independent. Then, (2) the angular momentum of the final system must be the same as that of the initial state despite the separation of the particles. Therefore, (3) the final spin state of the system should still be the singlet state. As a collateral argument, it is clear that without any spin-dependent interaction to disturb the system nor the individual fermions, the spin states of the fermions cannot change with respect to the initial state.

This logic is not clear after point number 2. Indeed, the final state of the system is expected to be the same as its initial state only as long as we observe it with an instrument that treats the system as a whole and does not "inquire" about the state of the subsystems represented by the fermions. For instance, the system must have the same charge as it initially had, but it may have disintegrated into many lighter particles.

The following remarks also seem relevant:

(A) Point number 3 may seem obvious on account of a natural intuition based exclusively on classical experiences. In the QM singlet state, each individual particle is not at all in any particular state, but it is, at the same time, in every state possible for a spin-$\frac{1}{2}$ object. We can hardly say that a particle will "remain" in its state; which one? We have shown in the previous section that only if we assume *aaad*'s can we conceive that the particles will remain in "all the states at the same time." Moreover, an interaction that leaves the individual particles in their initial state and yet produces the separation of the particle may not exist if the singlet state of the separated particles does not. We might recall the classical example of a bullet that, when shot by a rifle, acquires a spin without any spin action being exerted directly by the explosive.

(B) The total spin of the system when the particles are bound together can be measured—for instance, with a Stern-Gerlach apparatus. On the other hand, when the particles are separated, only the individual spins can be measured. If we could assert that the result of the measurement represents the spin state in which the particle "was before the measurement," then summing the two results would be equivalent to a measurement of the spin of the system; we could then expect that the two results would add to zero. However, such an assertion is in general not true; thus, it is not true that the individual measurements must give us the state of the system. It would be true, though, if the particles were still in the singlet state after separating. Therefore, the conservation of angular momentum demands the existence of the singlet state only if we assume that the separated particles are in the singlet state.

(C) It cannot be assumed that the experiments prove that the final state is the "singlet state for photons." The correlation of linear polarizations is indeed in agreement with such an assumption, and the helicity correlation will probably be shown to be in agreement also. However, that cannot be sufficient to "prove" such a miracle as *aaad*'s having not just one, but many incredible properties.[2]

(D) The fact that the individual spin states can only be measured after the separation might well indicate that the separation is the first step of a measurement. If we can accept the notion that a measurement of the left fermion can make the state of the distant right one "collapse" from an unpolarized state into a definite eigenstate when the particles are far apart, we could easier, we think, assume that the separation of two interacting fermions "somehow" collapses *ud-du* into one state *ud* of a mixture.

It is interesting to note that articles have appeared contemplating transition from a pure state to a mixture "in violation of QM."[25]

We want to conclude this point by saying only that surely the question of conservation of angular momentum must be understood better, but it is reasonable to think that it cannot be understood until the final state in the EPR experiment is known with certainty. As of now, we cannot see that considerations of angular momentum dispose of the EPR. The considerations of the previous section seem compellingly stronger.

Some other points we would like to make include: (E) All experiments on the EPR are consistent with the EPR state. However, the experiments have all been of the same type and could not give different views of the phenomenon observed, which might be more complex than we suspect. Another point to mention is that the experiments are not a reproduction of the gedanken-experiment (like the one described in the previous section) mainly because the pair of photons are emitted with an isotropic angular distribution independent from each other (rather than being emitted "back-to-back"). Thus, when one photon arrives at its detector, only one in a thousand times (approximately) does the other one also arrive at its detector. Such a feature is certainly undesirable because it leaves the door open for explanations based on enhancements and hidden variables.[21,26]

On the other hand, the experiments on the photons emitted from positron-electron annihilation—which do not suffer from that imperfection—also give a result in agreement with the EPR state.[14-16,27]

Therefore, we believe that the departure from the ideal situation will probably not be the explanation of the atomic photons experiments. However, we also believe that it is unwise to add unwarranted magic to those experiments by interpreting the beautiful work of Aspect *et al.*[13] as "proving" the existence of "superluminal" *aaad*'s. Indeed, the Paris experiment was apparently designed to observe *aaad*'s. However, the experiment gave no evidence at all for the contemplated effect. The result faithfully reproduced the previous ones of Clauser[11] and Fry.[12] To see in the Paris data an evidence of *aaad*'s and an evidence of superluminal speeds in order to explain that no evidence at all was seen is, we think, somewhat risky.

In addition, there is one further point to make: (F) With respect to the possibility of hidden variables explaining the atomic photons result, we want to briefly mention a yet unpublished experiment done by us at the University of California at San Diego (UCSD). The experiment was intended as a test to see whether the photons emitted from positron-electron annihilation are "normal" or whether they have peculiar properties (such as a spin larger than one). We had in mind that in order to reproduce the correlation predicted by the EPR state $(xy - yx)$ without actually being in that state, the annihilation photons should be "abnormal" in the sense that they should scatter with a sharper dependence on the angle between the initial polarization and the direction of scattering than that predicted by the Klein-Nishina (KN) formula. That formula is fundamental for the interaction of photons with electrons. In particular, it gives (with very good accuracy) the polarization that an unpolarized photon acquires after scattering from electrons.[28] If the abnormal photons did not obey the KN theory, they should also show some anomaly concerning the polarization after scattering.

We measured the polarization acquired by the annihilation photons after scattering at 60 and at 90 degrees. The results agreed very well with the KN prediction—indicating that the annihilation photons are very well described by QM—with spin one and without hidden variables or other additional features.

Given this result, it would be very surprising if the atomic photons did possess any unusual features such as hidden variables.

OUR CONCLUSIONS

The most important point concerning the EPR subject is to be convinced that it does not consist in an error caused by wrong concepts of reality, or by ignoring the uncertainty principles of QM, or by an excessive use of "common sense" (if such a thing is possible at all). Only if enough physicists can be convinced that the EPR state indeed contradicts QM and that aggressive research is still needed can we expect progress in the understanding of the phenomenon. At present, it seems that the experiments support the existence of the EPR state. We showed in the second section that that state is unacceptable. We believe that this contradiction is the real, interesting problem of the EPR issue, and its solution is not in sight because the charming *aaad*'s are too magical to be believed and the territory for "models" have shrunk to an uncomfortable size.

We also recall that puzzles just as big (like that of the energy nonconservation in beta decay) have eventually been solved in a harmonious fashion without inventions of appropriately designed miracles.

This situation, instead of inspiring pessimism, should suggest that the solution of the EPR will be a rewarding result of imaginative research.

ACKNOWLEDGMENTS

We are indebted to A. Wightman of Princeton University and R. Swanson of UCSD for stimulating discussions. We also wish to thank Pat Fisher, Brian Wright, and David Coblentz of UCSD for their very valuable collaboration in preparing this text.

REFERENCES

1. EINSTEIN, A., B. PODOLSKY & N. ROSEN. 1935. Phys. Rev. **47**: 777–780.
2. PICCIONI, O., P. BOWLES, C. ENSCOE, R. GARLAND & W. MEHLHOP. 1985. *In* Open Questions in Quantum Physics. G. Tarozzi & A. van der Merwe, Eds.: 103–118. Reidel. Dordrecht.
3. BOHR, N. 1935. Phys. Rev. **48**: 696.
4. D'ESPAGNAT, B. 1979. Sci. Am. **241**: 158; D'ESPAGNAT, B. 1983. In Search of Reality. Springer-Verlag. New York.
5. LAHTI, P. & P. MITTELSTAEDT. 1985. Symposium on the Foundations of Modern Physics, Joensuu, Finland. World Scientific. Singapore.
6. DAVIES, P. 1985. Superforce (1st edition). Simon & Schuster. New York.
7. FINE, A. 1982. Phys. Rev. Lett. **48**: 291.
8. PITOWSKI, I. 1982. Phys. Rev. Lett. **48**: 1299.

9. D'ESPAGNAT, B., Ed. 1971. Foundations of Quantum Mechanics. Academic Press. New York.
10. WHEELER, J. A. & W. H. ZUREK, Eds. 1983. Quantum Theory and Measurement. Princeton Univ. Press. Princeton, New Jersey.
11. CLAUSER, J. 1976. Phys. Rev. Lett. 36(21): 1223–1226.
12. FRY, E. S. & R. C. THOMPSON. 1976. Phys. Rev. Lett. 37(8): 465–468.
13. ASPECT, A., J. DALIBARD & G. ROGER. 1982. Phys. Rev. Lett. 49(25): 1804–1807.
14. WU, C. S. & I. SHAKNOV. 1950. Phys. Rev. 77: 136.
15. KASDAY, L. R. 1971. In Foundations of Quantum Mechanics. B. d'Espagnat, Ed.: 195. Academic Press. New York.
16. BRUNO, M., M. D'AGOSTINO & C. MARONI. 1977. Nuovo Cimento 40B: 142.
17. CLAUSER, J. F. 1976. Nuovo Cimento 33B(2): 740–746.
18. CLAUSER, J. F. & A. SHIMONY. 1978. Rep. Prog. Phys. 41: 1881–1927.
19. SELLERI, F. & G. TAROZZI. 1981. Riv. Nuovo Cimento 4(2): 1–53.
20. PIPKIN, F. 1978. Advances in Atomic Molecular Physics, vol. 14. S. D. R. Bates & B. Bederson, Eds.: 281. Academic Press. New York.
21. SELLERI, F. 1985. Phys. Lett. 108A: 197.
22. FORTUNATO, D., A. GARUCCIO & F. SELLERI. 1977. Int. J. Theor. Phys. 16(1): 1–6.
23. DUNCAN, A. J., W. PERRIE, H. J. BEYER & H. KLEINPOPPEN. 1985. The circular polarization correlation of two photons as a test of Bell's inequality. Second European Conference on Atomic and Molecular Physics. Amsterdam.
24. WEISSKOPF, V. F. 1980. Sci. Am. 242: 8.
25. ELLIS, J., J. S. HAGELIN, D. V. NANOPOULOS & M. SREDNICKI. 1984. Nucl. Phys. B241: 381–405.
26. MARSHALL, T. & E. SANTOS. 1985. Phys. Lett. 107A: 164. (Also see other references within.)
27. LANGHOFF, H. 1960. Z. Phys. 160: 186–193.
28. WIGHTMAN, A. 1948. Phys. Rev. 74: 1813.

Einstein-Podolsky-Rosen Interferometry[a]

MICHAEL A. HORNE[b] AND ANTON ZEILINGER[c]

Department of Physics
Massachusetts Institute of Technology
Cambridge, Massachusetts 02139

INTRODUCTION

Einstein, Podolsky, and Rosen[1] (abbreviated EPR) in their classic 1935 paper examined the quantum mechanical description of two spatially separated, yet correlated systems. They concluded that quantum mechanics is an incomplete theory of physical reality. The EPR argument uses a thought-experiment in which one may select to measure either the positions or the linear momenta of a pair of particles. Bell,[2] in 1965, continued the study begun by EPR and proved, surprisingly, that the completion of quantum mechanics envisioned by EPR implies instantaneous interactions between the spatially separated systems. Bell's theorem was presented in terms of another thought-experiment in which one measures select components of the spins of a pair of particles.

Bell's theorem, because it depends critically on the two-valuedness of these spin observables, is not easily extended to the continuously valued position and linear momentum observables originally considered by EPR. Bell does point out that the theorem can be extended to observables other than spin by considering two-dimensional subspaces in the state space of each system and defining operators, that is, observables, formally analogous to spin. However, in general, it may not be clear what apparatus actually corresponds to these formal "observables." In this paper, we wish to show explicitly how the Bell theorem can be extended to linear momentum, and to point out that the required apparatus already exists—namely, a perfect crystal interferometer.

Before describing this union of EPR and interferometry, we review a typical polarization-type EPR arrangement and also present some basic aspects of perfect crystal interferometry. We conclude with a discussion of experimental realizability.

EINSTEIN-PODOLSKY-ROSEN

FIGURE 1 depicts an idealized EPR experiment of the familiar polarization type, as considered by Bell. An atom in the source undergoes a cascade that emits two photons traveling in opposite directions. Photon 1 (2) traveling left (right) impinges on a linear polarization analyzer oriented at angle θ_1 (θ_2), and subsequently triggers a count in one

[a]This work was supported by the U.S. National Science Foundation under Grant No. 8513396-DMR.
[b]Permanent address: Stonehill College, North Easton, Massachusetts 02356.
[c]Permanent address: Atominstitut der Oesterreichischen, Universitaeten, Schuettelstraße 115, 1020 Wien, Austria.

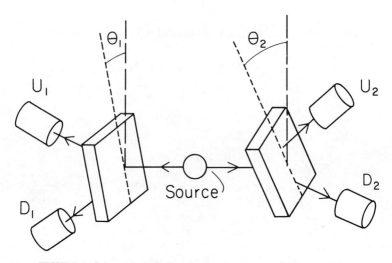

FIGURE 1. Schematic depiction of a polarization-type EPR experiment.

of the two detectors, U_1 or D_1 (U_2 or D_2). The probability of each of the possible outcomes depends upon the quantum mechanical polarization state of the photon pair, which in turn depends on the particular atomic cascade that produced them.

For example, if the atom cascades through angular momentum states, $0 \rightarrow 1 \rightarrow 0$, the state of the photon pair, as determined by angular momentum and parity conservation, is

$$\frac{1}{\sqrt{2}} \; [\, |R\rangle_1 |R\rangle_2 + |L\rangle_1 |L\rangle_2 \,], \tag{1}$$

where $|R\rangle_1$ means photon 1 is right-hand circularly polarized, etc. Note that equation 1 implies that neither photon separately has a state of definite polarization; all that can be said is that the pair of photons is in the state of equation 1. In fact, equation 1 implies that each photon separately is unpolarized and that the probability of a count in any of the four detectors is a constant independent of θ_1 and θ_2: namely,

$$P(U_1) = P(D_1) = P(U_2) = P(D_2) = \frac{1}{2}, \tag{2}$$

where $P(U_1)$ is the probability that detector U_1 will be triggered, etc. However, despite this insensitivity of each detector's count rate to the settings, θ_1 and θ_2, equation 1 also implies interesting correlations in the triggering of the detectors: the joint probabilities of coincident counts in two of the detectors are

$$P(U_1, U_2) = P(D_1, D_2) = \frac{1}{4} + \frac{1}{4} \cos (\theta_1 - \theta_2) \tag{3}$$

and

$$P(U_1, D_2) = P(D_1, U_2) = \frac{1}{4} - \frac{1}{4} \cos (\theta_1 - \theta_2). \tag{4}$$

It is these quantum mechanical predictions for the joint probabilities (i.e., coincident count rates in pairs of detectors) that Bell proves cannot be produced by any local theory of reality. However, these predicted count rates have been repeatedly confirmed experimentally.[3]

INTERFEROMETRY

FIGURE 2 depicts schematically a single-particle interferometer that is similar to ones currently used both with photons and with neutrons of approximately one-angstrom wavelength. The device uses diffraction at three perfect crystal slabs (S, M, S') to coherently split and recombine the particle's quantum mechanical wave function. In each crystal slab, the diffracting lattice planes are perpendicular to both the face of the crystals and to the plane of the figure. Because the slabs are connected portions of a single large crystal, the lattice planes of S, M, and S' are aligned.

Consider an incident plane wave of wavevector $\mathbf{K}$ that illuminates S at exactly the Bragg angle. Diffraction in S produces two plane waves behind the crystal—a forward wave with the same wavevector, $\mathbf{K}$, as the incident wave, and a Bragg diffracted wave with wavevector $\mathbf{K}' \equiv \mathbf{K} + \mathbf{G}$, where $\mathbf{G}$ is the reciprocal lattice vector of the diffracting planes. These two waves are coherent, and with a suitable choice for the thickness of S, they are of equal amplitude; hence, the symbol, S, to denote this crystal as a "splitter." Specifically, if the thickness T_S of S is one of the values,

$$T_S = (2n - \tfrac{1}{4}) \, \Delta, \qquad n = 1, 2, 3, \ldots, \tag{5}$$

where Δ is the pendellösung length,[4,5] the effect of S is given by

$$|\mathbf{K}\rangle \xrightarrow[S]{} \frac{1}{\sqrt{2}} \, [\,|\mathbf{K}\rangle + i\,|\mathbf{K}'\rangle], \tag{6}$$

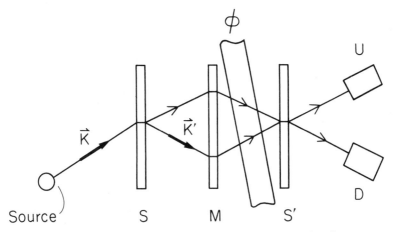

FIGURE 2. Schematic depiction of a perfect crystal single-particle interferometer.

$$|\mathbf{K}'\rangle \underset{S}{\to} \frac{1}{\sqrt{2}} \left[|\mathbf{K}'\rangle + i |\mathbf{K}\rangle \right]. \tag{7}$$

Here, $|\mathbf{K}\rangle$ denotes a plane wave state of wavevector $\mathbf{K}$, etc., with incident states to the left and corresponding outgoing states to the right of the arrow.

The two waves from S fall on the "mirror" crystal, M, whose thickness is one of the values,

$$T_M = (2n - \tfrac{1}{2}) \Delta, \qquad n = 1, 2, 3, \ldots, \tag{8}$$

and whose effect is simply

$$|\mathbf{K}\rangle \xrightarrow[M]{} i |\mathbf{K}'\rangle, \tag{9}$$

$$|\mathbf{K}'\rangle \xrightarrow[M]{} i |\mathbf{K}\rangle; \tag{10}$$

that is, each incident wave is totally diffracted by M.

The two waves from M fall on a slab of transparent refractive material, a phase plate, that imparts an additional relative phase, ϕ, to the two fields. We define ϕ to be $|\mathbf{K}'\rangle$-field-phase minus $|\mathbf{K}\rangle$-field-phase. The value of ϕ may be varied by simply rotating the phase plate so that it presents a different thickness to $|\mathbf{K}\rangle$ and $|\mathbf{K}'\rangle$. Finally, behind the phase plate, the two plane waves encounter a second splitter crystal, S', identical to S, so each wave incident on S' illuminates both the U and the D detectors.

All that is reported above concerning the diffraction processes can be derived for neutrons[5] (photons[4]) by applying Schrödinger's equation (Maxwell's equations) in the periodic potential (dielectric constant) of the crystal medium. Using the mirror and splitter equations 6, 7, 9, and 10, and including the phase, ϕ, one can calculate the amplitudes and hence the probabilities that the particle described quantum mechanically by the incident wave, $|\mathbf{K}\rangle$, will trigger the U or D detectors. The results are

$$P(U) = \tfrac{1}{2} + \tfrac{1}{2} \cos \phi \tag{11}$$

and

$$P(D) = \tfrac{1}{2} - \tfrac{1}{2} \cos \phi. \tag{12}$$

Note, for example, that if the phase plate is parallel to the crystal faces, the phase, ϕ, is zero and hence no particles land in D. Also note that equations 11 and 12 hold even when the relative phase, ϕ, is imparted not by a phase plate, but by gravity, Coriolis force, or Aharonov-Bohm effect, etc.

EINSTEIN-PODOLSKY-ROSEN INTERFEROMETRY

FIGURE 2 and the right half of FIGURE 1 are similar. Each has a single adjustable parameter: the relative phase, ϕ, in FIGURE 2, and the analyzer orientation angle, θ, in FIGURE 1. Each has two detectors. These similarities led us to consider FIGURE 3 as a possible analog to the EPR arrangement in FIGURE 1. Notice that neither side of the arrangement in FIGURE 3 contains the splitter crystal, S, present in the interferometer of FIGURE 2; here, the illumination of the crystals, M_1 and M_2, at the Bragg angle is to be supplied by an elementary emission event in the source that produces two suitably correlated particles (1 and 2).

Suppose, for example, that this two-particle state is

$$\frac{1}{\sqrt{2}} \left[| -\mathbf{K} \rangle_1 | \mathbf{K} \rangle_2 + | -\mathbf{K}' \rangle_1 | \mathbf{K}' \rangle_2 \right], \tag{13}$$

where $| -\mathbf{K} \rangle_1$ denotes a plane wave state for particle 1 with wavevector $-\mathbf{K}$, etc. Although equation 13 is the state of the pair of particles only in the region between M_1 and M_2, by repeated application of equations 6, 7, 9, and 10, we can calculate the amplitude in the region of the detectors and hence the probability, $P(U_1, U_2)$, that particle 1 triggers detector U_1 and particle 2 triggers detector U_2, etc. The probabilities obtained in this way are identical to equations 2, 3, and 4, except that the relative

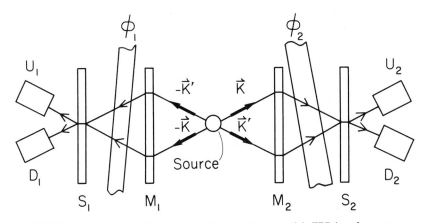

FIGURE 3. Schematic depiction of a perfect crystal two-particle EPR interferometer.

phases, ϕ_1 and ϕ_2, replace the analyzer orientations, θ_1 and θ_2. Thus, the EPR interferometer is a perfect analog to the polarization EPR arrangement.

EXPERIMENTAL REALIZATION

Can EPR interferometry be demonstrated in the laboratory? Positronium annihilation at rest produces a pair of photons whose momenta are angularly anticorrelated as in equation 13, thereby potentially providing a source. We must emphasize at this point that equation 13 is a superposition of products and that positronium annihilation does produce such a superposition, that is, not a classical mixture. The wavelength of the photons is 0.024Å. For this wavelength and the (400) planes of silicon (lattice spacing of 1.36Å), the Bragg angle is 0.52° and the pendellösung length, Δ, is 1.33 mm, indicating crystal diffraction can be performed at this wavelength. Silicon could also be used to construct phase-shifting devices; a thickness of 1.83 mm produces a 2π shift. Finally, these high energy photons are easily detectable.

In the laboratory, however, positronium is not often at rest; the positronium moves as dictated by the source temperature. At room temperature, this thermal motion of the positronium smears the ideal angular anticorrelation of each term in equation 13 into a milliradian angular window. Because the angular acceptance window for the Bragg diffraction is much smaller, namely, 0.2 arcseconds for these photons at silicon (400), there would be few pairs of photons that both diffract in their respective crystal interferometer, which is required for EPR interferometry. When one contemplates using the brightest existing sources[6] emitting 10^9 pairs/sec and using source cooling to the millikelvin region, the numbers begin to indicate a feasible laboratory demonstration.

ACKNOWLEDGMENTS

We wish to thank C. G. Shull for his hospitality at Massachusetts Institute of Technology, which brought us together and which permitted us to contemplate the possibility of a connection between neutron interferometry and EPR-Bell physics.

REFERENCES

1. EINSTEIN, A., B. PODOLSKY & N. ROSEN. 1935. Phys. Rev. **47:** 777.
2. BELL, J. S. 1965. Physics (N. Y.) **1:** 195.
3. CLAUSER, J. & A. SHIMONY. 1978. Rep. Prog. Phys. **41:** 1881.
4. BATTERMANN, B. W. & H. COLE. 1964. Rev. Mod. Phys. **36:** 681.
5. RAUCH, H. & D. PETRASCHECK. 1978. Neutron Diffraction. H. Dachs, Ed: 303. Springer-Verlag. Berlin.
6. BERKO, S. 1985. Private communication.

Quantum Mechanical Hamiltonian Models of Computers[a]

PAUL BENIOFF

Environmental Research Division
Argonne National Laboratory
Argonne, Illinois 60439

INTRODUCTION

Interest in the physical limitations of the computation process has been increasing in recent years.[1,2] Landauer[3-6] has discussed this subject extensively, particularly from the viewpoint of energy dissipation and reversible and irreversible computation. He has also stressed the fact that the computation process is necessarily implemented as a physical process and is thus subject to physical laws.

Much of the work in this area has been concerned with the construction of various models of the computation process with different properties. Bennett[7,8] and Likharev[9] have discussed thermodynamically reversible models that dissipate arbitrarily little energy if they proceed sufficiently slowly. Fredkin and Toffoli[10] have constructed ideal classical mechanical billiard-ball models of the computation process that do not dissipate energy and that evolve at a finite speed. Benioff has constructed quantum mechanical Hamiltonian models of Turing machines on spin lattices both with[11,12] and without[13,14] the use of scattering systems to drive the process.

Feynman[15] has outlined the construction of quantum ballistic models of the computation process. He has also shown that models can be constructed for which the Hamiltonian contains, at most, three body interactions. Margolus[16] has used Feynman's methods to construct quantum mechanical models of the classical billiard-ball models.[10] Peres[17] has constructed models that include redundancy to correct errors, and Zurek[18] has discussed the propagation of errors in classical and quantum mechanical models. Deutsch[19] and Pitowsky[20] have considered the computation power of more general types of quantum computers.

In this paper, Feynman's[15] methods will be used to construct quantum mechanical Hamiltonian models of Turing machines on a two-dimensional lattice of spin-$\frac{1}{2}$ systems. The Hamiltonians will be seen to be spatially local, simple, and such that the system state does not degrade as it evolves.

From the point of view of constructing physical models of these machines, these properties are desirable. Physically reasonable Hamiltonians are spatially local in that their interaction does not extend over all space with undiminished strength. A Hamiltonian is simple if its construction requires, at most, knowledge of the computer programs to be run. This is reasonable in that real computers require this knowledge for their operation. Knowledge of computation orbits is not needed. Evolution without

[a]This work was partially supported by the Applied Mathematical Sciences Subprogram of the Office of Energy Research, U.S. Department of Energy, under Contract No. W-31-109-Eng-38.

state degradation means that energy need not be dissipated during the model evolution to upgrade and correct the model state. This is important because for real computers built so far, the amount of computing power that can be packed into a given space-time volume is limited by the efficiency of heat removal. This limit disappears if no energy is dissipated (other than that needed to run the model in a noisy environment).

TURING MACHINES

In brief, a Turing machine consists of an infinite computation tape, T, divided into cells, and a computation head, I. Each cell of the tape can have any symbol, s, of a finite symbol alphabet, S, written on it. S includes the blank cell symbol, b. The head can be in any state, ℓ, of a finite set, L, of internal states. The head scans one tape cell at any given time. FIGURE 1 gives the setup.

The basic machine operations consist of changing the scanned symbol, s, to s' and/or shifting I one cell to the right or left. Each Turing machine is defined by a map $\tau : L \times S \rightarrow L \times S \times \{-1, 0, +1\}$, where τ defines the elementary machine steps. $\tau(\ell s) = (\ell' s' \alpha)$ means if I is in state ℓ and scans symbol s, then the machine operations will change s to s', change ℓ to ℓ', and shift I one cell to the right ($\alpha = +1$), one cell to the left ($\alpha = -1$), or leave it where it is ($\alpha = 0$). Successive steps of a machine

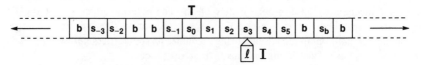

FIGURE 1. Schematic representation of a Turing machine.

computation are done by iterations of τ. The computation halts if I arrives in a state ℓ such that the state of the tape remains fixed under iterations of τ.

It is assumed that computations start and end with all cells of T blank (which are to the left of position 0), that the cell at position 0 is not blank, and that no two nonblank cells are separated by a blank cell. Initially, I is at position 0, and if the computation halts, I scans the rightmost nonblank cell.

The main restriction imposed here on τ is that it describes reversible Turing machines. Reversibility is equivalent to the requirement that τ have a well-defined inverse on $L \times S$. Because $L \times S$ is finite, such τ are one-to-one onto $L \times S$. For such τ, one also requires that the shift and read-write operations are separated. Further details are given elsewhere.[7]

The reversibility requirement also means that the overall computation process has no beginning or end. This is taken into account here by extending τ so that the head I moves in from the left with no changes in the tape system occurring until I reaches position 0. If the computation terminates, I moves to the right, away from the rightmost nonblank position, without further changes in T.

In what follows, it will be convenient to be able to designate for any τ with $\tau(\ell s) = (\ell' s' \alpha)$ the separate dependencies of ℓ', s', and α on ℓ and s. To this end, one needs to

define three functions—$\tau_1 : L \times S \rightarrow L$; $\tau_2 : L \times S \rightarrow S$; and $\tau_3 : L \times S \rightarrow \{-1, 0, +1\}$—
by $\tau(\ell s) = \{\tau_1(\ell s), \tau_2(\ell s), \tau_3(\ell s)\}$ for all ℓ and s.

It remains to discuss the completeness of the set of reversible one-tape machines. Bennett[7] has shown that to every Turing machine, there corresponds a reversible three-tape Turing machine that operates in three phases: compute and record history, copy result, and reverse compute and erase history. He also noted without discussion that equivalent reversible one-tape Turing machines should also exist. A proof of this will not be given here. However, relevant details of one proof include the following: The tape, T, is extended to consist of compute cells, c, copy cells d, and history cells, h, in a regular repeated order such as $\ldots cdhcdh\ldots$. Then L is expanded to contain $2M^2N + K$ symbols, where M is the number of quintuples in the original (not necessarily reversible, one-tape) τ. This expansion is needed because I must be able to carry codes for the just completed quintuple and the next one to be carried out. S is expanded to include the original S plus M new symbols. Two special markers are needed—one to mark the active c cell while I is away recording the history, and one to mark the available h cell while I is doing a compute step. N is the number of quintuples needed in the expanded machine for one step of the original τ, and K is the number of quintuples in the copy phase. The factor 2 results from the fact that states of I in the reverse phase must be distinct from those in the forward phase. From now on, τ will denote extended reversible machines as described above.

QUANTUM MECHANICAL MODELS

The Turing machine models are all constructed on a two-dimensional lattice of distinguishable spin-$\frac{1}{2}$ systems. FIGURE 2 gives some details. The lattice is finite in the y-direction and infinite in the x-direction. It consists of two distinct regions, Γ and Ω, corresponding to the tape, T, and the head, I, respectively. Each tape cell is modeled by a line of spins in the y-direction. The cell position is given by the x-coordinate of the line of spins. All spins are down in region Ω, except along some line in the y-direction. The position of I is given by the x-coordinate of this line.

It is assumed that one has a given representation of the symbols in S and the states in L as finite strings of 0's (spin down) and 1's (spin up) of length, ℓ_S and ℓ_L, respectively. From now on, s and ℓ denote either the symbols and state labels or their representation as strings of 0's and 1's. For any s and ℓ, $D_s = \{j | s(j) = 1\}$ and $D_\ell = \{j | \ell(j) = 1\}$ are the set of string places for s and ℓ that have 1's. Note that the blank symbol, b, is in S and that D_b is not empty. For reasons that will become clear shortly, it is required that the representations are such that for any pair, ℓ, ℓ', of I states, D_ℓ is not a subset of $D_{\ell'}$. It is also required that D_ℓ and $D_{\ell'}$ contain one or more elements in common. Similar relations are required to hold for D_s and $D_{s'}$ for any pair, s, s', in S (including the blank).

For any configuration, f, of spins on the lattice, Ψ_f denotes the configuration state that is the product of single spin states over the whole lattice. The state of the single spin system at each site (x, y) is $\binom{1}{0}$ if $f(xy) = 1$ and is $\binom{0}{1}$ if $f(x, y) = 0$. $\Psi_{\varrho\lambda j}$ denotes the configuration state in which I is in state ℓ and at position j and in which expression λ is on the tape. Here, one is limited to the set of all expressions λ such that, at most, a finite number of symbols are not blank. One can write $\Psi_{\varrho\lambda j} = \Psi_{\varrho j}^I \times \Psi_\lambda^T$, where the configuration state, $\Psi_{\varrho j}^I$, is limited to the region Ω of the lattice and has spins down everywhere except at position j. Ψ_λ^T is limited to region Γ and is given by

$$\Psi_\lambda^T = \times_j \Psi_{\lambda(j)}^T(j), \tag{1}$$

where $\lambda(j) = b$ except possibly for a finite number of j.

The operators are all constructed using raising, $\sigma^+(j, k)$, and lowering, $\sigma^-(j, k)$, operators for the spins at lattice site (j, k), where $\sigma^+ = \begin{pmatrix} 0 & 1 \\ 0 & 0 \end{pmatrix}$ and $\sigma^- = \begin{pmatrix} 0 & 0 \\ 1 & 0 \end{pmatrix}$. The

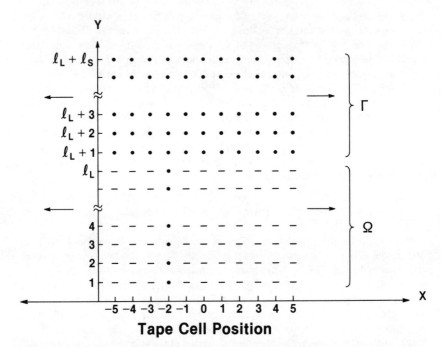

Tape Cell Position

FIGURE 2. Schematic representation of the spin lattice model of a Turing machine. The dashes denote lattice sites with spin down systems. Each column of dots at a fixed position denotes a line of spins with at least one spin up. I is shown at position -2, where it scans cell -2. The regions of the lattice that are used for T and I are denoted by Γ and Ω, respectively. The horizontal arrows denote infinite extent of the lattice in the x-direction.

operators, $\alpha_{\ell j}$ and α_{sk}, are defined by

$$\alpha_{\ell j} = \times_{h \epsilon D_\ell} \sigma^-(j, h) \tag{2}$$

and

$$\alpha_{sk} = \times_{h \epsilon D_s} \sigma^-(j, \ell_L + h). \tag{3}$$

The Hermitian adjoints, $\alpha_{\ell j}^\dagger$ and $\alpha_{sk}^\dagger$, are defined as above with σ^+ replacing σ^-. $\alpha_{\ell j}^\dagger$ and $\alpha_{\ell j}$ are referred to here respectively as the creation and annihilation operators for I in state ℓ at position j because they satisfy

$$\alpha_{\ell j}^{\dagger}\Psi_{mj}^{I} = \Psi_{\ell j}^{I}\delta_{m,-} \tag{4}$$

and

$$\alpha_{\ell j}\Psi_{mj}^{I} = \Psi_{-j}^{I}\delta_{m,\ell}. \tag{5}$$

Here, Ψ_{-j}^{I} denotes the configuration state on region Ω with all spins down in Ω (independent of j), and $\delta_{m,n} = 1$ if $m = n$ and $\delta_{m,n} = 0$ if $m \neq n$. These relations are seen to hold if and only if for all m and ℓ in L, D_ℓ is not a subset of D_m, and D_ℓ and D_m contain one or more elements in common. This is the reason the requirements noted before were placed on the representation.

The operators, $\alpha_{sk}^{\dagger}$ and α_{sk}, for creating and annihilating the symbol s in tape cell k satisfy

$$\alpha_{sk}^{\dagger}\Psi_t^T(k) = \Psi_s^T(k)\delta_{t,-}, \tag{6}$$

$$\alpha_{sk}\Psi_t^T(k) = \Psi_-^T(k)\delta_{t,s}. \tag{7}$$

The state, $\Psi_-^T(k)$, describes all spins down in tape cell k and is distinct from the state, $\Psi_b^T(k)$, which corresponds to cell k being blank. These relations hold provided D_s and D_t satisfy the requirements given before.

The Turing machine step operator, V^τ, is defined from the annihilation and creation operators as

$$V^\tau = \sum_{\ell \in L}\sum_{s \in S}\sum_{j=-\infty}^{\infty} V_{\ell sj}^{\tau}, \tag{8}$$

where

$$V_{\ell sj}^{\tau} = \alpha_{\tau_1(\ell s),j+\tau_3(\ell s)}^{\dagger}\alpha_{\ell j}\alpha_{\tau_2(\ell s)j}^{\dagger}\alpha_{sj}. \tag{9}$$

The action of V^τ on any state, $\Psi_{\ell\lambda j}$, is obtained from the above as

$$V^\tau\Psi_{\ell\lambda j} = V_{\ell sj}^{\tau}\Psi_{\ell\lambda j}^{\tau} = \Psi_{\tau_1(\ell s),\lambda',j+\tau_3(\ell s)}, \tag{10}$$

where $s = \lambda(j)$ and $\lambda'(k) = \lambda(k)$ for all $k \neq j$ and $\lambda'(j) = \tau_2(\ell s)$. Thus, V^τ carries out one Turing machine step on states of the form $\Psi_{\ell\lambda j}$, thereby converting ℓ to $\tau_1[\ell\lambda(j)]$, moving I from j to $j + \tau_3[\ell\lambda(j)]$, and converting $\lambda(j)$ to $\tau_2[\ell\lambda(j)]$.

The adjoint $V^{\tau\dagger}$ is obtained directly from the above as a sum over ℓsj of $V_{\ell sj}^{\tau\dagger}$ where

$$V_{\ell sj}^{\tau\dagger} = \alpha_{\ell j}^{\dagger}\alpha_{\tau_1(\ell s),j+\tau_3(\ell s)}\alpha_{sj}^{\dagger}\alpha_{\tau_2(\ell s)j}. \tag{11}$$

The action of $V_{\ell sj}^{\tau\dagger}$ on any state of the form $\Psi_{m\lambda k}$ gives 0 unless $m = \tau_1(\ell s)$, $\lambda(j) = \tau_2(\ell s)$, and $k = j + \tau_3(\ell s)$. In this case, one has

$$V_{\ell sj}^{\tau\dagger}\Psi_{\tau_1(\ell s),\lambda,j+\tau_3(\ell s)} = \Psi_{\ell\lambda'j}, \tag{12}$$

where $\lambda'(j) = s$ and $\lambda(h) = \lambda'(h)$ for all $h \neq j$.

The above shows that $V^{\tau\dagger}$ applied to any state $\Psi_{m\lambda k}$ carries out the computation inverse of τ. As a consequence, V^τ is unitary on the subspace of all lattice configuration states, with the subspace being spanned by all states of the form $\Psi_{m\lambda k}$. Note that on other lattice configuration states, the action of V^τ is quite complex and, in general, V^τ is not unitary. However, one is not interested here in these other states, and considerations will be limited here to states that are in the above noted subspace.

Consider a state, $\Psi_{\ell_i \lambda 0}$, for I in initial state, ℓ_i, at position 0 and T with a standard initial expression λ. The iteration of V^τ and $V^{\tau\dagger}$ on $\Psi_{\ell_i \lambda 0}$ gives the states, $(V^\tau)^m \Psi_{\ell_i \lambda 0} = \Psi_\lambda^m$, which describe forward $(m > 0)$ and backward $(m < 0)$ steps of the τ computation $[(V^\tau)^{-1} = V^{\tau\dagger}]$.

The set of states, Ψ_λ^m [denoted from now on by $|m\rangle$ with λ understood], describes the model computation orbit of τ for the initial tape expression λ. The states also span a subspace of states that is invariant and irreducible with respect to the action of V^τ. In particular, $V^\tau |m\rangle = |m + 1\rangle$. For each standard initial λ, one has a distinct computation orbit and a distinct invariant irreducible subspace on which V^τ is a bilateral shift. As such, the spectrum of V^τ is purely continuous and is the unit circle;[21] that is, one can write

$$V^\tau = \int_{-\pi}^{\pi} e^{-ip} d(Ep) \tag{13}$$

for each of the subspaces, where p denotes the orbit momentum of the system and Ep is the associated spectral measure.

Note that the orbit position and momentum denote the position and momentum of the overall system along the computation orbit. They do not correspond to the lattice position or lattice momentum of I along the tape.

Following Feynman's prescription,[15] the model Hamiltonian for each τ is defined by

$$H^\tau = K(2 - V^\tau - V^{\tau\dagger}), \tag{14}$$

where K is an arbitrary constant. The spectral representation of H^τ can be written as $H^\tau = \int_{-\pi}^{\pi} \omega_p d(Ep)$, where the orbit energy, ω_p, is given by

$$\omega_p = 2K[1 - \cos(p)]. \tag{15}$$

Equation 15 shows that, for small p, ω_p is proportional to p^2, which is the appropriate momentum dependence for the kinetic energy.

The system state evolution for this type of Hamiltonian is described as follows: An initial wave-packet state, $\Psi_\lambda(0)$, of the machine at time 0 can be written as a linear sum over orbit position states,

$$\Psi_\lambda(0) = \sum_{m=-\infty}^{\infty} d_m(0)|m\rangle. \tag{16}$$

At time t, the state $\Psi_\lambda(t)$ is given by

$$\Psi_\lambda(t) = \sum_{m=-\infty}^{\infty} d_m(t)|m\rangle, \tag{17}$$

where the coefficient, $d_m(t) = (m|\Psi_\lambda(t))$, is given by

$$d_m(t) = \int_{-\pi}^{\pi} dp \frac{e^{ipm - i\omega_p t}}{\sqrt{2\pi}} (p|\Psi_\lambda). \tag{18}$$

If the packet Ψ_λ is centered at orbit position, m_0, and at orbit momentum, p_0, then $d_m(t)$ is large when $m - m_0 \sim (d\omega_{p_0}/dp_0)t$ or $m \sim m_0 + 2Kt \sin (p_0)$. This shows that the group velocity, v, of the packet, which is also the computation speed with $v \approx 2K \sin (p_0)$, is independent of time and orbit position. More exactly, v is given by $v = -i \langle [\tilde{n}, H^\tau] \rangle = 2K\langle \tilde{q} \rangle$, where $\tilde{q} = i(V^\tau - V^{\tau\dagger})/2 = \sin (\tilde{p})$, $\tilde{n}$ is the orbit position operator, $\tilde{p}$ is the orbit momentum operator, and $[\tilde{n}, H^\tau]$ denotes the commutator of $\tilde{n}$ and H^τ.

It can also be shown, following methods given elsewhere,[22] that the dispersions, $\Delta\tilde{n} = (\langle \tilde{n}^2 \rangle - \langle \tilde{n} \rangle^2)^{1/2}$ and $\Delta\tilde{q} = (\langle \tilde{q}^2 \rangle - \langle \tilde{q} \rangle^2)^{1/2}$, satisfy an uncertainty principle relation given by

$$\Delta\tilde{n} \, \Delta\tilde{q} \geq \frac{1}{4} |\langle V^\tau + V^{\tau\dagger} \rangle|. \tag{19}$$

For a minimal packet, the spread, $\Delta\tilde{n}(t)$, along the orbit at time t can be shown, following methods given elsewhere,[22] to be given by

$$\Delta\tilde{n}(t)^2 = \Delta\tilde{n}(0)^2 + 4K^2t^2\Delta\tilde{q}^2, \tag{20}$$

where $\Delta\tilde{n}(0) = \Delta\tilde{n}$, and $\Delta\tilde{q}$ is independent of time. For a wave packet centered at orbit momentum state p_0 and with a small orbit momentum dispersion, $\Delta\tilde{p}$, one has $\Delta\tilde{q} \approx \Delta\tilde{p} \cos (p_0)$ in the above. For such packets, spreading is small if p_0 is close to $\pi/2$. However, this corresponds to a large orbit momentum in the model because the orbit velocity is close to its maximum value.

Use of the uncertainty relation gives the result that spreading is small for all times t such that $\Delta\tilde{n}(t) \approx \Delta\tilde{n}$ or $t \ll 2\Delta\tilde{n}^2/(K|\langle V^\tau + V^{\tau\dagger} \rangle|)$. Because $|\langle V^\tau + V^{\tau\dagger} \rangle| \leq 2$, spreading is certainly small if $t < \Delta\tilde{n}^2/K$. In addition, because vt is the total number of computation steps or τ iterations carried out in time t, the spreading is small for the first $2\Delta\tilde{n}^2\langle \tilde{q} \rangle$ steps of the process. The models described here are referred to as "quantum ballistic computation" models because the orbit momentum is a constant of the motion and the Hamiltonian is, in essence, the kinetic-energy operator for a free system on the computation orbits.

In order to apply the foregoing discussion to the Turing machine models, the initial state should be a wave packet centered on an orbit state, $|m_0\rangle = \Psi_{\ell_i\lambda j_0}$, with $j_0 \ll 0$. The linear superposition is over states corresponding to the iteration of V^τ both forward and backward (as $V^{\tau\dagger}$) from $|m_0\rangle$ and includes states in which I is in different lattice positions, k, for $k < 0$. The expression λ on T is unchanged. The width, $\Delta\tilde{n}$, is such that for all orbit positions, m, in equation 16, $d_m(0)$ is negligible for all m corresponding to an I lattice position of $k \geq 0$. Ψ_λ is also constructed so that the group velocity, v, and the momentum in the orbit are positive. FIGURE 3a gives the details graphically.

As the system evolves in time, I moves along the lattice, interacting with T and moving with an average lattice position velocity that is half of the orbit position velocity. This occurs because read and shift operations are separated in τ, and I must read the scanned T cell to see if it is blank before shifting. No change in the state of T occurs until t is such that the amplitudes for states $|m\rangle$ corresponding to positive lattice positions of I in $\Psi_\lambda(t)$ of equation 17 are appreciable. These $|m\rangle$ describe the beginning of the computation proper and the changing of the tape expression λ. Somewhat later, when $\Psi_\lambda(t)$ is centered well into the computation, the $d_m(t)$ are appreciable for states for which I is not in special initial or final states and for which I is in various lattice

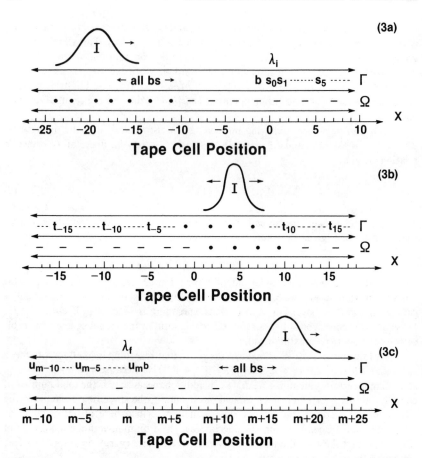

FIGURE 3. Representation of initial (a), intermediate (b), and final (c) states of the model quantum system. The lattice positions of tape cells are denoted on the x-axis. For clarity in presentation, the y-dimensions are shortened compared to those of FIGURE 2. The uncertainty in the states of spin systems in various lattice regions is indicated by dots and occurs in lattice regions where the amplitude in the orbit wave packet for finding I is appreciable. Definite symbols or long dashes (all spins down) indicate definite spin states in regions of the lattice where the amplitude for finding I is negligible. The I packet is narrower in (3b) than in (3a) or (3c) because the spread, $\Delta \tilde{n}(t)$, over orbit states during the computation phase is greater than the spread over lattice position states of I. The lattice position velocity of I along T is indicated by the arrows next to the wave packet.

positions, positive or negative , and T has various expressions on it. In particular, $\Psi_\lambda(t)$ does not correspond to T containing a definite expression or I being in a definite lattice position. FIGURE 3b gives details.

If and only if the computation halts, $\Psi_\lambda(t)$ evolves into a linear sum of orbit states representing the finished computation; that is, T has a definite final standard expression, λ_f, and I is positioned to the right of the rightmost nonblank symbol of λ_f. I continues moving with an average lattice velocity equal to one-half of the orbit velocity and with no further changes in the tape contents. This situation is shown in FIGURE 3c.

DISCUSSION

It has been seen that the evolution of quantum mechanical Turing machines, whose dynamics are given by the Feynman type of Hamiltonian, gives a satisfactory representation of the computation process. In particular, the state evolves from an initial wave-packet state that localizes the head I in the left-hand blank region of the tape (FIGURE 3a) to a final wave-packet state that localizes the head in the right-hand blank region of the tape (FIGURE 3c), thus moving it away from the nonblank region of the tape (provided the computation halts). In order that the states are so localized, it is sufficient to require that the spread, $\Delta \tilde{n}$, of the initial state be sufficiently large so that no significant spreading occurs during the calculation.

The effect of this requirement on the width of the initial state can be appreciable. For example, if one requires that model computation processes carry out at least 10^{14} steps before spreading becomes appreciable, the width, $\Delta \tilde{n}$, of the initial state must be about 10^7 orbit positions. This means that during times at which the computation is actually occurring, the state, $\Psi_\lambda(t)$, is completely uncertain regarding the lattice position and states of I and the expression on T because at least 10^7 different orbit positions in the sum of equation 17 have appreciable amplitudes. This is a typical quantum mechanical effect and occurs in spite of the fact that the computation is ballistic; that is, the expectation values for the position $\langle \tilde{n}(t) \rangle$ and momentum $\langle \tilde{p} \rangle$ (or $\tilde{q}$) along the orbit are well defined and follow the classical equations of motion for a free system.

As might be expected, the model works differently if $\Delta \tilde{n}$ is small. In the extreme case, in which $\Psi_\lambda = |m_0\rangle$ is a single orbit position state, the coefficients, $d_m(t)$, in equation 18 are given by

$$d_m(t) = \langle m|e^{-iHt}|m_0\rangle = e^{-2iKt}(i)^{m-m_0}J_{m-m_0}(2Kt), \qquad (21)$$

where $J_n(x)$ is the Bessel function of index n. The properties of Bessel functions are such that the magnitude of $d_m(t)$ is appreciable for $|m - m_0 \leq 2Kt$. Thus, if one starts in a single orbit state, $|m_0\rangle$, the model state spreads rapidly in both the forward and backward directions along the orbit with a maximum velocity of $2K$.

The Hamiltonians defined by equation 14 are simple in the sense noted in the INTRODUCTION because V^τ is simple. This can be seen from equations 8 and 9, which show that the construction of V^τ requires knowledge of the Turing machine step function τ. However, knowledge of the details of the position states in the computation orbits is not required.

The argument given at the beginning of this section shows that there is essentially no state degradation as the model evolves. In particular, the initial state wave packet can be moved sufficiently far away from the nonblank cells of T so that the part of it that represents I in the nonnegative region of the lattice has an arbitrarily small amplitude. Similarly, the component of the final state that represents the unfinished computation can be made very small by simply waiting. The magnitude of this component decreases asymptotically to a lower limit that is given by the wave packet spreading. The lower limit is a function of $\langle \tilde{q} \rangle / \Delta \tilde{q}$ and can be made arbitrarily small by decreasing $\Delta \tilde{q}$ or increasing $\Delta \tilde{n}$.

This shows that one need not dissipate energy to relocalize the system state, no matter how long the computation takes. Also because the orbit subspaces are H^τ invariant, no energy dissipation is required to correct for ingrowth of configuration component states lying outside of the orbit of interest. This shows (as has been recognized before[13,15]) that quantum mechanics with its uncertainty principles does not necessarily introduce energy dissipation into models of computation. (This argument assumes that the model operates in complete isolation from the environment. Operation in a noisy environment would require energy dissipation to keep the model "on course," unless the Hamiltonian is expanded, as described by Peres,[17] to include error-correcting components.)

An important property of the Hamiltonian models constructed here is that they are spatially local. This holds because V^τ defined by equations 8 and 9 is spatially local. By equation 9, each $V_{\ell sj}$ includes nearest-neighbor interactions only in the x-direction for the I system spins. The interaction range of $V_{\ell sj}^\tau$ in the y-direction is much longer as it extends over $\ell_S + \ell_L$ sites (FIGURE 2). This follows from the definition of the annihilation and creation operators.

Spatial locality means here that the interaction range of terms in the Hamiltonian does not depend on term labels (ℓsj) or on the number of steps in the computation, nor on the initial tape expression. The range can depend on the Turing machine being considered. If τ is the reversible extension of a universal Turing machine, then for the models constructed in this paper, all possible computations can be modeled by one Hamiltonian with an interaction range of $\ell_S + \ell_L$ sites, where ℓ_S and ℓ_L refer to the universal machine.

The above shows that the interaction range in the y-direction is considerable. One recalls that ℓ_S is the binary sequence length needed to express all elements in the expanded S (see section entitled TURING MACHINES) and that ℓ_L is the binary sequence length needed to represent all $2M^2N + K$ different internal states of I. (Recall the restrictions on D_ℓ and D_s noted earlier.) The minimum value for ℓ_L can be shown to be approximately equal to the base 2 logarithm of $2M^2N + K$. A similar minimum holds for ℓ_S.

One way to reduce the interaction range is by use of higher spin systems at the lattice sites. For instance, I can be represented by one system of sufficiently high spin, σ, so that each ℓ in L corresponds to a different one of the $2\sigma + 1$ spin projection states. If the same is done for each cell in T, the interaction range of V^τ becomes the nearest neighbor in both the x- and y-directions on the lattice.

The above discussion suggests that there may be trade-offs between the complexity of the Hamiltonian in terms of such features as the interaction range, n body interactions with n large, etc., and the rate of state degradation. State degradation did not occur in the models considered here because the Hamiltonians are sufficiently complex so that the subspaces generated by the computation orbits are H^τ invariant and irreducible. For (simpler) Hamiltonians for which the orbit subspaces are not invariant, the amplitudes for error components in the state increase quadratically with time.[18]

In the models described so far in the literature, it is clear that details of the trade-offs are complex and that computation efficiency may be involved. For instance,

Feynman[15] has outlined models in which no state degradation occurs and in which the Hamiltonian is simple (i.e., does not require prior knowledge of computation paths) and contains, at most, three body interactions. However, the spatial locality and the computation efficiency of these models relative to the Turing model considered here need more investigation. Other models described in the literature[13] also show no state degradation during the model evolution. However, it is an open question as to whether or not the Hamiltonians of these models require prior knowledge of the computation paths.

Quantum ballistic models are quite sensitive to measurements of the orbit position. Such a measurement will collapse the system wave-packet state into some orbit position state, $|m\rangle$. As was noted earlier, the collapsed state spreads forward and backward along the orbit. If one waits long enough (and the computation halts), most of the state will be spread into the initial state region and the final state region. Consequently, the probability is 0.5 that a measurement made much later will find the state in the final region.

Subsystem measurements, such as those to determine if the computation has halted, can be made most of the time without perturbing the system state. For instance, such a measurement would examine I to see if it is in special final states and whether it could be of finite time duration from t to $t + \delta$. However, the system state will not be perturbed by such a measurement only if the computation does not halt within the time interval, $t - \Delta \tilde{n}/v$ to $t + \delta + \Delta \tilde{n}/v$.

In this paper, models were developed for distinguishable spin-$\frac{1}{2}$ systems on a lattice in order to keep the formulae simple. Assuming that the spin-$\frac{1}{2}$ systems are indistinguishable, fermions can easily be accounted for by appropriate antisymmetrization of the wave functions and symmetrization of the operators.

In common with models developed elsewhere, the quantum ballistic models developed here are quite sensitive to external influences that can change the spin projections of systems at various lattice sites. Thus, they would be expected to run best at temperatures close to absolute zero. Another aspect is that the velocity or momentum of I along the lattice sites (spin wave velocity or momentum) is not the same as the orbit velocity or momentum. In particular, the lattice or spin wave momentum of I changes often during the computation, for example, whenever a shift operation occurs.

ACKNOWLEDGMENTS

The author wishes to thank Charles H. Bennett for his advice, help, and consultation on several aspects of Turing machines during the preparation of this paper.

REFERENCES

1. LANDAUER, R. & C. H. BENNETT. 1985. Sci. Am. **253**(1): 48–56.
2. ROBINSON, A. L. 1984. Science **233**: 1164–1166.
3. LANDAUER, R. 1984. Fundamental physical limitations of the computational process. *In* Computer Culture: The Scientific, Intellectual, and Social Impact of the Computer. H. R. Pagels, Ed. Ann. N.Y. Acad. Sci. **426**: 161–170.

4. LANDAUER, R. 1982. Int. J. Theor. Phys. **21:** 283–297.
5. LANDAUER, R. 1976. Ber. Bunsenges. Phys. Chem. **80:** 1048–1059.
6. LANDAUER, R. 1961. IBM J. Res. Dev. **5:** 183–191.
7. BENNETT, C. H. 1973. IBM J. Res. Dev. **17:** 525–532.
8. BENNETT, C. H. 1982. Int. J. Theor. Phys. **21:** 905–940.
9. LIKHAREV, K. K. 1982. Int. J. Theor. Phys. **21:** 311–326.
10. FREDKIN, E. & T. TOFFOLI. 1982. Int. J. Theor. Phys. **21:** 219–253.
11. BENIOFF, P. 1980. J. Stat. Phy. **22:** 563–591.
12. BENIOFF, P. 1982. Int. J. Theor. Phy. **21:** 177–201.
13. BENIOFF, P. 1982. Phys. Rev. Lett. **48:** 1581–1585.
14. BENIOFF, P. 1982. J. Stat. Phys. **29:** 515–545.
15. FEYNMAN, R. P. 1985. Opt. News **11:** 11–20.
16. MARGOLUS, N. 1984. Quantum computation. MIT preprint. (Also enclosed in this volume.)
17. PERES, A. 1985. Phys. Rev. **32A:** 3266–3276.
18. ZUREK, W. H. 1984. Phys. Rev. Lett. **53**(4): 391–394.
19. DEUTSCH, D. 1985. Proc. R. Soc. London **A400:** 97–117.
20. PITOWSKY, I. 1985. For Quantum Computers P=NP. Hebrew University preprint.
21. HALMOS, P. 1967. A Hilbert Space Problem Book, chapter 9. Van Nostrand. Princeton, New Jersey.
22. MESSIAH, A. 1961. Quantum Mechanics Vol. I, pp. 218–222 and 299–301. North-Holland. Amsterdam/New York.

Quantum Computation[a]

NORMAN MARGOLUS

Laboratory for Computer Science
Massachusetts Institute of Technology
Cambridge, Massachusetts 02139

INTRODUCTION

When we describe the operation of a computer, we are of course describing the dynamical evolution of a physical system. What distinguishes a computer from other physical systems is its ability to simulate many aspects of other physical processes (including, in particular, the logical operation of any other computer, given enough time and memory[1]). It is interesting to note that for several recent models of computation, the mapping between the computer and the underlying physics is quite direct. This leads us to ask the question: "how similar can the models used to describe computers be made to microscopic physics?"

This question is of some interest to the technologists because it is closely related to how efficiently and quickly physical degrees of freedom can be made to perform a computation for us.[2] Models in which there is a very direct mapping between the computational and the physical degrees of freedom can also act as bridges connecting concepts and techniques in physics and computation.[3]

A particularly simple classical-mechanical model of computation was found by Fredkin.[4] He showed that a gas of hard spheres with exactly prescribed initial conditions can be made to perform an arbitrary digital computation. This and other related logically reversible models of computation[b] have played a critical theoretical role in establishing the possibility of microscopic physical models of computation. They have also helped in clarifying issues related to fundamental thermodynamic constraints on the computational process.[4-9] But of course the world is quantum mechanical, and so what we would really like is a quantum model of computation.

It may well be that to take best advantage of the computational capabilities of QM systems, we must reformulate our notion of a computation. However, in this paper, I will restrict my attention to the more straightforward problem of asking to what extent

[a]This research was supported by grants from the Defense Advanced Research Projects Agency (N00014-83-K-0125), the National Science Foundation (8214312-IST), and the Department of Energy (DE-AC02-83ER13082).

[b]Computers that operate invertibly at every step have been described[3,4,6,7] and are found to be essentially not much more complex or difficult to use than conventional computers. It was a significant and somewhat surprising discovery that general-purpose computation can be carried out in a reasonable manner despite the severe constraints implied by invertible operation. In a reversible computer, no information can be lost at any step of the computation—you cannot simply erase unneeded partial results, or even the arguments to an addition. One way of effectively "erasing" partial results is to copy an answer once you have it, and then do an inverse computation so that all intermediate results go away and only the initial inputs and a copy of the answer remain.

a microscopic QM system can simulate an ordinary (classical) deterministic computation.[c] I will describe some of the work that has been done in this direction and point out some difficulties that remain. As a specific model for illustration, I will use a reversible cellular automaton model of computation that is closely related to the hard-sphere-gas computer mentioned above, and address the issues of spatial locality, cyclic operation, and parallelism in quantum computation.

APPROACHES TO QUANTUM COMPUTATION

I will discuss two approaches to the issue of Quantum Computation (QC). Because the time-evolution operator in QM is always a unitary (and hence invertible) operator, both approaches will be based on the notion of a reversible computer. The two approaches will be distinguished by whether the time-evolution operator or the Hamiltonian operator is taken as the starting point for the discussion.

Time-Evolution Operator Approach

The first discussion indicating that QC was not necessarily inconsistent with the formalism of QM was that of Paul Benioff.[12] It depends upon the observation that the Schrödinger evolution of the wave function is perfectly deterministic. If one associates a basis vector with each possible logical state of a reversible computer, then the one-step time-evolution that carries each state into the appropriate next state is a permutation on the set of basis states; therefore, it is given by a unitary operator. Formally, it is always possible to write down an Hermitian operator whose complex exponential equals this unitary operator. Given an initial logical-basis state, the Schrödinger evolution generated by this Hamiltonian will give the appropriate successor logical states at consecutive integer times.[d]

For example, if we let the possible configurations of the three-state "computer" described in FIGURE 1 be represented by

$$A = \begin{pmatrix} 1 \\ 0 \\ 0 \end{pmatrix} \quad B = \begin{pmatrix} 0 \\ 1 \\ 0 \end{pmatrix} \quad C = \begin{pmatrix} 0 \\ 0 \\ 1 \end{pmatrix},$$

[c]We will not consider here the very interesting issue of a computer that is a Universal Quantum Simulator.[10] Such a computer would be a QM system that, started from an appropriate initial state corresponding to a state of any given QM system, would evolve in time, t, proportional to that taken by the given system into a QM state corresponding to the t-evolved state of the given system. Measurements performed on the simulator would correctly reproduce the QM statistics that one would have obtained by performing an experiment on the original system. Such a simulator would provide an alternative to the present computational methods used to predict the consequences of QM models. Deutsch[11] discusses this problem, but does not address the important issue of the spatial locality of the Hamiltonian.

[d]Although the Schrödinger equation is a linear differential equation, in QM we allow a large enough set of basis vectors (one per configuration) so that a unitary operator can take a computer through an arbitrary invertible sequence of configurations. In particular, there is no difficulty in having the computer compute such "nonlinear" functions as logical AND and OR.

then the time-evolution given in FIGURE 1 can be represented by the unitary single-time-step operator,

$$U = \begin{pmatrix} 0 & 1 & 0 \\ 1 & 0 & 0 \\ 0 & 0 & 1 \end{pmatrix}.$$

Then from U, we can find an Hermitian matrix such that $U = e^{-iH}$. In this case,

$$H = \begin{pmatrix} \dfrac{\pi}{2} & -\dfrac{\pi}{2} & 0 \\ -\dfrac{\pi}{2} & \dfrac{\pi}{2} & 0 \\ 0 & 0 & 0 \end{pmatrix}.$$

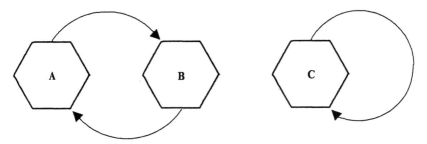

FIGURE 1. A simple three-state machine. If the "computer" is in state A, it will go into state B: State B goes into A, and C does not change.

Hamiltonian Operator Approach

One would like the Hamiltonian operator, H, to be given as a sum of pieces, each of which only involves the interaction of a few parts of the computer that are near to each other. The most direct way of ensuring that H is of this form is to write H down *ab initio*, rather than derive it from U.

Richard Feynman was the first to discuss this approach.[13] He realized that if the unitary operator, F, that describes one step of the desired forward evolution can be written as a sum of local pieces, then if we let $H = F + F^\dagger$ be the Hamiltonian operator, H will also be a sum of local (i.e., nearby-neighbor) interactions. The time-evolution operator, $U(t) = e^{-iHt}$, is then a sum of powers of F and $F^\dagger$ taken with various weights. Thus, if $|n\rangle$ corresponds to the logical state of a computer at step n (i.e., $F|n\rangle = |n + 1\rangle$), then $U(t)|n\rangle$ is a superposition of configurations of the computer at various steps in the original computation. This superposition contains no configurations that are not legitimate logical successors or predecessors to $|n\rangle$: if you make a measurement of the configuration of the computer, you will find it at some step of the desired computation. If, instead, you simply measure some piece of the configuration that tells you whether the computation is done or not, then when you see that it is done, you can immediately look elsewhere in the configuration to find the answer and be assured that it is correct. Alternatively, one may construct a superposition of configuration states that acts as a sort of wave-packet state in which the computation moves forward at a uniform rate.

In order to write $F = \Sigma F_i$ with F as a unitary operator, Feynman described a computer in which only one spot is active at a time. If instead of taking ΣF_i to be unitary we only require the F_i's to be local, it turns out that we can describe a computer where all sites are active at once, but where there is no longer a global time; that is, synchronization becomes a matter of local intercommunication.

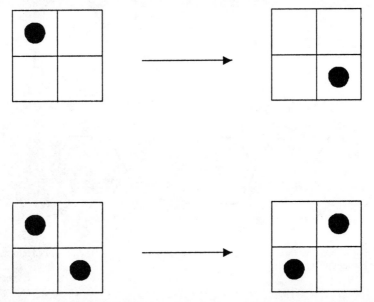

FIGURE 2. The BBMCA cellular automaton rule. For every 2×2 block, we count the number of 1's. If exactly one of the four cells contains a 1, we move the 1 to the opposite corner. If exactly two cells contain 1's, and they lie on a diagonal, we move them to the opposite diagonal. Otherwise, we leave the block unchanged.

A REVERSIBLE MODEL OF COMPUTATION

We will illustrate the two approaches in terms of a two-dimensional Cellular Automaton (CA) model of computation. This model is very similar to a lattice gas—in fact, it is derived from the classical mechanical gas model of computation called the Billiard Ball Model[4] and we will refer to it here as the BBMCA.[3] At each point with integer coordinates on a Cartesian lattice, we associate a two-state variable (0 or 1, say). Given an initial configuration of 0's and 1's, we partition the sites into blocks of four, with the upper-left site in each block having even coordinates. Then we apply the rule of FIGURE 2 to each block of four: a lone 1 moves to the opposite corner, exactly two 1's on a diagonal switch to the other diagonal, and all other cases remain unchanged. Now we change the grouping of sites so that the upper-left site in each block of four has odd coordinates, and we again apply the BBMCA rule to all blocks. We iterate this procedure to generate a dynamical evolution.

The evolution generated by this rule is exactly invertible: this property is inherited from the invertibility of the rule applied to each block. Furthermore, it has been shown[3] that starting from a suitable initial state, this system can do any computation that any general-purpose digital computer can do (1's move around on the lattice, act as signals, and interact with each other to do digital logic, much like the logic that goes on in the circuitry of any electronic digital computer).

This model is an obvious candidate for us to try to describe in terms of a lattice of QM spins. Here QM may even be superior to classical mechanics because it is more natural to have identical two-state systems in QM (cf. references 2 and 9). During one logical step in such a CA model, information has only to be communicated to nearby neighboring spins; data-paths are very short and so the impact of the finite light-speed restriction on computation speed is minimized.[e]

TIME-EVOLUTION OPERATOR APPROACH

In order to implement the BBMCA rule as a QM model, we will consider a two-dimensional lattice of spins, each of which is in a spin-component eigenstate with respect to the z-direction (which is taken to be perpendicular to the plane of the lattice). At each site, spin-up represents a logical 1 and spin-down represents a logical 0.

At a given lattice site with coordinates (i, j), the projection operator, $P_{ij} = (1 + \sigma^z_{ij})/2$, projects states that have a logical 1 at site (i, j), and the operator, $\bar{P}_{ij} = (1 - \sigma^z_{ij})/2 = 1 - P_{ij}$, projects states with 0 at (i, j). The operator, $a_{ij} = (\sigma^x_{ij} - i\sigma^y_{ij})/2$, lowers a 1 at (i, j) to a 0, while $a^\dagger_{ij} = (\sigma^x_{ij} + i\sigma^y_{ij})/2$ raises a 0 at (i, j) to a 1.

We can now construct a unitary operator that will implement the BBMCA rule applied to a block of four sites, with the upper-left corner at position (i, j):

$$\begin{aligned}
A_{ij} = &(a_{ij}a^\dagger_{i+1j+1} + a^\dagger_{ij}a_{i+1j+1})\,\bar{P}_{i+1j}\bar{P}_{ij+1} \\
&+ (a_{i+1j}a^\dagger_{ij+1} + a^\dagger_{i+1j}a_{ij+1})\,\bar{P}_{ij}\bar{P}_{i+1j+1} \\
&+ (a_{ij}a^\dagger_{i+1j}a^\dagger_{ij+1}a_{i+1j+1} + a^\dagger_{ij}a_{i+1j}a_{ij+1}a^\dagger_{i+1j+1}) \\
&+ 1 - (\bar{P}_{ij}\bar{P}_{i+1j+1} + \bar{P}_{i+1j}\bar{P}_{ij+1} - 2\bar{P}_{ij}\bar{P}_{i+1j}\bar{P}_{ij+1}\bar{P}_{i+1j+1}).
\end{aligned}$$

If A_{ij} is applied to a configuration of 1's and 0's, all of the lattice sites, except those in the block at (i, j), will remain unchanged; this block will change according to the BBMCA rule. If we let

$$U_0 = \prod_{ij\ \text{even}} A_{ij}, \quad U_1 = \prod_{ij\ \text{odd}} A_{ij},$$

---

[e] Only for computations that can take advantage of this architecture. For example, many problems that are usually described in terms of differential equations seem well suited to a CA solution.[14,15]

then $U = U_1 U_0$ is a unitary operator that exactly implements the BBMCA rule.^{f} $U(t) = U^{t/2}$ will exactly correspond to a BBMCA evolution at even-integral times.

Now we will try to write $U(t) = e^{-iHt}$, with H as a sum of local pieces. We begin by noting that $A_{ij}^2 = 1$ (which follows from the BBMCA rule). Therefore, $[(1 - A_{ij})/2]^2 = (1 - A_{ij})/2$ and $\exp[-i\pi(1 - A_{ij})/2] = A_{ij}$ (expand the exponential). If we let $H_{ij} = \pi(1 - A_{ij})/2$, then

$$U_0 = \prod_{ij\,even} A_{ij} = e^{-i\Sigma_{ij\,even}H_{ij}}, \qquad U_1 = e^{-i\Sigma_{ij\,odd}H_{ij}},$$

and $U(t) = e^{-iHt}$, where $H = \Sigma_{ij\,even}H_{ij}$ when the integer part of t is even and $H = \Sigma_{ij\,odd}H_{ij}$ when it is odd.

This U will reproduce the BBMCA evolution at all integer times. Intuitively, the reason we had to introduce a time dependence into H is because the H_{ij}'s at a single

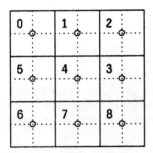

First 9 steps.

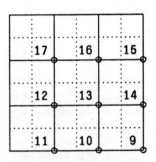

Next 9 steps.

FIGURE 3. A 6×6 lattice with periodic boundaries. All 2×2 blocks in the solid partition are updated first and then all blocks in the dotted partition are updated. Because of periodicity, numbers 9 through 17 mark the centers of dotted blocks.

time-step all refer to nonoverlapping blocks of spins, and so they all commute, thus allowing the product U_0 or U_1 of exponentials to be turned into an exponential of a sum. The even-block and odd-block H_{ij}'s do not all commute—because the blocks overlap, it makes a difference in which order the H_{ij}'s are applied.

HAMILTONIAN OPERATOR APPROACH

Serial Computer

We can use Feynman's method to arrive at a time-independent version of the BBMCA. We will use a 6×6 lattice (FIGURE 3) to illustrate the technique. The

---

^{f}It has been suggested[12,17] that in order to construct a time-independent H for a U such as this, it is necessary to know explicitly the configuration of 1's and 0's at each step of every possible computation in advance.

boundaries are periodic—we can imagine the lattice as being physically wrapped around into a torus so that opposite edges touch. Now we divide a complete updating of the lattice into 18 independent steps, as shown in FIGURE 3. The step during which each 2×2 block is updated is indicated near its center, and (i_k, j_k) are the coordinates of the upper-left-hand corner of the kth block. We introduce an extra "clock" spin at the center of each block and let $c_k = \sigma_k^x - i\sigma_k^y$ be the lowering operator acting on this clock-spin.

We can now write the unitary operator, F, which in 18 steps accomplishes one complete updating of all the even and then all of the odd blocks on the lattice, as a sum of operators, with each acting on one block only:

$$F = \sum_{k=0}^{17} F_k, \text{ where } F_k = A_{i_k j_k} c_{k+1}^\dagger c_k,$$

and where we start the lattice off with the clock-spin in block #0 up and all of the rest of the clock-spins down.

If $|0\rangle$ is the initial state, then $F|0\rangle = |1\rangle$, which is the state where block #0 has been updated and block #1 is waiting to be updated. Then $F|1\rangle = |2\rangle, \ldots, F|17\rangle = |18\rangle$, which is the state where one complete updating of all the blocks has been accomplished and the "up" clock-spin is once again in block #0, etc.

We have thus been able to write the forward time-step operator as a sum of local pieces by serializing the computation (only one block of the automaton is active during any given step).

Now, we may write down a Hamiltonian operator, $H = F + F^\dagger = \Sigma_k H_k$ (where $H_k = F_k + F_k^\dagger$), which is a sum of local interactions. If $|n\rangle$ is evolved for a time t, it becomes $e^{-iHt} |n\rangle$, which is a superposition of the configurations of the serialized automaton that are legitimate successors and predecessors of $|n\rangle$.

We would like to make our automaton evolve forwards at a uniform rate; we can do this by constructing a wave-packet state. If we let N be the step-number[g] operator $(N|n\rangle = n|n\rangle)$, then

$$\frac{d}{dt} \langle N \rangle = \left\langle \frac{[N, H]}{i} \right\rangle = \langle V \rangle, \quad \text{where } V = \frac{[N, H]}{i} = \frac{F - F^\dagger}{i}, \quad [V, H] = 0.$$

Thus, the eigenstates of V have $\langle N \rangle$ that changes uniformly with time, and they can be chosen to be simultaneous eigenstates of H also. This allows us to make a superposition state from V's eigenstates that has a fairly sharply peaked step-number and for which the computation proceeds at a uniform rate.

This corresponds closely to Feynman's original construction. Peres[17] noticed that we have the freedom to introduce coefficients of ω_k multiplying each H_k, and that with an appropriate choice (neglecting for a moment the A_{ij}'s), H becomes essentially the angular momentum operator, J_x. This technique would allow us to start the system in state $|0\rangle$ and be assured of finding the system in state $|17\rangle$ after some prescribed time, T, that sets the scale for the ω_k's. However, the system would then undo its evolution and be back in state $|0\rangle$ at time $2T$. Thus, this technique is not useful for making our

---

[g] $|0\rangle$ is distinguished from $|18\rangle$ by looking at the computation part (as opposed to the clock-spins part) of the state.

system run through a repeating computation cycle. If we want V to commute with H, then we are forced to set the ω_k's to a constant, which is what Feynman did.

This seems to be the best we can do with a serial computer that runs in a cycle. A Hamiltonian with a clock that gives exactly F when exponentiated (which is what we would ideally want) is necessarily nonlocal.[18]

Parallel Computer

In order to be able to write $F = \Sigma F_{ij}$ with F as a unitary operator, we described a computer in which only one spot was active at a time. We will now drop the restriction that ΣF_{ij} be unitary.

Let $H = \Sigma F_{ij} + F_{ij}^\dagger$. $U(t) = e^{-iHt}$ will now be a sum of terms involving all possible combinations of powers of the various F_{ij}'s and $F_{ij}^\dagger$'s. If $U(t)|0\rangle$ is to be a superposition of configurations that correspond to legitimate classical evolutions from $|0\rangle$, then states where part of the automaton has been updated (while other parts have not) must be allowed. This sort of cellular automaton where there is no global clock (as there has been in all of our preceding discussions) is called an Asynchronous Cellular Automaton (ACA).

An ACA can simulate an ordinary (synchronous) CA; all it needs is a little extra state information to force the places that get ahead to wait for their neighbors to catch up.[19] The synchronous CA is like a line of people marching in step: all cells take a step forward simultaneously. An ACA is like a line of people walking forward hand in hand: cells that walk too fast get held back by their neighbors. The state of each cell in the ACA will correspond to the state of the same cell in the synchronous CA at some particular moment of time. The ACA will have hills and valleys in time, but with a limited slope and no breaks.

The most important constraint in the asynchronous implementation of the BBMCA is that a block must not be updated unless all four cells of the block contain data corresponding to the same moment of the synchronous evolution (blocks can only step forward if none of their cells are ahead or behind the rest). To be able to tell whether or not this constraint is met, we will add an extra "guard" bit associated with each cell in the original BBMCA model. We will make a rule for changing the guard-bits, which ensures that if all four guard-bits in a 2×2 block of cells have the same value, then the information in all four cells corresponds to the same moment of synchronous evolution.

For the forward evolution, our rule for the guard-bits will be that even-blocks can be updated if all four guard-bits are 0's and that odd-blocks can be updated if they are all 1's. When a block is updated, its guard-bits are all flipped (complemented).

To understand how the synchronization works, it is enough to watch only the guard-bits because the computation just rides on top without affecting the guard-bits.

One particular one-dimensional cross-sectional view of the guard-bits' evolution might look like FIGURE 4. We start off with all guard-bits set to zero. By $t = 6$, the cell at $x = 2$ has moved three logical-steps forward.

If we imagine that the guard-bits are spins in a lattice that sits directly below our original BBMCA lattice, and let g_{ij} be the lowering operator for a spin at the site (i, j) on the guard-bit lattice, then our forward-step operator for the site (i, j) is given by $F_{ij} = A_{ij} g_{ij}^\dagger g_{i+1j}^\dagger g_{ij+1}^\dagger g_{i+1j+1}^\dagger$ for (i, j) even and $F_{ij} = A_{ij} g_{ij} g_{i+1j} g_{ij+1} g_{i+1j+1}$ for (i, j) odd.

Similarly, $F_{ij}^\dagger$ (which has the g's and $g^\dagger$'s interchanged, relative to the definition of F_{ij}) implements a possible step *backwards* rather than *forwards*. Thus, $H_{ij} = F_{ij} + F_{ij}^\dagger = A_{ij} (g_{ij}^\dagger g_{i+1j}^\dagger g_{ij+1}^\dagger g_{i+1j+1}^\dagger + g_{ij}g_{i+1j}g_{ij+1}g_{i+1j+1})$ for both even- and odd-blocks, and $H = \Sigma_{\text{even or odd blocks}} H_{ij}$ acting on a given configuration will produce a superposition of configurations, each of which has moved forwards or backwards one step at some location.

This model can be made to perform a computation by occasionally checking for a "computation done" flag; that is, some particular group of cells that the computation

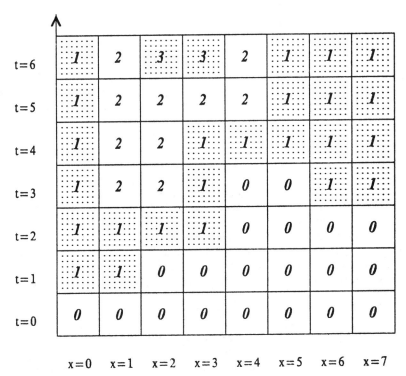

FIGURE 4. Cross-sectional view of asynchronous automaton evolution. The space is eight cells wide and we show the first seven time-steps. At $t = 0$, all guard-bits are set to zero. The shaded cells have guard-bits set to one. The number inside each cell indicates the number of times that the cell contents has been updated since time zero; this is also the equivalent synchronous time at that cell.

will set to certain values when it is done. The appearance of such a flag ensures that there is an unbroken chain of sites that connect the flag to the place that signaled it to appear, with none of which corresponding to moments of time in the equivalent synchronous evolution that precede the moment the signal passed that site. Thus, if the flag signal was produced by a process that first put the answer somewhere, the answer must still be available there when the "done flag" is seen.

Of course, what we would really like to do is to show that we can make this sort of computer run at a uniform rate. The difficulty here is that if we let N be an operator that, when applied to a configuration state, returns the average synchronous-step in that configuration, and $V = [N, H]/i$, we find that V does not commute with H, and so the situation is more complicated than it was in the serial-computer case.

I do not know if this computer can be made to "run" in a reasonable fashion. One approach to the question of reformulating computation to take better advantage of QM might be to see what the computing power of this model (and related models[16]) is without the guard-bits. In this case, it seems easy to construct wave packets for the individual 1's (which are the moving particles of this model).

CONCLUSIONS

An ideal computation—the most efficient imaginable—would map as closely as is possible onto all of the physical degrees of freedom of the computer. Such models would be fundamental theoretical tools in the study of the ultimate nature and limitations of the computational process and could perhaps play a role analogous to that of the ideal engine of thermodynamics.

As it is quantum mechanics that today embodies our most fundamental understanding of microscopic physical phenomena, we are naturally led to the problem of describing computing mechanisms that operate in an essentially quantum mechanical manner.

In this paper, I have attempted to extend Feynman's construction of a quantum computer in order to arrive at a more ideal model; namely, one in which the parallelism inherent in the operation of physical law simultaneously everywhere is put to use. Although this attempt has met with only limited success, I judge this problem to be an important one and worthy of further study. If better models of quantum computation can be found, then it may well be that quantum mechanics will provide the correct formalism within which to formulate and discuss the quantities and issues relevant to fundamental computer theory.

ACKNOWLEDGMENTS

I would like to thank P. A. Benioff, C. H. Bennett, R. P. Feynman, E. Fredkin, T. Toffoli, G. Y. Vichniac, and W. H. Zurek for useful discussions.

REFERENCES

1. MINSKY, M. 1967. Computation: Finite and Infinite Machines. Prentice–Hall. Englewood Cliffs, New Jersey.
2. LANDAUER, R. 1986. Computation and physics. To appear in Found. Phys.
3. MARGOLUS, N. 1984. Physics-like models of computation. Physica **10D:** 81.
4. FREDKIN, E. & T. TOFFOLI. 1982. Conservative logic. Int. J. Theor. Phys. **21:** 219.
5. LANDAUER, R. 1961. Irreversibility and heat generation in the computing process. IBM J. Res. Dev. **5:** 183.
6. BENNETT, C. H. 1973. Logical reversibility of computation. IBM J. Res. Dev. **17:** 525.
7. TOFFOLI, T. 1977. Computation and construction universality of reversible cellular automata. J. Comput. Syst. Sci. **15:** 213.

8. POROD, W., R. GRONDIN, D. FERRY & G. POROD. 1984. Dissipation in computation. Phys. Rev. Lett. **52:** 232; comments by: BENNETT, C. H., P. BENIOFF, T. TOFFOLI & R. LANDAUER. 1984. Phys. Rev. Lett. **53:** 1202.
9. ZUREK, W. H. 1984. Reversibility and stability of information processing systems. Phys. Rev. Lett. **53:** 391.
10. FEYNMAN, R. P. 1982. Simulating physics with computers. Int. J. Theor. Phys. **21:** 467.
11. DEUTSCH, D. 1985. Quantum theory, the church-turing hypothesis, and universal quantum computers. Proc. R. Soc. London Ser. **A400:** 97.
12. BENIOFF, P. A. 1980. J. Stat. Phys. **22:** 563; 1982. J. Stat. Phys. **29:** 515; 1982. Int. J. Theor. Phys. **21:** 177.
13. FEYNMAN, R. P. 1985. Quantum mechanical computers. Opt. News **11:** 11–20.
14. TOFFOLI, T. 1984. Cellular automata as an alternative to (rather than an approximation of) differential equations in modeling physics. Physica **10D:** 117.
15. FRISCH, U., B. HASSLACHER & Y. POMEAU. 1985. A lattice gas automaton for the Navier Stokes equation. Preprint no. LA-UR-85-3503, Los Alamos National Laboratory, New Mexico.
16. TOFFOLI, T. & N. MARGOLUS. 1986. Cellular Automata Machines: A New Environment for Modeling. To be published by MIT Press. Cambridge, Massachusetts.
17. PERES, A. 1985. Reversible logic and quantum computers. Phys. Rev. **A32:** 3266.
18. PERES, A. 1980. Measurement of time by quantum clocks. Am. J. Phys. **48:** 552.
19. TOFFOLI, T. 1978. Integration of the phase-difference relations in asynchronous sequential networks. *In* Automata, Languages, and Programming. G. Ausiello & C. Böhm, Eds.: 457–463. Springer-Verlag. Berlin/New York.

How to Take a Photograph of Another Everett World

DAVID ALBERT

Physics Department
University of South Carolina
Columbia, South Carolina 29208
and
Institute for the Philosophy of Science
Tel-Aviv University
Ramat Aviv, Tel Aviv, Israel

I want to tell you a story here that is essentially in the tradition of curious old stories about quantum mechanics like the story of Schrödinger's cat and the story of Wigner's friend. Those stories both begin with the assumption that all physical systems in the world (not merely subatomic particles, but also measuring instruments, tables, chairs, cats, people, oceans, and stars) are all quantum mechanical systems whose states evolve in accordance with linear quantum mechanical equations of motion. Furthermore, that assumption is precisely the content of the many-worlds picture of quantum theory, which is what my story is about. This last point, because it has been the subject of a great deal of confusion over the years, and because it forms the basis of everything that I shall have to say here, deserves special emphasis. The many-worlds picture (as I shall use that term here) is simply the thesis that every physical system in the world is a quantum mechanical system, that all such systems evolve entirely in accordance with the linear quantum mechanical equations of motion, and that every self-adjoint local operator of such systems can, at least in principle, be measured. Those are the rules of the game we are going to play here. Now, what I want to tell you about is a move that is possible within this game,[1] but that has not been considered before.

The old stories of Schrödinger's cat and Wigner's friend end at a point where (in the first case) the cat is in a superposition of states, namely, one in which it is alive, and another in which it is dead; or where (in the second case) the friend is in a superposition of states that entail various different and mutually exclusive beliefs about the result of some given experiment. Suppose, for example, that Wigner's friend carries out a measurement of the y-spin of a spin-$\frac{1}{2}$ particle, P, that is initially prepared in the state $|\sigma_z = +\frac{1}{2}\rangle_P$. He carries out the measurement by means of a measuring device that interacts with P, and he subsequently looks at this device in order to ascertain the result of the measurement. The end of that story looks like this:

$$
|\alpha\rangle \equiv \frac{1}{\sqrt{2}}\left[\left|\,\text{Believes that }\sigma_y = +\frac{1}{2}\right\rangle_{\text{Friend}} \cdot \left|\,\text{Shows that }\sigma_y = +\frac{1}{2}\right\rangle_{\substack{\text{Measuring} \\ \text{Device}}}\right.
$$

$$
\cdot \left|\,\sigma_y = +\frac{1}{2}\right\rangle_P + \left|\,\text{Believes that }\sigma_y = -\frac{1}{2}\right\rangle_{\text{Friend}}
$$

$$
\left.\cdot \left|\text{Shows that }\sigma_y = -\frac{1}{2}\right\rangle_{\substack{\text{Measuring} \\ \text{Device}}} \cdot \left|\,\sigma_y = -\frac{1}{2}\right\rangle_P\right].
$$

(The phrase, "Believes that $\sigma_y = \pm \frac{1}{2}$", of course, does not completely specify the quantum state of the very complicated brain of Wigner's friend. However, the many other degrees of freedom of that system—for example, those that specify what sort of ice cream Wigner's friend prefers—simply do not concern us here, and so, for the moment, we will ignore them.) Now, such endings as this are usually judged to be so bizarre and so blatantly in contradiction with our daily experience that they invalidate the assumption that gives rise to these stories; that is, these stories are usually judged to imply that there must be physical processes in the world that cannot be described by linear equations of motion—processes like the collapse of the wave function.

The content of the many-worlds picture is purely and simply a denial of this judgement. In effect, what Everett did was to point out that the endings of those old stories, albeit they are assuredly strange, are not, if one thinks it over calmly, so blatantly in contradiction with our everyday experience. Maybe, says Everett, that is really the way things are at the end of measuring processes.

It is probably too bad that this very simple thesis has come to be called the many-worlds interpretation at all, because that name has sometimes given rise to the false impression that there are supposed to be more physical universes around after a measurement than there were before it. It might have been better to call what Everett came up with a "many-points-of-view" interpretation of quantum mechanics, or something like that, because it is surely true of Everett's picture (as it is in all other pictures of quantum theory that I know about) that there is always exactly one physical universe. However, the rules of Everett's game, which he insists we play out to the very end, require that every one of the physical systems of which that universe is composed (including cats, measuring instruments, my friend's brain, and my own brain) can be, and often are, in those bizarre superpositions. The various elements of such a superposition, in the case of brains, correspond to a variety of mutually exclusive points of view about the world, as it were, all of which are simultaneously associated with one and the same physical observer.

Now, needless to say, in some given physical situation, different observers may be associated with different numbers of such points of view (they may, that is, inhabit different numbers of Everett worlds). Suppose, for example, that we add a second friend (friend no. 2) to the little story we just told. Suppose that at the end of that story, when the state of the composite system consisting of P, the measuring device for σ_y, and friend no. 1 is $|\alpha\rangle$, that friend no. 2 measures A, where A is a maximal observable of that composite system such that $A|\alpha\rangle = \alpha|\alpha\rangle$. Friend no. 2 carries out that measurement by means of an A-measuring device (which, according to the rules of our game, can always be constructed). This device interacts with that composite system, and friend no. 2 subsequently looks at the device in order to ascertain the result of the measurement. When that is accomplished (because the result of this measurement will with certainty be $A = \alpha$), things will look like this:

$$|\beta\rangle \equiv |\text{Believes that } A = \alpha\rangle_{\substack{\text{Friend} \\ \text{no. 2}}} \cdot |\text{Shows that } A = \alpha\rangle_{\substack{A \\ \text{Measuring} \\ \text{Device}}} \cdot |\alpha\rangle.$$

In this state, friend no. 1 inhabits two Everett worlds (the world where $\sigma_y = +\frac{1}{2}$ and the world where $\sigma_y = -\frac{1}{2}$), whereas friend no. 2 inhabits only one (the world where $A = \alpha$), which by itself encompasses the entire state $|\beta\rangle$. Moreover, in his single world, friend no. 2 is in possession of something like a photograph of the two worlds that friend no. 1 simultaneously inhabits (he is in possession, that is, of a recording in his measuring device of the fact that $A = \alpha$). By means of his measurement of A, friend no. 2 directly sees the full superposition of friend no. 1's brain states; indeed, he can even specify the relative sign between those states.

Nothing ought to be very surprising in all this, and, indeed, it was all very well known to Everett and his readers. So far as friend no. 2 is concerned, after all, friend no. 1, whatever else he may be, is a physical system out there in the external world; consequently, according to the rules of our game, friend no. 1 ought to be no less susceptible of being measured to be in superpositions than a single subatomic particle. However, this need not be the very end of the game. One more move that is fully in accordance with the rules of the game is possible; a move that Everett never mentions. Here it is: Suppose, at the end of the slightly longer story we just told, when the state of things is $|\beta\rangle$, that friend no. 2 shows the photograph that is now in his possession (which is, remember, a photograph of the two Everett worlds that friend no. 1 now simultaneously inhabits) to friend no. 1. Suppose, that is, that friend no. 1 now looks at the measuring apparatus for A. It is quite trivial to show that the result of such a move will be this:

$$|\gamma\rangle = |\text{Believes that } A = \alpha\rangle_{\substack{\text{Friend} \\ \text{no. 2}}} \cdot |\text{Shows that } A = \alpha\rangle_{\substack{A \\ \text{Measuring} \\ \text{Device}}}$$

$$\cdot \frac{1}{\sqrt{2}}\left[\left|\text{Believes that } A = \alpha, \text{Believes that } \sigma_y = +\frac{1}{2}\right\rangle_{\substack{\text{Friend} \\ \text{no. 1}}}\right.$$

$$\cdot \left|\text{Shows that } \sigma_y = +\frac{1}{2}\right\rangle_{\substack{\sigma_y \\ \text{Measuring} \\ \text{Device}}} \cdot \left|\sigma_y = +\frac{1}{2}\right\rangle_{P}$$

$$+ \left|\text{Believes that } A = \alpha, \text{Believes that } \sigma_y = -\frac{1}{2}\right\rangle_{\substack{\text{Friend} \\ \text{no. 2}}}$$

$$\cdot \left.\left|\text{Shows that } \sigma_y = -\frac{1}{2}\right\rangle_{\substack{\sigma_y \\ \text{Measuring} \\ \text{Device}}} \cdot \left|\sigma_y = -\frac{1}{2}\right\rangle_{P}\right].$$

This is in a number of respects a somewhat extraordinary state of affairs. Let us look at it carefully. To begin with, note that we have here brought an additional degree of freedom of friend no. 1's brain explicitly into consideration (I have called this degree of freedom the A-memory of friend no. 1.) This is the degree of freedom wherein friend no. 1 remembers the information in the photograph that friend no. 2 has just shown him. Now, what is going on in this state is that friend no. 1 still simultaneously inhabits two different and mutually exclusive Everett worlds (in one, $\sigma_y = +\frac{1}{2}$, and in the other, $\sigma_y = -\frac{1}{2}$), but now, in each of those two worlds separately, friend no. 1 knows that $A = \alpha$; he knows, that is, that another world exists. Indeed, he has literally seen what amounts to a photograph of that other world.

Perhaps I can make this a bit clearer by saying it in a few other ways. What is going on in the state $|\gamma\rangle$ is that friend no. 1 has simultaneous and completely accurate knowledge of two noncommuting observables, σ_y and A. Let us delineate that in some detail. Consider the world wherein $\sigma_y = +\frac{1}{2}$. Within that world, friend no. 1 is in a position to predict with certainty, and correctly, that any subsequent measurement of σ_y will necessarily produce the result of $\sigma_y = +\frac{1}{2}$. Furthermore, within that same $\sigma_y = +\frac{1}{2}$ world, friend no. 1 is also in a position to predict with certainty, and correctly, that any subsequent measurement of A (a measurement that, as it were, checks for the existence of worlds other than his own) will with certainty produce the result $A = \alpha$. Indeed, even if both A and σ_y are subsequently to be measured (in that order), friend no. 1 is in a position to predict correctly, and in advance, both results (however, note that the order in which these subsequent experiments are carried out is important: all this would not work if the σ_y measurement is carried out first). Moreover, neither friend no. 2 nor any observer in the world other than friend no. 1 can, even in principle, ever be in a position to simultaneously know the values of precisely those two observables (albeit they can, of course, know either one). The possibility of knowing both A and σ_y at the same time depends not merely on what sorts of measuring instruments or what sorts of ingenuity one has at one's disposal, but it also depends on one's identity as well.

It ought to be emphasized that there are no paradoxes in all of this, and there are no violations of quantum theory, from which it was all derived. We have simply discovered a new move—a move that is entirely legal within Everett's game—whereby we can directly and experimentally see other Everett worlds. This move just was not anticipated by the founders of quantum mechanics. It happens that when such a move is made, things begin to look very odd, and the uncertainty relations cease to apply in precisely the ways with which we have for so long been familiar.

This tactic of looking at photographs of one's self inhabiting some multiplicity of worlds at the same time is a rich and strange business, and we as yet understand only a little. Nonetheless, we already know of a few nice tricks one can pull off by means of tactics like this (tricks involving various kinds of quantum mechanical automata and computers) that have heretofore been thought to be impossible to pull off by any means whatsoever. Let me conclude by mentioning just one.

David Deutsch of Oxford University has recently exploited this tactic[2] in order to design quantum mechanical computers that can solve a variety of problems in fewer calculational steps than any of their possible classical counterparts. Deutsch's strategy is to break the problem up into separate parts, and to have the computer do those various parts simultaneously in various different Everett worlds. Then he collects all those results at the end by having the computer look at one of our pictures of itself. This strategy will not work for every problem, but we now know that problems exist for which it will work.

We know of some other tricks too (some of which are quite astonishing from a philosophical point of view), but what is fun in all of this is that it is obvious that there must be many more possible tricks of which we are as yet unaware.

REFERENCES

1. This move was first described by: ALBERT, D. 1983. Phys. Lett. **98A:** 5, 6.
2. DEUTSCH, D. 1985. Proc. R. Soc. London **A400:** 97–117.

Trajectories, Spin, and Energy Conservation in Time-Dependent Neutron Interferometry

JEAN-PIERRE VIGIER

Laboratoire de Physique Théorique
Institut Henri Poincaré
75231 Paris Cedex 05, France

INTRODUCTION

Neutron interferometry has recently become a very powerful tool in testing the physical basis of quantum theory. Indeed, the Austrian group of physicists working at the Laue-Langevin Institute in Grenoble has produced an exciting set of experiments on neutron interference with highly attenuated beams that has enabled us to really record neutron self-interference data.[1-4] In all of these experiments, quantum theoretical predictions have been undoubtedly confirmed. Therefore, this may be considered as another powerful success of the quantum formalism in predicting the outcome of measurements on quantum ensembles.

However, because the structure of these neutron interferometry experiments essentially reproduces Young's double-slit configuration in a new refined form, one is tempted to revisit, in this different context, the Bohr-Einstein controversy on the interpretation of the quantum formalism. We will not, though, restrict our presentation to that specific problem, but will, instead, simply present the interpretation of these experiments in the frame of the causal quantum potential model. Then, we will compare our theoretical pattern to the usual assertions of the Copenhagen School. By this procedure, we hope to contribute to a clarification of the theoretical context and hope to help the reader in comparing the different explanatory patterns: The quantum potential model and the scheme of the Copenhagen School concerning micropro-cesses.

In fact, it is quite straightforward to summarize the basic ingredients of the quantum potential model advanced by de Broglie[5] and Bohm.[6] The real and imaginary part decomposition of the Schrödinger equation,

$$(\hbar/i)(\partial \psi/\partial t) = (\hbar^2/2m)\nabla^2\psi,$$

with $\psi = R \exp(iS/\hbar)$, yields the essential aspects of the model in the simplest of the cases by means of a Hamilton-Jacobi type (HJ) equation and a continuity (c) equation,

$$\frac{\partial S}{\partial t} + \frac{(\nabla S)^2}{2m} + \left(-\frac{\hbar^2}{2m}\frac{\nabla^2 R}{R}\right) = 0 \quad \text{and} \quad \frac{\partial(R^2)}{\partial t} + \nabla \cdot \left(R^2\frac{\nabla S}{m}\right) = 0,$$

respectively. Here, the particle has definite space-time trajectories (with $v = \nabla S/m$) and is constantly subjected (even in the "free particle" case) to a context that is

503

dependent on the nonclassical quantum potential,

$$Q = -\frac{\hbar^2}{2m}\frac{\nabla^2 R}{R},$$

which produces the quantum interference effects and, generally speaking, all quantum features deviating from the macroscopic particle behavior. In this sense, we can think of the quantum entity as a particle surrounded by a field (de Broglie's "pilot wave") or a "particle + wave" entity that responds to quantum boundary conditions and experimental arrangements. Furthermore, no good reason exists why energy conservation should not hold; it is only that the total particle energy, $-\partial S/\partial t$, is no longer equal to the kinetic energy, but is determined by the quantum potential contribution. Energy balance operations have to take this fact explicitly into account. An analogue reasoning also leads to a generalized angular momentum conservation due to contributions ascribed to the action of "quantum forces" (i.e., quantum potential gradients and torques). This means that the quantum system is, in principle, an open system constantly coupled to a thermal bath, de Broglie's hidden thermostat,[7] or Dirac's ether[8] (a fact that is visualized by the action of the quantum potential). Only specific situations (and quantum boundary conditions) decouple the system from the "thermostat" and reestablish a quasi-classical conservation scheme.

On the other hand, the rather confusing and contradictory scheme uniformized under the label of the "Copenhagen Interpretation" (CIQM) cannot be exposed in a similar way because, as we believe, a vast amount of philosophical assertions have been mixed with the correct quantum formalism and have been exposed as a coherent physical theory. For Bohr, for example, complementarity means, in a rigorous formulation, the mutual exclusion of space-time coordination of events and conservation laws, which is a fact that is supposed to be a consequence of the quantum uncertainties, $\Delta x \cdot \Delta p \geq \hbar$ and $\Delta E \cdot \Delta t \geq \hbar$. Heisenberg deduces from the same uncertainties a statistical conservation of energy-momentum, but denies energy-momentum conservation in individual processes. For him, causality fails in the quantum domain, and the observer-independent microphysical reality has to be abandoned. In the best of the cases, physical reality is created by measurements due to the macroscopic character of the instruments, but sometimes observer consciousness intervenes as well (Wigner). Wheeler paraphrases the situation in the famous tautological statement: "No microphenomenon is a phenomenon until it becomes an observed phenomenon" (phenomenon in Greek = appearance). Because the probabilistic ψ description is complete according to CIQM, any question concerning independent physical realities such as particle trajectories, particle-spin, and conservation laws is irrelevant. The whole set of these (mostly contradictory) statements attached to the quantum formalism is then presented as "the quantum theory" or, more modestly, "the Copenhagen School." Then, with a little help from the spontaneous, positivistically flavored, common sense of the physicists, it attains the status of the dominant formulation of quantum mechanics. In what follows, we will not try to falsify this interpretation because a philosophical position cannot be shown wrong even by scientific means. However, we will simply argue that one can very well account for the experimental facts by retaining particle trajectories, definite spin-vectors, and energy-angular momentum conservation in time-dependent neutron interferometry. We will especially see this in the three characteristic examples given below.

TIME-DEPENDENT NEUTRON INTERFEROMETRY

The setup is represented in FIGURE 1. A strongly polarized monokinetic neutron beam (i.e., with the magnetic moments oriented in the $+z$ direction perpendicular to the plane of the figure by an external magnetic field) enters the interferometer. The beam intensity has been reduced by chopping to 2–3 neutrons/second with a velocity of $v \sim 2073$ ms^{-1} (with an error bar $\pm 1.4\%$). Because the Compton wavelength is $\sim 10^{-13}$ cm, this clearly establishes that only one wave packet can be present at a time in a device ~ 10 cm long. This is so because its passage takes ~ 30 μsec. Any detected neutron (with an efficiency $>99\%$) is thus observed long before the next has left its uranium atom within the pile. Observed interferences in such a situation clearly confirm that quantum particles (here neutrons) only interfere with themselves (because the neutrons are detected individually).

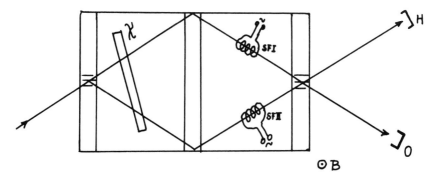

FIGURE 1. A neutron single-crystal interferometer with two spin-flip rf-coils.

On this basis, three time-dependent interference experiments can and have been performed:

Experiment I— Individual polarized neutron waves (i.e., the incoming wave packets), $\psi = |\uparrow_z\rangle$, are split by the Bragg planes of a first slab, a, cut in a silicon monocrystal ~ 10 cm total length. This separation gives rise to two partial beams, $\psi_I = e^{ix}|\uparrow_z\rangle$ and $\psi_{II} = |\uparrow_z\rangle$, where the term, e^{ix}, corresponding to the phase-shift induced by a movable rotating crystal (denoted χ in FIGURE 1) is introduced to yield a controllable difference of march between the paths I and II that will yield modulations. A check is made to ensure that the crystal is pure enough (i.e., its Bragg planes are sufficiently parallel) so that both waves, ψ_I and ψ_{II}, present no observable energy difference and no modification of their $\uparrow_z$ polarization. With both spin-flippers turned off, the wave packets, ψ_I and ψ_{II}, travel along both paths, are reflected on two slabs (b and c), recombine on the slab d, and superpose (interfere) on two beams, O and H (O containing a supplementary polarizer), where they are detected in detectors, D_H and D_O. Independently of any interpretation, the quantum mechanical formalism has been shown to be entirely correct in this case, with the superposition in O and H being modulated with the phase-shift, χ, to give the intensity,

$$I = (\psi_I + \psi_{II})^+(\psi_I + \psi_{II}) = 2(1 + \cos \chi),$$

while the polarization remains in the $+z$ direction, namely,

$$P = (P_x, P_y, P_z) = (0,0,1).$$

Due to Bragg reflection-transmission in d, one obtains two sinusoidal intensity patterns for O and H, where the maxima of O corresponds to the minima of H, and vice versa.

This first (successful) experiment by the Vienna group has been augmented in two additional ways:

Experiment II— (one spin-flipper only). The first way is to add to the setup one spin-flipper only (represented by the coil, SF_{II}, in FIGURE 1), which operates at ~100% efficiency. As is well known (and as has been checked experimentally), practically every neutron (>96%) whose wave packet, $|\uparrow_z\rangle$, goes through such a spin-flipper loses one photon to the coil by resonance, that is, it flips its spin to $|\downarrow_z\rangle$ with a loss of energy, $\Delta E = \hbar\omega_{rf} = 2\mu B_{rf}$, in the present setup. Here, the quantum formalism says that the superposition of $\psi_I = e^{i\chi}|\uparrow\rangle$ and $\psi_{II} = |\downarrow\rangle$ yields a constant intensity along with a final polarization of

$$P = [\cos(\omega_{rf}t - \chi), \sin(\omega_{rf}t - \chi), 0]$$

so that each neutron emerging from the interferometer is polarized in the x-y plane and has lost an energy, $\Delta E/2$. Thus, here too the quantum formalism has been shown to be verified by experiment.

Experiment III— (two spin-flippers). The second way is to have two synchronized spin-flippers working on both paths I and II simultaneously. Independently of any interpretation, the quantum formalism implies that the superposition on beams O and H is $e^{i\chi}|\downarrow\rangle + |\downarrow\rangle$, which yields the intensity,

$$I = 2(1 + \cos \chi),$$

and the polarization,

$$P = (0,0,-1).$$

It is these predictions that have just been verified in Grenoble (see FIGURE 2). Each individual neutron has thus been shown experimentally (1) to leave the interferometer with spin down, that is, to have lost an energy, ΔE, to the spin-flippers, and (2) to have interfered with itself.

THEORETICAL DISCUSSION

In order to account for the spin superposition features of the recent neutron interferometry experiments, the original causal interpretation of the Schrödinger equation has been generalized by Bohm et al.[9] to include the concept of spin. Therefore, it can be interpreted in terms of well-defined motions in the frame of the Pauli equation. The extra degrees of freedom in the two-component Pauli spinor are given by the Eulerian angles, θ, ψ, ϕ, that define a general state of rotation given by the spinor,

$$\Psi = R \begin{pmatrix} \cos\theta/2 & e^{i(\psi+\phi)/2} \\ i\sin\theta/2 & e^{i(\psi-\phi)/2} \end{pmatrix} = Re^{i\psi/2} \begin{pmatrix} \cos\theta/2 & e^{i\phi/2} \\ i\sin\theta/2 & e^{-i\phi/2} \end{pmatrix},$$

FIGURE 2. Intensity interference, $I(x)$, with both spin-flippers on (H beam). The rf-field is synchronized to 71, 96 kHz (reproduction by kind permission of Badurek, Rauch, and Tuppinger).

by means of which the spin vector is given as

$$\mathbf{S} = \frac{\hbar}{2} \frac{\Psi^+ \sigma \Psi}{\Psi^+ \Psi}.$$

The evolution of a Pauli spinor is then given by the Pauli equation,

$$i\hbar \frac{\partial \Psi}{\partial t} = H\Psi,$$

where

$$H = -\frac{\hbar^2}{2m}\left(\nabla - i\frac{e}{\hbar c}A\right)^2 + \mu(\sigma \cdot H) + V \quad \text{with} \quad \mu = -\frac{e\hbar}{2mc}$$

and Ψ as above. The equations of motion can be derived from the Pauli-Hamiltonian (as described by Bohm *et al.*[9]) by introducing in addition to $\rho = R^2, \psi/2$, the canonical variables, $\rho \cos \theta, -\phi/2$. We then find

$$\frac{\partial \rho}{\partial t} + \text{div} \,(\rho v) = 0,$$

that is, a continuity equation, and a Hamilton-Jacobi type equation,

$$\frac{\hbar}{2} \left(\frac{\partial \psi}{\partial t} + \cos \theta \, \frac{\partial \phi}{\partial t} \right) + \frac{1}{2} mv^2 + Q + V + H_s = 0.$$

Here,

$$Q = -\frac{\hbar^2}{2m} \frac{\nabla^2 R}{R}$$

is the normal quantum potential and H_s is a spin-dependent addition to the quantum potential (which introduces a new spin-orbit coupling), where

$$H_s = \frac{\hbar^2}{8m} \left[(\nabla \theta)^2 + \sin^2 \theta \, (\nabla \phi)^2 \right] - \frac{e}{mc} \mathbf{S} \cdot \mathbf{H}.$$

The equation of motion of the spin vector, S, can also be written as

$$\frac{d\mathbf{S}}{dt} = \frac{1}{m} \frac{\mathbf{S}}{\rho} \times \sum_i \frac{\partial}{\partial x^i} \left(\rho \frac{\partial \mathbf{S}}{\partial x^i} \right) - \frac{e}{mc} (\mathbf{S} \times \mathbf{H}),$$

where the term,

$$\frac{1}{m} \frac{\mathbf{S}}{\rho} \times \sum_i \frac{\partial}{\partial x^i} \left(\rho \frac{\partial \mathbf{S}}{\partial x^i} \right),$$

is an additional "quantum torque" that introduces a quantum mechanical precession of the spin vector. It is evident from these equations that even in the absence of magnetic fields, free-spinning particle trajectories will not coincide with Schrödinger trajectories, nor will the orientation of the spin vector remain constant if the particle is in a nonstationary spin state. The spin-dependent quantum potential and quantum torque are nonzero under these conditions because the spin orientation has nonzero spatial gradients, $\nabla \theta, \nabla \phi$. With this general scheme based on the Pauli equation, a detailed account of all three experiments can be given. In all cases, we assume both beams to have a Gaussian wave-packet profile.

For experiment I, it has been shown[10] that both beams have the same spin orientation, for example, $\binom{1}{0}$, and the combined wave function possesses the same spinor symmetry and exhibits a spatial interference pattern: As a consequence, the Euler angle $\theta = 0$, the spin vector has no spatial dependence, and the spin-dependent quantum potential and the quantum torque are zero. Every incoming neutron preserves its spin orientation for the constant external magnetic field, and therefore a full conservation of the spin-dependent part of the energy exists.

In experiment II, where an rf-spin-flipper operates in one of the beams, the situation is quite different. A detailed calculation shows[11] that due to the different partial beam spinor symmetry, the combined wave function does not exhibit spatial interference despite the phase difference between the beams. However, the Euler angles, θ and ϕ, have a spatial variation, and therefore the spin-dependent addition to the quantum potential and the quantum torque are nonzero. The beams emerging from the interferometer have definite spin vectors with $\theta = \pi/2$ and $\phi = -[\pi/2 - \omega_{rf}t + \chi]$, which are results that are in agreement with quantum predictions and experimental results. Originally, spin-up or spin-down vectors in the partial beams are twisted to the horizontal position (x-y plane) by the quantum torque, and they have opposite directions depending on which partial emerging beam the neutrons enter when leaving the superposition region. We point at this stage to the problem of energy and angular momentum conservation in the individual microprocess. A statistical conservation of both quantities is always guaranteed: before superposition, there is an average value of total spin zero ($\uparrow,\downarrow$); after the process, the spins in the forward and deviated beam lie in opposite directions in the x-y plane. However, in the causal interpretation (where definite trajectories exist for the spinning particles), the total angular momentum is also conserved in an individual passage of a neutron because the quantum torque rotates the spin vector from $+z$ or $-z$ direction into the x-y plane in the region of superposition.

A similar reasoning applies as well to the energy conservation. Every neutron entering the interferometer in the spin-up state has a definite energy in the external magnetic field. If it goes through the partial beam with no spin-flipper, an energy amount of $-\hbar\omega_{rf}/2$ is supplied by the spin-dependent quantum potential so that an energy balance is established with its final horizontal position in the superposition region. If, on the other hand, it passes through the spin-flipper and loses an amount, $\Delta E = \hbar\omega_{rf}$, it gains an amount of $\hbar\omega_{rf}/2$ due to the spin-dependent quantum potential so that the energy balance is again established. Of course, there is no need to say that this picture goes beyond the average energy conservation because it is also valid due to the equal relative frequencies of neutron passages through each of the two partial beams.

In experiment III, we have two rf-spin-flippers operating in both arms of the interferometer. A calculation in the frame of our general scheme shows that due to the equal particle-beam spinor symmetry (both spinor waves are inverted), the combined wave function exhibits spatial interference modulated by χ and no interferences in the spin-polarization. The Euler angles, θ and ϕ, have no spatial variation, and therefore, exactly as in experiment I, both the spin-dependent quantum potential and the quantum torque vanish. Angular momentum is absolutely conserved individually and statistically in a "classical" way because quantum torque effects are absent. In fact, every neutron that enters the interferometer with spin $\uparrow_z$ is found with spin $\downarrow_z$ in the superposition area due to the $S \times H$ term operating in the spin-flipper. This fact has a very serious theoretical implication: the two states, $\uparrow_z$ and $\downarrow_z$, differ by an energy amount, $\Delta E = \hbar\omega_{rf}$, that is exactly the resonance energy-exchange with the spin-flipper. Because this energy is exchanged with only one spin-flipper (due to the resonance condition), it seems to us that this is direct evidence of a neutron passage through one of the arms of the interferometer. Due to the lack of an explicit measurement process, we are not, of course, in a position to say through which spin-flipper the neutron has passed, but we can nevertheless advance the statement that the neutron has passed through the coil or the other. We are thus in a position to consistently use the combined wave + particle aspect of matter in the same experiment, which is contrary to the complementarity "no go" statements. Spatial interference exists and energy conservation implies a particle passage through one of the interferometer arms. This is precisely the reason why we proposed[12] this type of experiment: roughly speaking, we follow the neutron as a particle in the interferometer, while we observe, at the same time, interferences because spinor Ψ waves propagate at the same time through both arms of the apparatus.

Looking back at the set of the three experiments discussed in this section, we realize that our model accounts consistently for all features of the experiments preserving a space-time coordination of events as well as a strict validity of conservation laws (i.e., a "complementary monster" according to the orthodox philosophical point of view). Reality appears to be nonseparable in the sense that the quantum potential and quantum torque are context-dependent, but this same reality is analyzable and intuitively comprehensible, at least in principle.

What is the Copenhagen response to these experiments? One can only be sure that any argument advanced will be inevitably coupled with complementarity assertions and uncertainty discussions. According to this point of view, no neutron travels in space-time unless it is measured. This is so because if it were traveling along one path, then no interference would occur. Interference experiments manifest only propagation and superposition of probability amplitudes; nothing can be said about individual microprocesses. Questions along the lines of energy-momentum conservation are irrelevant because they go beyond the quantum "abstract mathematical description" and quantum completeness. All our above reasoning would then be an artifact that not only is irrelevant, but that should also lead to contradictions. However, we managed to show that no contradictions arise in our model because the results obtained are quite natural and self-consistent. On the other hand, we could ask the question of whether the acceptance of "quantum completeness' in the Copenhagen view and the assignment of irrelevancy to the conservation laws is not too high a price to pay for the adoption of this purely philosophical point of view. One could still argue that in the last resort, it is a matter of taste which point of view to adopt because the bare experimental facts are reproduced identically in both approaches. To our point of view, this problem exceeds personal preferences and is inevitably tied to an effort of distinguishing scientific from purely speculative reasoning.

In our opinion, in experiment III, if one assumes (1) that energy-momentum is always conserved in all individual microprocesses and (2) that quanta are indivisible, it would now seem difficult to escape the conclusion that Einstein and de Broglie were right (against Bohr and Heisenberg) in the Bohr-Einstein controversy.

REFERENCES

1. SUMMHAMMER, J., G. BADUREK & U. KISCHKO, 1982. Phys. Lett. **90A:** 110.
2. BADUREK, G., H. RAUCH, J. SUMMHAMMER, U. KISCHKO & A. ZEILINGER. 1983. J. Phys. **A16:** 1133.
3. SUMMHAMMER, J., G. BADUREK, H. RAUCH, U. KISCHKO & A. ZEILINGER. 1983. Phys. Rev. **A27:** 2523.
4. BADUREK, G., H. RAUCH & J. SUMMHAMMER. 1983. Phys. Rev. Lett. **51:** 1015.
5. DE BROGLIE, L. 1960. Nonlinear Wave Mechanics. Elsevier. Amsterdam.
6. BOHM, D. 1952. Phys. Rev. **85:** 166, 180.

7. DE BROGLIE, L. 1964. Thermodynamique cachée des particules. Gauthier–Villars. Paris.
8. DIRAC, P. A. M. 1951. Nature **168:** 906.
9. BOHM, D., R. SCHILLER & J. TIOMNO. 1955. Suppl. Nuovo Cimento Ser. X.
10. DEWDNEY, C., P. R. HOLLAND, A. KYPRIANIDIS & J. P. VIGIER. 1985. Trajectories and spin vector orientations in the causal interpretation of the Pauli equation. Preprint Inst. H. Poincaré. Submitted to Phys. Rev. D.
11. DEWDNEY, C., P. R. HOLLAND, A. KYPRIANIDIS & J. F. VIGIER. 1985. Spin superposition in neutron interferometry. Preprint Inst. H. Poincaré.
12. DEWDNEY, C., A. GARUCCIO, A. KYPRIANIDIS & J. P. VIGIER. 1984. Phys. Lett. **104A:** 325.

Making Consistent Inferences from Quantum Measurements[a]

ROBERT B. GRIFFITHS

Physics Department
Carnegie-Mellon University
Pittsburgh, Pennsylvania 15213

INTRODUCTION

Quantum mechanics has been a very successful theory, and presently it is the only successful theory for dealing with phenomena of the microscopic world: the motion of electrons, protons, nuclei, etc. We do not need quantum mechanics to describe the motion of large, macroscopic bodies (such as planets moving around the sun). However, it is absolutely essential for describing the invisible motion of electrons around an atomic nucleus.

The microscopic world described by quantum mechanics is not directly accessible to our senses. Hence, the experimental program for investigating this world demands a measuring apparatus that amplifies invisible events and makes them visible to us. Conversely, to interpret the visible results of experiments, we need a theory of how these have been produced by, or are related to, the microscopic or atomic events of interest. Quantum mechanics is this theory, if there is any theory at all that allows us to say something about electrons, atoms, etc., on the basis of experiments.

Nonetheless, it is widely acknowledged that there are conceptual difficulties (in particular, problems of logical consistency) in making inferences about microscopic phenomena from the results of experimental measurements. These difficulties are so severe that some physicists have despaired of even speaking about microscopic phenomena at all. Quantum mechanics, they say, allows us to predict the results of measurements (i.e., certain macroscopic things), but does not necessarily allow us to say anything sensible about the microscopic things (if there are such things) that our measurements are measuring.

I am not so pessimistic. It seems to me that it is possible to speak sensibly about microscopic phenomena and how they are related to measurements. However, the procedure for doing this, namely, the logical process of inference, must be appropriate to the domain of study and must be consistent with and indeed based on quantum theory itself. Elsewhere,[1] I have indicated one scheme for doing this. In the present paper, I shall focus on one particular difficulty: that of inferring properties of microscopic systems at times both before and after a measurement takes place.

PREDICTIONS AND RETRODICTIONS: THE QUANTUM DILEMMA

Let us begin with a "classical" example: A piece of paper that is either red or green (we do not know which) has been placed in an opaque envelope. A "measurement"

[a]This research has been supported by the National Science Foundation under Grant No. DMR-8108310 to Carnegie-Mellon University.

512

consists of opening the envelope, pulling out the piece of paper, observing that its color is green, and putting it back in the envelope. On the basis of this "measurement," we usually think it sensible to infer that the color of the paper was green both before the measurement took place and afterwards, with the paper back in the opaque envelope. The first of these is a retrodiction, to a time before the measurement, and the second is a prediction, to a time after the measurement. In both cases, we have to assume that the color is not sensibly altered by the passage of time, or by removing the piece from the envelope, or by putting it back in.

Now consider an analogous quantum situation (FIGURE 1) in which a spin-$\frac{1}{2}$ particle passes through an "improved" Stern-Gerlach apparatus[2] Z constructed so that a particle entering with $S_z = \hbar/2$ passes through a detector and then emerges with S_z still equal to $\hbar/2$, while the apparatus changes to a state, Z_+ (as indicated by a pointer

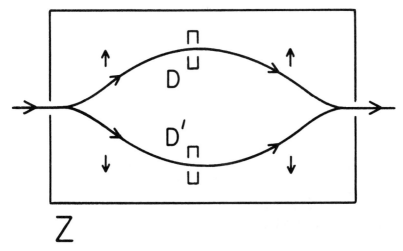

FIGURE 1. The improved Stern-Gerlach apparatus Z. The vertical arrows indicate the spin polarizations (S_z) of the particles passing through the detectors, D and D'.

or some other macroscopic change). On the other hand, a particle entering with $S_z = -\hbar/2$ emerges with $S_z = -\hbar/2$ after passing through a different detector, which makes the apparatus change to a state, Z_-. With z replaced by x and Z by X, the previous description describes an improved Stern-Gerlach apparatus X for measuring S_x.

In parallel with our previous reasoning about the color of a piece of paper, we might want to infer that if the passage of a particle leaves the apparatus in a state Z_+, then the particle had $S_z = \hbar/2$ before it entered the apparatus (retrodiction) as well as after it left (prediction). (We assume there are no magnetic fields, and thus no precession of the spin direction outside the apparatus.) However, the typical textbook[3] exposition of quantum mechanics (following the scheme laid down by von Neumann[4]) supports the predictive, but not (in general) the retrodictive inference; that is, after the measurement, the particle is in an eigenstate of S_z corresponding to the measured value (as a result of "collapsing" the wave function), whereas before the measurement, it is (in general) in a superposition of such states. What is it in quantum mechanics that produces a time asymmetry that seems to be absent in the classical case? Indeed, is this asymmetry intrinsic to quantum mechanics, or does it simply express a particular way of interpreting quantum mechanics that has come about by historical accident?

I find it hard to construct a compelling argument to support the thesis that quantum mechanics allows only predictive inferences to states of affairs after the time of a measurement. For each argument in favor of prediction, it seems to me that another can be constructed in favor of allowing retrodiction. Indeed, Aharonov, Bergmann, and Lebowitz[5] have pointed out that it is possible, at least for some purposes, to invert the time sequence when discussing the statistics of quantum measurements.

However, there is a serious problem if one allows for both prediction and retrodiction on an equal footing. Consider the situation shown in FIGURE 2: a Z polarization analyzer measures S_z at some time, t_1, while an X analyzer measures S_x at a later time, t_2. (For convenience in drawing the figure, both apparatuses have been shortened in the horizontal direction in comparison with FIGURE 1.) Suppose that a single particle produces the sequence, $Z_+ X_+$, in the two analyzers. We can then infer that at some time, t, between t_1 and t_2,

$$A: S_z = \hbar/2,$$

using prediction from the earlier measurement, and

$$B: S_x = \hbar/2,$$

using retrodiction from the later measurement. (Note that we cannot predict $S_z = \hbar/2$ for times later than t_2 because the magnetic fields in apparatus X will perturb S_z; similarly, nothing can be said about S_x for times earlier than t_1.)

The trouble, of course, is that quantum mechanics gives us no way to describe a particle for which A and B hold at the same time, and there is no apparatus that can measure S_x and S_z simultaneously. Any attempt to put prediction and retrodiction on an equivalent footing must, it seems to me, face up to the dilemma caused by the fact

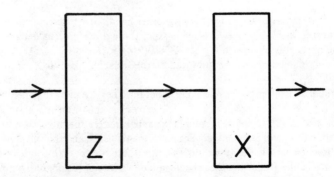

FIGURE 2. A Z apparatus followed by an X apparatus. (The horizontal dimension of each has been reduced relative to FIGURE 1.)

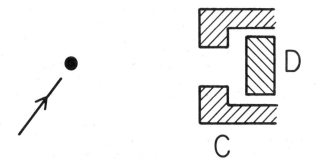

FIGURE 3. Particles from an incident beam (arrow) may be scattered from a target and trigger a detector, D, after passing through a hole in a collimator, C.

that an earlier measurement of one variable can be combined with a later measurement of a different variable to make an inference about the state of affairs at an intermediate time. If the operators for the two variable do not commute, we arrive at a situation that is difficult for ordinary quantum mechanics to deal with.

WAYS OUT OF THE DILEMMA

It seems to me that there are basically four ways for resolving the dilemma associated with prediction and retrodiction (apart from abandoning quantum mechanics entirely, or changing it in some radical fashion):

(1) Allow neither predictions nor retrodictions (at least to microscopic events).
(2) Allow only predictions.
(3) Allow only retrodictions.
(4) Allow both, but provide an alternative scheme to get around the paradoxes.

Because I am in favor of proposal 4, I am (psychologically) well prepared to tell you what is wrong with the other options. My complaint about schemes 1 and 2 is that they seem, to me, to ignore the way in which experimental physicists think about things.

Consider, for example, the situation shown in FIGURE 3, where a beam of particles strikes a target, and there is a detector placed behind a hole in a collimator. Suppose the detector registers the arrival of a particle. The experimenter will explain this as arising from the fact that a particle in the initial beam has been scattered by the target in a direction that allows it to pass through the hole in the collimator and thence into the detector. That is, he can infer from the fact that the detector is triggered (a macroscopic event) at some time, that at a slightly earlier time, a scattered particle had passed through the hole in the collimator. The event of the particle passing through the hole is a microscopic event (in that it involves a microscopic particle; the hole, of course, is macroscopic), but it is not a measurement, at least in the usual sense of that term. Nonetheless, it is important for understanding the experimental results because it is the hole in the collimator that determines the solid angle for detecting particles.

However, passing through the collimator hole just before detection is the sort of thing that schemes 1 and 2 do not allow us to talk about (at least in any simple way). What about the third scheme? Could we set up a quantum mechanical interpretation scheme using only retrodictions? It is an intriguing idea, but I do not think it will work. In a meaningful discussion of experiments of this type, one must make some use of the properties of the system at a still earlier time than that at which the particle reached the collimator hole (e.g., the fact that it was in the beam incident on the target). Thus, I suspect that predictions always enter the picture, at least implicitly, in some way.

The advantage of proposal 4 (at least in the way I have formulated it) lies precisely in the fact that it allows quantum mechanics to confirm what the experimenter believes: if the particle reaches the detector (and if certain earlier initial conditions are satisfied), then the particle did pass through the hole in the collimator on its way to the detector. And at a still earlier time, it was traveling on its way from the target towards the hole, etc.

The disadvantage of proposal 4, though, of allowing both prediction and retrodiction from quantum measurements is that one has to deal with paradoxes of the sort discussed earlier in connection with FIGURE 2. My own way[1] of doing this goes by the name of "consistent histories." I start with a generalization of the Born probability ansatz that permits the discussion of joint probabilities of events at several different times. However (and this is the key point), not every sequence of events is assigned a probability. Only those sequences, or histories, satisfying a consistency requirement are considered meaningful within the framework of the theory. Once such a sequence or history is identified, the corresponding probabilities are given their usual (classical) interpretation. However, events from separate consistent histories cannot, in general, be combined to form a single consistent history, and consequently, certain inferences that are automatic or "intuitively obvious" in classical logic are disallowed in the consistent history approach.

Let me stress that the consistency requirement is a mathematical requirement: whether a given sequence of events is or is not consistent is an issue of calculation, not physical or philosophical intuition. It turns out that at least some of the consistent sequences make good physical sense. Others are more problematical, but I have yet to find any that are nonsensical.

It is perhaps instructive to see how the consistent history approach deals with the situation in FIGURE 2. Given an appropriate initial state (particle headed for the Z analyzer, with both pieces of apparatus ready to register its polarization), and the final state in which the two apparatuses are in states, X_+ and Z_+, the event A, $S_z = \hbar/2$ at an intermediate time, can be incorporated in a consistent history and its (conditional) probability is one. Similarly, the event B, $S_x = \hbar/2$ at the same intermediate time, can be incorporated in a consistent history and has a (conditional) probability of one. However, there is no consistent history that contains both A and B (at the same time). Hence the usual conclusion that since A occurred and B occurred, the event "A and B" occurred does not follow, because there is no event "A and B" that one can talk about.

CONCLUSION

To summarize, making inferences for quantum measurements really is more complicated than is suggested by the simple analogy of pulling a piece of paper out of an envelope and noting its color. However, the approach that denies the possibility of making retrodictions to previous states of affairs on the basis of quantum measurements is unsatisfactory when it comes to thinking about laboratory experiments. The consistent history approach puts predictions and retrodictions on an equal footing, but it does so at the price of ruling out certain inferences allowed by classical logic and probability theory.

REFERENCES

1. GRIFFITHS, R. B. 1984. J. Stat. Phys. **36**: 219.
2. See: FEYNMAN, R. P. 1965. The Feynman Lectures on Physics, vol. III, p. 6–3. Addison–Wesley. Reading, Massachusetts. (I have added detectors to Feynman's apparatus.)
3. For example: COHEN-TANNOUDJI, C., B. DIU & F. LALOË. Quantum Mechanics, vol. I, p. 220. Wiley. New York.
4. VON NEUMANN, J. 1955. Mathematical Foundations of Quantum Mechanics, chap. V. Princeton Univ. Press. Princeton, New Jersey.
5. AHARONOV, Y., P. G. BERGMANN & J. L. LEBOWITZ. 1964. Phys. Rev. **134B**: 1410.

Variable Photon Detection as an Explanation of EPR Experiments

F. SELLERI

Dipartimento di Fisica
Università di Bari
INFN–Sezione di Bari
I-70126 Bari, Italy

VON NEUMANN AND BOHR

For those who work in the foundations of quantum physics, a great achievement has been the overcoming of von Neumann's theorem[1] (and of all the theorems of the same type[2]) that tried to forbid causal formulations of quantum theory. The opinion that von Neumann's theorem can now be ignored is one of the few on which there is agreement among the persons interested in these matters. This should be of no surprise because already in 1952, Bohm[3] succeeded in achieving precisely what von Neumann's theorem was supposed to forbid: that is, provide a causal formulation of the existing quantum theory. Later, some simpler models that reproduced a limited, but very meaningful part of quantum theory (the eigenvalues and the probabilities for the spin observables of a single spin-½ particle) were proposed.[4] It has recently been realized[5] that the existence of these models does not only provide an overcoming of von Neumann's theorem, but of Bohr's complementarity as well. Today, we can give a causal description in space and time of most fundamental quantum phenomena (double-slit experiment, neutron interferometric results, and so on). There is even a movie, produced by Chris Dewdney,[6] in which deterministic particle trajectories reproduce the quantum mechanical interferences in several interesting cases. Of course, one does not need to endorse the validity of the proposed models. Their value is mostly methodological because they show, in a detailed, rational way, how and why all the "impossibility proofs" (including complementarity) are today obsolete.

In defense of the old Copenhagen ideology (which considers the atomic phenomena as mysterious and basically nonunderstandable), two major points are often made:

(1) It is recalled that the Schrödinger equation for n particles represents quantum waves as propagating in an abstract $3n$-dimensional space and not in our ordinary physical space;

(2) It is stated that the experiments performed to check Bell's inequality have produced good agreement with the quantum-theoretical predictions, but disagreement with the idea of Einstein locality.

On the first point, we have little to say in the present paper. We can only recall that no "impossibility proof" has ever been proposed against an ordinary-space description of the quantum behavior of n particles. If the difficult task of overcoming von Neumann's theorem has been achieved, there can be no doubt that this "easier" problem will also eventually be solved.

Thus, we will instead discuss in detail the second point and show that the agreement of the experimental results with the quantum-theoretical predictions does not provide evidence against Einstein locality. We will do so by developing a new form of local realism that is far weaker than originally introduced by EPR.[7] The possibility to apply the original EPR approach to quantum mechanics no longer exists because the Wigner-Araki-Yanase theorem[8] has shown that the usual conservation laws of additive physical quantities do not allow one to make predictions with certainty, even in the case of a system initially in an eigenstate of the observable to be measured.

CAUSALITY AND DETERMINISM

The original formulation of the EPR paradox[7] based on the idea of deterministic and separable elements of reality cannot be considered fully satisfactory today. In fact, determinism may not apply to the quantum domain where random processes play an important role (action of the apparatus on the measured objects, distribution of individual lifetimes of unstable systems, values of impact parameters in collision processes, and so on).

Determinism is a narrow and particular form of causality. From the point of view proposed here, today it is possible to defend causality, but it is almost impossible to believe that determinism is universally valid. Hence, it can finally be stated that Laplacian deteminism is dead, that Brownian motion is an objectively causal phenomenon, and that objective causality is a part of causality.

The original proof of Bell's inequality[9] was also based on a deterministic philosophy, and therefore people tried immediately to find probabilistic formulations of Einstein locality. The best-known approach of this type was provided by the 1974 Clauser-Horne model[10] in which joint probabilities for two correlated objects are assumed to be factorable at some level, that is, after fixing a finite number of variables. It was shown elsewhere[11] that factorability is not an assumption with a well-defined status within the existing theory of probabilities. Therefore, it is doubtful whether it can provide the ground for a general proof of Bell's inequality based exclusively on Einstein locality. After all, factorable probabilities represent statistically independent phenomena, and it is hard to see why Einstein locality should be equivalent to statistical independence. Furthermore, the definition of probability is far from unique, and it was shown in reference 11 that within the most widely used definition (probability introduced as frequency in a statistical ensemble), the Clauser-Horne factorability condition cannot be generally true. For these reasons, a different formulation of Einstein locality in probabilistic terms will be presented in the following sections.

PROBABILISTIC EINSTEIN LOCALITY

Let a set, S, be given of physical objects of the same type (e.g., photons). We call the objects, $\alpha_1, \alpha_2, \ldots, \alpha_N$, and write

$$S = \{\alpha_1, \alpha_2, \ldots, \alpha_N\}. \tag{1}$$

Suppose a measuring instrument, I, is given with which it is possible to measure a dichotomic physical quantity, A, on the systems composing S. Let the possible results be A_1 and A_2. We assume that:

If it is possible to predict the existence of a subset, S', of S, then

$$S' = \{\alpha_{i_1}, \alpha_{i_2}, \ldots, \alpha_{i_N}\} \tag{2}$$

without disturbing the objects composing S' and S; if it is also possible to predict correctly that future measurements of A on S' will give the results, A_1 and A_2, with respective probabilities, p_1 and p_2, then it will be said that a physical property, λ', belongs to S' and that

$$p_1 = p_1(A; \lambda') \text{ and } p_2 = p_2(A; \lambda'). \tag{3}$$

The previous statement will be called the Generalized Reality Criterion (GRC); it constitutes a natural generalization of the famous criterion for (deterministic) reality put forward by Einstein, Podolsky, and Rosen (EPR) in 1935. Its most important use is in connection with EPR experiments, where each one of the systems, α_i, composing S is physically correlated with a (separated) system, β_i. Let the set of these new systems be

$$T = \{\beta_1, \beta_2, \ldots, \beta_N\}. \tag{4}$$

For instance, the particles, α_i and β_i, could have been produced simultaneously by the decay of an unstable system, M_i ($i = 1, 2, \ldots, N$). Also, suppose that at some time the space parts of the quantum mechanical wave packets describing an α-system and the corresponding β-system are separated by a very large distance: this requirement will be considered a sufficient condition for the validity of the Generalized Separability Principle (GSP), which is formulated as follows:

Measurements performed on T (β-systems) cannot generate the physical properties required by the GRC that belong to any subset, S', of S (α-systems). Of course, in the GSP, the roles of the sets, S and T, can also be exchanged.

In an EPR experiment, one will detect S' by measuring a (dichotomic) observable, B, on the β-particles: if $T' \subset T$ is the set of β-particles for which the result, $B = B_1$, has been found, it can often be predicted that another observable, A, will be found to have the values, A_1 and A_2, with respective probabilities, p_1 and p_2, in the subset S' of α-particles correlated with the β-particles belonging to T'.

Application of the GSP guarantees that the physical property, λ', is not created at a distance from the measurements performed on T. This property, λ', is a part of the physical reality of S' that is not detected directly in the usual experiments in which eigenvalues and probabilities are measured. It is, therefore, of the same general nature of the so-called "hidden variables," even though it is obviously more general than these because it is attributed to statistical ensembles rather than to individual systems. At present, the existence of λ' is conjectural, but if this conjecture were correct, it would obviously be possible to detect its existence with suitable experiments. Further comments on λ' are made in the next section.

WEAK REALISM FOR EPR EXPERIMENTS

In a typical (ideal) EPR experiment, there are two observers: O_α, who performs measurements of the observable A on the set S of the α-particles, and O_β, who measures B on the set T of the β-particles. Assuming that O_β performs the first set of measurements (in the laboratory frame) and that T' is the subset of T for which $B = B_1$ (constant) has been found, O_β himself can predict the existence of the subset S' (composed of the α-particles individually correlated with the β-particles composing T') for which, later, O_α shall find the results, $A = A_1$ and $A = A_2$, with respective probabilities, p_1 and p_2. Notice that p_1 and p_2 are in general different from the corresponding probabilities holding for the whole ensemble S. Therefore, if O_α later does find the probabilities predicted by O_β, it can be concluded that there is something in the physical reality of S' that somehow generates p_1 and p_2 if and when A is measured by O_α with the instrument I. It can also be concluded that these probabilities are not generated by I independently of the properties of the objects composing S' because neither the instrument I nor the observer O_α possesses information on the composition of S'. It is only when the experiment has been completed that O_β will tell O_α which subset of the indices $\{1, 2, \ldots, N\}$ should be used for composing S', for which the probabilities, p_1 and p_2, are predicted. In these conditions, it seems natural to attribute the predicted emergence of p_1 and p_2 (which are detected as frequencies) at least partly to the physical properties of S'. It is on this basis that the physical property, λ', is attributed to S': the value of λ' fixes p_1 and p_2, as can be seen in equation 3.

In general, the probabilities (which become concrete when the observable A is actually measured) could also depend on the instrument I that is used. This happens in many real experiments where the precision of the analyzers, the efficiency of the counters, and so on, affect the determination of the observed probabilities. Therefore, one can assume that these probabilities have, so to say, a double nature because they reflect the physical reality of the ensemble S' and of the instrument I. Therefore, the notation in equation 3 gives to the probabilities their true nature by making them dependent both on the physical property, λ', of S' and on the measured observable, A (for simplicity, in the symbol A, we include the properties of the instrument I, eventual local vacuum-fluctuation effects, and so on).

The foregoing discussion also shows why the probabilities, p_1 and p_2, were not attributed directly to S' as real, whereas the property, λ', was introduced. If we had defined the probabilities directly as real then in practice nothing would have changed in the results obtained in this paper. However, we would have exposed our approach to the criticism of having attributed to S', as real, something that can emerge only through the concrete intervention of the measuring apparatus ("counterfactuality"[12]).

The exact nature of λ' is not of interest here, though. It will generally result from the combination of a large number of "elements of reality" concurring to generate a situation for S' in which the probabilities are p_1 and p_2 and not different.

An important point to stress is that the property, λ', will be attributed to S', even if no actual measurement is carried out on S', provided that the previous and exhaustive experience with repetitions of the sets, S, S', and T, shows that the probabilities, p_1 and p_2, are correctly predicted. By this, nothing more is implied than the standard scientific procedure: if a large body of empirical evidence made by repeated observations proves that p_1 and p_2 show up invariably in S'—and, therefore, by the GRC, that the property, λ', belongs invariably to S'—then one can also conclude that λ' is real even if no future measurement on the given set S' will be made. Thereby, one excludes that the action of the instrument I on the α-particles creates a property, λ', on these particles retroactively in time. Retroaction has instead been proposed as a solution of the EPR paradox by other physicists.[13]

We can go a step further and completely disentangle the existence of λ' from all types of measurement by virtue of the GSP. Consider the measurement of B made by O_β on the set T of β-particles. The results, $B = B_1$ and $B = B_2$, split T into two subsets, T' (all cases where $B = B_1$) and T'' (all cases where $B = B_2$). Recall that T' is related to S' in the way stated and that λ' is a physical property of S'. Naturally, a completely symmetrical reasoning could be made for T'', the set of α-particles related to it, their predictable probabilities, and their physical property, λ''. The splitting of T into T' and T'' takes place if B is measured: it is this splitting that allows one to identify the sets, S' and S'', to which physical properties, λ' and λ'', can be attributed. However, these physical properties cannot be created at a distance by the measurements on T because this is excluded by the GSP. Therefore, an unknown, but concrete splitting of S into S' (with the property, λ') and S'' (with the property, λ'') exists even if no measurement at all is made on the β-particles. A mere conclusion of the existence of S' and S'' (with their respective properties, λ' and λ'') will, however, suffice for our purposes, as it will be shown later, even if it is not possible to identify those α-particles that compose S' and S''.

The considerations contained in this and in the previous section constitute our form of local realism, which is obviously far weaker and more general than the one originally proposed by EPR. Our GRC does not suffer from the limitations of the EPR reality criterion, for which it could be objected that one cannot see why a superposition should be less real than an eigenstate. The present approach can instead be used by starting both from eigenstates and from superpositions because probabilities can be predicted for all types of quantum mechanical wave functions. Furthermore, it is not limited to the world of quanta, but is applicable to all physical domains, also independently of the use of a theory for the prediction of probabilities; these can often be known simply because of previous experimental investigations.

FROM ENSEMBLES TO SINGLE OBJECTS

It will next be shown that our two assumptions (GRC and GSP) imply the existence of physical properties (and of probabilities) for the individual objects composing the ensembles, S and T.

We have shown that the property, λ' (λ''), can be attributed to S' (S'') on the basis of a pure reasoning (based on a theory whose predictions can be trusted, and/or on previous experimental activity) with no need to perform the actual experiments every time the GRC is used. This, of course, is in agreement with our realistic line. Therefore, even in the absence of measurements on set T, there exists an unknown, but concrete splitting of S into S' and S'', such that the following properties can be attributed:

$$\lambda'(B) \rightarrow S'(B); \lambda''(B) \rightarrow S''(B). \tag{5}$$

In equation 5, we wrote $\lambda'(B)$, $S'(B)$ and $\lambda''(B)$, $S''(B)$ to recall that the dividing line between S' and S'' depends on the observable B measured (or thought to be measured) on the set T of β-particles. The choice of the observable B is of course arbitrary. If a different observable, B', were chosen, then a different splitting of S should be considered. In addition, because it is well known both theoretically and experimentally that the new probabilities for the subensembles, $S'(B')$ and $S'''(B')$, are different from those deduced for the old subensembles, then on the basis of the GRC and of the GSP, one could conclude that the physical properties for the new ensembles should also be different (different effects require different causes). Therefore, one can write:

$$\lambda'(B') \rightarrow S'(B'); \lambda''(B') \rightarrow S''(B'). \tag{6}$$

There is, of course, no problem if the observables, B and B', are incompatible. We can assign the attributions in equations 5 and 6 simultaneously because, as mentioned before, we also consider the relevant sets as existing (but unknown) when B and B' have not been measured.

In order to understand what happens to the probabilities if a different splitting is considered, one must realize that the p_1 and p_2 introduced above for the set S' of α-particles actually depend also on the observable measured on the β-particles. In fact, they depend on $\lambda'(B)$ (see equation 3), which becomes $\lambda'(B')$ (in general, different from λ') when B becomes B'. This dependence does not imply some form of nonlocality or a contradiction with the GSP because it can more simply be attributed to the exclusion of some α-systems and to the inclusion of some other α-systems when the set $S'(B)$ is transformed in $S'(B')$. As one can see from FIGURE 1, when $S'(B) \rightarrow S'(B')$, the subset S_1 is excluded from S', while S_3 becomes now part of S'.

Under the generally valid hypothesis that $\lambda'(B') \neq \lambda'(B)$, we can now rule out that the subensembles in equations 5 and 6 be homogeneous. In fact, if they were, we should attribute the same physical property to every subset of each of them. In particular, referring to FIGURE 1 and noticing that S_2 is just the intersection of $S'(B)$ and of $S'(B')$, one could conclude that S_2, as a subset of $S'(B)$, should have the physical property, $\lambda'(B)$, while as a subset of $S'(B')$, it should have the different physical property, $\lambda'(B')$. However, this is impossible because these two physical properties lead to different probabilities for the same event.

We have thus proved that the considered ensembles cannot be homogeneous. This lack of homogeneity means, for instance, that a subset of $S'(B)$ has physical properties (and therefore gives rise to probabilities) different from those of the whole of $S'(B)$. However, subsets are also the individual systems. We can thus conclude that the physical properties required by the GRC for ensembles such as $S'(B)$ must arise from physical averages of individual physical properties that are, in general, different for different objects composing the ensemble. For every particle, α_i, we can therefore repeat the following:

The particle, α_i, possesses the physical property, λ_i, which gives rise to the probabilities, $p_{1i} = p_1(A; \lambda_i)$ and $p_{2i} = p_2(A; \lambda_i)$, for the two results, $A = A_1$ and $A = A_2$, respectively, if and when the observable A is measured on this particle ($i = 1, 2, \ldots, N$).

The above conclusion has been stated for all indices from $i = 1$ to $i = N$ (that is, for all particles, α, of the set S). This, of course, is possible because similar conclusions of the lack of homogeneity hold for S' and S'' and because the union of these two ensembles gives S.

The above particles can be generalized to two important cases. Firstly, to the β-particles because the previous reasoning can be repeated with the roles of the α- and β-particles interchanged. Following a long-lasting tradition, we will also call λ_i the new physical property of β_i. By this, it is of course not implied that the physical properties of α_i and β_i are really equal, but that the set of all the new properties of α_i and of β_i is described with a unique symbol for simplicity. Then, for the second case, it can be generalized to an arbitrary number of observables, $A, A', \ldots$, of the α-particles and $B, B', \ldots$, of the β-particles. The individual probabilities for the β-particles will be:

$$\begin{cases} q_{1i} = q_1(B; \lambda_i), & \text{for the result, } B = B_1, \\ q_{2i} = q_2(B; \lambda_i), & \text{for the result, } B = B_2. \end{cases}$$

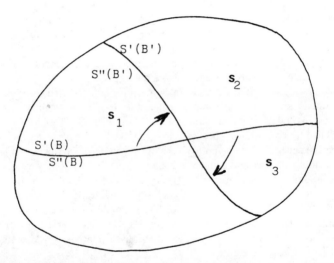

FIGURE 1. Two different splittings of the set S of the α-particles due to measurements of two different observables (B and B') on the set T of the β-particles.

The individual physical property, λ_i, will be assumed to be independent of the observable to be measured in the future on the particle to which it belongs and independent of the observable already measured on the separated other particle of the same pair. This is a new form of separability for the individual particles of our ensembles. As a consequence, the probabilities, $p_1(A; \lambda_i)$, $p_2(A; \lambda_i)$, $q_1(B; \lambda_i)$, and $q_2(B; \lambda_i)$, are also all local.

PROBABILITIES AND INEQUALITIES

By means of the individual probabilities, it is now possible to express all the interesting ensemble probabilities. Capital letters will be used for the probabilities relevant to the full ensembles, S and T. Thus, $P_1(A)$ and $P_2(A)$ will be the probabilities to measure A on (all) the α-particles composing S and to find the results, $A = A_1$ and $A = A_2$, respectively. The probabilities, $Q_1(B)$ and $Q_2(B)$, are similarly defined for the β-particles. One can write:

$$P_1(A) = \langle p_1(A; \lambda_i) \rangle_S; \quad P_2(A) = \langle p_2(A; \lambda_i) \rangle_S,$$

$$Q_1(B) = \langle q_1(B; \lambda_i) \rangle_T; \quad Q_2(B) = \langle q_2(B; \lambda_i) \rangle_T, \tag{7}$$

where the symbols, $\langle \ldots \rangle$, denote, as usual, the average.

The (conditional) probability for finding $A = A_m$ ($m = 1, 2$) on the α-particles if $B = B_n$ on the β-particles have previously been found ($n = 1, 2$) is given by

$$\begin{cases} p(A_m | B_1) = \langle p_m(A; \lambda_i) \rangle_{S'(B)} \\ p(A_m | B_2) = \langle p_m(A; \lambda_i) \rangle_{S''(B)}. \end{cases} \tag{8}$$

Similarly,

$$\begin{cases} q(B_n | A_1) = \langle q_n(B; \lambda_i) \rangle_{T'(A)} \\ q(B_n | A_2) = \langle q_n(B; \lambda_i) \rangle_{T''(A)} \end{cases} \tag{9}$$

with obvious meaning of the new symbols.

According to the general rules of the probability calculus, the joint probability of finding $A = A_m$ ($m = 1, 2$) on the α-particles and $B = B_n$ ($n = 1, 2$) on the correlated β-particles is given by

$$\omega(A_m, B_n) = p(A_m | B_n) Q_n(B) = q(B_n | A_m) P_m(A). \tag{10}$$

With the help of the joint probabilities, it is possible to calculate the correlation function, $P(A, B)$, which in the simpler case of $A_1 = B_1 = +1$ and $A_2 = B_2 = -1$ is given by

$$P(A, B) = \omega(A_1, B_1) - \omega(A_1, B_2) - \omega(A_2, B_1) + \omega(A_2, B_2). \tag{11}$$

By using equations 7 and 8, it is a simple matter to show that

$$P(A, B) = Q_1(B) \langle \Delta_i \rangle_{S'(B)} - Q_2(B) \langle \Delta_i \rangle_{S''(B)}, \tag{12}$$

where

$$\Delta_i = p_1(A, \lambda_i) - p_2(A, \lambda_i) \tag{13}$$

is the difference of two probabilities so that $|\Delta_i| \leq 1$.

Considering a new observable, A', of the α-particles and the old B for the β-particles, all the previous considerations can be repeated, and from equation 12 and an analogous formula for $P(A', B)$, one can easily deduce

$$|P(A, B) - P(A', B)| \leq Q_1(B) \langle |\Delta_i - \Delta_i'| \rangle_{S'(B)} + Q_2(B) \langle |\Delta_i - \Delta_i'| \rangle_{S''(B)}. \tag{14}$$

However, the right-hand side of equation 14 is just the average of $|\Delta_i - \Delta_i'|$ over the whole ensemble, $S = S'(B) \cup S''(B)$; in fact, $Q_1(B) [Q_2(B)]$ is the a priori probability of the set, $S'(B) [S''(B)]$, and, of course, $Q_1(B) + Q_2(B) = 1$. Therefore,

$$|P(A, B) - P(A', B)| \leq \langle |\Delta_i - \Delta_i'| \rangle_S. \tag{15}$$

A strictly analogous reasoning leads to

$$|P(A, B') + P(A', B')| \leq \langle |\Delta_i + \Delta_i'| \rangle_S. \tag{16}$$

By noticing that $|\Delta_i| \leq 1$ and $|\Delta_i'| \leq 1$, one can easily show that

$$|\Delta_i - \Delta_i'| + |\Delta_i + \Delta_i'| \leq 2. \tag{17}$$

By summing up the two inequalities in equations 15 and 16, and by using equation 17, one gets

$$|P(A, B) - P(A', B)| + |P(A, B') + P(A', B')| \leq 2, \tag{18}$$

which is Bell's inequality.

It will be shown elsewhere that the present approach allows one to obtain not only the inequality in equation 18, but also all the inequalities satisfied by the arbitrary linear combinations of correlation functions that can be deduced from Einstein locality.[14]

THE CASE OF LOW EFFICIENCY DETECTORS

In the preceding sections, it has implicitly been assumed that the instruments are perfect in the sense that they cannot fail to give one of the two possible values of the measured dichotomic observable. This is evident, for instance, from the assumption of $S = S'(B) \cup S''(B)$.

In a real experiment, things can often be rather different from the ideal case. In the performed experiments on the EPR problem with pairs of atomic photons, for instance, one has to consider the reduced efficiency of the counters, which typically have a probability of 10–20% of detecting an incoming photon. In an experiment of this type, one has analyzers placed on the trajectory of either one of the two correlated photons. The axes of the analyzers form angles a and b with respect to an arbitrarily chosen direction. In doing so, the dichotomic observables become dependent on these angular parameters, and they can be written: $A = A(a)$; $B = B(b)$. Now, the quantum mechanical predictions for an experiment of this type, for instance, in the case of the 0–1–0 cascade of calcium,[15] give the correlation function,

$$P_{qm}[A(a), B(b)] = \epsilon_-^{\alpha}\epsilon_-^{\beta}F\eta_{\alpha}\eta_{\beta} \cos 2(a - b), \tag{19}$$

where ϵ_-^{α} and ϵ_-^{β} are typical parameters of the analyzers that are often rather close to one, F is a geometrical factor very close to one, and η_{α} and η_{β} are the quantum efficiencies of the photomultipliers that are of the order of ten percent. The factor multiplying the cosine in equation 19 is around 0.01, which is so small that the linear combination of the correlation functions appearing in the left-hand side of Bell's inequality is always well below the value of 2. Therefore, Bell's inequality is not violated by quantum theory if no additional assumptions are made.

In the remaining part of this section, however, we will forget about quantum theory and prove that our probabilistic scheme can easily be adapted to the case of imperfect detectors. We will also show that Bell's inequality still follows.

The first measurement, performed by O_β on the β-particles, can produce three outcomes: the result, $B = B_1$, with probability $q_1(B, \lambda_i)$; the result, $B = B_2$, with probability $q_2(B, \lambda_i)$; no detection, with probability $q_0(B, \lambda_i)$. One, though, must have

$$q_0(B, \lambda_i) + q_1(B, \lambda_i) + q_2(B, \lambda_i) = 1. \tag{20}$$

Similar probabilities can be introduced for the second measurement. With an obvious generalization of the notation used in the previous sections, one has

$$p_0(A, \lambda_i) + p_1(A, \lambda_i) + p_2(A, \lambda_i) = 1. \tag{21}$$

These individual probabilities can be used, as before, to write simple expressions for the ensemble probabilities. One has, for instance,

$$\begin{cases} Q_0(B) = \langle q_0(B, \lambda_i) \rangle_T \\ Q_1(B) = \langle q_1(B, \lambda_i) \rangle_T \\ Q_2(B) = \langle q_2(B, \lambda_i) \rangle_T, \end{cases} \tag{22}$$

where $Q_0(B)$ is the ensemble probability of no detection, while Q_1 and Q_2 have the same meaning as before. In the case of the EPR experiments performed with pairs of atomic photons, it is both an empirical fact and a quantum-theoretical prediction that $Q_0(B)$ does not depend on B. This does not mean, however, that $q_0(B, \lambda_i)$ is necessarily constant. Already at this level, we see that our theoretical scheme contains variable detection probabilities. This new notion can be used for an elegant solution of the EPR paradox, as it will be seen later.

The considerations of the previous sections can be repeated with minor variations as well. One must keep in mind that the set S of the α-particles is now split into three sets by the measurement on the β-particles. The sets, $S'(B)$ and $S''(B)$, have the same meaning as before. The new set is $S^0(B)$, which contains the α-particles individually correlated with those β-particles that have escaped detection. Thus, one has $S = S^0(B) \cup S'(B) \cup S''(B)$. Consequently, it must be

$$Q_0(B) + Q_1(B) + Q_2(B) = 1, \tag{23}$$

which can easily be seen to follow from equations 20 and 22. All the considerations developed in the previous section from equation 7 to equation 14 can be repeated in the present case without any difficulty. A problem arises, though, when one tries to pass from equation 14 to equation 15 because it is not true anymore that the union of $S'(B)$ and $S''(B)$ gives S. The proof of equation 15 must now pass through the addition of the nonnegative quantity,

$$Q_0(B) \langle |\Delta_i - \Delta'_i| \rangle_{S^0(B)},$$

to the right-hand side of equation 14. By so doing, one obtains the inequality,

$$\begin{aligned} |P(A, B) - P(A', B)| \leq\ & Q_0(B) \langle |\Delta_i - \Delta'_i| \rangle_{S^0(B)} \\ & + Q_1(B) \langle |\Delta_i - \Delta'_i| \rangle_{S'(B)} \\ & + Q_2(B) \langle |\Delta_i - \Delta'_i| \rangle_{S''(B)}. \end{aligned} \tag{24}$$

However, the right-hand side of equation 24 can now be recognized to be the average of $|\Delta_i - \Delta'_i|$ over the whole ensemble S. Therefore, we have proved equation 15. In a similar way, equation 16 can also be shown to hold. The consequence is again Bell's inequality (equation 18).

ROLE OF THE ADDITIONAL ASSUMPTIONS

In 1969, Clauser, Horne, Shimony, and Holt (CHSH)[16] assumed that:

If a pair of photons emerges from two polarizers, the probability of their joint detection is independent of the orientation of the polarizers' axes.

From this assumption coupled to a certain factorable structure of probabilities, they were able to show that the following inequality must hold:

$$|P(A, B) - P(A', B)| + |P(A', B') + P(A', B')| \leq 2\eta_\alpha\eta_\beta. \tag{25}$$

The great interest of this inequality was in the fact that it could be violated by the quantum mechanical formula (equation 19), which leads to the left-hand side of equation 25 being as large as $2\sqrt{2}\ \epsilon_-{}^\alpha\epsilon_-{}^\beta\ F\eta_\alpha\eta_\beta$ for a suitable choice of the angles. The above value is in many concrete instances larger than the right-hand side of equation 25.

The same result was obtained by Clauser and Horne (CH) in 1974[10] from a systematic use of factorable probabilities and from the following additional assumption:

For every atomic emission, the probability of a count with a polarizer in place is not larger than the probability with the polarizer removed.

Thanks to these additional assumptions, several experiments were performed,[17] and we must now say that the CHSH and CH assumptions had a positive historical role. Believing in their validity is quite another matter, as will next be shown. These additional assumptions (A.A.) are more than natural within the usual quantum mechanical way of thinking: they are true. If they were at least natural within alternative schemes, such as the probabilistic Einstein locality proposed in this paper, it would perhaps be reasonable to accept them. However, if instead they cut away essential degrees of freedom and arbitrarily limit the possible developments of the causal way of thinking (as it turns out to be the case), they must necessarily be overcome. If one considers the measurement process as a two-step process, as it was in the performed experiments, one must remember that each photon crosses an analyzer before its detection in a photomultiplier. If the analyzer is a two-way prism from which a transmitted and a reflected beam emerge with photons in two orthogonal states of linear polarization, then it is natural to assume that the result, $A = A_1\ [A = A_2]$, refers to the transmitted [reflected] beam. The previously introduced probabilities, $p_{1,2}$ and $q_{1,2}$, should now be written as transmission/reflection probability (T/R) multiplied by a detection probability (D). Assuming for simplicity that the two photomultipliers give rise to the same detection probability, one can write

$$\begin{cases} p_1(A, \lambda_i) = T_\alpha(A, \lambda_i)\,D_\alpha(A, \lambda_i) \\ p_2(A, \lambda_i) = R_\alpha(A, \lambda_i)\,D_\alpha(A, \lambda_i) \end{cases} \tag{26}$$

for photon α_i, and

$$\begin{cases} q_1(B, \lambda i) = T_\beta(B, \lambda_i)\,D_\beta(B, \lambda_i) \\ q_2(B, \lambda i) = R_\beta(B, \lambda_i)\,D_\beta(B, \lambda_i) \end{cases} \tag{27}$$

for photon β_i. The A.A.'s can now be written as:

CHSH: The product, $D_\alpha(A, \lambda_i)\,D_\beta(B, \lambda_i)$, is independent of A and B;
CH: $D_\alpha(A, \lambda_i) \leq D_\alpha(\infty, \lambda_i)$ and $D_\beta(B, \lambda_i) \leq D_\beta(\infty, \lambda_i)$, where the symbol, ∞, indicates that the prism has been removed.

Obviously, the CHSH assumption is equivalent to the statement that $D_\alpha(A, \lambda_i)$ is independent of A and that $D_\beta(B, \lambda_i)$ is independent of B. Once this is taken for granted, no model based on Einstein locality can agree with quantum theory because it must satisfy equation 25. If experiments had agreed with equation 25, but not with quantum theory, the problem could have found a solution. However, the well-known fact is that experiments agree with quantum theory, and the only inference that one can draw from this is either that Einstein locality does not hold in nature, or that the A.A.'s are false. Because these do not have any empirical support, but are just arbitrary, ad hoc assumptions, the choice is easy, at least for the present writer.

PROOF OF FACTORABILITY

In the present section, it will be shown that the joint probabilities introduced before must be factorable if the GRC and the GSP are taken for granted.

If $N'(B)$ is the population of $S'(B)$, one sees from equation 8 that

$$p(A_1|B_1) = \langle p_1(A, \lambda_i)\rangle_{S'(B)} = \frac{1}{N'(B)} \cdot \sum_{i \in S'(B)} p_1(A, \lambda_i). \tag{28}$$

The a priori probability that the set $S'(B)$ be obtained must coincide with the frequency with which elements of the same set are concretely present in S. Therefore,

$$Q_1(B) = N'(B)/N. \tag{29}$$

By using equation 10, one obtains for the joint probability,

$$\omega(A_1, B_1) = \frac{1}{N} \cdot \sum_{i \in S'(B)} p_1(A, \lambda_i). \tag{30}$$

Suppose, for concreteness, that there is only a finite number of values of the new physical property, λ_i. Let these be

$$\mu_1, \mu_2, \ldots, \mu_\ell, \tag{31}$$

which are produced in the source with respective frequencies,

$$\rho_1, \rho_2, \ldots, \rho_\ell. \tag{32}$$

Suppose furthermore that $N'(B)$ is so much larger than ℓ that even the least probable of the values, μ_κ, will be found a very large number of times in S. Now, the value μ_κ will be present in $S'(B)$ every time that the value, $B = B_1$, is found by the second observer; that is, with a frequency, $q_1(B, \mu_\kappa)$, times the frequency with which μ_κ is produced by the source. Therefore, equation 30 can now be written as

$$\omega(A_1, B_1) = \sum_{\kappa=1}^{\ell} \rho_\kappa \, q_1(B, \mu_\kappa) \, p_1(A, \mu_\kappa). \qquad (33)$$

This is the factorability formula for $\omega(A_1, B_1)$. It can easily be extended to all $\omega(A_m, B_n)$ with $m = 1, 2$ and $n = 1, 2$. Also, the extension to continuous values of the physical property, μ, does not present essential difficulties and thus leads to

$$\omega(A_1, B_1) = \int d\mu \, \rho(\mu) \, p_1(A, \mu) \, q_1(B, \mu). \qquad (34)$$

We, therefore, see that our axiomatic approach gives a very solid foundation to the factorability of probabilities (and of correlation functions) for EPR pairs. If the general ideas of reality and of separability proposed at the beginning of this paper are assumed, then individual probabilities must be introduced and the "factorability formula" must hold. To this, one can add the possibility to explain rationally the experiments performed on the EPR paradox. The overall scheme thus seems fruitful enough.

EFFECTS OF VARIABLE PHOTON DETECTION

Already a considerably large literature exists in which variable detection probability models are studied.[18] It is not the purpose of this section to give a review of these proposals, but only to give an idea of how they work by presenting a very simple model. First of all, we will limit the discussion to experiments in which only one channel is studied for each photon: the formalism of the preceding sections can still be used if it is assumed that the reflection channels correspond to an absorption so that $R_\alpha = R_\beta = 0$. Consequently, one must have $p_2(A, \lambda_i) = q_2(B, \lambda_i) = 0$ for all photons. Every photon is assumed to have two physical attributes—a polarization vector, $\hat{\ell}$, and a detection vector, $\hat{\delta}$: this corresponds to a splitting of the general symbol, λ, used before, into two variables. The probability of the α-photon crossing a polarizer with axis a is assumed δ-independent and is given by

$$T_\alpha[A(a), \ell] = \cos^2 (\ell - a), \qquad (35)$$

where $\ell - a$ is the angle formed by $\hat{\ell}$ and $\hat{a}$ (Malus law). The polarization, $\hat{\ell}$, is naturally assumed to become $\hat{a}$ after crossing the polarizer.

The probability of photon detection by a photomultiplier with quantum efficiency, η_α, is assumed dependent both on $\hat{\delta}$ and on the photon polarization, and is assumed to be given by

$$D_\alpha(\delta - a) = {}^8\!/\!_3 \cos^4 (\delta - a) \, \eta_\alpha \qquad (36)$$

for a photon that arrives in the photomultiplier with linear polarization, $\hat{a}$. Equation 36 can be readily written as

$$D_\alpha(\delta - a) = [1 + {}^4\!/\!_3 \cos 2(\delta - a) + {}^1\!/\!_3 \cos 4(\delta - a)] \, \eta_\alpha. \qquad (37)$$

Assuming that a statistical ensemble of photons (polarized or not) has δ distributed uniformly from 0 to π, it can be seen immediately that the δ-averaged value of D_α is just η_α, which is the quantum efficiency. Therefore, for single photons, D_α can always be substituted by η_α; the whole single-photon physics is therefore reproduced by this model.

In the 0–1–0 cascade of calcium, pairs of photons emitted by the same atom travel in opposite directions, impinge over polarizers with axes, $\hat{a}$ and $\hat{b}$, and eventually enter the photomultipliers with quantum efficiencies, η_α and η_β. For such pairs considered within the present variable detection probability model, we assume the polarization vectors, $\hat{\ell}$ and $\hat{\ell}'$, to rotate in opposite directions around the common propagation axis and to be uncorrelated so that the two expressions of the type in equation 35 for T_α and T_β should be averaged independently over $\hat{\ell}$ and $\hat{\ell}'$. Furthermore, we assume that:

(i) the vector, $\hat{\delta}$, is the same for the two photons of a given pair;
(ii) it is distributed uniformly from 0 to π over the statistical ensemble;
(iii) it is left unchanged by the photon crossing of a polarizer.

The probability of a double count is thus given by

$$\omega(a - b) = \langle \cos^2 (\ell - a) \rangle \langle \cos^2 (\ell' - b) \rangle \frac{1}{\pi} \int_0^\pi d\delta$$

$$\cdot \frac{8}{3} \cos^4 (\delta - a)\eta_\alpha \frac{8}{3} \cos^4 (\delta - b)\eta_\beta. \quad (38)$$

By using equation 37, one can easily obtain

$$\omega(a - b) = \tfrac{1}{4} [1 + \tfrac{8}{9} \cos 2(a - b) + \tfrac{1}{18} \cos 4(a - b)] \, \eta_\alpha \eta_\beta. \quad (39)$$

This result agrees well with the result of the first Orsay experiment,[17] namely,

$$\omega(a - b) = [0.249 + 0.218 \cos 2(a - b)]\eta_\alpha \eta_\beta. \quad (40)$$

The presence of a small extra term proportional to $\cos 4(a - b)$ is a necessary consequence of the present model and of other models of the same type, and this could lead to experimental controls of these proposals. Of course, the present model is only one of the many models with variable detection probability leading to violations of the inequality in equation 25 because of the correlations of the δ-enhanced photon detection processes that can be conceived.

These models open a new door for the investigation of the EPR paradox. Bell's theorem maintains all its great validity, but is limited, in practice, in the case of photons, because of the fact that high efficiency detectors do not exist. For low efficiencies, no theorem as general as that of Bell has yet been found. Nevertheless, several exciting new ideas are emerging and the feeling of this writer is that we are getting closer to a really deeper understanding of the behavior of atomic systems.

REFERENCES

1. VON NEUMANN, J. 1955. The Mathematical Foundations of Quantum Mechanics. Princeton Univ. Press. Princeton, New Jersey.

2. BELINFANTE, F. J. 1973. A Survey of Hidden-Variables Theories. Pergamon. Oxford.
3. BOHM, D. 1952. Phys. Rev. **85:** 166, 180.
4. BELL, J. S. 1966. Rev. Mod. Phys. **38:** 447.
5. SELLERI, F. 1985. Bohr's complementarity in the light of modern researches in the foundations of quantum theory. Invited paper at the International Symposium on Niels Bohr, University of Roma, Nov. 25–27, 1985. In press.
6. DEWDNEY, C. 1985. Invited paper at the International Conference on "Microphysical Reality and Quantum Formalism", Urbino, Sept. 25–Oct. 3, 1985. In press.
7. EINSTEIN, A., B. PODOLSKY & N. ROSEN. 1935. Phys. Rev. **47:** 777.
8. WIGNER, E. P. 1952. Z. Phys. **133:** 101; ARAKI, H. & M. M. YANASE. 1961. Phys. Rev. **120:** 622.
9. BELL, J. S. 1965. Physics **1:** 195.
10. CLAUSER, J. F. & M. A. HORNE. 1974. Phys. Rev. **D10:** 526.
11. SELLERI, F. 1985. Paper presented at the International Conference on "Microphysical Reality and Quantum Formalism", Urbino, Sept. 25–Oct. 3, 1985. In press.
12. STAPP, H. P. 1982. Found. Phys. **12:** 363.
13. COSTA DE BEAUREGARD, O. 1979. Nuovo Cimento **B51:** 267; RIETDIJK, C. W. 1978. Found. Phys. **8:** 815; STAPP, H. P. 1979. Found. Phys. **9:** 1; WHEELER, J. A. 1980. Delayed-choice experiments and the Bohr-Einstein dialog. Paper presented at the Joint Meeting of the American Philosophical Society and the Royal Society, London, June 5, 1980.
14. GARUCCIO, A. & F. SELLERI. 1980. Found. Phys. **10:** 209.
15. PIPKIN, F. M. 1978. Prog. Atom. Mol. Phys. **14:** 281; CLAUSER, J. F. & A. SHIMONY. 1978. Rep. Prog. Phys. **41:** 1881; TAROZZI, G. & F. SELLERI. 1981. Riv. Nuovo Cimento **4:** 1.
16. CLAUSER, J. F., M. A. HORNE, A. SHIMONY & R. A. HOLT. 1969. Phys. Rev. Lett. **23:** 880.
17. FREEDMAN, S. J. & J. F. CLAUSER. 1972. Phys. Rev. Lett. **28:** 938; HOLT, R. A. & F. M. PIPKIN. 1974. Harvard University preprint; FRY, E. S. & R. C. THOMPSON. 1976. Phys. Rev. Lett. **37:** 465; ASPECT, A., P. GRANGIER & G. ROGER. 1981. Phys. Rev. Lett. **47:** 460; ASPECT, A., P. GRANGIER & G. ROGER. 1982. Phys. Rev. Lett. **49:** 91; ASPECT, A., J. DALIBARD & G. ROGER. 1982. Phys. Rev. Lett. **49:** 1804; PERRIE, W., A. J. DUNCAN, H. J. BEYER & H. KLEINPOPPEN. 1985. Phys. Rev. Lett. **54:** 1790.
18. MARSHALL, T. W., E. SANTOS & F. SELLERI. 1983. Phys. Lett. **98A:** 5; GARUCCIO, A. & F. SELLERI. 1984. Phys. Lett. **103A:** 99; MARSHALL, T. W. & E. SANTOS. 1985. Phys. Lett. **107A:** 164; SELLERI, F. 1985. Phys. Lett. **108A:** 197; FERRERO, M. & E. SANTOS. 1985. Phys. Lett. **108A:** 373; HOME, D. & T. W. MARSHALL. 1986. Phys. Lett. In press; FERRERO, M. & E. SANTOS. 1986. Phys. Lett. In press.

The Locality Problem in Stochastic Mechanics

EDWARD NELSON

Department of Mathematics
Princeton University
Princeton, New Jersey 08544

CORRELATED SPIN EXPERIMENTS AND
CLASSICAL LOCAL FIELD THEORIES

Stochastic mechanics is a theory of quantum phenomena described in terms of classical random processes. An immediate objection is that such a theory is impossible due to Bell's inequalities[1,2] and their violation in experiment.[3] Let us begin by confronting this problem.

Consider a random field, ϕ. For each test function, f, on space-time, M, $\phi(f)$ is a random variable depending linearly on f. This is a classical, not a quantum, field: the $\phi(f)$ for all f have joint probability distributions. More generally, consider a family of random fields, ϕ_j, where j denotes an external current that can be coupled to the system; we think of j as being subject to the experimenter's control. Can a family of random fields describe nature (in particular, correlated spin experiments) correctly? The usual response to this is no, not without violating locality.

The word, "locality," has too many meanings to be used unambiguously without a modifier. Let us distinguish between two notions. We say that the family, ϕ_j, of random fields is *actively local* if whenever two currents, j and k, agree except on a region A in M, the fields, ϕ_j and ϕ_k, agree except on the future cone of A. This means that the experimenter operating in A cannot send a signal to a spacelike separated region; this requirement is a consequence of special relativity and causality, and there is not the slightest experimental evidence to raise doubts about its validity. We say that the family, ϕ_j, is *passively local* if for all bounded spacelike separated regions, A and B, of M, there is a region, X, disjoint from their future cones such that (given a knowledge of ϕ_j on X) the fields, ϕ_j on A and ϕ_j on B, are conditionally independent. The reason suggested for imposing this requirement is that we can choose X to include the intersection of the past cones of A and B. The knowledge of the field on X might not be sufficient to predict its behavior on A, but if it decides to behave in a certain random way on A, how can B know anything about this other than from its memory of their common past? In Bell's phrase,[2] supplementary information from B could "reasonably be expected to be redundant."

Bell has shown[2] that a family of random fields that is both actively and passively local cannot give the same predictions as quantum theory for correlated spin experiments. One version[4] of this result is the following:

Theorem: Let ϕ_j be a family of random fields that is both actively and passively local. Let j_μ and k_ν, for $\mu, \nu = 1, 2, 3$, be currents localized respectively in the spacelike separated bounded regions, A and B, of M, and let $Pr_{\mu\nu}$ denote the probability measure for the field with current $j_\mu + k_\nu$. Then, there do not exist random variables, α_μ and β_ν, that are functions of the field in A and B, respectively, each equal to ± 1, such that

(1) $Pr_{\mu\mu}\{\alpha_\mu\beta_\mu = -1\} = 1$,
(2) $Pr_{\mu\nu}\{\alpha_\mu\beta_\nu = -1\} < \frac{1}{2}, \mu \neq \nu$.

The context of this theorem is a correlated spin experiment. Two photons of total spin 0 are emitted and travel to A and B. The experimenter chooses one of three coplanar equally spaced directions to measure the polarization at A (the choice corresponds to applying the current j_μ and the outcome to α_μ) and similarly at B. Then, quantum theory predicts that (1) and (2) hold (in fact, with $Pr_{\mu\nu}\{\alpha_\mu\beta_\nu = -1\} = \frac{1}{4}$ for $\mu \neq \nu$), and this prediction is confirmed by the experiments of Aspect et al.[3]

The proof of the theorem is easy. Let X be as in the definition of passive locality and let $Pr_{\mu\nu}\{\ldots | X\}$ denote the conditional probability given a knowledge of the field on X. Suppose that active locality, passive locality, and equation 1 hold. Then,

$$Pr_{\mu\nu}\{\alpha_\mu = 1 \ \& \ \beta_\nu = -1 | X\} = Pr_{\mu\nu}\{\alpha_\mu = 1 | X\} \, Pr_{\mu\nu}\{\beta_\nu = -1 | X\}$$

by passive locality. Because A and X are disjoint from the future cone of B,

$$Pr_{\mu\nu}\{\alpha_\mu = 1 | X\} = Pr_{\mu\mu}\{\alpha_\mu = 1 | X\}$$

by active locality, and similarly,

$$Pr_{\mu\nu}\{\beta_\nu = -1 | X\} = Pr_{\nu\nu}\{\beta_\nu = -1 | X\}.$$

However, by (1), this is equal to $Pr_{\nu\nu}\{\alpha_\nu = 1 | X\}$. Abbreviating this by p_ν, we find

$$Pr_{\mu\nu}\{\alpha_\mu = 1 \ \& \ \beta_\nu = -1 | X\} = p_\mu p_\nu,$$

and similarly,

$$Pr_{\mu\nu}\{\alpha_\mu = -1 \ \& \ \beta_\nu = 1 | X\} = (1 - p_\mu)(1 - p_\nu).$$

Therefore,

$$Pr_{\mu\nu}\{\alpha_\mu\beta_\nu = -1 | X\} = p_\mu p_\nu + (1 - p_\mu)(1 - p_\nu).$$

Taking the average over $\mu \neq \nu$, we have

$$\frac{1}{6}\sum_{\mu \neq \nu} Pr_{\mu\nu}\{\alpha_\mu\beta_\nu = -1 | X\} = \frac{1}{6}\sum_{\mu \neq \nu} [p_\mu p_\nu + (1 - p_\mu)(1 - p_\nu)] \geq \frac{1}{2}$$

because the minimum occurs at $p_1 = p_2 = p_3 = \frac{1}{2}$. Thus, we have the same inequality for the unconditional probabilities:

$$\frac{1}{6}\sum_{\mu \neq \nu} Pr_{\mu\nu}\{\alpha_\mu\beta_\nu = -1\} \geq \frac{1}{2},$$

but this contradicts (2).

The conclusion is that a family of random fields with both active and passive locality cannot describe nature correctly. This is usually interpreted as meaning that although one cannot signal from B to A, the choice of direction at B somehow influences the outcome at A. I will argue against this interpretation.

One way to construct a family of random fields is the following: Take a classical relativistic field equation, $\Box \phi = G$, where G is a function of ϕ, its first derivatives, and the current j. Suppose that it admits a unique smooth global solution for any smooth choice of initial data, and that the choice of j in a region, A, affects the solution only in the future cone of A. By putting any probability distribution on the initial data in the remote past, we obtain a family of random fields. Let us call the result of this construction a *smooth* family of random fields. It is actively local by assumption, and because we can choose X to contain the remote past, it is trivially passively local since a knowledge of the field on X tells us everything about its behavior on both A and B. Therefore, a smooth family of random fields cannot describe nature correctly. This construction expresses the traditional notion of randomness as due to ignorance of the initial conditions.

Here is a second way to construct a family of random fields. Again, start with a classical relativistic field equation, $\Box \phi = G$, but one for which existence and uniqueness of a smooth global solution to the initial value problem fails. Impose a space cutoff, L, and a momentum cutoff, K; that is, let G_{LK} be the truncated (at K) Fourier series of G in a spatial box of side L. Then, $\Box \phi = G$ is equivalent to a system of ordinary differential equations that will exhibit chaotic behavior as L and K increase. Impose a probability distribution on the initial data in the remote past and choose a limiting probability measure as $L, K \to \infty$. Let us call the result of this construction a *chaotic* family of random fields. In this construction, randomness is inherent in the temporal development of the system. The understanding of randomness as being of dynamical origin is distinct both from the understanding of randomness as an expression of ignorance of the initial conditions and from the instrumentalism to which quantum theory so easily lends itself.

There is no reason at all to expect a chaotic family of random fields to be passively local. For each L and K, the cutoff family will be passively local (because the solution of a system of ordinary differential equations is determined by the initial conditions), yet it may well happen that information relevant to what happens in A is stored in B in a stable way (which persists in the limit $L, K \to \infty$), but that the corresponding information in X (utterly precise knowledge of the initial conditions for the cutoff system) disappears in the limit.

Similar phenomena are well known to occur in the theory of random fields. This is not some mathematical pathology, but just what one would expect from the physics of a correlated spin experiment. No matter what care the experimenter exercises to reproduce the same initial conditions in X, the outcome at A is random. However, if conservation of angular momentum is to hold exactly during the chaotic evolution of the system, then we must expect a failure of passive locality: the supplementary information from B may reasonably be expected to be relevant. In this picture, there is no transmission of any influence from B to A.

The imposition of the requirement of passive locality is a remnant of deterministic modes of thought. One feels that if the field can develop in several different ways, then something should tell it which way to develop, and this something should be localized somewhere. However, this is not a necessary requirement on the dynamics of a chaotically evolving local relativistic field. Perhaps the results of correlated spin experiments are ultimately no more, and no less, mysterious than is the random growth of snowflakes with global hexagonal symmetry.

Thus, there is no reason to expect Bell's inequalities to hold for a chaotic family of random fields; not for the cutoff family because it is not actively local, and not for the limiting family because it may fail to be passively local. There is, therefore, no known impediment to the description of nature by means of classical local relativistic fields in which randomness is of dynamical origin.

STOCHASTIC MECHANICS

The starting point of stochastic mechanics is a classical Lagrangian, L; in its simplest form,

$$L = \frac{1}{2}m_{ij} v^i v^j - V.$$

The tensor, m^{ij}, has the right form to be the diffusion tensor for a classical Markov process with continuous trajectories, except that dimensional considerations require the insertion of a factor with the dimensions of action; in this way, Planck's constant enters phenomenologically. The Markov property is kinematically time-symmetric: the past and the future are conditionally independent given the present. In addition, so is the conservative dynamics of stochastic mechanics: the expected action,

$$\left\langle \int_{t_1}^{t_2} \left[\frac{1}{2} m_{ij} \xi^i \xi^j - V(\xi) \right] dt \right\rangle,$$

is required to be stationary. Due to the nondifferentiability of the trajectory, ξ, this expression is singular, but after an infinite constant (which is independent of the particular trajectory) is subtracted, it becomes well defined. The result is that a Markov process is critical for the classical action if and only if $\psi = \sqrt{\rho} e^{iS}$ satisfies the Schrödinger equation, where ρ is the probability density of the process and S is the stochastic analogue of Hamilton's principal function. For a detailed account of stochastic mechanics, including spin, statistics, interference, bound states, and scattering, see reference 5, the references contained therein, and the recent articles of Carlen.[6-8]

Because the probability density, ρ, of stochastic mechanics is always equal to $|\psi|^2$, the predictions of stochastic mechanics agree with those of quantum mechanics. Nevertheless,[4] the theory fails to satisfy the nonrelativistic analogue of active locality, and it gives ambiguous predictions about experiments in which two observations that should be noninterfering are made at distinct times. These difficulties arise in situations where a particle picture is perhaps not appropriate. It is widely maintained that a field-theoretic description is the fundamental one, with particle descriptions only being valid in certain circumstances, so let us turn our attention to the random fields of stochastic mechanics.

STOCHASTIC MECHANICS OF FIELDS

The first to apply the methods of stochastic mechanics to the study of fields were Guerra and Ruggiero[9] in 1973. Despite some later investigations,[10-12] this program is still in its infancy.

For each finite energy solution, μ, of the classical Klein-Gordon equation, $(\Box + m^2)\mu = 0$, on M, there is a corresponding coherent state, $\Gamma(\mu)$, in the Fock space for the free scalar quantum field, θ, of mass, m. (For $\mu = 0$, we obtain the vacuum state.) For a test function, f, on M, we set $\mu(f) = \int Mf(x)\mu(x)d^4x$. Combining the stochastic quantization method of Guerra and Ruggiero[9] with a result of Guerra and Loffredo[13] concerning coherent state processes, one finds[4] that the corresponding random field, θ_μ, is a Gaussian field such that

$$\langle \theta_\mu(f) \rangle = \mu(f).$$

However, this is also equal to $\langle \Gamma(\mu), \theta(f)\Gamma(\mu) \rangle$, and because the coherent states are a determining set, this uniquely specifies θ. From this point of view, the operator-valued quantum field, θ, is a mathematical device giving a succinct expression for expectation values of classical random fields.

When a scalar current, j, is put on the right-hand side of the Klein-Gordon equation, and μ_j is the corresponding retarded solution, we obtain a family of random fields, θ_{μ_j}, with

$$\langle \theta_{\mu_j}(f) \rangle = \mu_j(f),$$

that is actively, but not passively local.[4]

For interacting Bose fields, there has been an intensive study of the random fields in the vacuum state. In this state, at least for scalar fields, it is a matter of convention whether the field is viewed as living on M or, as has been customary in constructive quantum field theory,[14] on Euclidean space. However, the random fields corresponding to noncoherent states have not yet been studied, even for the free field. Does active locality persist?

MOTIVATION

Why study these questions when quantum theory gives a perfectly adequate account of experimental results? Let me suggest several reasons.

One wants to understand as well as predict. There are problems in the interpretation of quantum theory that simply refuse to go away. For a long time, it was thought that the phenomena of organic chemistry were governed by principles qualitatively different from those of inorganic chemistry. However, understanding in science comes from reduction. Can physical phenomena on the microscopic scale be understood in terms of classical local field interactions in which randomness is of dynamical origin? We do not know, and it is important to answer the question one way or another. Chaos in classical dynamical systems is currently of great mathematical and physical interest; it may be that the phenomena described by quantum theory are a manifestation of chaos in classical local field theories.

The mathematical techniques of random field theory have proved very useful in constructive quantum field theory and are potentially of greater utility as they are studied in real time. In addition, stochastic mechanics has proved to be a useful tool in some problems[15-18] of physics.

Finally, no one can predict the future needs of physical theory, and thus it is advisable to maintain a variety of seed corn.

ACKNOWLEDGMENTS

I thank W. Faris, S. Goldstein, M. Campanino, J. S. Bell, J. Lafferty, and R. Graham for conversations that decreased my ignorance concerning locality.

REFERENCES

1. BELL, J. S. 1964. On the Einstein-Podolsky-Rosen paradox. Physics 1: 195–200.
2. BELL, J. S. 1975. The theory of local beables. CERN preprint no. TH-2053. Reproduced in Epistem. Lett. (Association Ferd. Gonseth, CP1081, CH-205, Bienne) 9(11).
3. ASPECT, A., J. DALIBARD & G. ROGER. 1982. Experimental test of Bell's inequalities using time-varying analyzers. Phys. Rev. Lett. 49: 1804–1807.
4. NELSON, E. 1985. Field theory and the future of stochastic mechanics. In Stochastic Processes in Classical and Quantum Systems. Proc. First Int. Ascona-Como Meeting, Subm. Lect. Notes Phys. S. Albeverio, G. Casati & D. Merlini, Eds. Springer-Verlag. Berlin.
5. NELSON, E. 1985. Quantum Fluctuations. Princeton Univ. Press. Princeton, New Jersey.
6. CARLEN, E. 1985. The pathwise description of quantum scattering in stochastic mechanics. In Stochastic Processes in Classical and Quantum Systems. Proc. First Int. Ascona-Como Meeting, Subm. Lect. Notes Phys. S. Albeverio, G. Casati & D. Merlini, Eds. Springer-Verlag. Berlin.
7. CARLEN, E. 1985. Potential scattering in stochastic mechanics. Ann. Inst. Henri Poincaré (Phys. Series) 42: 407–428.
8. CARLEN, E. 1985. Existence and sample path properties of the diffusions in Nelson's stochastic mechanics. Proc. BiBoS. I Conf., Springer Lecture Notes. To appear.
9. GUERRA, F. & P. RUGGIERO. 1973. A new interpretation of the Euclidean-Markov field in the framework of physical Minkowski space-time. Phys. Rev. Lett. 31: 1022–1025.
10. GUERRA, F. & M. I. LOFFREDO. 1980. Stochastic equations for the Maxwell field. Lett. Nuovo Cimento 27: 41–45.
11. DAVIDSON, M. 1982. Stochastic quantization of the linearized gravitational field. J. Math. Phys. 23: 132–137.
12. DeSIENA, S., F. GUERRA & P. RUGGIERO. 1983. Stochastic quantization of the vector meson field. Phys. Rev. D27: 2912–2915.
13. GUERRA, F. & M. I. LOFFREDO. 1981. Thermal mixtures in stochastic mechanics. Lett. Nuovo Cimento 30: 81–87.
14. GLIMM, J. & A. JAFFE. 1981. Quantum Physics: A Functional Integral Point of View. Springer-Verlag. New York.
15. JONA-LASINIO, G., F. MARTINELLI & E. SCOPPOLA. 1981. The semiclassical limit of quantum mechanics: a qualitative theory via stochastic mechanics. Phys. Rep. 77: 313–327.
16. JONA-LASINIO, G., F. MARTINELLI & E. SCOPPOLA. 1981. New approach to the semiclassical limit of quantum mechanics I—Multiple tunnelings in one dimension. Commun. Math. Phys. 80: 223–254.
17. JONA-LASIMIO, G., F. MARTINELLI & E. SCOPPOLA. 1982. Decaying quantum-mechanical states: An informal discussion within stochastic mechanics. Lett. Nuovo Cimento 34: 13–17.
18. RUGGIERO, P. & M. ZANNETTI. 1985. Stochastic quantization at finite temperature. Riv. Nuovo Cimento 8.

Suppose the State Vector Is Real: The Description and Consequences of Dynamical Reduction

PHILIP PEARLE

Physics Department
Hamilton College
Clinton, New York 13323

INTRODUCTION

Probably sometime you have said "the wave function of the electron" when you might have said "the wave function of an ensemble of identically prepared electrons" or "the wave function describing my knowledge of the electron." You might also have said "the wave function of the many universes, each containing the electron, but only one containing me" or "the wave function describing all possible experiments I might do upon the electron if I wanted to." Perhaps you were just saving your breath. Then again, perhaps, deep in the physics psyche (the classical part), there is the belief, hope, or yearning that quantum theory describes an individual physical system in nature.

However, quantum theory unaltered does not do this. Schrödinger made the point most clearly in his famous "cat paradox" paper:[1] in the quantum theory description of a measurement, the Schrödinger unitary evolution leaves the state vector in a superposition of macroscopically distinguishable states (e.g., "cat-alive" plus "cat-dead"), whereas in nature, the apparatus is left in one of those states (e.g., "cat-alive"). Fifty years ago, Schrödinger wrote:[1]

> For each measurement, one is required to ascribe to the ψ-function a quite sudden change . . . from which alone it is already quite clear that this second kind of change of the ψ-function has nothing whatever in common with its orderly development *between* two measurements. The abrupt change by measurement . . . is the most interesting point of the entire theory. It is precisely *the* point that demands the break with naive realism. For *this* reason one can *not* put the ψ-function directly in place of the physical thing . . . because from the realism point of view observation is a natural process like any other and cannot *per se* bring about an interruption of the orderly flow of events.

In this paper, we shall review the current status of a particular approach to "the most interesting point of the entire theory," namely, an approach to solving the problem posed by Schrödinger of how to reconcile "naive realism" with "the orderly flow of events."

We hypothesize that the state vector is in one-to-one correspondence with the physical state of an individual system in nature. This is "naive realism." One may view the realist theories of de Broglie–Bohm[2] and Nelson[3] as having a "many-to-one" character, in that the state vector and a point in configuration space correspond to a single physical system. One may view the nonrealist interpretation of quantum theory, that the state vector corresponds to an ensemble of identical physical systems,[4] as having a one-to-many character. Our hypothesis is intermediate in this view.

We seek to modify the Schrödinger equation so that it describes the "orderly" evolution of the superposition,

$$|\psi, t\rangle = \Sigma_n a_n(t)|\phi_n, t\rangle \tag{1.1}$$

(where each $|\phi_n, t\rangle$ corresponds to a macroscopic experimental outcome and includes experimental apparatus), into the state,

$$|\psi, t\rangle = 1 \cdot e^{i\theta_m(t)}|\phi_m, t\rangle. \tag{1.2}$$

This evolution is called the "reduction of the state vector." Schrödinger's problem is resolved if there really is in nature a (nonlocal) interaction between macroscopically distinct states of a single system that results in state vector reduction. We assume this is the case, and look for a dynamical theory to describe it.

The hope is that there will be theoretical and experimental constraints that will help delimit such a theory. On the theoretical side, not just any old equation will produce state vector reduction, and there may be aesthetic or additional properties that make one set of equations preferable. On the experimental side, a new kind of time evolution raises the possibility of predictions of experimental outcomes different from quantum theory. One may try to ensure that known experimental results and the expected results of thought-experiments are correctly predicted.

In the first half of this paper, I present my current favorite dynamical reduction equation and describe its properties. Remarkably, it turns out that Schrödinger's equation itself, properly written, is quite a satisfactory dynamical reduction equation. Other examples will be mentioned. In the rest of the paper, experimental implications for the theory will be discussed, including discussions of rapidly repeated experiments with and without interference, nonsuperluminal communication, and nonviolation of conservation laws.

THE "SCHRÖDINGER REDUCTION EQUATION"

In order to present the reduction equation, consider first the Schrödinger equation,

$$id|\psi, t\rangle/dt = H|\psi, t\rangle + \dot{B}|\psi, t\rangle, \tag{2.1}$$

where H is the usual Hamiltonian, but $\dot{B}$ is an unusual operator. $\dot{B}$ is at first to be negligibly small, but then it grows in magnitude as the preferred basis states in equation 1.1,

$$|\phi_n, t\rangle \equiv e^{-iHt}|\phi_n, 0\rangle, \tag{2.2}$$

become more macroscopically distinct, with

$$\dot{B}|\phi_n, t\rangle = \Sigma_m|\phi_m, t\rangle\dot{B}_{mn}(t), \tag{2.3}$$

where $\dot{B}_{mn}(t)$ is a Hermitian matrix element and $\dot{B}_{nn} = 0$ (no self-interaction). (In this last sentence, I have tucked some of the major unresolved problems for the theory: what determines the preferred basis, what precisely is meant by macroscopically distinct, and how do $\dot{B}$'s magnitude, time-dependence, and nonlocal structure arise?)

Substitution of equation 1.1 into equation 2.1, along with the use of equations 2.2 and 2.3, yields the equation for the amplitudes:

$$ida_n(t)/dt = \Sigma_{m \neq n} \dot{B}_{nm}(t) a_m(t).$$ (2.4)

In terms of the magnitudes, x_n, and phases, θ_n, of the amplitudes,

$$a_n(t) \equiv \sqrt{x_n(t)} e^{i\theta_n(t)}.$$ (2.5)

We rewrite equation 2.4 as difference equations,

$$dx_n = i\Sigma_{m \neq n} \sqrt{x_n x_m} [dB_{nm} e^{i(\theta_n - \theta_m)} - dB_{mn} e^{-i(\theta_n - \theta_m)}],$$ (2.6a)

$$d\theta_n = -2^{-1}\Sigma_{m \neq n} \sqrt{x_n^{-1} x_m} [dB_{nm} e^{i(\theta_n - \theta_m)} + dB_{mn} e^{-i(\theta_n - \theta_m)}],$$ (2.6b)

where $\dot{B}_{nm} dt \equiv dB_{nm}(t)$.

If $B_{nm}(t)$ is a continuous function of t, then in the limit of $dt \rightarrow 0$, equation 2.6 of course is equivalent to equation 2.4, and the amplitudes, a_n, undergo ordinary Schrödinger evolution. However, if $B_{nm}(t)$ fluctuates randomly with a correlation time scale less than dt, I claim that in the limit of $dt \rightarrow 0$, equation 2.6 reduces the state vector.

The particular time-dependence of $B_{nm}(t)$ determines which outcome (equation 1.2) of the experiment will actually occur. Because dynamical equations 2.6a and 2.6b depend upon the random functions of time, $B_{nm}(t)$, this is called a stochastic dynamical reduction theory. The first dynamical reduction theory, due to Bohm and Bub,[5] is deterministic in the sense that the outcome of each experiment is determined by certain constants (Wiener-Siegal[6] hidden variables) that are fixed parameters in the dynamical equations, although they are randomly assigned. It is by attributing to nature a random behavior outside experimental control that dynamical reduction theories explain what quantum theory cannot, namely, why a particular event occurs.

We shall take $B_{nm}(t)$ to be (complex) independent Brownian motion functions,

$$\langle dB_{nm}(t) \rangle = 0, \langle dB_{nm}(t) dB_{rs}(t) \rangle = \sigma_{nm}^2 dt \delta_{ns} \delta_{mr} \quad (n \neq m)$$ (2.7)

($\langle \rangle$ means expectation value; $B_{nn} = 0$), and model equations 2.6a and 2.6b as Itô stochastic differential equations.[7] Then equations 2.6a and 2.6b describe a Markov process, and it can be shown[8] that the probability density, $\rho(x,\theta;t)$, describing the behavior of the ensemble of solutions of these equations obeys the diffusion equation,

$$\partial\rho/\partial t = 2^{-1}\Sigma_{nm}\sigma_{nm}^2(\partial/\partial x_n - \partial/x_m)^2 x_n x_m \rho$$ (2.8)

$$+ 4^{-1}\Sigma_{nm}\sigma_{nm}^2(x_m x_n^{-1}\partial^2/\partial\theta_n^2 + \partial^2/\partial\theta_n\partial\theta_m)\rho.$$

The same result can be obtained[9] by less restrictive assumptions on $B_{nm}(t)$ using techniques other than Itô's: what is needed is that the phases of the B_{nm}'s fluctuate randomly and independently with a small correlation time.

It should be emphasized that equation 2.6, as an Itô stochastic differential equation, is suggested by differential equation 2.4, but is not equivalent to it. It is equivalent to the Stratonovich stochastic differential equation,

$$ida_n/dt = \Sigma_{m \neq n} \dot{B}_{nm} a_m(t) + 2^{-1}a_n^{*-1}\Sigma_m\sigma_{nm}^2[|a_n|^2 - |a_m|^2],$$ (2.9)

which means that if $B_{nm}(t)$ is a sequence of functions that converge to Brownian motion, then in the limit, the solution of equation 2.9 is identical to that of equation 2.6.

The behavior of the solutions of equations 2.6a and 2.6b (except for a set of measure 0) can be read from equation 2.8, and that is what we shall do. However, first we shall mention two places where diffusion equation 2.8 (without the angular part) arises.

GAMBLER'S RUIN AND GENETIC DRIFT

Consider a gambling game with N gamblers, where the ratio of the money possessed by the nth gambler to the total money possessed by all gamblers is x_n (so $\Sigma_n x_n = 1$). They randomly pair off (say, the nth and m^{th} gamblers play) and each pair tosses a fair coin. The outcome of the toss determines which gambler wins and which loses. This results in the exchange of a fraction, ϵ_{nm}, of the total money in the game (x_n increases or decreases by ϵ_{nm}). If a gambler loses all his money, he drops out.

This is the "gambler's ruin" game.[10] It has the properties that eventually one gambler wins all the money (one x_n equals 1, and $x_{\neq n} = 0$), and if a gambler starts each game with $x_n(0)$ of the money, he will win all the money in a fraction, $x_n(0)$, of the ensemble of games.

The analogy with a dynamical reduction theory should be clear. In fact, it can be shown[11] that if $\epsilon_{nm} \sim \sqrt{x_n x_m \Delta t}$, where Δt is the time between coin tosses, in the limit $\Delta t \to 0$, the evolution of the ensemble of games is described by diffusion equation 2.8 (without the angular part). Thus, we may think of the various macroscopic states in the superposition (equation 1.1) as playing the gambler's ruin game until one of them wins.

I was recently interested to discover that equation 2.8 (with all σ_{nm}'s equal and without the angular part) has been known for a long time to population geneticists.[12] Suppose there are N different alleles (genes) for eye colors. Consider a fixed population of alleles, with x_n equal to the frequency in the population of nth-color alleles. The Wright-Fisher model for reproduction of the next generation of alleles is the rule: select one allele at a time from the population, with replacement, until an equal size population has been chosen.

This is called a "neutral model" (because there is no bias by natural selection) of "genetic drift" (because the x_n's change with the generations). It has the property that the population is eventually composed of one allele (it is then said that the population is "fixed"; the physics term, "reduced," would be equally appropriate). The probability that this happens equals the initial frequency of that allele. Equation 2.8, modified as mentioned, is called the diffusion approximation of the Wright-Fisher model of genetic drift, which holds for a large population and a time scale large compared to the time between generations.

PROPERTIES OF THE REDUCTION EQUATION

Properties 0–10 below follow from equation 2.8. The first five are most important because they establish that equations 2.6a and 2.6b reduce the state vector.

Property 0: $\Sigma_n x_n = 1$ for each state vector in the ensemble:
Because the derivatives $(\partial/\partial x_n - \partial/\partial x_m)$ commute with any function of $\Sigma_n x_n$, if ρ is initially proportional to $\delta(1 - \Sigma_n x_n)$ then it remains so.

Property 1: $x_n(\infty) = 1$, $x_{\neq n}(\infty) = 0$ for each state vector in the ensemble (reduction property):
By multiplying equation 2.8 by $x_n x_m$ $(n \neq m)$ and integrating over x, θ, we find

$$d\langle x_n x_m \rangle dt = -\sigma_{nm}^2 \langle x_n x_m \rangle, \quad n \neq m, \tag{4.1}$$

where we have introduced the notation,

$$\langle f[x(t), \theta(t)] \rangle \equiv \int_0^1 dx \int_0^{2\pi} d(\theta/2\pi) \rho(x, \theta; t) f(x, \theta). \tag{4.2}$$

According to equation 4.1, $\langle x_n x_m \rangle \to 0$ as $t \to \infty$. However, because x_n, x_m, and ρ are positive, this is only possible if, in the integrand (equation 4.2), $\rho(x, \theta; \infty)$ vanishes (except for a set of measure 0) wherever $x_n \neq 0$ and $x_m \neq 0$. Applied to all pairs, n, m, this means that $\rho(x, \theta; \infty)$ can only be nonvanishing where at most one $x_n \neq 0$. However, by property 0, this x_n must equal 1.

It is interesting that so much information about individual state vector amplitudes can be gleaned from the behavior of just the second moments.

Property 2: $x_n(0) =$ the fraction of state vectors in the ensemble for which $x_n(\infty) = 1$ (fundamental property):
I call this property "fundamental" because it causes predictions to be in agreement with those of quantum theory for experiments in which the reduction proceeds uninterrupted to completion.

By multiplying equation 2.8 by x_n and integrating over x, θ, we find

$$d\langle x_n \rangle / dt = 0. \tag{4.3}$$

A diffusion equation satisfying equation 4.3 is said to be a Martingale.

It follows from equation 4.3 that

$$\langle x_n(0) \rangle = \langle x_n(\infty) \rangle. \tag{4.4}$$

If we take $t = 0$ to be the time just before the state vector commences reduction, then $\langle x_n(0) \rangle = x_n(0)$ because there is just one state vector in the ensemble at that time. According to property 1, $x_n(\infty)$ equals either one or zero, so $\langle x_n(\infty) \rangle = 1 \otimes$ [fraction of state vectors for which $x_n(\infty) = 1$]. Thus, equation 4.4 implies the fundamental property.

One can look at this another way. It is hard to understand why quantum theory uses the squared modulus of a complex number as a probability. If one takes the reduction seriously as a real physical process, this quantum rule arises because the reduction possesses the Martingale property (equation 4.3).

Property 3: $x_n(0) = \langle x_n(t) \rangle$ (constant mean or Martingale property):
This follows from equation 4.3. The dynamical reduction theory of Bohm and Bub[5] satisfies equation 4.4, but not the more stringent constant mean property (equation 4.3). We will see in the section entitled EXPERIMENTS that this latter property ensures agreement of predictions with those of quantum theory even when the reduction caused

by one experiment is interrupted by another experiment, for a wide class of experiments. Because of this, I suggest that all dynamical reduction theories should have this property, which I call the "constant mean hypothesis."

Property 4: The reduction takes a finite time:

It can be shown, using Dynkin's equation for the mean first passage time, that the mean reduction time is finite.[13] Thus, the time for each state vector to reduce must be finite (except for a set of measure 0).

Conceptually, this is an important property. A superposition that lasts forever, even if all amplitudes except one become exponentially small (which is the case in Bohm-Bub's theory[5] and in a recent stochastic reduction theory of Gisin[14]), is still a superposition, and it is difficult to reconcile this with a unique macroscopic experimental outcome.

Note that the exponential decay of $\langle x_n x_m \rangle$ (see equation 4.1) is due to an exponentially decreasing number of incompletely reduced state vectors, and not due to the exponential decay of x_n.

It also is true that the mean reduction time is independent of the number of basis states playing the reduction "game" for large N.

Property 5: Two uncorrelated systems may reduce independently:

If x'_r, θ'_r satisfy equations 2.6a and 2.6b with matrix elements, dB'_{rs}, which are statistically independent of dB_{nm}, then it is straightforward to show[9,11] that $x_{nr} \equiv x_n x_r$, $\theta_{nr} \equiv \theta_n + \theta_r$, satisfy equations 2.6a and 2.6b with matrix elements, $dB_{nr,ms} = dB_{nm}\delta_{rs} + \delta_{nm}dB'_{rs}$.

Property 6: The reduction is invariant under uniform scaling of amplitudes:

As in quantum theory, the equations are invariant under the transformation of $x_n \rightarrow \lambda x_n$.

Property 7: The reduction is invariant under arbitrary phase translation of the preferred basis states:

The irrelevance of arbitrary phase factors in quantum theory holds here as well (for the ensemble, but not for the evolution of an individual state vector). Suppose each basis state, $|\phi_n, 0\rangle$, is replaced by $|\phi_n, 0\rangle \exp i\Delta_n$, so that the initial phase angles are $\theta_n(0) - \Delta_n$ instead of $\theta_n(0)$. Because the diffusion coefficients in equation 2.8 do not depend upon θ, it follows that if $\rho(x,\theta; t)$ is a solution with initial angle $\theta_n(0)$, then $\rho(x, \theta + \Delta; t)$ is also a solution with initial angles, $\theta_n(0) - \Delta_n$.

Property 8: The density matrix obeys the backward diffusion equation associated with equation 2.8:

The density matrix elements in the preferred basis $\{|\phi_n t\rangle\}$ are

$$D_{nm}(t) = \langle a_n a_m^* \rangle = \langle \sqrt{x_n x_m} e^{i(\theta_n - \theta_m)} \rangle. \tag{4.5}$$

Because equation 2.8 describes a Markov process, $\rho(x, \theta; x_0, \theta_0; t)$ also obeys the backward diffusion equation in the initial conditions, $x_0 \equiv x(0)$, $\theta_0 \equiv \theta(0)$:

$$\partial\rho/\partial t = 2^{-1}\Sigma_{rs}\sigma_{rs}^2 x_{r0}x_{s0}(\partial/\partial x_{r0} - \partial/x_{s0})^2\rho \tag{4.6}$$
$$+ 4^{-1}\Sigma_{rs}\sigma_{rs}^2(x_{r0}x_{s0}^{-1}\partial^2/\partial\theta_{r0}^2 + \partial^2/\partial\theta_{r0}\partial\theta_{s0})\rho.$$

Both sides of this equation can be multiplied by $\sqrt{x_n x_m}$ exp $i(\theta_n - \theta_m)$ and integrated over all x, θ, which replaces ρ in equation 4.6 by $D_{nm}(x_0, \theta_0; t)$.

Property 9: During reduction, the diagonal elements of the density matrix remain constant, the off-diagonal density matrix elements' moduli decrease to zero, and (if the density matrix is initially pure) their phase-angles remain constant:
$D_{nn} = \langle x_n \rangle$ by equation 4.5, which remains constant by equation 4.3. If any solution of equation 4.6 is expanded in a Fourier exponential series in the phase factors, exp $i\theta_{n0}$, it follows from equation 4.6 that each Fourier coefficient (which depends upon x_0) evolves independently according to a real homogeneous equation. By property 8, D_{nm} obeys equation 4.6, and its initial value is $D_{nm}(0) = \sqrt{x_{n0}x_{m0}}$ exp $i(\theta_{n0} - \theta_{m0})$ (initially pure density matrix). Thus, the Fourier series for $D_{nm}(t)$ remains a single term with a real time-dependent coefficient whose initial value is $\sqrt{x_{n0}x_{m0}}$. The eventual vanishing of the coefficient follows from reduction property 1.

Property 10: If a density matrix element ever vanishes, it vanishes thereafter. In particular, a diagonal density matrix remains diagonal:
This follows from equation 4.6, which D_{nm} obeys.

OTHER STOCHASTIC DYNAMICAL REDUCTION THEORIES

A class of stochastic dynamical reduction theories[8] can be specified by the Stratonovitch equations,

$$ida_n/dt = a_n^{*-1}\Sigma_m B_{nm}(a_n a_m^*)^r. \tag{5.1}$$

My previous favorite[8,9,11,15] was equation 5.1 with $r = 1$. The Itô equations are identical to equations 2.6a and 2.6b except for a minus sign on the right-hand side of equation 2.6a. This does not affect the associated diffusion equation (equation 2.8), so all properties in the previous section are satisfied for this theory. For $r \geq 2$, the reduction takes an infinite time (property 4 is violated), and for $r \neq 1$, properties 5 and 6 are violated.[9,11]

Recently, Gisin has published a stochastic dynamical reduction theory with Itô equations,

$$dx_n = x_n\Sigma_m(S^{-1}x_m - \delta_{nm})\, dB_m, \quad d\theta_n = 0, \tag{5.2}$$

where $S \equiv \Sigma_n x_n$ and dB_m are independent Brownian motion functions. The associated diffusion equation is

$$\partial\rho/\partial t = (\sigma/2)^2\Sigma_{nm}(\partial/\partial x_n - \partial/\partial x_m)^2 x_n x_m[(x_n + x_m)/S - \Sigma_k(x_k/S)^2]\rho. \tag{5.3}$$

The density matrix has the nice property that its off-diagonal elements decay exponentially because it follows from equation 5.3 that

$$d\langle\sqrt{x_n x_m}\rangle dt = -(\sigma/2)^2\langle\sqrt{x_n x_m}\rangle \tag{5.4}$$

and the phases do not evolve. However, each state vector takes infinite time to reduce[16,17] (property 4 is violated). This theory will play an important role in the discussion of superluminal communication (see later section).

EXPERIMENTS

There is a hierarchy of conceivable classes of experiments of increasing difficulty that constrain dynamical reduction theories. These theories are designed to produce agreement with the predictions of quantum theory as long as the reduction process is allowed to go to completion without interruption. Thus, in the first class of experiments (normal experiments), this is what occurs. The theory must then satisfy properties 0, 1, 2, and 4.

The second class I call interrupted reduction experiments. Each experiment consists of successive measurements that are separated by an interval less than the mean reduction time. This may produce predictions that differ from those of quantum theory.

However, if the constant mean hypothesis is satisfied (property 3), it can be shown[15,17,18] (see next section) that the predictions agree with those of quantum theory as long as a measurement does not involve interference among the macroscopically distinct state vectors produced by a previous measurement. This is most likely the case because measurements most often involve an irreversible change in a macroscopic apparatus.

Therefore, to obtain possible disagreement with quantum theory, we turn to interrupted reduction interference experiments, where a second measurement does produce interference among preferred basis states of the previous measurement.

Such experiments address the following important issue: The interaction between the preferred basis states (which may be thought of as "pointer positions") is supposed to grow as these states become macroscopically distinct, thus triggering the reduction "game." The problem is, what is meant by "macroscopically distinct"? Distinguishing properties that have been mentioned are mass, separation, and complexity. Presumably, the photon packets in the different arms of a Michelson interferometer do not spontaneously reduce, even with a macroscopic separation, either because of the small mass of the photon or because of its lack of complexity.

One particular issue is the question of the need for complexity, and how to define it. I will distinguish two hypotheses. In the first, the reproducibility hypothesis, the state vector just prior to reduction is capable of being prepared (reproduced) to arbitrary accuracy. It is the mass of the system and the spatial separation of the different "pointer" states that trigger the reduction: complexity plays no role. In this case, it is possible to do interrupted reduction interference experiments.

For example, consider a two-slit neutron-interference experiment, or a double-Stern-Gerlach experiment with a suitably massive neutral particle. In both cases, the wave packet separation is macroscopic by atomic standards, and the particle is reasonably massive by electron standards. It is possible that at least a slow reduction may ensue as the packets separate (the first "measurement"), with one packet slightly growing at the expense of the other, until they are brought together and detected (the second measurement). This "spontaneous reduction" (so-called because the first "measurement" would not normally be regarded as such, except that it triggers reduction) would result in a slight washout of the interference pattern in the neutron-interference experiment[18] and a slight tilt of the spin in the Stern-Gerlach experiment. The former experiment has actually been performed by Zeilinger et al.,[19] who report 1% agreement with the predictions of quantum theory, which translates to the statement that the reduction time in their experiment had to exceed eight seconds. This, of course, is consistent with there not being enough mass or complexity to trigger the reduction.

The second hypothesis, the irreproducibility hypothesis, is that an experimenter cannot precisely reproduce the state vector prior to reduction to the extent that the experimenter's "effective" density matrix (the density matrix corresponding to the ensemble of initial state vectors traced over the variables that are not under the experimenter's control) is diagonal prior to reduction. Then, by property 10, it remains diagonal. In this case, interrupted reduction interference experiments yield no results different from quantum theory.

I would prefer the reproducibility hypothesis because of the experimental possibilities for testing the theory. However, it turns out that with the reproducibility hypothesis, there is the possibility of superluminal communication.[17] Therefore, I presently opt for the irreproducibility hypothesis.

INTERRUPTED REDUCTION EXPERIMENTS

Here we show the utility of the constant mean hypothesis. Consider a sequence of (for simplicity) instantaneous measurements. The outcome of the first measurement (at $t = T_0$) is described by one of the states, $|\phi_k\rangle$, the outcome of the first two measurements (the second taking place at $t = T_1$) is described by $|\phi_{km}\rangle$, etc.

According to quantum theory, the succession of state vectors describing these measurements is

$$|\Psi_1, t\rangle = \Sigma_k a_k(t) |\phi_k\rangle \qquad T_0 \leq t < T_1, \qquad (7.1a)$$

$$|\Psi_2, t\rangle = \Sigma_{km} a_k(T_1) b_{km}(t) |\phi_{km}\rangle \qquad T_1 \leq t < T_2, \qquad (7.1b)$$

etc., where $|\phi_k\rangle$ evolves into $\Sigma_m b_{km} |\phi_{km}\rangle$ at $t = T_1$ and where $|a_k(t)|^2, |b_{km}(t)|^2, \ldots$, do not change with time. Thus, for example, the probability predicted by quantum theory of the km outcome is

$$P_{km} = |a_k(T_1)|^2 |b_{km}(T_2)|^2 = |a_k(T_0)|^2 |b_{km}(T_1)|^2. \qquad (7.2)$$

According to a dynamical reduction theory; equation 7.1a also holds for $T_0 \leq t < T_1$, but all that can be asserted is

$$\langle |a_k(t)|^2 \rangle = \langle |a_k(T_0)|^2 \rangle = |a_k(T_0)|^2 \qquad T_0 \leq t \leq T_1, \qquad (7.3a)$$

where the first equality in equation 7.3a follows from the constant mean hypothesis, and the second equality is due to the fact that reduction has not yet begun. For $T_1 \leq t < T_2$, $|\psi_2, t\rangle = \Sigma_{km} a_{km} |\phi_{km}\rangle$ with

$$\langle |a_{km}(t)|^2 \rangle = \langle |a_{km}(T_1)|^2 \rangle = \langle |a_k(T_1)|^2 |b_{km}(T_1)|^2 \rangle = |a_k(T_0)|^2 |b_{km}(T_1)|^2, \; (7.3b)$$

where the first equality in equation 7.3b is due to the constant mean hypothesis, the second equality is due to the measurement, and the third follows from equation 7.3a.

Consider a sequence of two consecutive such measurements, after which the reduction goes to completion. The diagonal density matrix element (equation 7.3b) is the probability of the km outcome, and this equals the quantum theory prediction (equation 7.2). (This is true for any number of successive measurements.)

It is not hard to show, if the constant mean hypothesis is not obeyed in some time interval and an experiment in the sequence is done in that interval, that the prediction for the sequence will deviate from equation 7.2. Thus, the constant mean hypothesis is necessary and sufficient for the predictions for this class of experiments to agree with those of quantum theory.

SUPERLUMINAL COMMUNICATION

I will simply quote the results of a rather involved analysis.[17] All results hold for the most general stochastic dynamical reduction theory (which is therefore described by a diffusion equation having properties 0, 1, and 2, like equation 2.8 but more general) obeying the constant mean hypothesis and having phase invariance (properties 3 and 7).

The first result is that superluminal communication can occur unless the off-diagonal elements of the density matrix decay with a universal time constant, as in Gisin's theory (see equation 5.4 and the section it is in). This is proven by considering correlated interrupted reduction interference experiments such as a "double-double-Stern-Gerlach experiment": two double-Stern-Gerlach experiments performed on correlated, but widely separated particles, with the recombination of packets being performed at arbitrarily chosen times and the spins being measured thereafter in arbitrarily chosen directions. The reduction is then finally allowed to go to completion. Upon requiring the reduced density matrix associated with one particle (obtained by tracing over the variables associated with the other particle) to be independent of the arbitrary time and direction associated with the measurement on the other particle, this result is obtained.

Actually, because the time constant must be universal (this is essentially because the dependence upon the parameters of the other experiment, for example, the mass and separation of the packets of the other particle, must not be discernible in the reduced density matrix), it must be as "fast" as the fastest experiment. It is then likely that it is so "fast" that two consecutive experiments could not practically be done within the allotted time, assuming that the reduction is triggered at all. Thus, the reproducibility hypothesis in this case and the irreproducibility hypothesis come to the same thing: no practical experimental test of the theory.

The second result is that Gisin's theory is the unique stochastic reduction theory, without angular evolution, for which the off-diagonal density matrix elements decay with a universal time constant.

The third result is that in any stochastic reduction theory in which the off-diagonal density matrix elements decay with a universal time constant, with or without angular evolution, no state vector (except perhaps for a set of measure 0) ever reduces in a finite time.

To summarize, it appears we have three choices: (1) reproducibility hypothesis: an experimentally testable theory with finite reduction time, but with the possibility of superluminal communication; (2) no superluminal communication: an experimentally untestable theory with infinite reduction time; or (3) irreproducibility hypothesis: an experimentally untestable theory without superluminal communication and with finite reduction time. I prefer choice 3, as I mentioned at the end of the section entitled EXPERIMENTS.

CONSERVATION LAWS

In this section, we point out that dynamical reduction, hypothesized in certain circumstances such as two-slit neutron interference or double-Stern-Gerlach experiments, can violate conservation laws. We discuss the implications of this result. We also present reasonable sufficient conditions for nonviolation of conservation laws during reduction.

It should first be noted that quantum theory itself, with the reduction postulate indiscriminately applied, does not necessarily satisfy the conservation laws. Consider a system described by the wave function in equation 1.1. If a conserved quantity is S, with eigenvalues, s, and eigenvectors, $|s, \lambda\rangle$ (λ is a degeneracy index), then the probability of measuring s on the system is

$$\Sigma_\lambda |\langle s, \lambda|\psi, t\rangle|^2 = \Sigma_{nm\lambda} a_n a_m^* \langle \phi_m, t|s, \lambda\rangle\langle s, \lambda|\phi_n, t\rangle. \tag{9.1}$$

However, if the state vector is interpreted, via a reduction postulate, as implying that $|a_n|^2$ is the probability of the nth outcome described by $|\phi_n, t\rangle$, then the probability of measuring s is

$$\Sigma_{n\lambda} |a_n|^2 |\langle s, \lambda|\phi_n, t\rangle|^2, \tag{9.2}$$

which differs from equation 9.1 by terms that may not vanish. For example, if a wave packet is split into two orthogonal pieces, then unless the wave functions of the pieces in momentum space do not overlap, the momentum distribution in the pieces is not equal to the momentum distribution in the original packet. Obviously, the violation or nonviolation of a conservation law depends upon the preferred basis states to which the reduction postulate is applied.

The discussion here was stimulated by Y. Aharonov (private communication), who suggested that, in the two-slit neutron interference experiment, once the neutron passes through the screen, its momentum perpendicular to the slits and parallel to the screen might not be conserved during its "spontaneous reduction." Indeed, it is not: the unreduced momentum probability distribution associated with the sum of the two neutron packets differs from the completely reduced momentum probability distribution of the separate packets. The difference between the two probability distributions decreases with increasing slit separation to slit width ratio and depends upon the momentum range and resolution.

If one believes that spontaneous reductions may take place, but not if they appreciably violate conservation laws, one might find this to be an acceptable explanation of why Zeilinger *et al.* did not observe reduction.

If the $|\phi_n, t\rangle$ are macroscopically distinguishable states (i.e., composed of many particles and spatially separated, which is the circumstance in which the reduction postulate of quantum theory is generally used), in reasonable models, the difference between equations 9.1 and 9.2 can be shown to vanish or be unmeasurably small. No matter how small, however, if it is nonvanishing, then it is still a violation of a conservation law. That is a serious problem for quantum theory with a reduction postulate. For a dynamical reduction theory, it is an opportunity. It raises intriguing possibilities of deeper insights into the nature of the theory—for example, the possibility that the fluctuating medium that causes the reduction may exchange energy and momentum with the quantum system,[20] or the possibility of rules for choosing the preferred basis states so that conservation law violation is minimized.

In the remainder of this section, I wish to discuss the conservation laws during the reduction process when the condition,

$$\langle \phi_n, t | S^N | \phi_m, t \rangle = 0, \quad n \neq m, \tag{9.3}$$

is satisfied for certain values of N. Intuitively, the left side of equation 9.3 should be quite small if the $| \phi_n, t \rangle$ describe spatially separated states and S is a local operator like energy, momentum, and angular momentum. It vanishes if the $| \phi_n, t \rangle$ are (nondegenerate) eigenstates of an operator that commutes with S. If equation 9.3 is true at one time, it will always be true because the $| \phi_n, t \rangle$ evolve by the Hamiltonian, H, that commutes with S.

The point to be made is that this is a sufficient condition for conserved quantities and preferred basis states to satisfy in order to avoid conservation law violation during reduction.

We distinguish the situation where $| \psi, t \rangle$ is an eigenstate of S from the qualitatively different situation when this is not the case. In the former situation, every reducing state vector must also be an eigenstate of S with the same eigenvalue if the conservation law is to hold. In the latter situation, it is only the ensemble of reducing state vectors that must have the same probability distribution of eigenvalues of S as the initial state vector.

Therefore, first consider that the initial state vector, $| \psi, 0 \rangle$, is an eigenstate of S with eigenvalue s. Suppose this state vector evolves by the usual Schrödinger evolution to the superposition (equation 1.1) just prior to the commencement of the reduction. Suppose further that we can prove the assertion that each preferred basis state, $| \phi_n, t \rangle$, is also an eigenstate of S with eigenvalue s. Then, while the amplitudes, a_n, fluctuate during the reduction dynamics, the state vector remains an eigenstate of S with eigenvalue s, and the reduction process respects the conservation law.

We prove the assertion as follows. We assume equation 9.3 with $N = 1, 2, 3$. It follows from $S | \psi, 0 \rangle = s | \psi, 0 \rangle$ and $[S, H] = 0$ that $S | \psi, t \rangle = s | \psi, t \rangle$. Taking the scalar product of this with $\langle \phi_n |$, and using equations 1.1 and 9.3, we obtain $\langle \phi_n | S | \phi_n \rangle = s$. Therefore, we may always decompose the vector, $S | \phi_n \rangle$, into

$$S | \phi_n \rangle = s | \phi_n \rangle + | \lambda_n \rangle, \quad \langle \phi_n | \lambda_n \rangle = 0. \tag{9.4}$$

Consider $s^2 = \langle \psi, t | S^2 | \psi, t \rangle$:

$$s^2 = \Sigma_{nm} a_n^* a_m \langle \phi_n | S^2 | \phi_m \rangle = \Sigma_n | a_n |^2 \langle \phi_n | S^2 | \phi_n \rangle \tag{9.5a,b}$$

$$= \Sigma_n | a_n |^2 ((\langle \phi_n | s + \langle \lambda_n |)(s | \phi_n \rangle + | \lambda_n \rangle)) = s^2 + \Sigma_n | a_n |^2 \langle \lambda_n | \lambda_n \rangle. \tag{9.5c,d}$$

Equation 9.5a follows from the expansion in equation 1.1, equation 9.5b follows from equation 9.3, and equations 9.5c,d follow from equation 9.4. Thus, $0 = \Sigma | a_n |^2 \langle \lambda_n | \lambda_n \rangle$, so $| \lambda_n \rangle = 0$, and according to equation 9.4, the assertion is proved.

Second, consider that $| \psi, T \rangle$ (T is the time just before the reduction begins) is not an eigenstate of S. We can easily show that the expectation value of S^N does not change during the reduction. During the reduction, the density matrix is

$$D = \Sigma_{nm} \langle a_n a_m^* \rangle |\phi_n\rangle\langle\phi_m| \qquad (9.6)$$

and so the ensemble expectation value of S^N is

$$\text{tr } DS^N = \Sigma_{nm} \langle a_n a_m^* \rangle \langle\phi_m|S^N|\phi_n\rangle = \Sigma_n \langle |a_n|^2 \rangle \langle\phi_n|S^N|\phi_n\rangle \qquad (9.7\text{a,b})$$

$$= \Sigma_n |a_n(T)|^2 \langle\phi_n|S^N|\phi_n\rangle = \Sigma_{nm} a_n(T)a_m^*(T)\langle\phi_m|S^N|\phi_n\rangle, \qquad (9.7\text{c,d})$$

$$\text{tr } DS^N = \langle\psi, T|S^N|\psi, T\rangle. \qquad (9.7\text{e})$$

Equations 9.7b,d follow from equation 9.3, and equation 9.7c follows from the constant mean hypothesis.

Now, because two (appropriately analytic) probability distributions are equal if they have the same moments, we have proved that the probabilities of the eigenvalues s during the reduction always equal the probabilities predicted by quantum theory if equation 9.3 holds for all N.

CONCLUDING REMARKS

The purpose of this work was to explore the consequences of the hypothesis stating that the state vector describes a single system in nature. I see no reason yet to abandon the hypothesis; on the contrary, it still continues to be stimulating.

ACKNOWLEDGMENT

I would like to acknowledge, with pleasure, collaboration with Toru Ohira on the material reported in the section entitled CONSERVATION LAWS.

REFERENCES

1. SCHRÖDINGER, E. 1935. Naturwissenschaften **23**: 807, 823, 844.
2. DE BROGLIE, L. 1930. An Introduction to the Study of Wave Mechanics. Dutton. New York; BOHM, D. 1952. Phys. Rev. **85**: 166, 180.
3. NELSON, E. 1966. Phys. Rev. **150**: 1079; 1985. Quantum Fluctuations. Princeton Univ. Press. Princeton, New Jersey.
4. PEARLE, P. 1967. Am. J. Phys. **35**: 742; BALLENTINE, L. E. 1970. Rev. Mod. Phys. **42**: 358; BELINFANTE, F. 1975. Measurements and Time Reversal in Objective Quantum Theory. Pergamon. Oxford.
5. BOHM, D. & J. BUB. 1966. Rev. Mod. Phys. **38**: 453.
6. WIENER, N. & A. SIEGAL. 1956. Phys. Rev. **101**: 429.
7. WONG, E. 1971. Stochastic Processes in Information and Dynamical Systems. McGraw–Hill. New York; ARNOLD, L. 1974. Stochastic Differential Equations: Theory and Applications. Wiley. New York; SCHUSS, Z. 1980. Theory and Applications of Stochastic Differential Equations. Wiley. New York.
8. PEARLE, P. 1979. Int. J. Theor. Phys. **48**: 489; 1986. Models for reduction. *In* Quantum Concepts in Space and Time. R. Penrose & C. Ischam, Eds. Oxford Univ. Press. Oxford.

9. PEARLE, P. 1976. Phys. Rev. **D13:** 857; 1986. Statevector Reduction as a Dynamical Process. *In* Fundamental Questions in Quantum Mechanics. A. Inomata & L. Roth, Eds. Gordon & Breach. New York.
10. FELLER, W. 1950. An Introduction to Probability Theory and Its Applications, chap. 14. Wiley. New York.
11. PEARLE, P. 1982. Found. Phys. **12:** 249.
12. EWENS, W. J. 1979. Mathematical Population Genetics. Springer-Verlag. New York.
13. PEARLE, P. 1986. J. Stat. Phys. **41:** 719.
14. GISIN, N. 1984. Phys. Rev. Lett. **52:** 1657; **53:** 1776.
15. PEARLE, P. 1984. Dynamics of the reduction of the statevector. *In* The Wave-Particle Dualism. S. Diner, D. Fargue, G. Lochak & F. Selleri, Eds. Reidel. Dordrecht.
16. PEARLE, P. 1984. Phys. Rev. Lett. **53:** 1775.
17. PEARLE, P. 1986. Phys. Rev. **33:** 2240.
18. PEARLE, P. 1984. Phys. Rev. **D29:** 235.
19. ZELLINGER, A., M. A. HORNE & C. G. SHULL. 1983. Proc. Int. Symp. Found. Quantum Mech. Tokyo **389.**
20. KÁROLYHÁZY, F., A. FRENKEL & B. LUKÁCS. 1982. On the possibility of observing the eventual breakdown of the superposition principle. *In* Physics as Natural Philosophy. A. Shimony & H. Feshbach, Eds. MIT Press. Cambridge, Massachusetts; 1986. *Article in* Quantum Concepts in Space and Time. R. Penrose & C. Isham, Eds. Oxford Univ. Press. Oxford.

A Research Program with No "Measurement Problem"[a]

H. PIERRE NOYES,[b] CHRISTOFFER GEFWERT,[c] AND
MICHAEL J. MANTHEY[d]

[b]Stanford Linear Accelerator Center
Stanford University
Stanford, California 94305

[c]Academy of Finland
Helsinki, Finland

[d]Computer Science Department
New Mexico State University
Los Cruces, New Mexico 88003

INTRODUCTION

Quantum mechanics has to be adjoined to a "measurement theory" that has never been formulated in a satisfactory way; it is in the words of Wheeler,[1] a "law without law." For us, "measurement" is part of any research program in physics; if we construct physics as a research program, the "measurement problem" cannot be given a separate locus. We[2] first formulate what we mean by a participatory research program, which will specify the criteria and the steps that can allow us to conclude that the program is complete. We present this schema in FIGURE 1. The implied philosophical position has been discussed by one of us (C.G.) elsewhere.[3] Although participation is involved in the creation of the program by virtue of the meaning-conferring acts of judgment entailed, the end result is objective in that, if successful, the program provides the same explanation of meaning for any participant when applied.

To show the objectivity, the technique we use is to code the program, and hence insure that it is computable. The program uses arbitrary numbers, in McGoveran's sense, generated by the nondeterminism born of the communication between asynchronous processes over a shared memory.[e] The basic entities in the program are ordered strings of the symbols "0, 1" generated either by adding one arbitrary bit to each extant string, or by discriminating between strings and adjoining a novel result to the bit string universe. The act of concatenating each extant string with an arbitrary bit is our representation of a "quantum event," which changes the entire bit string universe whenever discrimination between extant strings fails to produce demonstrable novelty.

[a]This work was supported by the Department of Energy, Contract No. DE-AC03-76SF00515.
[e]D. McGoveran uses "arbitrary" to mean "not due to any finite, locally specifiable algorithm"; because computer hardware is finite and attempts to be locally deterministic, he would replace Manthey's term, "nondeterminism," by the term, "multideterminism" (private communication).

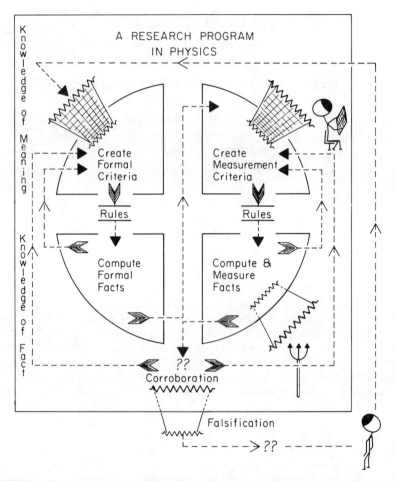

FIGURE 1. The relation between the knowledge of meaning and the knowledge of fact, theory, and measurement for a research program in physics.

Clearly, such events are nonlocal, which is currently an experimentally implied requirement for quantum events. The problem is rather to show that in the articulation of the theory, they do not allow supraluminal signaling.

The means used to connect the bit string universe to the practice of particle physics is to assume that:

> any *elementary event,* under circumstances which it is the task of the experimental physicist to investigate, can lead to the firing of a counter.

We call this the "counter paradigm." It allows us to connect the "quantum events" that occur in our computer program with laboratory counter firings in such a way as to provide our theory with both predictive power and corrigibility. We identify the three

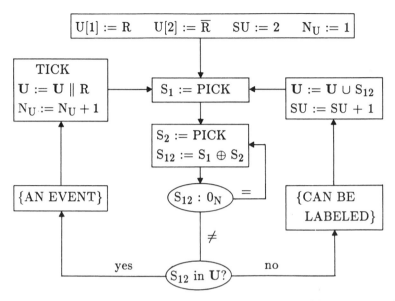

FIGURE 2. Program universe: no. strings = SU; length = N_U; element $U[i]$; $i \in 1, 2, \ldots, SU$; $R \rightarrow 0, 1$ (flip bit); *PICK*: = some $U[i]$, $p = 1/SU$; *TICK* U: $= U \| R$; $\overline{S} = 1_N \oplus S$.

or four bit strings defining any quantum event as the basis states needed to construct a finite-particle-number, relativistic (i.e., constrained by the "limiting velocity for signals") quantum scattering theory (including the conserved quantum numbers encountered in the "standard model" of quarks and leptons) and to make a start on computing the scale constants of modern physics.

CONSTRUCTING A BIT STRING UNIVERSE

The basic entities in the theory are ordered strings of the symbols, "0", "1" [labeled below by $a, b, \ldots$], defined by $S^a(N_U) = (\ldots, b^a_n, \ldots)_{N_U}$, where $b^a_n \in 0, 1$ and $n \in [1, 2, \ldots, N_U]$. The strings combine by "XOR": $S^a \oplus S^b = (\ldots, b^a_n +_2 b^b_n, \ldots)_{N_U}$ (for 0, 1 bits), or by $S^a \oplus S^b \equiv [\ldots, (b^a_n - b^b_n)^2, \ldots]_{N_U}$ (for 0, 1 integers). This fruitful ambiguity allows us to refer to either operation as discrimination. The null string is called $0_N \equiv (0, 0, \ldots, 0)_N$, $S^a \oplus S^a = 0_N$; the antinull string is symbolized by $1_N \equiv (1, 1, \ldots, 1)_N$, allowing us to define the "bar operation," $\overline{S}^a(N) \equiv 1_N \oplus S^a(N)$, which interchanges "0"('s) and "1"('s) in a string.

We generate the strings according to the flow chart in FIGURE 2. The program is initiated by the arbitrary choice of two distinct bits: $R := 0$ or 1, $\overline{R} = 1 \oplus R$. Entering at *PICK*, we take $S_1 := PICK$; $S_2 := PICK$; $S_{12} := S_1 \oplus S_2$. If $S_{12} = 0_{N_U}$, we return to picking S_2 until we pass this test. We then ask if S_{12} is already in the universe. If it is not, we adjoin it, $U := U \cup S_{12}$, $SU := SU + 1$, and return to *PICK*. If S_{12} is already in the universe, we go to our third (and last) arbitrary operation called *TICK*. This simply adjoins a bit (via R), arbitrarily chosen for each string, to the growing end of each string, $U := U \| R$, $N := N + 1$, and returns us to *PICK*; here, "$\|$" denotes string concatenation. *TICK* results either from a *3-event*, which guarantees that at that N_U the universe contains three strings constrained by $S^a \oplus S^b \oplus S^c = 0_{N_U}$, or a *4-event* constrained by $S^a \oplus S^b \oplus S^c \oplus S^d = 0_{N_U}$. That these are the only ways that events can happen in the bit string universe is demonstrated in FIGURE 3.

Given two distinct (linearly independent or l.i.) non-null strings, a, b, the set, $\{a, b, a \oplus b\}$, closes under discrimination. Observing that the singleton sets, $\{a\}$, $\{b\}$, are closed, we see that two l.i. strings generate three discriminately closed subsets (DCsS's). Given a third l.i. string, c, we can generate $\{c\}$, $\{b, c, b \oplus c\}$, $\{c, a, c \oplus a\}$, and

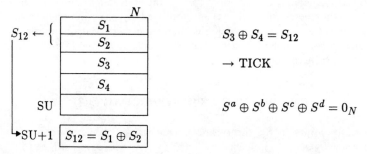

3-EVENTS

$$S'_{12} \| t_{12} = S'_1 \| t_1 \oplus S'_2 \| t_2$$

$$t_{12} = t_1 \oplus t_2$$

$$\rightarrow \text{TICK}$$

$$S^a \oplus S^b \oplus S^c = 0_N$$

4-EVENTS

$$S_3 \oplus S_4 = S_{12}$$

$$\rightarrow \text{TICK}$$

$$S^a \oplus S^b \oplus S^c \oplus S^d = 0_N$$

FIGURE 3. How events happen in program universe. Each *TICK* "records" a unique event "somewhere" in the universe.

$\{a, b, c, a \oplus b, b \oplus c, c \oplus a, a \oplus b \oplus c\}$ as well. In fact, given j l.i. strings, we can generate $2^j - 1$ DCsS's because this is the number of ways we can choose j distinct things at one, two, $\ldots$, up to j at a time. This allows us to construct the combinatorial hierarchy[4] by generating the sequence, $(2 \longrightarrow 2^2 - 1 = 3)$, $(3 \longrightarrow 2^3 - 1 = 7)$, $(7 \longrightarrow 2^7 - 1 = 127)$, $(127 \longrightarrow 2^{127} - 1 \simeq 1.7 \times 10^{38})$, mapped by the sequence, $(2 \longrightarrow 2^2 = 4)$, $(4 \longrightarrow 4^2 = 16)$, $(16 \longrightarrow 16^2 = 256)$, $(256 \longrightarrow 256^2)$. The process terminates because there are only $256^2 = 65,536 = 6.5536 \times 10^4$ l.i. matrices available to map the fourth level, which are far too few to map the $2^{127} - 1 = 1.7016 \ldots \times 10^{38}$ DCsS's of that level. This (unique) hierarchy is exhibited in TABLE 1. The closure of the hierarchy

TABLE 1. The Combinatorial Hierarchy[a]

ℓ	$B(\ell+1) = H(\ell)$	$H(\ell) = 2^{B(\ell)} - 1$	$M(\ell+1) = [M(\ell)]^2$	$C(\ell) = \sum_{j-1}^{\ell} H(j)$
Hierarchy level (0)	—		(2)	—
1	2	2	4	3
2	3	3	16	10
3	7	7	256	137
4	127	127	$(256)^2$	$2^{127} - 1 + 137$
	$2^{127} - 1$	$2^{127} - 1$		

[a] Level 5 cannot be constructed because $M(4) < H(4)$.

allows us to divide the strings generated by the program into a finite initial segment (called the label) and a growing remainder. The labels close in some representation of the 4-level combinatorial hierarchy with exactly $2^{127} + 136$ strings of fixed length, which are then used to label address ensembles, as is discussed in more detail in reference 2 and elsewhere.

Each event results in a *TICK*, which increases the complexity of the universe in an irreversible way. Our theory has an ordering parameter (N_U) that is conceptually closer to the "time" in general relativistic cosmologies than to the "reversible" time of special relativity. The arbitrary elements in the algorithm that generates events preclude unique "retrodiction," while the finite complexity parameters (SU, N_U) prevent a combinatorial explosion in statistical retrodiction. In this sense, we have a fixed (though only partially retrodictable) past and a necessarily unknown future of finite, but arbitrarily increasing complexity. Only structural characteristics of the system, rather than the bit strings used in computer simulations of pieces of our theory, are available for epistemological correlations with experience.

SCATTERING THEORY

Now that we have established the formal elements of the theory and the rules that allow us to compute formal facts, we must establish measurement criteria. This is done by relating the bit strings to the basis states of a relativistic, unitary, and "crossing symmetric" quantum particle scattering theory, and by deriving the "propagator" of that theory, which connects events as some system within the universe evolves. The labels are used to define quantum numbers—symmetric between "particles" and "antiparticles"—that are conserved in connected events. The labeled address strings are interpreted as the velocities associated with these quantum numbers; by appropriate definition, they are measured in units of the limiting velocity, "c". Since quantum scattering theory associates quantum numbers with discrete conserved masses, and 3-momentum is conserved in evolving systems, we also use the labeled address strings to define velocities (in units of the limiting velocity) which when multiplied by the appropriate discrete masses conserve 3-momentum in the discrete "3 + 1 space" that our events allow us to construct. Because the labels close, these quantum numbers and masses, m_w (which it will become the task of the theory to compute self-consistently), retain an invariant significance no matter how long the program runs, or how long and large the address string ensembles become.

The scattering theory on which we rely[5] starts from three distinguishable particles and a linear, unitary quantum dynamics based on relativistic three-particle Faddeev equations (which can be viewed as the summation of quantum events with appropriate statistical weights). The basic entities for "Yukawa coupling" are a particle, an antiparticle (number of particles minus number of antiparticles conserved), and a quantum (with zero particle quantum number) to which this pair can coalesce, or which can disassociate into the pair; a quantum can be emitted or absorbed by a particle (or antiparticle) without changing the particle quantum number. Particles and quanta may carry other conserved quantum numbers allowing a definition of "antiquanta," but there must always be one quantum state that carries only null quantum numbers. The "quantum" associated with that state is indistinguishable from its "antiquantum."

We symbolize any string by $S^w = [L^w(N_L), A^w(N)]$. Our basic quantum number scheme for three linearly independent strings of bit length 4 is given in FIGURE 4, which meets the requirements set above. For any address string $A^w(N)$, the parameter, $k_w = \Sigma_{n-1}^N b_n^w$, allows us to define a signed rational fraction, β_w, for each address string by taking $2k_w = N(1 + \beta_w)$; clearly, $\beta_w \in [-1, -(N - 1)/N, \ldots, (N - 1)/N, + 1]$. Thus, a 3-event initiates a state, $|N; k_a, k_b, k_c\rangle$, defined by four integers (referring to the address string, and at least two quantum numbers each for a, b, and c as discussed above) that specify three scalar rational fractions; these we interpret as velocities in units of the limiting velocity, c.

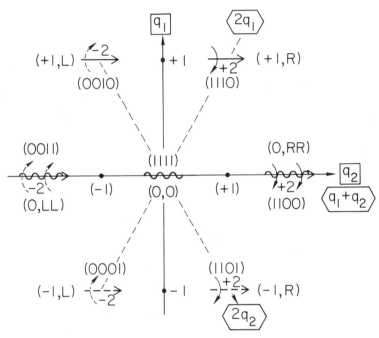

FIGURE 4. The quantum numbers for a string (b_1, b_2, b_3, b_4) defined by $q_1 = b_1 - b_2 + b_3 - b_4$ and $q_2 = b_1 + b_2 - b_2 - b_4$ plotted on a square mesh and $2q_1, 2q_2, q_1 + q_2$ plotted on a hexagonal mesh.

Because the basic discriminations also define the strings, $A^{ab} = A^a \oplus A^b = A^c$ (a, b, c cyclic), and hence $\beta_{ab} = \beta_c$, we conclude that each pair has the same velocity as the third, or spectator, system. The three velocities, the three pair-velocities, and the three masses provide 9 of the 12 degrees of freedom of the three 4-vectors in a conventional description, while the remaining three cannot be specified without specific context because our construction has geometrical isotropy. We note that the "bar" operation, $\bar{S} = 1_{N_U} \oplus S$, reverses the sign of all velocities and all quantum numbers at the same time. In contrast, if we reverse only the velocities, the helicities do not reverse, thus showing that they are "pseudo-vectors." Our basis states have the characteristics needed for "crossing symmetry" and "CPT invariance."

To obtain the statistical connection between events, we start from our counter paradigm, and note that because of the macroscopic size of laboratory counters, there will always be some uncertainty, $\Delta\beta$, in measured velocities that is reflected in our integers, k_a, by $\Delta k = \frac{1}{2}N\Delta\beta$. Thus, if we start with some specified spread of events corresponding to laboratory boundary conditions and tick away, the fraction of connected events we need consider diminishes in the manner illustrated in FIGURE 5. Because the "off shell propagator" of quantum scattering theory refers to the probability that two states that do not conserve energy will be connected, we claim that we could, given more space, conclude from this calculation that the propagator is proportional to

$$\frac{1}{(E - E' \mp i0^+)}.$$

Now that we have masses and the limiting velocity, and we know from the hierarchy construction that the simplest unit of mass to use will be either the proton or the Planck mass, the only remaining dimensional constant to assign is the unit of action, or angular momentum. In previous treatments, we have used the digital structure of the address strings and velocities to describe a drunkard's walk between events weighted by $\frac{1}{2}(1 + \beta)$ with step length, hc/E, which implies a coherence length, h/p, and hence the usual relativistic de Broglie phase and group velocities. Recent work on discrete topology by McGoveran[6] makes it likely that the digital structure also implies the usual relation, $\ell_x\ell_y = i\hbar\ell_z$, resulting from the "torsion" inherent in defining "distance" in a finite, digital space. A self-consistent definition of h, $\hbar$, and π along this route is a formal criterion we hope to meet in the near future.

THE STANDARD MODEL

We interpret one dichotomous quantum number for each of the four levels as helicity. Because Level 1 has only two independent states, and these are coupled by the "bar" operation to the sign of the velocities that they label, we interpret these two basis states as chiral (two component) neutrinos. The next two quantum numbers (Level 2) allow for particle-antiparticle (or "charge") discrimination with helicity $\pm\frac{1}{2}$ coupled to two ± 1 helicity states and the degenerate $(0_4, 1_4)$ zero helicity state. We take these to be charged leptons coupled to a massless "spin 1" quantum, and the associated "coulomb" interaction. If we were constructing a "field theory," this would restrict us to the "physical" or "coulomb" gauge. In a finite particle number theory with exact unitarity, this is not a restriction, but a conceptual necessity.

For Level 3, we concatenate a string of length 4 (interpreted as defining particle and helicity states, q_1, q_2) with a string defining the color octet. One way of getting the SU_3 octet from our strings is given in TABLE 2 (or implied in FIGURE 4). For color, we could take red = (0001), anti-red = (1110); yellow = (0010), anti-yellow = (1101); blue = (1100), anti-blue = (0011). Then, three colors or three anticolors give the color singlet (1111), as do the appropriate combinations of color and anticolor. The three basis strings so constructed give us a colored quark and the associated gluons. Because $a \oplus a \oplus a \equiv a$, three colored quarks (or antiquarks) add to give a color singlet, and they yield the spin and helicity states of a nucleon (antinucleon). Doubling the first four bits

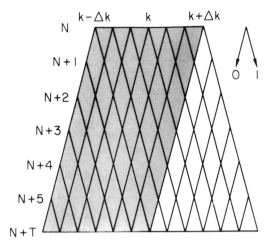

FIGURE 5. The connection between the address strings in tick-separated events resulting from an initial uncertainty in velocity measurement: If k, k' represent two values of "k" allowed by the velocity uncertainty, $\Delta\beta$, and the corresponding integral uncertainty, Δk, the correlated probability of having both, normalized to unity when they are the same, is

$$f(k,k') = \frac{2\Delta k \mp (k' - k)}{2\Delta k \pm (k' - k)},$$

where the positive sign corresponds to $k' > k$. The correlated probability of finding two values, k_T, k'_T, after T ticks in an event with the same labels and same normalization is $f(kT, k'_T)/f(k, k')$. This is 1 if $k' = k$ and $k'_T = k_T$. However, outside of this specific requirement, we can see that this ratio, written as

$$\frac{1 \pm \dfrac{2(\Delta k - \Delta k_T)}{(k' - k)} + \dfrac{4\Delta k \Delta k_T}{(k' - k)^2}}{1 \mp \dfrac{2(\Delta k - \Delta k_T)}{(k' - k)} + \dfrac{4\Delta k \Delta k_T}{(k' - k)^2}},$$

goes to 0^* in the large number or sharp resolution limits, thus correlating the limits to an ordering dependent on the sign of the velocity.

TABLE 2. The SU_3 Octet for "I, U, V Spin"[a]

	$(b_1 b_2 b_3 b_4)$	$2I_z$	$2U_z$	$2V_z = 2(I_z + U_z)$
String:	1110	$+1$	$+1$	$+2$
	0010	-1	$+2$	$+1$
	1100	$+2$	-1	$+1$
	1111	0	0	0
	0000	0	0	0
	0011	-2	$+1$	-1
	1101	$+1$	-2	-1
	0001	-1	-1	-2

[a]$2I_z = b_1 + b_2 - b_3 - b_4$; $2U_z = -2b_1 + b_2 + 2b_3 - b_4$; $2V_z = -b_1 + 2b_2 + b_3 - 2b_4$.

gives us a second flavor of quark, and we get a second nucleon when we form a color singlet using two of the first type and one of the second. Details will be presented elsewhere. Speculatively, because the scattering theory employed allows three states of the same mass to combine to the single state of that mass, we can take both the quark and the nucleon mass to be the same; this would mean that quark structure would only appear at the 3-Gev level, which is desirable if nuclear physics is to continue to use mesons and nucleons as a first approximation. Level 4 gives us a combinatorial explosion of higher generations with the same structure, but it only weakly coupled because of the large number of combinatorial possibilities.

The final step at this stage in the development of our theory is to set the mass ratio scale by invoking the Parker-Rhodes calculation.[7] As we have argued several times, our interpretation of quantum numbers and construction of $3 + 1$ "space" allows us to take this over intact, and we claim that

$$m_p/m_e = \frac{137\pi}{\langle x(1 - x)\rangle\langle 1/y\rangle},$$

with $0 \le x \le 1$ and $0 \le (1/y) \le 1$, where x is the charge in units of $e^2 = \hbar c/137$ and y is the radial distance from the center of symmetry limited from below by the minimal radial distance for a system at rest, $h/2m_p c$. The statistical calculation is straightforward, and for three degrees of freedom, it gives $\langle x(1 - x)\rangle = (3/14)[1 + (2/7) + (2/7)^2]$ and $\langle 1/y\rangle = 4/5$. Hence, m_p/m_e is predicted to be $1836.151497\ldots$ in comparison with the accepted value of 1836.1515 ± 0.0005. Although this result has been published and presented many times, we know of no published challenge to the calculation.

CONCLUSIONS

As we have said before,[2]

The idea of a theory as a *theory of constructions* is valid independent of the "information content" of the theory. In order for a research program to succeed, it must create complete understanding in the way we have developed the theory. Whatever "machinery" is formulated as a theory of constructions, the participator idea implicit in the theory structure is necessary in order to understand.

In this paper, we have proved that by starting from bit strings generated by *program universe* and labeled by the $2^{127} + 136$ strings provided by any representation of the four-level *combinatorial hierarchy*, one gets an S-matrix theory with the usual C, P, T properties, *CPT* and crossing invariance, manifest covariance, and a candidate to replace quantum field theory by an N-particle scattering theory which will not be in conflict with practice for some sufficiently large *finite N*. Arbitrary ("random") choice and nonlocality provide the supraluminal correlations experimentally demonstrated in EPR experiments without allowing supraluminal transmission of information. As is true for any quantum mechanical theory, ours stands because of the outcome of Aspect's and similar experiments, and would have to fall if these are rejected. We claim to have arrived at an *objective* quantum mechanics with all the needed properties.

REFERENCES

1. WHEELER, J. A. 1983. Law without law. *In* Quantum Theory and Measurement. J. A. Wheeler & W. H. Zurek, Eds.: 182–213. Princeton Univ. Press. Princeton, New Jersey.

2. NOYES, H. P., C. GEFWERT & M. J. MANTHEY. 1985. In Symposium on the Foundations of Modern Physics, June 16–20, 1985, Joensuu, Finland. P. Lahti & P. Mittelstaedt, Eds.: 511–524. World Scientific. Singapore; see also: 1983. Toward a constructive physics. SLAC-PUB-3116 (Sept.), and references therein.

3. GEFWERT, C. 1983. A participator: the metaphysical subject. SLAC-PUB-3277 (Dec.). Synthese. To be submitted; 1984. The proposition-as-rules idea. SLAC-PUB-3303 (March). Synthese. To be submitted; On the logical form of primitive recursive functions. SLAC-PUB-3334 (May). J. Philos. Logic. To be submitted; On the logical form of mathematical language. SLAC-PUB-3344 (May). J. Philos. Logic. To be submitted.

4. BASTIN, T. 1966. Stud. Philos. Gandensia 4: 77.

5. NOYES, H. P. & J. V. LINDESAY. 1983. Aust. J. Phys. 36: 601; LINDESAY, J. V., A. J. MARKEVICH, H. P. NOYES & G. PASTRANA. 1986. A self-consistent, Poincaré invariant, and unitary three-particle scattering theory. Phys. Rev. D33: 2339–2349.

6. MCGOVERAN, D. 1985. Seventh Annual International Meeting of the Alternative Natural Philosophy Association, King's College, Cambridge. Proceedings available from F. Abdullah, City University, University of London.

7. PARKER-RHODES, A. F. 1981. The Theory of Indistinguishables. Synthese Library 150: 182–185. Reidel. Dordrecht.

A Derivation of Quantum Phenomena from a Wave System Model

T. B. ANDREWS[a]

A new wave system model of elementary particles has been developed from which basic quantum phenomena may be derived and logically understood. In this wave model, the elementary particles are hypothesized to be the constructive interference peaks of a wave system that extends throughout the universe.

The basic problem with this hypothesis, specifically, the stability of the constructive interference peaks, has been solved by assuming that the parameters, T and σ, of the classical wave equation,

$$(\partial/\partial x)[T(x)\partial y/\partial x] = \sigma(x)\partial^2 y/\partial t^2,$$

are proportional to the energy density. The stability of the peaks then depends on the fact that a wave system with variable parameters has a lower frequency than a comparable constant parameter system. Consequently, the system frequency is reduced because the concentration of energy at the constructive interference peaks results in large values of the parameters at the peaks and very small parameter values in the destructive interference regions.

Because the frequency reduction is proportional to the number of wave modes constructively interfering ($N = 10^{45}$), and any reduction in the constructive interference would then require a large energy input, the constructive interference is very stable. At the same time, increased constraints on the wave system as N increases tend to raise the system frequency. This effect establishes a lower bound on the system frequency.

This wave model of elementary particles is taken very seriously because important theoretical results have been obtained. For example, the dependence of the ratio of the electrostatic to the gravitational force on the number of wave modes, and the existence of a cosmological (relative) gravitational potential that explains both the Hubble redshift and the "missing mass" in galaxies and galaxy clusters.

The de Broglie wavelength and the Schrödinger equation are derived from a Lorentz transformation of the classical wave equation subject to the condition that the peaks stay in-phase with the wave modes. This derivation, plus the localized nature of the constructive interference peaks, is proposed as a solution to the "measurement" problem in quantum theory. For example, in the two-slit interference experiment, the particle must stay in-phase with the wave modes to minimize its frequency and energy. Because the in-phase condition is equivalent to the de Broglie wavelength of a particle, the interference from many particles corresponds to the pattern produced by a classical wave with a de Broglie wavelength.

It is concluded from the wave system model that the general applicability of quantum theory is due to the wave nature of all phenomena.

---

[a]Present address: 3828 Atlantic Avenue, Brooklyn, New York 11224.

A Proposal for the Completion of the Realization of Wigner's Gedanken-Experiment

M. BOŽIĆ

Institute of Physics
11001 Beograd, Yugoslavia

The perfect-crystal neutron interferometer coupled with spin-flipper and phase-shifter has been used recently[1] to produce two widely separated coherent beams of neutron waves with polarization states, "$+z$" and "$-z$", and to recombine them subsequently. The set consisting of the accelerator coil, the $\pi/2$-spin turn-coil, and the Heusler-crystal analyzer situated behind the interferometer serves to determine the direction of the polarization vector, $\vec{P}$, of the recombined beam. The experiment shows[1] that the polarization, $\vec{P}$, is directed along the vector,

$$\vec{n} = \cos \chi \vec{i} + \sin \chi \vec{j}, \qquad (1)$$

that is,

$$\vec{P} = c\vec{n}, \qquad (2)$$

where χ is the phase difference between two coherent beams and c is a constant that has not been measured here.

In this way, this experiment directly verifies from left to right the spin state superposition principle,

$$|\pi/2, \chi\rangle = [|\uparrow_z\rangle + \exp(i\chi)|\downarrow_z\rangle]/\sqrt{2}, \qquad (3)$$

according to which the superposition,

$$[|\uparrow_z\rangle + \exp(i\chi)|\downarrow_z\rangle]/\sqrt{2}, \qquad (4)$$

is the eigenstate of the operator,

$$\hat{S}_z = \hat{S}_x \cdot \cos \chi + \hat{S}_y \cdot \sin \chi. \qquad (5)$$

The importance of the experiment[1] comes also from the fact that it is considered to be the realization of Wigner's gedanken-experiment[2] (FIGURE 1) and that it resolves the dilemma in the theory of measurement in favor of the orthodox interpretation. We propose a minor modification of the original apparatus[1] in order to complete the realization of Wigner's experiment. This modification should consist of the replacement of the Heusler-crystal analyzer, the accelerator coil, and the $\pi/2$-spin turn-coil by the Stern-Gerlach (SG) magnet of variable orientation. The sketch of the modified apparatus is shown in FIGURE 2. With an SG magnet whose field is along the vector, $\vec{n}$, one would directly answer Wigner's question, of which a little generalized form is: Will the beam be deviated or split by the SG magnet with the field along the vector $\vec{n}$?

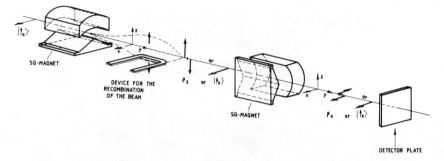

FIGURE 1. The scheme of Wigner's gedanken-experiment.

The deviation would mean that the neutrons emerging from the interferometer in the direction O before entering the SG magnet are in a pure state (equation 3), whereas the splitting would indicate that they are in the mixed state described by the density matrix,

$$\rho_z = [\,|\uparrow_z\rangle\langle\uparrow_z| + |\downarrow_z\rangle\langle\downarrow_z|\,]/2. \tag{6}$$

In the case of splitting, one could conclude that after passing through the SG magnet, the state of neutrons is described by the density matrix,

$$\rho_{\vec{n}} = [\,|\uparrow_{\vec{n}}\rangle\langle\uparrow_{\vec{n}}| + |\downarrow_{\vec{n}}\rangle\langle\downarrow_{\vec{n}}|\,]/2. \tag{7}$$

The modified experiment would also be relevant for the verification of the spin state superposition principle. With the field along $\vec{n}$, it would verify equation 3 from

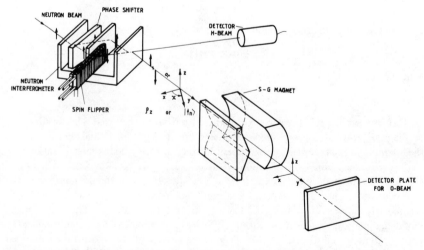

FIGURE 2. The apparatus for the realization of Wigner's experiment based on neutron interferometry.

right to left, whereas with the field along the z-axis, it would verify the same equation from left to right.

We want to point out that in all of the experiments mentioned here, one answers the question of whether the state of the measured object is a pure state or a mixture; on the other hand, the dilemma in the theory of measurement is between a pure and a mixed state of the object + apparatus after their mutual interaction.

According to the orthodox interpretation, after the interaction between the object and apparatus, but before the reduction of the state, the system object + apparatus is in a pure state. Consequently, the measured object is in a mixed state.[3] In the most-often considered alternative interpretation of the orthodox one, the state of the object + apparatus after the interaction is a mixture, as is the state of the object.

However, in the experiment studied, one finds that the measured object (neutron) is in a pure state. Thus, we consider that it does not follow from the mentioned result that the orthodox interpretation is valid. Instead, the above experiments suggest a new alternative interpretation of the measuring process. In it, the state of the object, ψ_ν, after the interaction with the apparatus changes into another pure state, $\psi_{\nu'}$.

ACKNOWLEDGMENTS

I am grateful to Z. Marić and J-P. Vigier for their inspiration and help.

REFERENCES

1. BADUREK, G., H. RAUCH, J. SUMMHAMMER, U. KISCHKO & A. ZEILINGER. 1983. J. Phys. **A16:** 1133–1139.
2. WIGNER, E. P. 1963. Am. J. Phys. **31:** 6–15.
3. LONDON, F. & E. BAUER. 1939. La Theorie de l'Observation en Méchanique Quantique, p. 37. Hermann. Paris.

Two-Time States of a Spin-Half Particle in a Uniform Magnetic Field

SUSAN S. D'AMATO

Physics Department
Furman University
Greenville, South Carolina 29613

Recent investigations[1-3] have shown that two-time measurements on a quantum mechanical system may create correlations between the values of noncommuting observables of the system at different times, and that, moreover, these correlations may be interpreted as an indication that such measurements place the system in a two-time

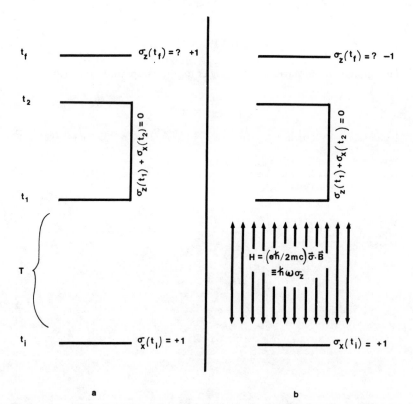

a   **b**

FIGURE 1. Given that spin measurements carried out on a particle at t_i and t_1/t_2 yield $\sigma_x(t_i) = +1$ and $\sigma_z(t_1) + \sigma_x(t_2) = 0$, the outcome of a measurement of σ_z at t_f depends on whether or not the particle experiences a uniform magnetic field in the z-direction in the interval between t_i and t_1. (a) In the absence of such a field, $\sigma_z(t_f) = +1$. (b) If such a field is switched on for a time $T = \pi/2\omega$, then $\sigma_z(t_f) = -1$.

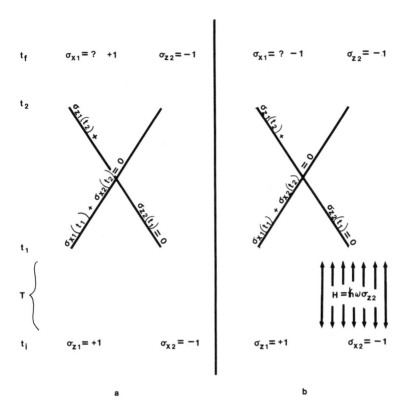

FIGURE 2. Given that the spin measurements carried out on two particles at t_i and t_1/t_2 yield $\sigma_{z1}(t_i) = +1$, $\sigma_{x2}(t_i) = -1$, and $\sigma_{x1}(t_1) + \sigma_{x2}(t_2) = \sigma_{z1}(t_2) + \sigma_{z2}(t_1) = 0$, the outcome of a measurement of σ_{x1} at t_f depends on whether or not particle 2 experiences a uniform magnetic field in the z-direction in the interval between t_i and t_1. (a) In the absence of such a field, $\sigma_{x1}(t_f) = +1$. (b) If such a field is switched on for a time $T = \pi/2\omega$, then $\sigma_{x1}(t_f) = -1$.

state (a state that is an eigenstate of the measured observable). In the present work, it is shown that the two-time states of a system store information about the history of the system in a way that its single-time states cannot.

Consider a spin-half particle subjected to a series of spin measurements. Suppose that, as illustrated in FIGURE 1a, these measurements reveal that $\sigma_x(t_i) = +1$ and that $\sigma_z(t_1) + \sigma_x(t_2) = 0$, where the σ_i are the Pauli matrices. (The two-time measurement at t_1/t_2 might be achieved by passing a particle beam through two appropriately oriented Stern-Gerlach instruments, and then recombining the two emerging beams for which $\sigma_z = -\sigma_x$.) If a measurement of σ_z is then carried out at some final time, t_f, what will be the result?

By projecting the known two-time state of the particle at t_1/t_2 [the eigenvalue-zero eigenstate of $\sigma_z(t_1) + \sigma_x(t_2)$] onto the particle's initial state in the manner explained in reference 3, it can easily be shown that the measurement at t_f must yield $\sigma_z(t_f) = +1$ if the particle's Hamiltonian is independent of spin in the intervals between the measurements. If, however, the particle experiences a uniform magnetic field in the

z-direction in the interval between t_i and t_1 for the length of time specified in FIGURE 1b, then the measurement of $\sigma_z(t_f)$ must yield -1 rather than $+1$. Therefore, the z-component of the particle's spin at t_f contains a record of the presence or absence of a field in the z-direction at an earlier time.

This result can be attributed to the correlation between $\sigma_z(t)$ and $\sigma_x(t')$ that is introduced by the two-time measurement at t_1/t_2. Because of this correlation, any change in σ_x that occurs prior to t_1 (such as the sign change induced by the magnetic field in the present example) must produce a corresponding change in the measured value of σ_z at times subsequent to t_2. In contrast, if no correlation is established at t_1/t_2, that is, if σ_z and σ_x are measured separately at those times, then the presence or absence of a magnetic field prior to t_1 has no effect on the measured value of $\sigma_z(t_f)$: the results of $+1$ and -1 are equally likely in that case, no matter if the particle experiences a magnetic field prior to t_1 or not. Therefore, a system subjected to two-time measurements (in other words, a system characterized by two-time states) "remembers" its history in a way that a system subjected only to single-time measurements does not.

It is interesting to observe this effect in a system of two spacelike-separated spin-half particles. If interparticle correlations are established in this case by two-particle, two-time measurements carried out at t_1/t_2, then, as shown in FIGURE 2, the outcome of a measurement of σ_{x1} at t_f depends on the presence or absence of a uniform field in the neighborhood of particle 2 in the interval between t_i and t_1. No relativistic paradox exists, however. The measurement of the two-time observables can be achieved only by passing particle beams at x_1 and x_2 through an appropriate array of Stern-Gerlach instruments and then combining the four emerging beams for which $\sigma_{x1}(t_1) + \sigma_{x2}(t_2) = \sigma_{z1}(t_2) + \sigma_{z2}(t_1) = 0$. Only through the interference of these beams can the sign of $\sigma_{x1}(t_f)$ (whether $+$ or $-$) be predicted with certainty.

REFERENCES

1. AHARONOV, Y. & D. Z. ALBERT. 1984. Phys. Rev. **D29:** 223–227.
2. D'AMATO, S. S. 1985. Multiple-time measurements on quantum mechanical systems. *In* Fundamental Questions in Quantum Mechanics. L. M. Roth & A. Inomata, Eds.: 225–239. Gordon & Breach. New York.
3. AHARONOV, Y., D. Z. ALBERT & S. S. D'AMATO. 1985. Phys. Rev. **D32:** 1975–1984.

Continuously Variable Spin Vectors and Spin Measurements in the Causal Interpretation of Quantum Mechanics

C. DEWDNEY

Laboratoire de Physique Théorique
Institut Henri Poincaré
75231 Paris Cedex 05, France

In the causal interpretation of the Pauli equation proposed by Bohm *et al.*,[1] spin may be understood in terms of an intuitive model in which the Pauli spinor is interpreted as defining the orientation of a spinning body in terms of the Euler angles, θ, ϕ, and ψ. As we have shown in specific calculations, the well-defined spin vector may have a continuously variable orientation.[2,3] According to the equations of motion derived by casting the Pauli equation in pseudoclassical form, a spinning particle is subject to an additional quantum torque and spin-dependent quantum force. These may be thought of as quantum mechanical features arising from a quantum addition to the scalar and vector potentials, and they introduce a new form of spin-orbit coupling. An analysis of the measurement of the spin component along a particular direction using a Stern-Gerlach apparatus (SGA) reveals how the quantum torque and force account for the dichotomous results ($+h/2$, $-h/2$).

In such a measurement, the system variable is the spin, whereas the apparatus variable is the actual particle position. This is so because by observing the position, we can infer a unique value for the spin. Let us assume that the particle traveling in the y-direction arrives at the aperture of the SGA with its spin vector pointing along the x-direction, and that the field is in the z-direction. Assuming the aperture has a Gaussian transmission, then the distribution of particle positions (apparatus hidden variables) will be Gaussian. The equations of motion will then enable the calculation of the correlated evolution of the system and the apparatus hidden variables (the actual spin vector and particle position). The results are shown in the figures.

FIGURE 1 shows the ensemble of possible motions of the apparatus coordinate (particle trajectories) from a Gaussian distribution of initial positions. FIGURE 2 shows the evolution of the spin vector as the initial packet splits into two eventually separated packets (we plot the orientation to the z-axis at a matrix of points, z, y). The "measurement" is thus shown to be a transformation in which the system variable and the apparatus coordinate undergo a correlated evolution. Evidently, once the initial spin orientation is given, this determines the position of the bifurcation plane in the wave packet. The outcome of a particular "measurement" then depends sensitively on the actual initial value of the apparatus coordinate. The role of the apparatus hidden variable enables us to understand the fact that if a further measurement is made (say, in the x-direction) on one of the emerging beams, there is an equal probability of finding the result of $+h/2$ or $-h/2$. If the spin vector lies along the z-axis, the wave packet will bifurcate this time along the y, z-plane. Of course, if the original orientation of the spin vector is not perpendicular to the field, then the bifurcation takes place

571

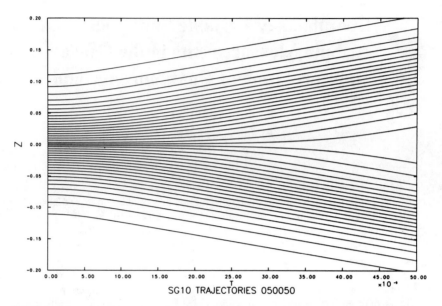

FIGURE 1. The ensemble of possible motions of the apparatus coordinate (particle trajectories) from a Gaussian distribution of initial positions.

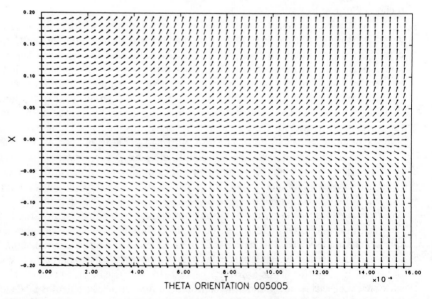

FIGURE 2. The evolution of the spin vector as the initial packet splits into two eventually separated packets.

away from the center of the packet. Thus, two unequal separating packets are formed, in each of which the spin vector is rotated to align with or opposed to the field. Furthermore, this analysis indicates that in the EPR Bohm experiment[4] carried out on two spin-half particles in the singlet state, the positions of the two particles at the entrance to the SGAs must play an essential role in determining the correlations. Correlations in the positions of the particles imply that the apparatus hidden variables are correlated in addition to the system variables. Thus, we see how it is possible for the two particles to have well-defined spin vectors and yet maintain correlations in the results of measurements carried out in arbitrary directions.

REFERENCES

1. BOHM, D., R. SCHILLER & J. TIOMNO. 1955. Nuovo Cimento Suppl. (series X) 1: 48.
2. DEWDNEY, C., P. R. HOLLAND, A. KYPRIANIDIS & J. P. VIGIER. 1986. Trajectories and spin vector orientations in the causal interpretation of the Pauli equation. Institut Henri Poincaré preprint.
3. DEWDNEY, C., P. R. HOLLAND, A. KYPRIANIDIS & J. P. VIGIER. 1986. Spin superposition in neutron interferometry. Institut Henri Poincaré preprint.
4. BOHM, D. 1951. Quantum Theory, chap. 22. Prentice-Hall. Englewood, New Jersey.

On a Lorentz Invariant Quantum Theory of Measurement

G. N. FLEMING

Department of Physics
Pennsylvania State University
University Park, Pennsylvania 16802

I propose a pervasive and consistent replacement of the concept of time dependence by the concept of dependence on spacelike hyperplanes in the formalism and interpretation of Lorentz invariant quantum theory. This replacement enables one to: (i) formulate a Lorentz invariant reduction postulate (a development of a proposal of Aharonov and Albert[1]) to the end of resolving apparent paradoxes relating to sets of measurements in Minkowski space-time; (ii) interpret the spacelike dispersion of frame-dependent localization of particles (à la Hegerfeldt[2]) in a covariant manner that removes the threat of superluminal signal propagation and causal anomalies; and (iii) resolve the time-ordering ambiguities of state reduction in the discussion of relativistic aspects of the EPR experiment by Shimony.[3] The developed formalism[4] appears to accommodate the covariant description of single particles interacting with a large class of hyperplane-dependent external potentials, as well as field theoretic interactions both local and nonlocal.[5]

The proposal involves three closely related parts. First, time-dependent state functions are to be replaced by hyperplane-dependent state functions. Second, in the Heisenberg picture, time-dependent observables and their time-dependent eigenvectors are to be replaced by hyperplane-dependent observables and eigenvectors. Third, and most important for the quantum theory of measurement, state vector reductions at definite instants of time are to be replaced by state vector reductions on definite spacelike hyperplanes. Consistency demands that in the presence of several measurements with spacelike separations, the assignment of reduced state vectors to the various possible hyperplanes follow certain rules.[4]

Consider the example of three measurements employing the spacelike interaction regions, R_1, R_2, and R_3. Let R_1 and R_2 be wholly spacelike with respect to each other, while R_3 is partly future timelike with respect to both R_1 and R_2 (see FIGURE 1). Now, consider the subensemble of systems beginning in the state, $|\psi\rangle$, which yields the results 1, 2, and 3 from the measurements executed in R_1, R_2, and R_3, respectively. Then, the assignment of reduced state vectors to the various possible hyperplanes for the subensemble is indicated in FIGURE 1 with, hopefully, self-evident notation. Notice that no state vectors are associated with hyperplanes passing through any interaction regions because on such hyperplanes the quantum system is coupled to the environment and, in general, has no state vector of its own.

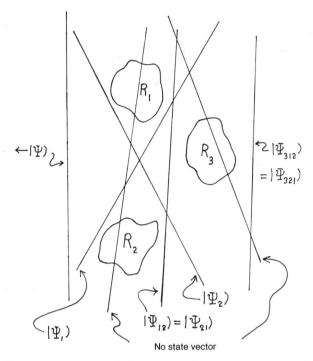

No state vector

FIGURE 1. Three measurements employing the space-time interaction regions, R_1, R_2, and R_3 (see text).

REFERENCES

1. AHARONOV, Y. & D. Z. ALBERT. 1984. Phys. Rev. **D29**: 228. Ultimately, the idea goes back to: TOMONAGA, I. 1946. Prog. Theor. Phys. **1**: 27; SCHWINGER, J. 1948. Phys. Rev. **74**: 1439.
2. HEGERFELDT, G. C. 1985. Phys. Rev. Lett. **54**: 2395.
3. SHIMONY, A. 1986. Events and processes in the quantum world. *In* Quantum Concepts in Space and Time. C. Isham & R. Penrose, Eds.: 182. Oxford Univ. Press. London/New York.
4. FLEMING, G. N. 1986. Towards a Lorentz invariant quantum theory of measurement. *In* Mini-Course and Workshop on Fundamental Physics. Univ. of Puerto Rico Press. To appear (presently available as a Penn State University preprint).
5. FLEMING, G. N. Lectures on Lorentz invariant quantum theory of measurement. In preparation. For earlier work on the idea of hyperplane dependence, see: FLEMING, G. N. 1964. Phys. Rev. **137B**: 188; 1966. J. Math. Phys. **7**: 1959; 1968. J. Math. Phys. **9**: 193.

Lagrangian with Nonlinear Terms for the Self-Energy and Particle-Particle Interactions

PAUL HARRIS[a]

The free spinor-particle Lagrangian of Proca[1] can be extended by inclusion of a particle-particle interaction term, $(\xi^+\eta)$ $(\eta^+\xi)$, and self-energy terms, $(\xi^+\xi)$ and $(\eta^+\eta)$, where ξ represents one particle, and η the other. The result is

$$L = \frac{1}{2}\left(\frac{d\xi^+}{d\tau}\xi - \xi^+\frac{d\xi}{d\tau}\right) + \frac{1}{2}\left(\frac{d\eta^+}{d\tau}\eta - \eta^+\frac{d\eta}{d\tau}\right) + \lambda_e^{(1)}(\dot{x}_{(1)}^e - \xi^+\gamma^e\xi)$$

$$+ \lambda_e^{(2)}(\dot{x}_{(2)}^e - \eta^+\gamma^e\eta) + \alpha_0(\xi^+\xi)^2 + \alpha_0(\eta^+\eta)^2 + \alpha_1(\xi^+\eta)(\eta^+\xi), \quad (1)$$

where the α_i are constants, and the sub(super)scripts "(1)" and "(2)" denote the particle number. The Euler-Lagrange equations then give the interesting results of

$$u_{(1)}^e = \xi^+\gamma^e\xi, \quad u_{(2)}^e = \eta^+\gamma^e\eta, \quad (2)$$

$$\frac{dU_{(1)}^\sigma}{d\tau} \equiv \frac{du_{(1)}^\sigma}{d\tau} + 2\lambda_e^{(1)}M_{(1)}^{e\sigma} = \alpha_1\langle(\xi^+\gamma^\sigma\eta)(\eta^+\xi) - (\eta^+\gamma^\sigma\xi)(\xi^+\eta)\rangle, \quad (3)$$

$$\frac{dU_2^\sigma}{d\tau} \equiv \frac{du_2^\sigma}{d\tau} + 2\lambda_e^{(2)}M_{(2)}^{e\sigma} = -\frac{dU_1^\sigma}{d\tau}, \quad M_{(1)}^{e\sigma} \equiv -\frac{1}{2}\xi^+[\gamma^e,\gamma^\sigma]\xi, \quad (4)$$

$$\frac{d(\xi^+\xi)}{d\tau} = \frac{d(\eta^+\eta)}{d\tau} = 0, \quad (5)$$

$$\lambda_e^{(1)} = \text{constant}, \quad \text{and} \quad \lambda_e^{(2)} = \text{constant}. \quad (6)$$

Equations 2 define four-velocities. Equations 3 and 4 yield action = reaction acceleration terms that suggest a center of mass and a "zitterbewegung" decomposition similar to that recently identified by Barut and Zanghi[2] for a single particle with a vector potential interaction term. $(\xi^+\xi)$ and $(\eta^+\eta)$ remain parametrically (relative to τ) invariant, suggesting a possible definition of electric charge, and the $\lambda_e^{(i)}$ are identifiable as the four-component bare mass actions.[1]

For $\alpha_1 = 0$, one can show that

$$\frac{d^2(S_{(1)}^{-1}\xi)}{d\tau^2} = -[\lambda_{(1)} - 2i\alpha_0\gamma^4(\xi^+\xi)]^2(S_{(1)}^{-1}\xi), \quad (7)$$

where S is a diagonalization matrix, $S_{(i)}^{-1}(\lambda_e^{(i)}\gamma^e)S_{(i)} = \pm i\lambda_{(i)}$, and $\lambda_e^{(i)}\lambda^{e(i)} \equiv -\lambda_{(i)}^2$. Thus, the self-energy terms introduce $\pm$ mass splittings relative to the $\lambda_{(i)}$. Working to

---

[a]P.H. is associated with the City College of New York. Present address: 7 Hamilton Road, Morristown, New Jersey 07960.

the lowest order in nonvanishing contributions to equation 3 gives a piece of $dU^\sigma_{(1)}/d\tau$ proportional to

$$2\alpha_1(\eta^+\xi)^2\tau(u^\sigma_{(1)} - u^\sigma_{(2)}). \tag{8}$$

The above expression compares in form to $mc^2(du^e/ds) = qF^{eu}u_u$, where F^{eu} is the electromagnetic stress-energy tensor and q is the charge. Thus, there also appears to be the possibility of interpreting electromagnetic fields in terms of local spinor variables. The $(\Delta u)\tau$ contained in expression 8 is also suggestive of a Coulomb's law behavior in that $dv/dt = \beta r^{-2} = \beta[r_0 + (\Delta v)t]^{-2}$ gives $dv/dt \sim \beta r_0^{-2}[1 - 2(\Delta v)t/r_0]$.

REFERENCES

1. PROCA, A. 1954. J. Phys. Radium **15**: 65.
2. BARUT, A. O. & N. ZANGHI. 1984. Phys. Rev. Lett. **52**: 2009.

Can Single Quantum Events Carry Superluminal Signals?

NICK HERBERT

Consulting Physicist
Boulder Creek, California 95006

On grounds more general than quantum theory, John Bell proves that any conceivable model of how individual events acquire their attributes must be nonlocal, that is, superluminally connected.[1] On the other hand, Eberhard has shown, within quantum theory, that event averages (quantum measurements) are never nonlocal.[2] We are forced to conclude that our world consists of locally connected patterns made up of nonlocally connected individual events. Because nature is connected superluminally at the individual event level, can humans use these connections to signal faster-than-light (FTL)?

We show that if Heisenberg's principle constrains ensembles and not individual measurements, then FTL signaling is possible. For instance, FTL signaling follows from an EPR setup if the polarization state of a single photon is measurable (FLASH proposal).[3]

We show here that a noiseless nonselective gain-of-two laser amplifier suffices to make such a measurement, but a more realistic amplifier due to L. Mandel[4] fails. We conclude that although you may "know for sure" how a particular photon is polarized, it is experimentally impossible to actually verify this knowledge; that is, a single photon's polarization is a kind of "hidden variable."

"Elements of reality" was what Einstein called such special known-with-certainty quantum attributes.[5] Our result that the purportedly certain value of an "Einstein attribute" cannot actually be verified suggests that the nature of quantum attributes is more subtle than is generally imagined.

REFERENCES

1. HERBERT, N. 1985. Quantum Reality: Beyond the New Physics. Chapter 12. Doubleday Anchor Press. New York.
2. EBERHARD, P. 1978. Nuovo Cimento **46B:** 392–419.
3. HERBERT, N. 1982. Found. Phys. **12:** 1171–1179.
4. MANDEL, L. 1983. Nature **304:** 188.
5. EINSTEIN, A., B. PODOLSKY & N. ROSEN. 1935. Phys. Rev. **47:** 777–780.

Locality, Causality, and the Aharonov-Bohm Effect

P. R. HOLLAND

Laboratoire de Physique Théorique
Institut Henri Poincaré
75321 Paris Cedex 05, France

Aharonov and Bohm[1] showed that if one adheres to the principle of the localizability of the interaction of matter and radiation, then the electromagnetic potentials have a physical significance in quantum mechanics that goes beyond their auxiliary role in classical physics. They argued that although one could formally replace the potentials by line integrals of the field strengths, this did not make quantum mechanics essentially nonlocal. In addition, such a procedure tended to contradict the very reason for introducing the notion of field in the first place. Recently, the assumption of locality has been questioned[2] by claiming (with particular reference to the AB effect) that the quantum mechanical one-body problem contains nonlocal features. We shall analyze this question in terms of the quantum potential model.[3] In fact, many discussions of the AB effect tacitly use the notion of an electron trajectory in the interferometer, but they do not do so consistently by adopting the causal interpretation.

Writing $\psi = Re^{iS/\hbar}$, the Schrödinger equation is equivalent to a Hamilton-Jacobi equation, from which we derive the equation of motion,

$$m\frac{dv}{dt} = -\nabla(Q + V) + F, \quad Q = -\frac{\hbar^2}{2m}\frac{\nabla^2 R}{R}, \tag{1}$$

where F is the Lorentz force and $mv = \nabla S - (e/c)A$, together with a conservation law and

$$\oint mv \cdot dx = nh - \frac{e}{c}\Phi, \quad \Phi = \oint A \cdot dx \tag{2}$$

for a spacelike circuit. The trajectories, $x = x(t)$, may be plotted by solving $\dot{x} = v$ if the initial conditions on ψ are supplemented with the initial particle position in a packet. The AB effect occurs where $F = 0$ in a region accessible to the particles, but where the potentials are nonvanishing. The necessity of such an action follows from equation 2 because if $\Phi \neq nch/e$, then uniform motion is not possible. Although the external field does not appear explicitly in equation 1 in this case, the particle is at all times locally acted upon by the quantum potential, Q. This is derived from the quantum state by solving Schrödinger's equation with all the boundary conditions, and therefore it contains information on slit widths, particle mass, packet velocities, etc., as well as the presence of the flux, which is a result of the sampling of the environment by the quantum field. Q thus provides a vehicle for the action of the potentials.

The objection to the potentials being physically effective hinges on their gauge dependence and their consequent "unobservability." However, an indirect, but local action of the potentials on particles via the gauge invariant quantum potential explains why the AB effect arises in quantum mechanics when no such effect is anticipated in classical physics. This happens because in the latter domain, $Q = 0$ (a similar result holds for gravity[4]). Thus, while observable results may depend only on certain global attributes of a given physical process (e.g., Φ), this does not mean that the physical actions that determine the experimental outcome are irreducibly of this kind. From this point of view, the AB effect is no more mysterious than two-slit interference itself because the information in Q relating to the slits does not fall off with distance. One may throw further light on this problem by asking what happens if the flux is switched on during an interference experiment.[5] The causal interpretation can give a precise answer to this question because the notion of the distance between particle and screen has a well-defined meaning for all electron positions in the interferometer. One sees that the effect of the field is propagated locally through space-time, and causality is preserved. In fact, one might conceive of introducing a time dependence into any of the other parameters on which Q depends because there is no essential difference between this and the changes in the external field.

Therefore, the quantum mechanical one-body problem is a local, but context-dependent field theory in which the wave function is an objectively real field whose time-dependent evolution determines particle motions. The fact that localized boundary conditions (e.g., slit width) have distant effects is a consequence of the fact that Q depends on the whole quantum state. However, this feature should not be termed "nonlocality" because the effect of any change in external fields or boundary conditions will be propagated at a finite speed to a distant point. The term "nonlocality" should be reserved for a many-body system whose associated quantum potential in configuration space does not decompose into a sum of quantum potentials where each is dependent only on the coordinates of one of the particles in the system.

REFERENCES

1. AHARONOV, Y. & D. BOHM. 1959. Phys. Rev. **115:** 485; 1961. Phys. Rev. **123:** 1511; 1962. Phys. Rev. **125:** 2192; 1963. Phys. Rev. **130:** 1625.
2. AHARONOV, Y. 1984. Proc. Int. Symp. on Foundations of Quantum Mechanics (1983). Phys. Soc. Japan. Tokyo.
3. PHILIPPIDIS, C., D. BOHM & R. D. KAYE. 1982. Nuovo Cimento **71B:** 75.
4. HOLLAND, P. R. & J. P. VIGIER. 1985. Nuovo Cimento **88B:** 20.
5. VAN KAMPEN, N. G. 1984. Phys. Lett. **106A:** 5; TROUDET, T. 1985. Phys. Lett. **111A:** 274.

Information Mechanics Perspective on Some Assumptions in Classical Mechanics and Quantum Mechanics about Measurement

F. W. KANTOR[a]

Classical mechanics (CM) and quantum mechanics (QM) do not provide quantitative treatment of information transport by the motion of a mass object: both assume that quantity to be infinite (see section entitled QUANTUM MECHANICS EXAMPLE). Because of this deficiency, CM and QM are not proper tools for constructing a quantitative theory of measurement; information "bookkeeping" is needed. Early work in information mechanics (IM) proceeded via the development of a sequence of information "bookkeeping theorems," of which the first few were subsequently replaced in the mid-1970s during the axiomatization of IM. In 1977, John Wiley & Sons published the original research notes in IM (including axiomatic IM) as a book entitled *Information Mechanics* (ISBN 0-471-02968-8; QC28.K36). This book[1] is literally the defining work for the field, and is required reading for anyone seriously pursuing theoretical, experimental, and/or applied work in IM.

For those interested in the history of physics, in FIGURES 1A and 1B is an informal outline, abstracted from the older, nonaxiomatic treatment, showing how information bookkeeping was originally extended in IM to include mass objects.

QUANTUM MECHANICS EXAMPLE

Consider a box, *B1*, containing a mass system, *S1*, described using quantum mechanics (QM). QM has an assumption used in classical mechanics (CM): namely, that the measurement of *S1* designates one out of an infinite set of distinguishable possibilities. This can be seen in assumption of calculus of infinitesimals in Schrödinger's formulation, and of infinite dimensional function space (Hilbert space) in Heisenberg's formulation. Using definition 1 (FIGURE 1A), the designation of one out of infinitely many would represent an infinite amount of information. *B1* supposedly would transport its contained information in moving. Because QM requires discreteness, in QM, transport of an infinite amount of information from one place to another in finite time would require an infinite amount of energy. Such a box, *B1*, might be imagined about any object in uniform, linear motion. Thus, in at least this way, it would seem that, taken on its own terms, quantum mechanics is a mechanics of immovable objects.

This difficulty appears to be due to combining discreteness with the requirement that one assume it to be possible to designate one out of infinitely many distinguishable

[a]F. W. Kantor is an independent inventor/physicist. His present address is: 523 West 112th Street, New York, New York 10025.

USING PART OF NON-RELATIVISTIC
QUANTUM MECHANICS ('NRQM') AND PART OF
ELECTROMAGNETIC THEORY ('EMT'),
WRITING 'LOG BASE 2' AS 'LOG2', AND
WRITING INFORMALLY, HERE IS AN OUTLINE
OF SOME OF THE EARLY (NON-AXIOMATIC)
RESULTS FROM INFORMATION MECHANICS
('IM'), ABSTRACTED FROM: KANTOR, F.W.
1977. INFORMATION MECHANICS. JOHN
WILEY & SONS. NEW YORK, NY. ISBN 0-
471-02968-8. QC28.K36 :

DEF.1. 'INFORMATION' IS
SPECIFICATION OF ONE FROM J>1
POSSIBILITIES, AND IS MEASURED IN
'BITS' BY LOG2(J); RESTRICTED TO 'THAT
INFORMATION WHICH CAN BE ENCODED FOR
COMPLETE AND UNAMBIGUOUS TRANSMISSION
AND DETECTION IN A PERFECT QUANTUM
MECHANICAL SYSTEM'.
'INFORMATION' MAY OCCASIONALLY BE
USED HEREIN TO MEAN 'AMOUNT OF
INFORMATION'.

--- ABOUT BOXES AND PHOTONS:

1. BECAUSE OF UNITARITY OF NRQM TIME
DEVELOPMENT OPERATOR FOR AN ISOLATED
FINITE QM SYSTEM, INFORMATION THEREIN
IS CONSERVED.

2. FOR BOX B CONTAINING ONLY
ELECTROMAGNETIC ENERGY; FROM NRQM, A
PERFECT QM DETECTOR PLACED AGAINST B
WOULD TAKE FOREVER TO UNAMBIGUOUSLY
DETECT AND ASSIGN EVERY ONE OF THE
PHOTONS TO ITS PHOTON STATE, SO ALL
INFORMATION IN B IS REPRESENTABLE BY
PHOTON-STATE OCCUPATION NUMBERS,
WITHOUT PHASE.

3. FOR ISOLATED BOX B2 CONTAINING BOX
B1 OF PHOTONS, AMOUNT OF INFORMATION
REPRESENTED IN B2 DOES NOT DEPEND ON
DECOMPOSITION INTO INTERNAL AND
EXTERNAL INFORMATION OF B1, BECAUSE
OPENING B1 WOULD NOT CHANGE THE FACT
OF B2 BEING ISOLATED.

--- EXTENDING THE INFORMATION
BOOKKEEPING TO INCLUDE MASS OBJECTS:

DEF.5. A 'SOFT' BOX IS ONE WHICH
CONTAINS PHOTONS WHILE ALLOWING
NONPROPAGATING NONZERO FIELD OUTSIDE.

DEF.6. LET BO DENOTE A SOFT BOX WHICH
ITSELF HAS NO MASS, APPEARING TO
CONTAIN WHEN SEEN SUBSTANTIALLY AT
REST TWO PHOTONS WITH EQUAL AND
OPPOSITE MOMENTA IN ITS LOWEST STATE,
WITH TOTAL REST CONTAINED PHOTON
ENERGY EO.
(NOT 'STANDING WAVE' 'PHOTONS')

4. IMAGINE BO CONTAINED IN MUCH LARGER
BOX B2, WITH BO SO SOFT IT MIGHT BE
CONSIDERED A FRAME OF REFERENCE WITHIN
WHICH THE TWO PHOTONS ARE LOCKED INTO
HAVING THE SAME FREQUENCY. THEN, IF
YOU DECOMPOSE THE WAVES ALONG THE LINE
OF MOTION AS SEEN BY AN OBSERVER
SUBSTANTIALLY AT REST IN B2, ONE OF
THE PHOTONS WOULD APPEAR UP-SHIFTED IN
FREQUENCY, 'Fup', AND THE OTHER DOWN-
SHIFTED, 'Fdown' (DOPPLER SHIFT). FROM
EMT, THESE TWO PHOTONS WOULD HAVE TO
SATISFY BOUNDARY CONDITIONS IN B2. TO
DO THIS, THE WAVELENGTH, 'Lb', OF
THEIR BEAT FREQUENCY WOULD HAVE TO FIT
INTO B2 AN INTEGER NUMBER OF TIMES.

BECAUSE THIS LINE OF REASONING IS
USED LATER FOR DERIVING, WITH
LIMITATION, EINSTEIN'S BASIC
ASSUMPTION FOR SPECIAL RELAVITY, AN
APPROXIMATE VALUE FOR Lb WAS OBTAINED
USING THE NON-RELATIVISTIC
APPROXIMATION ('NRA'), IN WHICH TERMS
OF ORDER (V/C)##2 AND HIGHER ARE
DROPPED, WHERE V IS VELOCITY, C IS
SPEED OF LIGHT, AND 'N##2' MEANS 'N TO
THE POWER 2'. AFTER RELATIVITY WAS
DERIVED IN IM, THIS EXTENSION OF
BOOKKEEPING WAS REWRITTEN AND TESTED
OK, BUT IT MIGHT HAVE BEEN LOGICALLY
IMPROPER TO HAVE USED A RELATIVISTIC
DERIVATION INITIALLY.
FOR TOTAL PHOTON ENERGY EO IN BO,
EACH OF THE TWO PHOTONS WOULD HAVE
ENERGY IN BO OF ~ EO/2, AND, FROM
NRQM, EACH WOULD HAVE FREQUENCY
FO ~ EO/(2#h), WHERE h IS PLANCK'S
CONSTANT. THE TWO DOPPLER-SHIFTED
FREQUENCIES WOULD THEN BE
    Fup ~ FO/(1-(V/C))   FORWARD
    Fdown ~ FO/(1+(V/C))   BACKWARD
THEIR DIFFERENCE (BEAT) FREQUENCY Fd,
    Fd ~ (Fup) - (Fdown) ,
WITH BEAT WAVELENGTH Lb,
    Lb = ~/Fd
      ~ C/(Fup - Fdown)
      ~ C/(FO#(1/(1-V/C) - 1/(1+V/C))
      ~ C/(FO#(2#V/C)/(1-(V/C)##2))
      ~ ((C##2)/(2#FO#V)) # (1-(V/C)##2),
NEGLECTING TERMS OF ORDER (V/C)##2 IN
COMPARISON TO 1 (NRA),
    Lb ~ C##2 /(2#FO#V) ,
AND, SUBSTITUTING EO/h = 2FO,
    Lb ~ ((C##2) # h) / (EO # V) .
FOR THE POSSIBLE STATES OF BO IN B2,
ALLOWED BY THE EMT REQUIREMENT THAT
BOTH PHOTONS SATISFY BOUNDARY
CONDITIONS IN B2, V IS SUCH THAT Lb
FITS INTO B2 AN INTEGER NUMBER OF
TIMES.
FROM NRQM, A PARTICLE P, WITH MASS
Mp AND VELOCITY V, HAS (De BROGLIE)
WAVELENGTH Lp, Lp ~ h / (Mp # V) , AND
P'S POSSIBLE STATES IN A BOX B2 ARE
THOSE FOR WHICH Lp FITS INTO B2 AN
INTEGER NUMBER OF TIMES. BECAUSE BO
AND P BOTH HAVE THE SAME 1/V RELATION
BETWEEN VELOCITY AND WAVELENGTH, ONE
COULD CAUSE BO AND P TO HAVE THE SAME
SET OF POSSIBLE V STATES IN B2, BY
FINDING A VALUE FOR TOTAL PHOTON
ENERGY EO IN BO WHICH WOULD MAKE
Lb ~ Lp FOR ALL V<<C; IF WE DO THIS,
THEN DESIGNATION BY P OF ONE STATE OUT
OF ALL OF P'S POSSIBLE V STATES IN B2
WOULD REPRESENT THE SAME AMOUNT OF
INFORMATION AS DESIGNATION BY BO OF
ONE STATE OUT OF ALL OF BO'S POSSIBLE
V STATES IN B2:
    FOR   Lb ~ Lp,
SUBSTITUTING,
((C##2)#h)/(EO#V) ~ h/(Mp#V),
CANCELLING V AND h ON BOTH SIDES,
    (C##2) / EO ~ 1 / Mp ,
AND, SOLVING FOR EO,
        EO ~ Mp # (C##2).
THE INFORMATION 'BOOKKEEPING' WAS
THUS EXTENDED TO INCLUDE MASS
PARTICLES, WITH THE AMOUNT OF
INFORMATION REPRESENTED BY AN AMOUNT M
OF MASS COUNTED AS BEING THE SAME AS
WOULD HAVE BEEN REPRESENTED BY AN
AMOUNT M#(C##2) OF ENERGY.
THIS WAS THE FIRST DEEP RESULT IN
IM. IT TELLS US THAT THE UNDERLYING
REASON WHY MASS AND ENERGY CAN BE

FIGURE 1A. Informal outline showing how, in early (nonaxiomatic) IM, information "book-keeping" was originally extended to include mass (continued in FIGURE 1B).

INTERCONVERTED IS THAT 'MASS' AND 'ENERGY' ARE NAMES FOR WAYS IN WHICH INFORMATION CAN BE REPRESENTED, WITH FUNDAMENTALLY THE SAME QUANTITY: THE AMOUNT OF INFORMATION REPRESENTED BY A PHYSICAL SYSTEM. IT ALSO TELLS US, ON THE BASIS OF INFORMATION BOOKKEEPING, THE CONVERSION FACTOR TO USE BETWEEN MASS UNITS AND ENERGY UNITS.

DEF.7. CALL A PHOTON REPRESENTATION FOR THE INFORMATION REPRESENTED BY A MASS PARTICLE, USING TOTAL ENERGY $Mp*(C**2)$, A 'NONRELATIVISTIC PHOTON PARTICLE REPRESENTATION', OR 'NRPPR'.

NOTE THAT THIS DERIVATION SO FAR HAS NOT USED EINSTEIN'S SPECIAL THEORY OF RELATIVITY.

5. WITH NRPPR, INFORMATION CONTENT OF BOX B2 DEPENDS ON ITS ENERGY CONTENT, INDEPENDENT OF PARTITIONING INTO PHOTONS, BOXES OF PHOTONS, MASS PARTICLES, OR COMBINATIONS THEREOF, BECAUSE ALL OF THE MASS PARTICLES COULD BE EXPRESSED AS BO'S AND ALL THE BOXES OF PHOTONS, INCLUDING ANY BO'S, OPENED, WITHOUT CHANGING THE FACT OF B2 BEING ISOLATED.

ONE MIGHT CHOOSE B2 AS LARGE AS A FINITE UNIVERSE, SO, WITH NRPPR, IN A FINITE UNIVERSE, INFORMATION REPRESENTED BY ANY CONFIGURATION COMPOSED ENTIRELY OF ELECTROMAGNETIC ENERGY AND/OR MASS DEPENDS ONLY ON ITS TOTAL ENERGY, COUNTING MASS M AS ENERGY $M*(C**2)$.

6. WITH NRPPR, BY IMAGINING IT TO BE BROKEN DOWN INTO MANY BO'S, ONE FINDS THAT THE AMOUNT OF INFORMATION REPRESENTED BY ANY ELECTROMAGNETIC AND/OR MASS CONFIGURATION IS SUBSTANTIALLY PROPORTIONAL TO ITS TOTAL ENERGY, COUNTING TOTAL MASS AS $M*(C**2)$.

--- WHY DOES RELATIVITY WORK?

7&8. HAVING EXTENDED THE INFORMATION BOOKKEEPING TO INCLUDE MASS PARTICLES, ONE FINDS THAT THE AMOUNT OF INFORMATION REPRESENTED BY A PARTICLE IN A BOX B1 IS FINITE AND, THEREFORE, THAT THE NUMBER OF POSSIBLE STATES IN THAT SYSTEM IS FINITE. SO, ONE COULD IN PRINCIPLE ACCELERATE B1 VERY GENTLY; IF THE UNIVERSE U WERE INFINITE, ONE COULD MAKE THE ACCELERATION SO GENTLE THAT IT WOULD NOT INDUCE ANY QM TRANSITION IN ANY ELECTROMAGNETIC AND/OR MASS SYSTEM INSIDE B1, IN WHICH CASE, ALL INFORMATION REPRESENTED INSIDE B1 WOULD BE EXACTLY PRESERVED -- AN OBSERVER O LIVING INSIDE B1 WOULD NOT KNOW THAT THIS HAD HAPPENED, AND O'S LAWS AND CONSTANTS OF PHYSICS WOULD APPEAR THE SAME. THIS IS WHY RELATIVITY WORKS.

BUT, IN A FINITE UNIVERSE, WHEN A BO WENT FAST ENOUGH, ITS DOWN-SHIFTED PHOTON WOULD BE IN ONE OF THE LOW-LYING STATES IN U, AND ITS BEHAVIOUR WOULD BECOME 'GRAINY' ENOUGH TO BECOME OBSERVABLE INSIDE B1 -- IN WHICH CASE, O WOULD KNOW THAT B1 WAS MOVING. ALTERNATIVELY, IN AXIOMATIC IM, ONE WOULD KEEP TRACK OF B1'S ACCELERATION

HISTORY, TO FIND WHEN THE REPRESENTATION OF INFORMATION INSIDE B1 STOPPED BEING ADEQUATELY DESCRIBABLE AS SEPARATE FROM THE REPRESENTATION OF INFORMATION OUTSIDE B1. THE TWO RESULTS WERE SUBSTANTIALLY THE SAME: THE ISOLATION WOULD BREAK DOWN FOR B1 MOVING SO FAST THAT THE UNIVERSE WOULD LOOK TO O ABOUT TWICE AS LONG AS B1. THIS IS A WAY IN WHICH RELATIVITY WOULD FAIL. THUS, THERE IS NO PARADOX, UNLIKE WHAT HAPPENS IF ONE ASSUMES THAT RELATIVITY WOULD WORK ALL THE WAY UP TO THE SPEED OF LIGHT.

USING LANGUAGE FAMILIAR FROM QM, THIS INFORMAL OUTLINE OF EARLY, NON-AXIOMATIC WORK IN IM SHOWS HOW IM WAS FIRST APPLIED TO CONCEPTUAL QUESTIONS WHICH COULD NOT BE ASKED WITHIN THE OLDER THEORIES OF CM AND QM.

A THEORY IS UNABLE TO EXPLAIN ITS OWN ASSUMPTIONS; A THEORY WHICH TRIES TO DO SO IS CALLED A TAUTOLOGY. ARE PUT INTO CM AND QM AS ASSUMPTIONS. FOR THIS REASON, IT IS NOT POSSIBLE FOR CM AND/OR QM TO EXPLAIN ANY OF THEM: A FUNDAMENTALLY DIFFERENT TOOL, WHICH DOES NOT USE THOSE ASSUMPTIONS, IS NECESSARY.

ULTIMATELY, DOES AN OBSERVER KNOW ANYTHING ABOUT A UNIVERSE OTHER THAN INFORMATION WHICH THAT OBSERVER HAS RECEIVED FROM THAT UNIVERSE? IF NOT, THEN, IS IT NECESSARY FOR ANY THEORY CONSTRUCTED BY THAT OBSERVER ABOUT THAT UNIVERSE TO CONTAIN ANY ASSUMPTION(S), ANY POSTULATE(S), OTHER THAN POSTULATE(S) ABOUT INFORMATION? ARE ALL THESE WORDS -- 'MASS', 'ENERGY', 'SPACE', 'TIME', 'CHARGE', 'GRAVITY', 'SPIN' -- JUST LABELS, HUNG UPON PARTIAL INTERPRETATION OF INFORMATION RECEIVED?

IN AXIOMATIZING IM, THE EARLY PART OF IM WAS REPLACED; NUMBERING FOR NEW DEFINITIONS, LEMMA, THEOREMS, AND COROLLARIES STARTED WITH '1', WITH THE PREFIX 'A-' (FOR 'AXIOMATIC'). THE ACRONYM, 'IM', NOW REFERS TO AXIOMATIC INFORMATION MECHANICS.

ALTHOUGH THIS BRIEF DISCUSSION HAS INCLUDED THE FIRST OF THE DEEP RESULTS IN EARLY IM, IN AXIOMATIC FORM IM IS DEEPER, MORE POWERFUL, AND MORE BEAUTIFUL -- BUT THE DERIVATIONS ARE WRITTEN IN THE LANGUAGE OF INFORMATION MECHANICS, AND I WILL NOT TRY TO PRECIS THEM HERE. FOR AXIOMATIC IM, LET ME REFER YOU TO THE PUBLISHED WORK CITED ABOVE, AND END THIS SUMMARY BY STATING, FROM THE AXIOMATIC FORM, THE FIRST DEFINITION AND THE THREE POSTULATES OF IM:

A-DEF.1. AMOUNT I IN 'BITS' OF INFORMATION EQUALS $LOG2$ OF NUMBER OF POSSIBILITIES FROM WHICH ONE IS DESIGNATED.

('INFORMATION' MAY OCCASIONALLY BE USED HEREIN TO MEAN 'AMOUNT OF INFORMATION')

POSTULATES:

1. INFORMATION IS CONSERVED.
2. INFORMATION IS COMMUNICABLE.
3. INFORMATION IS FINITELY ACCESSIBLE.

FIGURE 1B. Continued from FIGURE 1A.

possibilities (that is, that one assume infinite information). For at least this reason, it would seem that it is not possible to form any internally consistent theory of measurement that recognizes discreteness and requires this assumption; this includes, by way of example and without limitation, quantum mechanics, and mixtures of QM with classical mechanics.

REFERENCE

1. KANTOR, F. W. 1977. Information Mechanics. Wiley. New York.

Einstein-Podolsky-Rosen Constraints on Quantum Action-at-a-Distance

The Sutherland Paradox

A. KYPRIANIDIS

Laboratoire de Physique Théorique
Institut Henri Poincaré
75231 Paris Cedex 05, France

One of the models proposed in order to account for nonlocal correlations emerging in EPR-singlet states of spinning particles is based on a "retroaction in time" mechanism.[1] This model proposes a time-arrowless microcausality, a transition between the prepared and measured state instead of a retarded unitary evolution, an explicit use of acausal Pauli-Jordan rather than Feynman propagators, a combination of wave function collapse and retrocollapse, and, finally, a time zigzagging of positive energies as a manifestation of psychokinetic effects. Apart from general objections and criticism resting essentially on the fact that CPT-invariance only manifests the existence of antiparticles (along with Feynman zigzags preserving the time-arrow and irreversibility), a powerful objection has been formulated recently by Sutherland[2] for the case of two EPR-singlet particles on which a spin-measurement is performed at M'_1 and M_2, with $M'_1 M_2$ being a timelike interval (FIGURE 1): Because the "retroaction" mechanism is insensitive to the interval character between measurements and the M_2 result depends on the M'_1 instrument setting, we can modulate the original M'_1 setting after the M_2 measurement by a timelike signal and produce a paradox. We can do this because for certain configurations of settings, no spin-measurement outcome is consistent. Sutherland suggests that a correct model should imply that M_1 must affect M_2 when M_1 is outside the forward light cone of M_2, but not when it is inside.

This is exactly the constraint satisfied by the nonlocal quantum potential model that obeys Einstein causality and individual conservation laws. This model, treated for simplicity for scalar particles, results out of a Madelung-type decomposition of the Klein-Gordon equation,

$$\left(\Box + \frac{m^2 c^2}{\hbar^2}\right)\psi = 0 \quad (\text{where } \psi = e^{P + iS/\hbar}),$$

in

$$\frac{m^2 c^2}{\hbar^2} - \frac{1}{\hbar^2}\partial_\mu S \partial^\mu S + (\Box P + \partial_\mu P \partial^\mu P) = 0$$

and

$$\partial_\mu\left(e^{2P}\frac{\partial^\mu S}{m}\right) = 0$$

585

(that is, a Hamilton-Jacobi type equation and a continuity equation), and exhibits well-defined trajectories,

$$v^\mu = \frac{\partial^\mu S}{M},$$

and physical observable values (e.g., momentum, spin, etc.) that are context-dependent, and that, in the many-body case, are correlated by a causal action-at-a-distance. In the two-body case, we can verify that the two Klein-Gordon

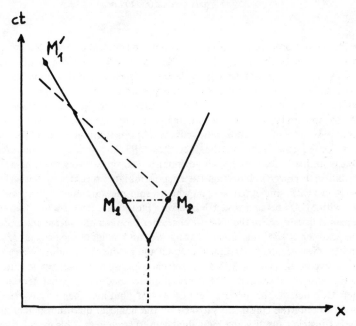

FIGURE 1. Two EPR-singlet particles on which a spin-measurement is performed at M_1' and M_2. $M_1'M_2$ is a timelike interval (see text).

equations,

$$\left(\Box_i + \frac{m_i^2 c^2}{\hbar^2}\right)\psi(x_1, x_2) = 0 \quad (i = 1, 2),$$

can be mapped onto a system of two relativistic particles submitted to nonlocal potentials described by the Hamiltonians,

$$H_i = \frac{P_i^2}{2} + Q = \frac{m_i^2}{2},$$

where the relativistic quantum potential map, $Q(x_1, x_2)$, has the following functional dependence:[4]

$$Q(\widetilde{x_1^\mu - x_2^\mu}) = Q\left[(x_1^\mu - x_2^\mu) - \frac{[(x_1^\nu - x_2^\nu)P_\nu]P^\mu}{P^2}\right],$$

where $P^\mu = P_1^\mu + P_2^\mu$. A transformation to the center of mass (C.M.) rest frame yields

$$Q(\widetilde{x_1^\mu - x_2^\mu}) = Q(x_1 - x_2);$$

that is, it does not depend anymore on the relative time, $x_1^0 - x_2^0$. Because $P^\mu(\widetilde{x_{1\mu} - x_{2\mu}}) = 0$, we deduce that this action-at-a-distance exists only in a surface perpendicular to the timelike C.M. momentum, P^μ; that is, on a spacelike surface. It becomes instantaneous only in the C.M. rest frame. Furthermore, because the difference of the two Hamiltonians is constant,

$$H_1 - H_2 = \frac{m_1^2 - m_2^2}{2},$$

we deduce that no exchange of energy occurs in the C.M. rest frame.

The generalization of this scheme to the case of spinning particles enables us to solve the Sutherland paradox along the following lines:

(1) Spinning particle equations (Feynman-Gell-Mann for spin $\frac{1}{2}$, Proca for spin 1) introduce an additional spin-spin action-at-a-distance, specifically, the "quantum torque," which is again active only in spacelike separations. The spins of the particles are now constantly spacelike nonlocally correlated, and so are the spacelike separated measurement results.

(2) A measurement of M_2 twists also the spin of particle 1 at M_1 to an antiparallel direction with respect to S_2, although it is not measured. A subsequent measurement at M_1' that occurs along the same lines will yield either (a) a correlated result if S_2 preserves the measured value at M_2 or (b) a decorrelated result if S_2 is perturbed and relaxes to a superposition of ↑ and ↓. However, no nonlocal or retroactive influence exists between the settings of the instruments because the measurement correlations result out of the permanent action-at-a-distance correlation of the spins of the two particles.

Concluding, we wish to stress that the Sutherland paradox is a conceptual one that is tied to the shortcomings of idealized quantum measurement theory and the creation of the reality of an observable by means of measurement. It is, however, a very useful one because it discredits "time retroactive" approaches.

REFERENCES

1. COSTA DE BEAUREGARD, O. 1985. Found. Phys. **15:** 871–887.
2. SUTHERLAND, R. I. 1985. Nuovo Cimento **88B:** 114–118.
3. BOHM, D., 1952. Phys. Rev. **85:** 166–179.
4. CUFARO-PETRONI, N., PH. DROZ-VINCENT & J. P. VIGIER. 1981. Lett. Nuovo Cimento **31:** 415–420.

Minimal Uncertainty and Maximal Information for Quantum Position and Momentum

PEKKA J. LAHTI

Department of Physical Sciences
University of Turku
Turku, Finland

For any two observables, A and B, the product of their variances in a state, ϕ,

$$\text{Var}\,(A, \phi) \cdot \text{Var}\,(B, \phi), \tag{1}$$

has a lower bound, $\frac{1}{4}|\langle\phi|[A, B]\phi\rangle|^2 + \frac{1}{4}\,\text{Cov}_\phi\,(A, B)^2$, with $\text{Cov}_\phi\,(A, B)$ denoting $\langle\phi|\{A, B\}_+\phi\rangle - 2\langle\phi|A\phi\rangle \cdot \langle\phi|B\phi\rangle$, which, in general, depends on the state, ϕ. A state, ϕ, that minimizes the uncertainty product (equation 1) is a state of minimal uncertainty for A and B. Similarly, for any two observables, A and B, the sum of their informations in a state, ϕ,

$$I_\phi(A) + I_\phi(B), \tag{2}$$

may or may not have an absolute or state-dependent upper bound, $I^o(A, B)$ or $I^o_\phi(A, B)$. A state, ϕ, that would maximize equation 2 would be a state of maximal information for A and B.

In recent years, several attempts have been done to define $I_\phi(A)$ for an arbitrary observable, A, and to compare equation 2 with equation 1. Until now, the problem has been solved to a satisfactory degree only for (generalized) position and momentum observables and for discrete (generalized) observables. (See reference 1 and references therein.) Here, our main concern is on the question, "To what degree of certainty can some particular values of any two given observables, A and B, be known simultaneously?" Therefore, we restrict our considerations to simple observables, and for them, we compare various characterizations of "maximal information" and show their relation to "minimal uncertainty." Finally, we apply the results to the spectral projections of position and momentum observables.

Let A and B be simple-effect-valued observables with ranges, $\{0, E, E^\perp, I\}$ and $\{0, F, F^\perp, I\}$ ($0 \le E, F \le I$, $E^\perp = I - E$, $F^\perp = I - F$). For such observables, the quantity,

$$I_\phi(E) + I_\phi(F) \;\; (\le 0), \tag{3}$$

with $I_\phi(E) = E_\phi\,\ell n\,(E_\phi) + E_\phi\,\ell n\,(E_\phi)$ (where $E_\phi = \langle\phi|E\phi\rangle$), measures the joint information on E and F in the state, ϕ. However, the probabilistic quantities,

$$E_\phi + F_\phi \;\; (\le 2) \tag{4}$$

and

$$E_\phi \cdot F_\phi \;\; (\le 1), \tag{5}$$

588

would do as well. The question now is whether a maximum (or even the supremum) exists for equations 3, 4, or 5, and whether it is attainable for some state, ϕ; furthermore, if it exists, does it minimize the uncertainty product (equation 1). The answers are:[1]

(i) Any state, ϕ, that maximizes equations 3, 4, or 5 gives Var $(E, \phi) \cdot$ Var(F, ϕ) $= \frac{1}{4}$ Cov$_\phi$ $(E, F)^2$, which thus minimizes the uncertainty product;

(ii) If E and F are projection operators, then the maxima of equation 3, if they exist, coincide with those of one of the quantities, $E^i_\phi + F^j_\phi$ and $E^i_\phi \cdot F^j_\phi$, with $E^i_\phi \in \{E, E^\perp\}$ and $F^j_\phi \in \{F, F^\perp\}$. Thus, for projection operators, the quantities in equations 3–5 lead to identical characterizations of maximal information.

As an application of these results, let E and F stand for the spectral projections, $E^Q(X)$ and $E^P(Y)$, with $X, Y \in \mathcal{B}$ ($\mathbb{R}$), of position, Q, and momentum, P. (1) If the value sets, X and Y, are bounded, then $E \wedge F = E^\perp \wedge F = E \wedge F^\perp = 0,$[2] so $E_\phi + F_\phi <$ 2 for all states, ϕ. However, sup $\{E_\phi + F_\phi | \phi \in \mathcal{H}_1\} = 1 + a_o$, where $a_o < 1$ is the largest eigenvalue of EFE, and the value, $1 + a_o$, can be attained with a state, ϕ_{mi}, that can explicitly be constructed.[3] ϕ_{mi} maximizes not only equation 4, but also equations 3 and 5, and it minimizes the uncertainty product. However, as $E^\perp \wedge F^\perp \neq 0$ now, sup $\{I_\phi(E) + I_\phi(F) | \phi \in \mathcal{H}_1\} = 0$. (2) If X and Y are half-lines, then $E \wedge F = E^\perp \wedge F = E \wedge F^\perp = E^\perp \wedge F^\perp = 0,$[2] and no state of maximal information exists.[1] However, because E and F are "almost commutative" now, this leads to the fact that sup$\{E_\phi + F_\phi | \phi \in \mathcal{H}_1\} = 2$ [and sup $\{I_\phi(E) + I_\phi(F) | \phi \in \mathcal{H}_1\} = 0$, sup $\{E_\phi \cdot F_\phi | \phi \in \mathcal{H}_1\} = 1$, and, as always for projections, inf $\{$Var $(E, \phi) \cdot$ Var $(F, \phi) | \phi \in \mathcal{H}_1\} = 0]$. (3) If $X = X + d$ and $Y = Y + 2\pi/d$ are periodic sets, the E and F commute,[2] and any ϕ in $\{\phi \in \mathcal{H}_1 | E\phi = \phi, F\phi = \phi\}$ ($\neq 0$) is a maximal information state.

REFERENCES

1. BUSCH, P. & P. LAHTI. 1985. Minimal uncertainty and maximal information for quantum position and momentum. Univ. of Turku preprint no. FTL-R85; J. Phys. A: Math. Gen. In print.
2. BUSCH, P. & P. LAHTI. 1985. To what extent position and momentum do commute. Univ. of Turku preprint no. FTL-R87; 1986. Phys. Lett. A115: 259–264.
3. LAHTI, P. 1985. States of minimal uncertainty and maximal information for position and momentum observables in quantum theory. Rep. Math. Phys. In print.

Causal Description of Measurement in Quantum Mechanics

ULF LARSEN

Physics Laboratory
University of Copenhagen
H. C. Ørsted Institute
Universitetsparken 5
DK 2100 Copenhagen Ø, Denmark

The evolution in the state of a system consists in a sequence of transformations caused by operations. Every such transformation of state, $W \to w$, is expressible in the form,[1]

$$w = \sum_j E_j W E_j^+ , \tag{1}$$

where $\mathscr{E} = \{E_j\}$ is a countable set that specifies the operation.

We shall present new, axiomatically simple criteria according to which there exist operations, $\mathscr{E}$, that, while admitting a causal description, still cause transformations that qualify as measurements. A new class of measuring operations discovered in this way turns out to reveal remarkably fundamental aspects of quantum theory.

The traditional "reduction" by means of orthogonal projectors, $\mathscr{E} = \{P_n\}$, also satisfies our criteria. However, it does not explain *how* the measurement is done in the same sense in which a Hamiltonian, H, can display the *causes* of a unitary transformation, $U = \exp(-iHt/\hbar)$; that is, a pure evolution in time, $\mathscr{E} = \{U\}$.

Suppose we measure a property, A, defining a spectral representation in terms of a Hilbert space basis, $\{|n\rangle\}$. Our criteria are:

(i) Compatibility: $[A, w] = 0$, whereby $\langle n|w|k \rangle = w_n \delta_{nk}$. The spectra are $\{A_n\}$ and $\{w_n\}$, where w_n is the fraction of specimens that register the value A_n in a sorting arrangement by $\{n\}$ (detectors, counters, etc.). This is feasible because it is what the definition of a state, w, entails.[2]

(ii) Reproducibility: $W = P_n \Rightarrow w = P_n$, where the projector, $P_n = |n\rangle \langle n|$, is an arbitrary state in which A_n is certain, that is, $w_n = 1$, and remains unaltered after a measurement of a property with which it is compatible.

(iii) Objectivity: w depends on W, but not on $\mathscr{E}$. Thus, w contains information about the "object state," W, but apart from the decision on A, w must not depend on the operations that are carried out to get it. Mathematically, the representation in equation 1 is not unique, so several operations may cause the same transformation; that is, the property A can perhaps be measured with different instruments. This new concept of "objectivity" is fully compatible with quantum mechanics and sharper than the traditional viewpoint.

It is straightforward to verify that $\mathscr{E}$ must then satisfy the condition,

$$\sum_j \langle k|E_j|l \rangle \langle m|E_j^+|n \rangle = \delta_{kl}\delta_{lm}\delta_{mn}, \tag{2}$$

and that it is now a theorem (rather than a postulate) that

$$w_n = \langle n|W|n \rangle \equiv P(n). \tag{3}$$

Measurements change the state of the system in such a way that the *empirically* defined *statistical weights*, $\{w_n\}$, in the new state, w, agree with the *theoretically predicted probabilities*, $\{P(n)\}$, of the old state, W. An operation, $\mathscr{E}$, that satisfies equation 2 therefore accomplishes what an *experimental measurement* is supposed to do when carried out in practice.

Reproducibility extends to any state (i.e., $W \rightarrow w \rightarrow w$) repeating the measurement of A. Hence, $\{w_n\}$ is a *reproducible statistics*.

The cases when $[A, E_j] = 0$ for all j have $\langle k|E_j|l \rangle = E_l(j)\delta_{kl}$, and equation 2 is merely a condition of orthogonality,

$$\sum_j E_l(j)E_m^*(j) = \delta_{lm}, \tag{4}$$

with a reassuring versatility. The projectors have $E_l(j) = \delta_{lj}$.

To be specific, let us consider a causally more rewarding example in the shape of a momentum measurement: $A = p$, with $\mathscr{E}$ based on a set of unitary operators,

$$E_j = \alpha_j \exp(iQ_j p/\hbar), \qquad \xi_j = |\alpha_j|^2, \qquad \sum_j \xi_j = 1, \tag{5}$$

corresponding to *translations*, $\{Q_j\}$, *generated by the measured property*, p, *itself*. With periodic boundary conditions over the position interval, $0 \leq q \leq L$, the condition (equation 2) is

$$\sum_j \xi_j \exp[iQ_j(p_l - p_m)/\hbar] = \delta_{lm}, \tag{6}$$

where the momentum spectrum is $p_l = (h/L)l$. This measurement can be performed with g equidistant translations, $Q_j = jQ + Q_o, j = 0, 1, \ldots, g - 1$, provided $\xi_j = 1/g$ and $gQ = L$, while Q_o and $g \geq 2$ are arbitrary.

To see how this works, suppose $W = |\psi\rangle \langle \psi|$ is a pure state with a wave function, $\psi(q) = \langle q|\psi\rangle$, and a predicted probability density, $P(q) = \langle q|W|q \rangle = |\psi(q)|^2$. The measurement proceeds through a mixture of subsystem translations, $|\psi\rangle \rightarrow |\psi_j\rangle$, so that $w = \Sigma_j \xi_j |\psi_j\rangle \langle \psi_j|$ is no longer a pure state. The resulting probability density is

$$p(q) = \sum_j \xi_j P(q - Q_j). \tag{7}$$

This convex combination shows how the momentum measurement *causes* a loss of precision in the position determination (this occurs by a process quite like the shaking of a photographic exposure). As the explicit realization shows, the consequent position *indeterminacy*, $\delta q = gQ = L$, is as large as it can get.

In an expanded space, say, $L' = 10\ L$, the former basis, $\{|n\rangle\}$, is no longer complete. Briefly stated, whereas it remains perfectly feasible, the operation $\mathscr{E}$ gets to be an "incomplete" measurement. Everything concerning A remains in effect, but because $\{A_n\}$ is now a decimation of the new momentum spectrum, it corresponds to a limited *resolution,* $dp = h/L$. The new momentum measurement would now give ten times better resolution, $dp' = h/L'$, at the cost of ten times greater position indeterminacy, $\delta q' = L'$.

Nevertheless, complete or not, and no matter how the measurement is performed,

$$\delta q \, dp = h. \tag{8}$$

This holds true even though the details (equation 7) of what happens differ. By Fourier reciprocity, there is, for position measurements, an analogous relation,

$$dq \, \delta p = h, \tag{9}$$

between its position resolution, dq, and the consequent momentum indeterminacy, δp.

Suppose we start with a state, W, wherein $P(q)$ predicts position and momentum *uncertainties,* Δq and Δp, in the usual way. We can measure momentum to any resolution, dp, and because of the compatibility, it will not affect Δp. However, to become *operationally* entitled to presume Δp we require $dp \leq \Delta p$. Consequently, we thereby create an indeterminacy, $\delta q = h/dp \geq h/\Delta p$. One can choose to regard this as a "preparation", but it makes no difference in the present context.

In the new state, $p(q)$ predicts an enhanced position uncertainty, $\Delta q \geq \delta q$. Therefore, in no tandem measurement where we subsequently verify this Δq can we establish both position and momentum to better statistically reproducible precision than

$$\Delta q \Delta p \geq h. \tag{10}$$

The subsequent position measurement in order to resolve to $dq \leq \delta q$ creates momentum indeterminacy, $\delta p = h/dq \geq h/\delta q$, such that the operational reason for the uncertainty relation (equation 10) is a corresponding relation,

$$\delta q \, \delta p \geq h, \tag{11}$$

between the indeterminacies that must be created by *actually* measuring both position and momentum.

Of course, there is no way to measure them simultaneously because they are complementary properties, and the corresponding sets, $\mathscr{E}$, are incompatible operations ("boosts" and translations). Each of them alone can be measured with arbitrarily good resolution. There is, obviously, no reciprocal relationship between the tandem resolutions, dq and dp. However, as soon as both are measured one after the other, it creates a reciprocal indeterminacy that agrees with the uncertainty relation (equation 10).

We conclude that quantum mechanics requires that its properties (the operators, p and q) be established by actual measurement. Its predictions concern situations where these are performed in reality. We found a causal description of such measurements that involves *a concert of precisely those operations that are generated by the measured operators themselves.* This result established the *fundamentally* operational nature of the properties of systems: They are operators mathematically because they generate the actual physical operations that constitute their measurement. It also suggested the clarifying distinction between resolution, indeterminacy, and uncertainty in the context of the uncertainty relation.

NOTES AND REFERENCES

1. LARSEN, U. 1986. Irreversibility in new class of quantum evolutions. Phys. Lett. **114A**: 359–364. This source contains references to earlier work and establishes the theorem in full generality.
2. VON NEUMANN, J. 1955. Mathematical Foundations of Quantum Mechanics. Princeton Univ. Press. Princeton, New Jersey. In chapter V, it is shown how a system can be separated into subsystems in pure states corresponding to the orthogonal projectors that define its statistical operator (by means of "semipermeable membranes," for example) with no loss of purity, but not into any of the alternative convex combinations of Schrödinger's.[3] It is clear, therefore, that the crucial stage in the measurement consists in turning the initial state into one that is compatible with the measured property.
3. SCHRÖDINGER, E. 1936. Probability relations between separated systems. Proc. Cambridge Philos. Soc. **32**: 446–452.

Relativistic Quantum Measurement and the Quantum Electrodynamic Arrow of Time

DARRYL LEITER[a]

National Aeronautics and Space Administration
Goddard Space Flight Center
Greenbelt, Maryland 20771

The microscopic classical electrodynamic measurement process contains no self-energy infinities and is described in a basically time-irreversible manner when the Abelian gauge symmetry Measurement Color is imposed upon classical electrodynamics.[1,2] The quantum field theory generalization, Measurement Color Quantum Electrodynamics (MC-QED), is found to a nonlocal, relativistic quantum electrodynamic field theory of the measurement process that also contains a dynamically irreversible retarded physical arrow of time generated from stability conditions internal to theory.[3]

In order to compare QED to MC-QED, let us refer to the numbered lines in TABLE 1 as we develop the structure of the theory. From line 1, we see that Measurement Color is an Abelian integer ($K = 1, 2, \ldots, \infty$) labeling of quantum field operators. This labeling represents the operator name of "microscopic fermion objects" and "microscopic fermion detectors," which interact in line 2 via a Lagrangian that dynamically excludes all time-symmetric Measurement Color self-interaction from the formalism. In an indefinite metric Hilbert space of states, the MC-QED operator equations of motion and the equal-time commutation relations follow directly from a standard canonical quantization procedure on the action (they are given in lines 3 through 6). Like its classical counterpart,[1,2] the physical solutions to the MC-QED formalism must obey the time-symmetric requirements of (a) positive definite radiation field energy, and (b) the asymptotic condition on the amplitudes in the $t \rightarrow \mp\infty$ limit.

Because of the absence of time-symmetric Measurement Color self-interaction in the Hamiltonian operator, condition (a) excludes $A_\mu^{(o)}$, the free local photon operators, in favor of a nonlocal photon operator, $A_{\mu(-)}^{(KJ)}$, with a negative parity under mathematical time reversal. This makes MC-QED into a nonlocal quantum field theory, and by virtue of the dynamic stability requirements associated with condition (b), this constrains the formalism to contain a retarded physical arrow of time (line 7 and 8). The MC-QED nonlocal photon operator, $A_{\mu(-)}^{(KJ)}$, generates Feynman photon propagators (line 9) given by

$$D_{F_{\mu\nu}}^{(KJK'J')}(x - x') = (\delta^{KJ} \delta^{K'J'} - \delta^{KK'} \delta^{JJ'}) D_{F_{\mu\nu}}(x - x').$$

The effect of this photon propagator is to allow only $K \neq J$ measurement color fermions to interact via virtual photons in the associated Feynman diagrams.

---

[a]Mailing address: 1730 Easy Lane, Charlottesville, Virginia 22901.

The nonlocal-in-time negative time parity photon field operator, $A_{\mu(-)}^{(KJ)}$, causes the MC-QED Hamiltonian operator (line 10) to contain an irreversible quantum measurement operator, V_{MEAS}, that is nonlocal-in-time. This irreversibility can be shown to be invariant under an extended form of T and CPT symmetry that preserves the dynamically chosen internal MC-QED physical arrow of time. Retarded quantum

TABLE 1. Measurement Color Transcription of QED into MC-QED

QED	MC-QED
(1) ψ, A_μ	$\psi^{(K)}, A_\mu^{(KJ)} \quad K, J = 1, 2, \ldots, \infty$
(2) $\int dx^4 J_\mu A^\mu$	$\int dx^4 \left(\sum\limits_{K=1}^{\infty} \sum\limits_{\substack{J \neq K \\ -1}}^{\infty} J_\mu^{(KK)} A^{\mu(JJ)} - J_\mu^{(KJ)} A^{\mu(JK)} \right)$
(3) $(-i\not{\partial} + m - e\not{A})\psi = 0$	$(-i\not{\partial} + m)\psi^{(K)} - e/2 \sum\limits_{\substack{J \neq K \\ -1}}^{\infty}$ $\cdot (\not{A}^{(JJ)}\psi^{(K)} - \not{A}^{(JK)}\psi^{(J)}) = 0$
(4) $\Box A_\mu = J_\mu, \langle \partial_\mu A^\mu \rangle = 0$	$\Box A_\mu^{(KJ)} = J_\mu^{(KJ)}, \left\langle \sum\limits_{K=1}^{\infty} \partial_\mu A^{\mu(KK)} \right\rangle = 0$
(5) $\{\psi(x, t), \psi^\dagger(x, t)\} = \delta^3(x - x')$	$\{\psi_{(x,t)}^{(K)}, \psi_{(x',t)}^{(J)\dagger}\} = \delta^{(KJ)}\delta^3(x - x')$
(6) $[A_\mu(x, t), \partial_t A_v(x', t)] = i\eta_{\mu v}\delta^3(x - x')$	$[A_\mu^{(KJ)}(x, t), \partial_t A_v^{(OBS)(K'J')}(x', t)]$ $= i\eta_{\mu v}\delta^{KJ'}\delta^{JK'}\delta^3(x-x')$
(7) $A^\mu = (A_{(ret)}^\mu + A_{(o)}^\mu)$	$A_\mu^{(OBS)(KJ)} = \left[\left(\delta^{KJ} \sum\limits_{\ell=1}^{\infty} A_{\mu(ret)}^{(\ell\ell)} - A_{(ret)}^{(KJ)}\right) + A_{\mu(-)}^{(KJ)}\right]$
(8) $A_{(o)}^\mu$ Local Photons	$A_{\mu(-)}^{(KJ)} = \frac{1}{2}(A_{\mu ret}^{(KJ)} - A_{\mu adv}^{(KJ)})$ Nonlocal Photons
(9) $\langle 0 \| T(A_{\mu(o)}(x) A_{v(o)}(x')) \| 0 \rangle$ $= D_{F_{\mu v}}(x - x')$	$\langle 0 \| T(A_{\mu(-)}^{(KJ)}(x) A_{v(-)}^{(K'J')}(x')) \| 0 \rangle$ $= D_{F_{\mu v}}^{(KJK'J')}(x - x')$
(10) $H = (H_o + V_{QM})$ Local-in-Time	$H = (H_o + V_{QM} + V_{MEAS})$ Nonlocal-in-Time
(11) $H\|\Psi\rangle = i\hbar\partial_t\|\Psi\rangle$ Reversible in Time	$H\|\Psi\rangle = i\hbar\partial_t\|\Psi\rangle$ Irreversible in Time

operator differential-delay effects generated by the V_{MEAS} operator make the MC-QED Schrödinger equation become nonlocal-in-time as well as nonlocal-in-space (line 11). Thus, in the MC-QED theory, the dynamical cause of quantum statistical effects in the time evolution of the "quantum potentia" generated by $(H_o + V_{QM})$ into the "quantum actua" of physical events is due to the fact that local-in-time preparations of the state vector, $|\Psi\rangle$, do not prepare the nonlocal-in-time quantum measurement interaction, V_{MEAS}, in the MC-QED theory.

We find that MC-QED mimics the results of QED with one major difference: Einstein relativity is compatible with quantum nonseparability in the quantum measurement process.

REFERENCES

1. LEITER, D. J. 1984. Found. Phys. **14:** 849.
2. LEITER, D. J. 1985. Lett. Nuovo Cimento **44:** 665.
3. LEITER, D. J. 1986. Submitted for publication.

A Geometric Introduction to Quantum Mysteries

VICTOR MANSFIELD[a] AND DAVID HENDERSON[b]

[a]Department of Physics and Astronomy
Colgate University
Hamilton, New York 13346

[b]Department of Mathematics
Cornell University
Ithaca, New York 14853

We seek to deepen the understanding of quantum phenomena through the geometry of Hilbert Space in a way that is accessible to a wide audience. We first give our presentation of Mermin's[1] version of the experiments designed to test Bell's inequality. Making the usual assumptions of locality (no superluminal communication), realism (properties of objects exist independent of measurement), and that the photons detected are representative of the entire population, we carefully show that a realistic

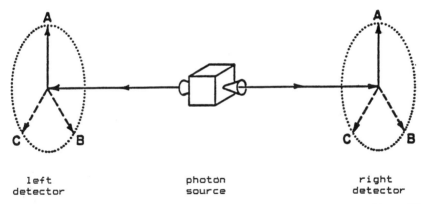

left detector photon source right detector

FIGURE 1. A source of correlated photon pairs is directed toward detectors with possible directions, A, B, and C, separated from each other by 120° as seen from the source.

or local hidden variable explanation of the two photon correlation experiments is inconsistent with the experimental data.

A geometric quantum mechanical analysis is given of the experiment. We use the following notation: Directions of the polarization detectors (separated by 120° as seen along the direction of photon propagation) are given by A, B, and C (see FIGURE 1). The possible measurements are correspondingly a^+ (photon passes through the detector set at A), a^- (does not pass the detector set at A), b^+, b^-, etc. The corresponding states in Hilbert Space are given by $|a^+\rangle$, $|a^-\rangle$, $|b^+\rangle$, etc. Although

Hilbert Space can be complex and can have an infinite number of dimensions, we rigorously treat this experiment using a real four-dimensional Hilbert Space denoted H. The following Quantum Mechanical Assumptions (QMA) are required:

QMA 1: Each possible state of the physical system under consideration is a disk in H. All of these disks have no thickness, a radius of 1, and common centers at 0, which is their only point of intersection.

QMA 2: If a photon is in state $|d\rangle$ and e is a possible result of measurement, then the probability that e will be measured is equal to the area of the orthogonal projection of the disk, $|d\rangle$, onto the disk, $|e\rangle$, divided by the area of a disk (pi).

QMA 3: Any geometric symmetry of a particular physical system must be represented by a corresponding geometric symmetry of the states in H.

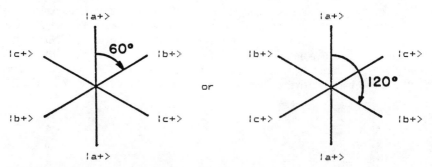

FIGURE 2. Two equivalent configurations of the angular relations of the disks in Hilbert Space corresponding to the states of possibility.

With these QMAs, along with the symmetries in the system and some simple physics of polarization, we derive the theorem:

Theorem 1: The angles between the disks in Hilbert Space can be pictorialized in a two-dimensional plane.

This theorem allows us to make the exact quantum mechanical calculation for the photon correlation experiment by just using simple plane geometry (see FIGURE 2). Throughout the presentation, the conceptual and philosophical meanings are stressed, and an effort is made to visualize all geometrical relations. We also include a technical appendix for the advanced reader.

REFERENCE

1. MERMIN, N. D. 1985. Phys. Today 38(4): 38–47.

The Problem of Internal Properties in Quantum Mechanics

ANDRE MIRABELLI

Saint Peter's College
Jersey City, New Jersey 07306

Any theory, to be theoretically complete, must permit thought-experiments, consistent with that theory, that fix the values of all the numbers that the theory requires to make its predictions. One crucial set of numbers required by all known physical theories is the set of values assigned to internal properties such as mass and charge ratios.

For instance, it must be possible, completely within the theory of classical mechanics, to construct a thought-experiment that determines the values of the masses and charges of a set of bodies and that does not require prior knowledge of the values of the masses and charges of other bodies. Thus, a beam balance cannot be used to determine the ratio of the masses of the first two particles considered because the mass and charge distributions of the beam are crucial, but, by hypothesis, are unknown.

Within classical mechanics (CM), special relativity (SR), and general relativity (GR), it is possible to construct thought-experiments that will determine standard clocks, standard rods, force-free volumes, and inertial frames, and that then will determine the values of the mass and charge (ratios) of particles.

For instance, CM can test for a force-free volume and an inertial frame within which to perform a two-body Machian experiment, and then it can apply the set of equations:

$$m_i a_{ij} = (G m_i m_j - K q_i q_j)/r^2.$$

The values of the distance, r, and the accelerations, a_{ij}, can be measured for all paired combinations of four particles. This provides enough equations to solve for the values of all of the internal properties (m_i and q_i).

An analogous procedure can be explicitly carried out for GR in the post-Newtonian approximation. Because the basic equations to be solved (while using the same kinematic data as in CM) will be different in GR than in CM, the values assigned to the internal properties must necessarily be different. Thus, it is impermissible to use CM values for internal properties within GR.

Similarly, it is impermissible to use either CM, SR, or GR values in quantum mechanics (QM) because QM relates m and q to the kinematic data in a different manner than does either CM, SR, or GR. However, QM cannot itself provide a thought-experiment that determines the values it requires. This is because, in principle, all measurements in QM require macroscopic apparatus, and we are considering the initial determination of the values for internal properties. Thus, as in the case of the beam balance, the mass and charge distribution of the extended measuring apparatus are unknown, making it impossible to use such an apparatus in an experiment that determines the values of internal properties for any initial set of bodies.

The conclusion is that QM cannot consistently borrow the values of the internal properties of (some or all) particles from classical physics, nor can QM determine these values itself. Thus, in principle, QM cannot make consistent predictions because its basic equations (e.g., the Schrödinger equation) require the values of the masses and charges of the bodies being considered.

It is also to be noted that this problem is different in kind from all other known problems with the interpretation of QM. All the other problems can be avoided, in the weak sense that they at least do not make quantum theory internally inconsistent, if one is willing to take the following solipsistic stance: I alone reduce any and all wave packets when they interact with my consciousness. However, the consistency problem posed here is not avoided even by such a radical move.

Quantum Mechanics Determines the Dimension of Space

R. MIRMAN[a]

A simple argument[1] gives the dimension of space $\leq 3 + 1$ (orthogonal transformations of real coordinates induce unitary transformations of complex state functions; thus orthogonal and unitary algebras must be isomorphic—possible only in $3 + 1$ or fewer dimensions). This implies that quantum mechanics, which uses complex state functions, determines the dimension. Are quantum mechanics and field theories possible in higher dimensions? Or do the dimension (and other properties of spacetime) and theories place such constraints on each other as to be (almost) uniquely determined?

The transformations under which a linear differential equation is invariant form a group, and give all solutions when applied to any one. Transformations linking solutions leave the equation invariant; they consist of pairs, with isomorphic group algebras, on coordinates (or momenta, p) and on solutions (the functions given by transformations on a solution of a group with algebra isomorphic to that on the p's). The solutions are the states of a representation of the largest invariance group of the equation.

What is this group for the $(n + 1)$-Dirac equation (besides spinning particles, orbiting scalar particles can be studied) with any metric signature whose solutions have k components? A sum, with complex coefficients, of solutions for the same p's is a solution. Coordinates (or p's) can go into linear combinations (of the orthogonal group—with complex parameters—but not the unitary group for then the phase of a p could be varied so that the phase of a γ would have to be, but $\gamma^2 = 1$). Also, the state function can be replaced by another (of the new coordinates), and the γ's can be replaced by a sum—a new realization that need not be considered for this similarity transformation gives the same solutions.

Coordinates transform under $O(n + 1)$, or $CO(n + 1)$, or a complex extension, and solutions transform under the (if any) homomorphic unitary group. The invariance group is $U(k/2) \times CO(n + 1)$. This must be homomorphic to the group on the k-component solution (a complex extension of) $U(k)$. With $n + 1 = 2\nu$ (or $n + 1 = 2\nu + 1$), so $k = 2^\nu$, $CO(n + 1)$ has $2\nu(2\nu \pm 1)$ generators, $U(k/2)$ has $2^{(2\nu-2)}$, and $U(k)$ has $2^{2\nu}$. The numbers of generators are equal only for $\nu = 2$ and an even-dimensional space, so $n + 1 = 4$ (signature not given by this counting argument, but see reference 1). With $O(n + 1)$, $\nu = 1$ and $n + 1 = 3$. For higher-dimensional spaces, $SU(k)$ is larger than the invariance group of the equation; thus, not all of its transformations give a solution.

Interactions (nonlinear terms) act as $SU(k)$ transformations; in higher-dimensional spaces on solutions to the linear equation (say, in-states), they give functions (out-states) that are not solutions (and not expandable in terms of solutions because the space given by the interactions is larger than that of the solutions of the free

[a]Present address: 155 East 34th Street, New York, New York 10016.

equation). The equation of motion corresponds to a Hamiltonian eigenvalue equation, so the resulting states are not eigenfunctions of the (same) Hamiltonian as the in-states, and possibly of none. This implies that they do not have definite energy (nor definite momentum) and that there is no group for which the state functions are eigenfunctions of physically meaningful representation labels.

Quantum mechanics and field theory may not be possible in higher-dimensional spaces—a reason for the dimensionality of our space.

Besides these conditions from the homomorphism (which is needed for consistent physics; otherwise, calculations, say of the number of lines in a Stern-Gerlach experiment, would give different results depending on how they are done for there would be no consistent way to transform to different coordinate systems—a mathematical operation—so scalar products would not be invariant) and the number of spinor components (determined by the dimension, thus placing a restriction on it), there are others imposed by the representations.

The state function of a system—a unitary-group representation basis state—has k components of j sets with the sets mixed by rotations, but members of each are not mixed. Therefore, $CO(n + 1) \times SU(k/j)$ must be homomorphic to $SU(k)$ to avoid inconsistencies. The number of parameters and of commuting generators must be equal, giving $2\nu(2\nu \pm 1) + (k/j)^2 = k^2$ and $\nu + k/j = k$. The simultaneous solutions for j, ν, and k all have to be integers. There is only one such solution, and it is the same as for the spinor, giving again a $3 + 1$-dimensional space. A 3-dimensional space does not satisfy, so a 4-dimensional one, a direct sum of two 3-dimensional spaces, does not either. This gives the dimension and signature—quantum mechanics requires relativity. Thus, quantum mechanics requires relativistic quantum mechanics. The theories are restricted (determined?) by consistency.

All of these conditions have integer solutions (there seems no a priori reason any should), and the solution is the same for all. Except for these coincidences, if any of these numbers were changed by even one, no universe would be possible. Or would we just have a different formalism?

If these were not met, then consistent physics would not be possible with formalisms and concepts anything like the ones we now use. Would physics be possible at all? Can an inconsistent universe exist? Is there any formalism for spaces of other dimensions; or is there a reason why the dimension of space and the laws of physics have to be what they are?

A space of different dimensionality would be very different in many other ways; some have been considered in papers previously referenced.[1] The problems that arise would likely make life and intelligence and probably any reasonable physics impossible. These give conditions satisfied in only a few spaces (for some only one); all hold in $3 + 1$ dimensions. The fact that the universe is possible, reasonable, and hospitable is due to a remarkable set of coincidences. There are many others, not only in physics, but in our circumstances—in the distance of the Earth to the sun, in the details of the history of the universe, the solar system, and the Earth, and of life itself. There seems no reason why any requirement would be met. Yet, all are.

There are other properties of space. It is real (all physics is ultimately quantum mechanical, and quantum mechanics uses complex objects; why is distance real?). Space can be defined by translation operators, generators of the inhomogeneous group, and a representation of its homogeneous part. There must be invariants in the space, like distance, mass, or angle; consistent physics would be unlikely otherwise. This restricts the inhomogeneous part, and thus space is real. State vectors are eigenfunctions of translations, which are nonlinear operators, so they are complex.

There are reasons for the nature of the universe and the laws of physics. Coherence and consistency provide very strong restrictions. Is the universe they allow unique?

REFERENCE

1. MIRMAN, R. 1984. The dimension of spacetime. Lett. Nuovo Cimento **39:** 398; Space-time dimensionality. Bull. Am. Phys. Soc. **29**(#1): 75, JF4.

The Coherence Properties of Particle Beams

K. RUBIN AND I. EFREMOV

Department of Physics
The City College of the City University of New York
New York, New York 10031

The quantum mechanical description of a beam of particles is not at all well understood. Consider, for example, particles exiting from an oven. The equilibrium state inside the oven can be described in terms of a set of incoherent eigenstates. However, when the particle exits from the oven, one can detect a localized object. Such a localization requires the superposition of a set of coherent waves (i.e., a wave packet). How does this localization come about? Was it there initially, or was it caused by the detection process? If we consider experiments involving a beam of particles, this question is directly related to the coherence properties of the beam. For example, can the initial state of a beam of particles in a scattering experiment be described as a set of incoherent plane waves, or should it be described as a superposition of coherent wave packets?

This question can be answered in such an experiment by making the appropriate observations. To demonstrate this, it is convenient to formulate the scattering problem in terms of a density matrix. Consider the scattering of a beam of particles from a fixed scattering center. If the incoming beam is represented by the density matrix, ρ_{in}, and the outgoing beam by ρ_{out}, where ρ_{out} is equal to $S^+ \rho_{in} S$, and S is the scattering matrix, then the matrix elements of the scattered beam are given by

$$\langle k | \rho_{out} | k' \rangle = -(\hbar^2/m\pi)\{ \mathrm{Im} \int \delta(E_{k''} - E_{k'}) \langle k | \rho_{in} | k'' \rangle f(\hat{k}'' \cdot \hat{k}') d^3k \}$$
$$+ (\hbar^2/m)^2 \{ \int\int \delta(E_k - E_{k''}) f^*(\hat{k} \cdot \hat{k}'')$$
$$\cdot \langle k'' | \rho_{in} | k''' \rangle f(\hat{k}''' \cdot \hat{k}') \delta(E_{k'''} - E_{k'}) d^3k''' d^3k'' \}, \quad (1)$$

and the radial component of the scattered current density, $j_s(r)$, is given by

$$(\hbar/mr^2)\{ -4\pi \int\int \mathrm{Im}[\langle k\hat{r} | \rho_{in} | k\hat{r}' \rangle g(\hat{r} \cdot \hat{r}')] d\Omega_{r'} k \, dk$$
$$+ \int\int\int g^*(\hat{r} \cdot \hat{r}') g(\hat{r} \cdot \hat{r}'') \langle k\hat{r}' | \rho_{in} | k\hat{r}'' \rangle d\Omega_{r'} d\Omega_{r''} k \, dk \}, \quad (2)$$

where r is the radius vector from the scattering center to the detector, k is the wave vector, $g(\hat{r} \cdot \hat{r}')$ is the dimensionless parameter defined by $g(\hat{r} \cdot \hat{r}') = kf(k, \hat{r} \cdot \hat{r}')$, and f is the elastic scattering amplitude. The first term in equation 2 gives the current density of particles scattered out of the incoming beams, while the second term gives the differential scattering current.

It is the first term in the above expression that clearly demonstrates the effect of the coherence properties of the incoming beam on the observed scattering current. The current represented by this term is the difference between the current reaching the detector with and without the scattering center present, and is the result of an interference between the incoming and the scattered beam. In a plane wave description, this term gives rise to the optical theorem. In a scattering experiment, the incoming beam is collimated to make it possible to distinguish between the incoming and scattered particles. The incoming beam, therefore, has components in some range of angles, and the question now arises as to whether the beam can be considered as an incoherent superposition of plane waves traveling in a range of angles or as some superposition of wave packets. (There is, of course, some coherence produced by the collimating slits, but this effect will be very small.) In the one extreme, that of the incoherent superposition of plane waves, the density matrix, ρ_{in}, would have the form, $\Sigma_s P_s |Ks\rangle\langle Ks|$, where $|K_s\rangle$ is a plane wave state and P_s is the probability that this state will be found in the beam. For a continuous distribution of plane wave states, the matrix elements, $\langle k\hat{r}|\rho_{in}|k\hat{r}'\rangle$, have the form, $\int P(K)\delta(k\hat{r} - K)\delta(K - k\hat{r}')d^3K$, producing a scattered current density,

$$j_s^{inc}(r) = (\hbar/mr^2)\{-4\pi \,\mathrm{Im}\, g(0) \int P(k\hat{r})k\,dk + \int\int P(k\hat{r}')|g(\hat{r}\cdot\hat{r}')|^2 d\Omega_{\hat{r}'}k\,dk\}, \quad (4)$$

which is just the usual plane wave result. In particular, the decrease of the current in

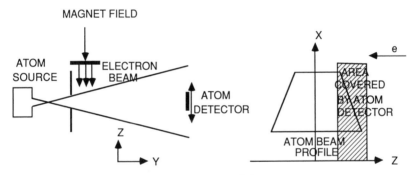

FIGURE 1. Schematic view of the apparatus.

any direction (given by the first term in equation 4) is proportional to the incoming current in that direction. The fraction of atoms scattered out of the beam should, in this case, be independent of the angle of observation. On the other hand, if the incoming beam is a superposition of wave packets, where the eigenstate, $|\Psi_s\rangle$, of a packet is given by $\int |k\rangle\varphi_s(k) \, d^3k$, the scattering current becomes

$$j_s(r) = (\hbar/mr^2)\sum_s P_s\{-4\pi \int\int \mathrm{Im}\, [\varphi_s^*(k\hat{r})\varphi_s(k\hat{r}')g(\hat{r}\cdot\hat{r}')]\, d\Omega_{\hat{r}'}k\,dk$$

$$+ \int\int\int g^*(\hat{r}\cdot\hat{r}')g(\hat{r}\cdot\hat{r}'')\varphi_s^*(k\hat{r}')\varphi_s(k\hat{r}'')\, d\Omega_{\hat{r}'}d\Omega_{\hat{r}''}k\,dk\}. \quad (5)$$

It is clear that, in this case, the first term in equation 5 is no longer proportional to the incoming current. A measurement of the fraction of particles scattered out of the incoming beam as a function of position within the shadow of the beam should therefore give information concerning the off-diagonal elements of the density matrix of the incoming beam. We have made such observations for the scattering of low energy electrons from potassium. The data were obtained in a crossed beam experiment in which measurements were made of the fraction of atoms scattered as a function of position within the shadow of the incoming atom beam. A schematic view of the apparatus and a plot of the results are shown in the FIGURES 1 and 2. It is clear that the fraction of atoms scattered is dependent upon the detector position, and that there are oscillations in the results that have the appearance of a diffraction pattern. It is possible to explain these oscillations by assuming that the incoming beam consists of

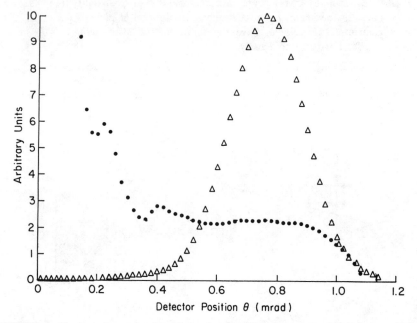

FIGURE 2. The experimental value of the fraction of atoms scattered (circles), and the experimental atom-beam profile (triangles).

wave packets localizing at different points in space, r_s. The first term in equation 5 will then contain a factor of the form, $\int\int e^{ik|\hat{p}-\hat{p}'|\cdot\hat{r}_s} d^3r_s\ k\ dk$. Integrating over a spherical region of radius, a, we obtain a term proportional to $1 - \sin(x)/x$, where $x = ka\vartheta$. From our data, we find a value for a of the order of 0.25×10^{-6} cm. This is of the order of magnitude of the radius of the scattering cross section, and the results would seem to indicate that the scattered particles are those particles whose wave packets have localized in the region of the cross section before scattering. Also, note from equation 2 that the coherence properties of the outgoing and incoming beams differ.

Proposed Experimental Investigation of Uncertainty Relations by Measuring the Velocity Dispersion of Localized Neutrons

J. SCHEER AND M. SCHMIDT

Department of Physics
University of Bremen
D-2800 Bremen 33, Federal Republic of Germany

In the EPR discussion, the original topic of the Einstein-Bohr debate that was related to the completeness of quantum mechanics has been overshadowed by the nonlocality question that has emerged from it. The original question was whether one could know more about an individual object than the quantum mechanics is able to tell because of the uncertainty relation. Therefore, the original idea was to propose a way to disentangle the situation where the very determination of one quantity physically disturbs the conjugated quantity, as, for instance, in the gamma-ray microscope. In that case, it was not at all clear

(1) whether the micro-object actually had the two properties simultaneously, but that they never could be determined that way;

(2) whether they did not have objective properties at all, and that they were created by the observer; or

(3) whether they actually existed and could by some means be determined in individual cases: the Heisenberg uncertainty relations being reinterpreted then as representing dispersion relations on an ensemble of particles.

Now EPR's idea was:

(a) to determine one quantity directly, say, the spatial coordinate, with a given uncertainty, and

(b) to obtain knowledge about the conjugated quantity without disturbing the previous determination by an indirect measurement.

Furthermore, their idea, of course, was to obtain knowledge about the momentum by measuring the momentum of the other particle that had been together with the first one at rest before:[4] this is a proposal that amounts to assuming the absolute conservation of energy momentum in all individual microprocesses.

Should the current interpretation of the EPR experiments be maintained and the criticism of Selleri and others not be upheld (see reference 5), then it is possible that EPR's "bad luck" was that, in such a situation, this disentanglement was not possible because of nonlocal effects specifically holding for such pairs of particles. If this is the case, then a different experiment (one that we should like to propose here) may do what EPR had in mind. The idea is still to determine the spatial coordinate with a given uncertainty, while also being able to obtain knowledge about the conjugated quantity by an indirect measurement without disturbing in any conceivable way the determination of the former.

The proposed experiment (see FIGURE 1) was inspired by an idea of Robinson,[1] who has proposed an investigation of the uncertainty relations involving electrons with selected velocities. The simple idea is to use thermal neutrons that are detected with a very small spatial uncertainty; they will be detected by using a special detector to be developed for this purpose. It consists of a thin cadmium layer, and the neutron-capture gamma rays are detected by the NaJ scintillators surrounding it, which gives the stop signal for a time-of-flight measurement.[a] Hereby, one obtains knowledge about the spatial coordinate indirectly by detecting gamma rays, thus knowing precisely where they came from. Completely independent of this indirect coordinate determination, the velocity of the neutron can be prepared with a particular velocity uncertainty by, for example, a double-chopper apparatus. This would imply, by

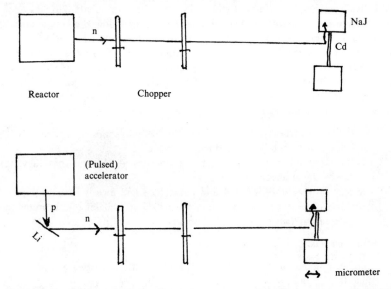

FIGURE 1. The proposed experiment inspired by an idea of Robinson. See text for details.

Heisenberg's relations, a certain spatial uncertainty that would be much larger than the actual detector layer width. Note that this Δx is in the direction of flight, not vertical to it, as is discussed in numerous arrangements, where the coordinate vertical to the flight direction is determined by a slit or diaphragm. Therefore, considerations like Feynman's[6] do not apply here. Here, the precision of the x-coordinate is not determined by an obstacle having its effect on the corresponding momentum precision, but simply by the presence of nuclei serving to detect the neutrons.

A possible experiment may involve thermal neutrons with velocity, $v = 10^5$ cm/sec,

---

[a] The recoil range prior to gamma emission is negligible ($v_R \approx 10^3$ cm/sec; $\tau_R < 10^{-15}$ sec; $\gamma_R < 10^{-12}$ cm).

gate time $= 10^{-5}$ sec, flight path $= 10^2$ cm, flight time spread $=$ velocity spread 1%, and velocity spread, $\Delta v = 10^3$ cm/sec. This, by Heisenberg's relation, implies a spatial spread, $\Delta x = 10^{-6}$ cm, but the actual spatial spread (one atomic layer) is 10^{-8} cm. Considering the fact that the nuclei are contained between much closer planes, the uncertainty is less than 10^{-11} cm. The discrepancy is so large that angular spreads, etc., in an actual experiment play no important role. The essential point, of course, is that the determination of the velocity is completely disentangled from the determination of the spatial uncertainty. Thus, an influence of the kind wherein which the choice of the layer thickness might affect the speed of the incoming neutrons is hard to imagine. The idea is similar to the one of Fitchard,[7] who proposed an experiment involving electrons, but it is simpler to perform, and the discrepancy between experimental and theoretical Δx is much larger. It may also be noted that there could be only one neutron per time in the apparatus, excluding any interaction.

Now, of course, the expected result is not new to the realistic interpretation that regards the Heisenberg relations as not limiting the measurement of an individual object, but only limiting the preparation of an ensemble of them.[2] The experiment described so far agrees with this because the neutron is captured, that is, practically destroyed by its detection.

This assertion can, however, be tested by a different experiment where the neutrons are produced by a threshold reaction, say, Li^7 (p, n), just above the threshold, with a pulsed beam on a thin layer that is subsequently chopped.

With a time spread of 10^{-6} sec, cold neutrons with $v = 10^3$ cm/sec, a flight path of 10^2 cm, a flight time of 10^{-1} sec, $\Delta v/v = 10^{-5}$, and $\Delta v = 10^{-2}$ cm/sec can be produced, thus implying, by Heisenberg's relation, a spatial uncertainty of $3 \cdot 10^{-1}$ cm $= 3$ mm. However, in an actual arrangement in 1-m distance, one can produce a spread of only 10^{-3} cm, which is a difference that by a foil detector described above can actually be detected by mechanical means and with the naked eye.

We think that Heisenberg's relation always refers to a situation where the preparation of the magnitudes of conjugated quantities is somehow interconnected. This means that these relations give the "natural" uncertainties; if you limit Δv and do nothing else, then there will be a Δx as an effect of the stochastic nature of the subquantum medium. Bohm has shown that Planck's h can be derived in this context[3] from properties of the subquantum medium referring to the fields existing in it. This means that the uncertainty refers to the guiding field (which is how the wave function is considered in the realistic interpretation), and normally this is all one knows about the particle. In special situations, however, one may prepare the properties more precisely provided that these procedures do not interfere with each other.

While the second experiment is somewhat difficult to be actually performed, the first one should be feasible: If $\sigma = 2 \cdot 10^{-20}$ cm, $\rho = 10^{+1}$ g/cm^3 (Cd), $x = 10^{-8}$ cm, $N_L = 6 \times 10^{23}$ Loschmidt-no., $1/M = 10^{-2} = 1/$molecular weight, $\Omega = 10^{-2}$ solid angle of the γ-detector, and $A = 10^{-1}$ response of the γ-detector, then $Z = N_n \cdot \sigma \cdot x \cdot \rho \cdot N_L/M \cdot \Omega \cdot A \approx N_n \cdot 10^{-8}$, and with $N_n \sim 10^8 - 10^7$, one has count rates on the order of 1/sec or 1/min.

We are presently constructing the foil detector, and we are looking for a facility to take it to. We will be very surprised if the experiment should yield different results from the ones that one would expect according to Einstein's views.

ACKNOWLEDGMENTS

We acknowledge valuable discussions with J. Robinson, E. J. Sternglass, J. P. Vigier, and W. Zeitz.

REFERENCES

1. ROBINSON, J. 1980. J. Phys. A: Math. Nucl. Gen. **13:** 877; 1982. J. Phys. A: Math. Nucl. Gen. **15:** 113, 3379.
2. BALLENTINE, J. 1970. The statistical interpretation of quantum mechanics. Rev. Mod. Phys. **24:** 358.
3. BOHM, D. *In* Advanced Quantum Mechanics. Blake, Ed.; see also: CUFARO-PETRONI, N., J. P. VIGIER, C. DEWDNEY, P. HOLLAND & T. KYPRIANIDIS. 1985. Phys. Rev. **D32:** 137.
4. EINSTEIN, A., B. PODOLSKY & N. ROSEN. 1935. Phys. Rev. **47:** 777.
5. SELLERI, F. 1985. Phys. Lett. **108A:** 197.
6. THE FEYNMAN-LECTURES ON PHYSICS, III. 2–1 ff.
7. FITCHARD, E. E. 1979. Found. Phys. **9:** 525.

A Comment on Bell's Inequality; Mental Activity and Physical Reality

DOUGLAS M. SNYDER[a]

COMMENT ON BELL'S INEQUALITY

The significance of Bell's inequality lies in its application to physical events that experiment has demonstrated are correctly described by quantum mechanics (specifically, in terms of probability amplitudes amenable to superposition and governed by the uncertainty principle) and not by a classical framework. Bell's inequality is generally not applied to macroscopic physical systems, for example, because it is not in doubt that a classical theoretical framework provides a correct description in the large majority of cases. B. d'Espagnat[1] considered realism as the view that consistencies in observation are due to a physical reality independent of human observers. He[1] derived Bell's inequality using the spin angular momentum of a particle, which is a quantity whose theoretical foundation is found in quantum mechanical and relativistic considerations, and not in a solely classical view. Even if spin is not considered with regard to this theoretical foundation, experimental evidence has shown that it is correctly described by quantum mechanics, which, of course, involves the uncertainty principle. For example, experimental evidence, in accord with quantum mechanics, indicates that only one spin component along an axis can be measured by an instrument at a time. In developing the argument leading to Bell's inequality, d'Espagnat wrote that if a physicist accepts the premises of local realistic theories, then conclusions can be drawn regarding the values of all three spin components. In considering a new bunch of paired protons in the singlet state that have not been measured with regard to spin,

> he [the physicist] can infer that in every pair, one proton has the property $A+$ [spin up along the A axis] and the other has the property $A-$ [spin down along the A axis]. [Reference 1, p. 166.]

In a similar manner, d'Espagnat wrote that the physicist can conclude that one proton in every pair has the property of spin up along the B axis (i.e., $B+$) and one has the property of spin down along the B axis (i.e., $B-$), and that one has spin up along the C axis (i.e., $C+$) and one has spin down along the C axis (i.e., $C-$).

> These conclusions require a subtle but important extension of the meaning assigned to a notation such as $A+$. Whereas previously $A+$ was one possible outcome of a measurement made on a particle, it is converted by this argument [the acceptance of a local realistic theoretical framework] into an attribute of the particle itself . . . . the physicist has been led to the conclusion that both protons in each pair have definite spin components at all times . . . . he [the physicist] can argue from the premises of local realistic theories that the values [of the spin components] are quite definite in the absence of any measurements. [Reference 1, p. 166.]

[a]Mailing address: Post Office Box 228, Berkeley, California 94701.

611

However, granting that each proton has the property $A+$ or $A-$, $B+$ or $B-$, and $C+$ or $C-$, it should be possible in principle to measure more than one spin component for a proton at a time. If this is not possible, then the view that is called realism and that is part of the basis for d'Espagnat's development of Bell's inequality actually takes on a positivistic character (specifically, the notion that properties of particles cannot be assumed to characterize the particle unless, and only during the course of which, they are measured). As noted, experimental data have indicated such measurements are not possible. Thus, the consideration of spin (or, for that matter, any other physical quantity to which Bell's inequality might be significantly applied) from the local realistic standpoint used to derive Bell's inequality contradicts experimental data. If Bell's inequality is to be of significance, then the argument supporting Bell's inequality is critically flawed.

Given a reasonable definition of realism (i.e., a definition that does not exhibit a strong positivistic character), the argument presented concerning Bell's inequality leads to the result that hidden variables are not a valid logical possibility for explaining physical quantities for which this inequality may be of significance. The above analysis can be applied to Mermin's[2] formulation of the key idea of Bell's inequality, specifically, Mermin's postulate that both members of each pair of particles released by a box carry identical instruction sets. The usefulness of Mermin's assignment of these instruction sets depends on the components of these sets being real characteristics of the particles, that is, on the enduring nature of all the components independent of whether a measurement is made on any particular component of a set.

MENTAL ACTIVITY AND PHYSICAL REALITY

Results[3] have been obtained that support a theory that allows for an influence with a velocity greater than that of light on physical events. The question arises as to the nature of this influence. Is it strictly a physical influence, or is it an influence that has a mental component? The latter possibility becomes distinctly plausible because any physical influence would violate special relativity. A test of the possible influence of mental activity on the measurements of physical events is theoretically possible and is a simple extrapolation of the general type of experimental design that has been used to test Bell's inequality. In the Aspect et al. experiment,[3] machines were used to randomly determine the settings of the measuring devices. Physicists have assumed that the use of random selection of the settings of the measuring devices by machines in tests of Bell's inequality would be equivalent to the free choice of these settings by human experimenters, with the latter emphasized by Bohr as being at the foundation of quantum mechanical theory. This assumption is now called into question. If the results of an experiment using machines to determine the settings of the measuring devices differ from the results obtained when people freely choose these settings, the thesis that this influence has a mental component would be supported. Specifically, as the Aspect et al. results support quantum mechanical predictions, a violation of the expected quantum mechanical pattern in the experiment using human experimenters to freely decide on the settings would provide evidence of a mental component.

In fact, the Aspect et al. experiment already provides significant evidence to support such an influence. In special relativity, simultaneity for a Newtonian frame of reference is defined as the time required by a ray of light to travel from a spatial point A to a spatial point B being equal to the time required for a ray of light to travel from point B to point A.[4] It is this formulation of time, rather than the instantaneous nature of simultaneity in Newtonian physics, that leads to the conclusions of special relativity. Spacelike separated events may be defined as events for which the absolute value of the quotient obtained by dividing the spatial distance between the events by the temporal interval between the events is greater than the velocity of light. As spacelike separated events are partially defined in terms of the difference in their temporal coordinates, their definition presupposes a common time of the clocks involved so that these temporal coordinates can be meaningfully compared. Thus, when spacelike separated events are generally considered, the nature of the time underlying these events is unclear. The theoretical framework of special relativity does not support the consideration of these events. It is proposed that when scientists discuss spacelike separated events and obtain experimental evidence to support their hypotheses in which such events are thought to be involved (as in the Aspect et al. experiment), scientists have engaged in a mental, or theoretical, development of physical reality (including time) that is confirmed by their experimental work. The only other alternative for establishing a temporal basis for the consideration of these events is for the common time to have the instantaneous nature found in Newtonian mechanics. This alternative is just what special relativity has refuted.

REFERENCES

1. D'ESPAGNAT, B. 1979. The quantum theory and reality. Sci. Am. **241**(5): 158–181.
2. MERMIN, N. D. 1981. Bringing home the atomic world: quantum mysteries for anybody. Am. J. Phys. **49**(10): 940–943.
3. ASPECT, A., J. DALIBARD & G. ROGER. 1982. Experimental test of Bell's inequalities using time-varying analyzers. Phys. Rev. Lett. **49**(25): 1804–1807.
4. EINSTEIN, A. 1952. On the electrodynamics of moving bodies. *In* The Principle of Relativity, a Collection of Original Papers on the Special and General Theory of Relativity. H. Lorentz, A. Einstein, H. Minkowski & H. Weyl, Eds.: 35–65. (W. Perrett & G. Jeffrey, Translation.) Dover. New York. (Original work published in 1905.)

The Quantum Condition and the Non-Euclidean Nature of Space-Time

E. J. STERNGLASS

Radiation Physics Laboratory
University of Pittsburgh
Pittsburgh, Pennsylvania 15261

The origin of the Bohr–de Broglie quantum condition for the stability of atomic and nuclear systems can be interpreted in terms of a locally high Gaussian curvature of space-time equivalent to a large value of the gravitational constant along the lines suggested by Motz[1] for the stability of the electron. Assuming the mass is purely electromagnetic in origin and that hadrons are composed of highly relativistic electron-positron pairs in "charmonium" or heavy, integrally charged, quarklike arrangements, and also by adopting a symmetrical definition of the electromagnetic force between two moving particles as proposed by Einstein in 1905, one arrives at the existence of a minimum approach distance as well as a changing source size or rest mass for the electron and positron in highly relativistic orbits of pion mass that form the basis of all hadrons (FIGURE 1).[2]

The existence of a minimum approach distance between the fundamental entities is equivalent to a non-Euclidean geometry with a high local G similar to that of Motz, except that this local G is found to increase inversely as the square root of the pair mass during the course of the evolution of the universe by internal pair-production. This process begins with the Newtonian value of G and increases up to a maximum value of e^2/m_o^2, starting with a single massive "Lemaitre-atom"-like electron-pair of mass equal to that of the universe, M_U, at the Planck density, $c^5/\hbar G^2$.[3]

As a result, the charges in equilibrium orbits move along geodesics of the local space so that they do not radiate, which is contrary to classical electromagnetic theory. In these orbits, the tangential Lorentz contraction of the field source is exactly equaled by the radial contraction produced by the local space-curvature, thus reducing the source to the spherical shape associated with a state of rest. This provides a simple physical or geometrical explanation of the Bohr–de Broglie quantum condition, which can be applied to the stability of electron orbits and, thus, to all matter.

Because hadrons appear to be describable as molecular arrangements of highly relativistic electrons and positrons whose masses, sizes, and lifetimes can be accounted for in terms of the basic electromagnetic constants, e, m_o, c, and $\hbar$, without any other arbitrary constants or adjustable parameters,[2] and because the electron and positron may in turn be regarded as self-stabilized, spinning sources of a single field[1] analogous to "twisted geons," "vortex rings," or "strings" in a fluidlike space-time continuum or ether, the wave-particle nature of matter finds a simple physical explanation. In this model, there is no "hard" or "ponderable" matter. Instead, all matter "particles" consist of stable, spinning sources of electromagnetic fields of finite inner size, with the size of the source determining the rest mass. This explains the relation of heavy quarks to leptons, including their small, pointlike size and spin ½.

In this model, the strong force is explained as a relativistic form of the electromagnetic interaction that changes the static Coulomb force constant, e^2, to γe^2, where γ is the Lorentz factor. Here, the "weakness" or "slowness" of beta-decay emerges as a consequence of the reduced source size associated with the abnormally high mass of the relativistic pairs in their π-type ground state.[2]

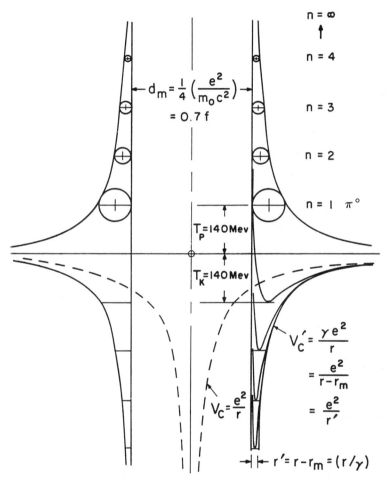

FIGURE 1. Schematic diagram of the non-Euclidean potential for the interaction of a relativistic electron pair at increasing energy.

In such a model, the gravitational force is found to be an effect of the space-time curvature associated with the finite source size of the spinning electron "vortex" and the resulting finite minimum approach distance of electron-positron pairs. It therefore appears that the key to the origin of gravitation and its connection to quantum theory is the necessity to introduce only finite minimum and maximum values for all measurable

TABLE 1. Implications of an Electromagnetic Theory of Matter

Basic Constants
$e, m_o, c,$ and $\alpha = e^2/\hbar c = 1/137.03604(05)$

Derived Quantities		
Radius of electron at rest	$r_{cl} = (1/2)e^2/m_o c^2$	1.4090×10^{-13} cm
Minimum distance between relativistic $e^+ e^-$	$d_{min} = (1/4)e^2/m_o c^2$	0.7045×10^{-13} cm
Mass of $n = 1$ relativistic $e^+ e^-$	$M_{\pi^o} = [(2/\alpha) - 10]m_o$	$264.072\, m_o$
Spin average mass of relativistic $e^+ e^-$	$\langle M_\pi \rangle = [(2/\alpha) - 2]m_o$	$272.072\, m_o$
Masses of hadrons	Molecular rotators composed of π's	(See reference 2)
Minimum distance between π's	$d_{\pi\pi} = r_{cl} = r_p = \hbar/M_\pi c$	1.4090×10^{-13} cm
Strong coupling constant $(\pi\pi)$	$\alpha_s = 2[(2/\alpha) - 1]\alpha \exp(-r/d_{min})$	0.539 for $r = d_{\pi\pi}$
Weak coupling constant	$g = (\alpha r_{cl})^2 e^2$	2.8439×10^{-49} erg cm^3
Effective field en. radius of $e^+ e^-$	$\langle R_{ee} \rangle = 4r_{cl}$	5.6359×10^{-13} cm
Effective field en. volume of $e^+ e^-$	$V_o = (8/\alpha)\langle R_{ee} \rangle^3$	$1096\, r_{cl}^3$
Maximum possible density (Planck)	$\rho_{max} = c^5/\hbar G^2$	5.176×10^{93} gm cm^{-3}
Maximum mass of relativistic $e^+ e^-$	$M_{max} = \rho_{max} V_o = 2\langle M_\pi \rangle 2^{(2/\alpha)}$	$1.7361 \times 10^{85}\, m_o$
Mass of universe	$M_U = M_{max}$	$9.4551 \times 10^{81}\, M_p$
Local curvature constant	$G_{loc} = (e^2/m_o^2)(m_o/M_{ee})^{1/2}$	Function of M_{ee}
Newton's constant	$G = (e^2/m_o^2)(m_o/M_U)^{1/2}$	6.6721×10^{-8} cgs^a
Schwarzschild radius of universe	$R_{sch} = \langle R_{ee} \rangle (M_U/m_o)^{1/2}$	2480×10^9 light-years
Einstein radius of universe	$R_E = (1/8\pi^2)R_{sch}$	31.41×10^9 light-years
Einstein's cosmological constant	$\Lambda = 1/R_E^2$	1.1325×10^{-57} cm^{-2}
Hubble constant (min. value)	$H_o = c/R_E$	9.5446 km sec$^{-1}/10^6$ light-years
Rotational period of universe	$\tau_o = 2\pi R_{sch}/c$	1.5596×10^{13} years^b
Dirac number	$N_D = (e^2/m_o^2 G) = (M_U/m_o)^{1/2}$	4.1667×10^{42}

^{a}Compare with the most recent measured value of $6.6726(05) \times 10^{-8}$ cgs (citation 15 in reference 3).
^{b}Compare with the 6×10^{13} years arrived by: BIRCH, P. 1982. *Nature* **298:** 451.

physical quantities such as distances between the fundamental entities, and their source-sizes, masses, charges, and relative velocities.

Thus, both the existence of a minimum quantum of action or angular momentum and the existence of a non-Euclidean physical space or gravitation appear to be logically required extensions of classical electrodynamics dictated by the need for a principle of finiteness that allows only unambiguously definable, finite quantities to enter into any internally consistent physical theory. The fundamental entities, here, are extended field sources of finite size and mass that, nevertheless, behave in all collisions as if they were ideal, structureless, infinitely small mathematical points.

The hypothesis that both the quantum condition and the non-Euclidean nature of physical space-time are consequences of a self-consistent electromagnetic theory of matter is strongly supported by the fact that not only the masses, sizes, spins, and lifetimes of hadrons can be calculated using only e, m_o, c, and $\hbar$ or α,[2] but also the large Dirac number, and thus the mass and size of the universe, as well as the numerical value of Newton's gravitational constant (see TABLE 1).[3]

REFERENCES

1. MOTZ, L. 1962. Nuovo Cimento 26: 672.
2. STERNGLASS, E. J. 1961. Phys. Rev. 123: 391; 1965. Nuovo Cimento 35: 227; 1965. Proc. 2nd Conf. on Resonant Particles, Ohio University. B. A. Munir, Ed. Ohio Univ. Press. Athens, Ohio.
3. STERNGLASS, E. J. 1984. Lett. Nuovo Cimento 41: 203.

Derivation of the Schrödinger Equation from Hamilton-Jacobi Theory in a Complexified Space with Extra Dimensions

CHRISTIAN J. TOURENNE

Department of Physics
Maharishi International University
Fairfield, Iowa 52556

The derivation of the Schrödinger equation (SE) from the classical Hamilton-Jacobi equation (HJE) is rigorous only for a free particle or for a particle in a potential in the classical limit ($\hbar \rightarrow 0$) of the optical analogy.[1] The complex quantum HJE[2] in one dimension

$$\partial F/\partial t + (\partial F/\partial x)^2/2m + V(x, t) = (i\hbar/2m)\partial^2 F/\partial x^2,$$

which can be derived from the one-dimensional SE for a wave function, $\Psi(x, t)$ [where $F = (\hbar/i) \ln \Psi$], usually involves a real continuity equation for the probability density and the assumption of a stochastic,[3] geometrical,[4] or dynamical model.[5] In this paper, an attempt is presented to establish the quantum HJE in the context of a complex HJ theory and to show that the term, $[(-i\hbar/2m) \, \partial^2F/\partial x^2]$, has the nature of a kinetic energy. The first assumption is that the motion of the particle takes place in an orthogonal complex geometry; complex position and momentum vectors are defined, as well as a complex trigonometry involving complex trigonometric functions. Quantum effects result from the complexification of the classical dimension and from the addition of an extra curvilinear complexified dimension. The second assumption is that the particle obeys a dynamics described by an HJE:

$$\partial F/\partial t + H = 0,$$

in which the Hamilton's function, F, and the Hamiltonian, H, are complex. The complex total momentum, $\vec{p}_T$, is the sum of two perpendicular momenta ($\vec{p}_T = \vec{p}_x + \vec{p}_\Sigma$), and makes the particle follow continuous trajectories in a cylindrical complex geometry. The momentum, $p_x = \partial F/\partial x$, makes the particle move along the complexified classical dimension, X_x ($dX_x = dx \exp [i\alpha(x, t)]$), corresponding to the axis of the cylinder, and p_Σ corresponds to a perpendicular motion along a curvilinear complexified dimension, σ_x, on which the particle is located by a position vector, R_x, from the origin.

The linear complex momentum along σ_x gives rise to two angular momenta of nonclassical origin. Two quantum constraints are postulated by which the integral of each angular momentum over the corresponding rotational angle and along a bundle of trajectories is proportional to $\hbar$. These quantum conditions show that quantum effects are equivalent to a constrained dynamics. The quantum HJE description is then equivalent to a complex Newtonian dynamics taking place on a smooth surface in a complexified geometry. The reaction of the surface on the particle does no work and is calculable by the theory. The optical analogy is reestablished in the context of a complex geometry by our derivation.

The theory establishes the term, $[(-i\hbar/2m)\ \partial^2 F/\partial x^2]$, as the kinetic energy of rotation of the particle along the dimension, σ_x:

$$p_\Sigma = (-i\hbar\ \partial^2 F/\partial x^2)^{1/2}.$$

It also derives a formula for the position vector, R_x:

$$R_x = (1/2\pi)[i\hbar/(\partial^2 F/\partial x^2)]^{1/2}.$$

R_x vanishes in the classical limit ($\hbar \rightarrow 0$), which results in the classical real dynamics. Like the generalized stochastic approach,[6] the approach described in this paper suggests the existence of nonobservable complex trajectories[7] and of non-Hermitian operators in nonrelativistic quantum mechanics. Differences and analogies are noticed with other interpretations[4,5] of the quantum theory.

REFERENCES

1. YOURGRAU, W. & S. MANDELSTAM. 1979. Variational Principles in Dynamics and Quantum Theory. Dover. New York.
2. GOLDSTEIN, H. 1950. Classical Mechanics. Addison–Wesley. Reading, Massachusetts.
3. GUERRA, F. 1981. Phys. Rep. **77**(3): 263.
4. SANTAMATO, E. 1984. Phys. Rev. **D29**(2): 216.
5. BOHM, D. 1952. Phys. Rev. **85**: 180.
6. ARON, J. C. 1981. Found. Phys. **11**(9–10): 699.
7. COMISAR, G. 1965. Phys. Rev. **B138**(5): 1332.

The Predictability of the Results of Measurements of Noncommuting Variables

LEV VAIDMAN AND YAKIR AHARONOV

Department of Physics
University of South Carolina
Columbia, South Carolina 29208
and
Department of Physics
Tel Aviv University
Ramat Aviv, 69978 Tel Aviv, Israel

In the orthodox understanding of quantum mechanics, two variables, A and B, cannot simultaneously have the definite values $A = a$ and $B = b$, if neither $[A, B] | A = a \rangle$ nor $[A, B] | B = b \rangle$ vanishes. Suppose, however, that at time t_1 A is found to have the value a, and that at time t_2 B is found to have the value b. Then, by means of prediction from time t_1, and retrodiction from time t_2, the values of both A and B at time t, where $t_1 < t < t_2$, can obviously be ascertained. We have found that there are situations in which we can ascertain not only the simultaneous values of two noncommuting variables, but rather of an infinite number of noncommuting variables. Roughly, these situations are, in some sense, linear superpositions of the situations wherein we can ascertain (by means of prediction and retrodiction together) the values of the noncommuting variables. The proper way to describe those situations is by using the language of multiple-time states,[1] but we can understand them also if we look on a specific part of a composite system at times between two measurements on the whole system.

We use here a generalization of the formula[2] for the probability of the result of measurements at time t, given the states of the system at times t_1 and t_2, where $t_1 < t < t_2$. The probability of finding $C = c$ at time t, if at time t_1 the state is $| \phi_1 \rangle$ and at time t_2 the state is $| \phi_2 \rangle$, is

$$P(C = c) = \frac{| \langle \phi_2 | \mathbf{P}_{C=c} | \phi_1 \rangle |^2}{\Sigma_i | \langle \phi_2 | \mathbf{P}_{C=c_i} | \phi_1 \rangle |^2},$$

where $\mathbf{P}_{C=c_i}$ is the projection operator on the subspace of states for which $C = c$ and where the sum in the denominator goes over all possible values of C.

We consider the spin-$\frac{1}{2}$ particle within a time interval between two measurements on the composite system that consists of this particle and another, "external," spin-$\frac{1}{2}$ particle. (The second particle takes the place of the measuring device of the multiple-time measurement.[3]) It was found that there are situations wherein the result $\sigma_\xi = 1$ (i.e., if spin is measured in the direction $\hat{\xi}$, the result is "up" with probability 1) is true simultaneously for a continuum of directions $\hat{\xi}$. It was proven that such a continuum of rays takes the form of a cone. For example, we consider the superposition of the situations: $\sigma_x(t_1) = 1$ and $\sigma_y(t_2) = 1$, $\sigma_y(t_1) = 1$ and $\sigma_x(t_2) = 1$. The spin-$\frac{1}{2}$

particle behaves as if it is in this superposition provided that the composite system is prepared at time t_1 in the state

$$|\phi_1\rangle = \frac{1}{\sqrt{2}} (|\uparrow_z\rangle_{\text{ext}}|\uparrow_x\rangle + |\downarrow_z\rangle_{\text{ext}}|\uparrow_y\rangle),$$

and is found at time t_2 in the state

$$|\phi_2\rangle = \frac{1}{\sqrt{2}} (|\uparrow_z\rangle_{\text{ext}}|\uparrow_y\rangle + |\downarrow_z\rangle_{\text{ext}}|\uparrow_x\rangle).$$

We assume that the system has zero Hamiltonian, and no measurement is performed on the external spin-$\frac{1}{2}$ particle between t_1 and t_2. The cone of directions $\hat{\xi}$ for which $\sigma_\xi = 1$ include, in this case, the axes $\hat{x}$, $\hat{y}$, and $\hat{z}$.

REFERENCES

1. D'AMATO, S. 1984. Ph.D. thesis. University of South Carolina.
2. AHARONOV, Y. *et al.* 1964. Phys. Rev. **B134:** 1410.
3. AHARONOV, Y. & D. ALBERT. 1984. Phys. Rev. **D29:** 223.

Simultaneous Particle and Wave Knowledge in Quantum Theory

ALLAINE YA'SIN AND DANIEL M. GREENBERGER

Department of Physics
The City College of the City University of New York
New York, New York 10031

With the neutron interferometer, one is able to alter the relative phase and intensity of two coherently partitioned beams (FIGURE 1). We will exploit this capacity to develop particle and wave information measures. Here, particle knowledge corresponds to the predictability of the neutron's trajectory (whether it will traverse the interferometer via beam I or II), and wave knowledge is indicated by the sharpness of the interference pattern.[1]

If an absorber is placed at F in FIGURE 1, the disturbance at the counters is

$$\Psi = Ae^{ikx} + Be^{i\phi}e^{-ikx},$$ (1)

where A and B are the amplitudes of beams I and II, respectively. The contrast is given by

$$C = \frac{I_{max} - I_{min}}{I_{min} + I_{min}} = \frac{2AB}{A^2 + B^2},$$ (2)

where I_{max} = maximum intensity and I_{min} = minimum intensity. The contrast provides the measure of wave knowledge, and is equal to its maximum when $A = B$.

The probability that the neutron is in beam I is

$$P_I = \frac{A^2}{A^2 + B^2} \quad (A > B).$$ (3)

The measure of particle knowledge is determined by taking the relative value of P_I to the probability for the case when we have no knowledge and then normalizing:

$$P = \left(\frac{A^2}{A^2 + B^2} - \frac{1}{2}\right)\bigg/\frac{1}{2} \quad \text{or} \quad P = \frac{A^2 - B^2}{A^2 + B^2}.$$ (4)

Let

$$A = R\cos\gamma \text{ and } B = R\sin\gamma.$$ (5)

The development of the neutron's wave and particle potentialities therefore satisfy

$$P^2 + C^2 = 1$$

because

$$P = \cos 2\gamma \text{ and } C = \sin 2\gamma.$$ (6)

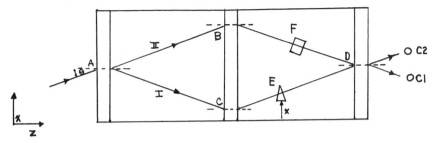

FIGURE 1. Top view of the neutron interferometer. The neutron interferometer is fabricated from a single cylindrical silicon crystal. Laue diffraction occurs at points A, B, and C. At D, the beams interfere coherently and enter the He^3 counters, C1 and C2. By inserting an aluminum wedge (E) and varying x (which alters beam I's optical path length), the dependence of the beams' relative phasing on the distance, x, is acquired. If a phase-shifting device is now positioned at F, its effects are easily probed as a function of the wedge's location. (After: GREENBERGER, D. M. 1983. *Rev. Mod. Phys.* **55**: 875.)

The information theoretical measure discovered by Shannon[2] yields similar results. The amount of information that we lack about a system that can be in any of K states with the probability, P_k, for being in the k-th state is defined to be $H(p)$, where

$$H(p) = -\sum_{k=1}^{k} P_k \ln P_k, \quad \sum_{k=1}^{k} P_k = 1. \tag{7}$$

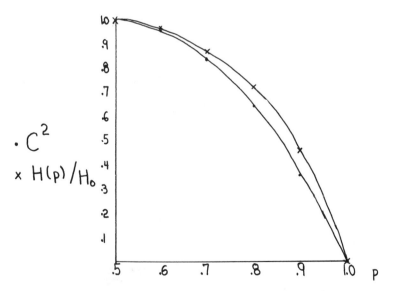

FIGURE 2. $H(p)/H_o$ (the relative amount of unknown information) and C^2 (the square of the contrast) versus the probability, p.

For our particular case,

$$P_1 = p = \frac{A^2}{A^2 + B^2}, \quad P_2 = 1 - p. \tag{8}$$

H is a maximum when $p = \frac{1}{2}$:

$$H(\tfrac{1}{2}) \equiv H_o = \ln 2 = 0.693. \tag{9}$$

The ratio, $H(p)/H_o$, designates the relative amount of unknown information regarding the neutron's path. In FIGURE 2, $H(p)/H_o$ is compared to C^2.

In conclusion, we have provided a quantitative description of the simultaneous development of a system's wave and particle properties, and thereby manifested the complementarity principle's structure.[3]

REFERENCES

1. For a review, see: GREENBERGER, D. M. 1983. Rev. Mod. Phys. **55:** 875; GREENBERGER, D. M. & A. W. OVERHAUSER. 1979. Rev. Mod. Phys. **51:** 43.
2. SHANNON, C. E. 1948. Bell Syst. Tech. J. **27:** 379.
3. WOOTTERS, W. K. & W. H. ZUREK. 1979. Phys. Rev. **D19:** 473. This article shows the feasibility of obtaining both wave and particle knowledge; however, our analysis is analytically simpler.

Quantum Mechanics and General Relativity

HÜSEYIN YILMAZ

Hamamatsu Photonics, K. K.
Hamamatsu City, 435 Japan
and
Electro-Optics Technology Center
Tufts University
Medford, Massachusetts 02155

In any space-time (curved or otherwise), let there be a Hamiltonian, $H = H(p, x)$, for particles, and a dispersion relation, $\omega = \omega(k, x)$, for waves. Suppose also that we wish to connect or unify waves and particles via the quantum mechanical relations, $H = \hbar\omega$ and $p = \hbar k$. It follows that

$$v = \partial H/\partial p = \partial\omega/\partial k = v_g;$$

namely, the group velocity, v_g, of a wave must be equal to the Hamiltonian velocity, v, of a particle. Note that this is a "classical" condition as $\hbar$ dropped out. Because the concept of a wave and of a particle are classically mutually exclusive, the interpretation of the "unified object" is necessarily statistical: the probability of finding a particle at x is equal to the normalized square, $|\Psi(x)|^2$, of the wave function at x. Assuming the intended unification is achievable in this manner, the experimental correspondence must involve both particles and waves, and it must sometimes go to one limit or the other, depending on the experimental setup and the measurements performed.

However, is there anything new here that is not presently known? Take any space-time and form the Hamiltonian-Jacobi equation using the metric. Also, form the dispersion relation using the (covariant) wave equation of the same metric. Letting $H = p_0$, $\omega = k_0$, and $c = \hbar = 1$, one has $p^\mu p_\mu = m_0^2$ and $k^\mu k_\mu = m_0^2 + \Gamma$, where Γ is a multiple of $\partial_\nu(\sqrt{-g}\,g^{\mu\nu})$. Γ occurs because the covariant d'Alembertian is a differential operator and creates more terms than there are in the Hamiltonian. Clearly, the intended unification is not possible unless

$$\partial_\nu(\sqrt{-g}\,g^{\mu\nu}) = 0,$$

which is a condition of compatibility (gauge) with quantum mechanics and acts on the space-time metric. It can be proved that the time-independent metric, $g_{00} = D(x, y, z)$, $-g_{ii} = A(x, y, z)$, can have multiparticle solutions, and $-g_{ik} = B_{ik}(z, t)$, $i, k = 1, 2$, can have multimode $T = T$ gravity waves carrying energy-momentum only when the above gauge condition is satisfied. The key words here are "multiparticle" and "multimode" solutions carrying energy-momentum. We know that quantum mechanics (especially the quantum field theory) requires multiparticle and multimode solutions. The following items are then proved:

(1) In the Einstein-Infeld-Hoffmann theorem, the multiparticle solution, $\phi = \Sigma_j m_j/|x - x_j|$, needed for the proof of N-body equations cannot survive in second order

unless the above condition is satisfied. What blocks the multiparticle solution is a (nonlinear) second-order condition, $(\beta + \delta - 2)\Omega_{ik} = 0$, $\beta + \delta - 2 \neq 0$,

$$\Omega_{ik} = \phi\phi_{ik} - 3\phi_i\phi_k + \delta_{ik}(\nabla\phi)^2 - \delta_{ik}\phi\nabla^2\phi.$$

Here, $i, k = 1, 2, 3$, and β and δ are second-order PPN parameters in the expansion, $g_{00} = 1 - 2\phi + 2\beta\phi^2$, $-g_{ii} = 1 + 2\phi + 2\delta\phi^2$. The gauge condition leads to $\beta + \delta - 2 = 0$, and hence gets rid of Ω_{ik}. If $(\beta + \delta - 2) \neq 0$, one has only a single particle solution, $\phi = m_1/|x - x_1|$. Then, in the Newtonian N-body equations, Σ'_j reduces to Σ'_{k-1}. Because Σ'_j means $j = k$ is excluded, the right-hand side leads to $m_1 d^2x_1/dt^2 = 0$, that is, only to the uniform motion of a "single" particle.

(2) The 529″ cy^{-1} planetary perturbative (Newtonian) component of Mercury's perihelion advance requires the N-body solution; hence, it cannot be reproduced unless the above gauge condition holds.

(3) Under the gauge condition above, quantum mechanics can be set up in curved-space (they are then compatible), leading to two experimental confirmations (isotropy of inertia and neutron phase-shift) and a complete computation (prediction) of gravity radiation from the binary pulsar (quadrupole computation from the two-body solution, the radiation from the $T=T$ waves) in agreement with experiment. Other known effects such as the redshift, light deflection, time-delay, moon-ranging, and the 43″ cy^{-1} post-Newtonian component of the perihelion advance (relativistic correction) are all satisfied because the PPN parameters are $\alpha = \gamma = \beta = \delta = 1$. The existence of the N-body solution in second and higher orders determines the δ as $\delta = 1$. It is interesting that the gauge condition relates the first- and second-order parameters because it gives $\beta + \delta - 2\alpha\gamma = 0$, $\alpha = \gamma$, which are sufficient to eliminate the unwanted Ω_{ik}. These considerations show that there is an urgent need to revise general relativity if we are to recover, among other things, the 529″ cy^{-1} Newtonian advance of the perihelion and the two-body quadrupole moment for gravity radiation from the binary pulsar; we also need to do this if we are to establish consistent contact with quantum mechanics.

Does Distribution Fail in the Logic of Quantum Theory?

SILVIO ZENONE

Physics Department
Concordia University
Montreal, Quebec H3G 1M8

Proof that the distributive law breaks down in quantum mechanics was given by Birkhoff and von Neumann in a well-known article (1936)[1] that presented the following thought-experiment: if A represents the experimental observation of a wave packet, ψ, on a side of a plane in ordinary space, if A' represents the observation of ψ on the other side, and if B represents the observation of ψ in a state symmetric about the plane, then

$$B \cap (A \cup A') = B \cap I = B > \odot = (B \cap A)$$

$$= (B \cap A') = (B \cap A) \cup (B \cap A'), \quad (1)$$

which shows violation of the distribution rule,

$$A \cap (B \cup C) = (A \cap B) \cup (A \cap C).$$

In equation 1, I stands for "identically true" and $\odot$ stands for "identically false" from a logical standpoint, and the symbols, $\cap$ and $\cup$, represent the "meet" and "join," respectively, of propositions. The above proof is based on the assumption that $(A \cup A')$ is an identically true proposition; that is, $(A \cup A') = I$ is a necessary conclusion if a bivalent logic is assumed. However, assuming that A corresponds to a position observation and that B corresponds to another, noncommuting observable, then logical proposition A (also A') may be undecided. Consequently, $(A \cup A')$ will not be logically true, so $B \cap (A \cup A') = B \cap I = B$ (and violation of the distributive law) will not follow. In fact, assuming a three-valued logic that allows the truth-values, T, F, and U (true, false, and undecided), the following rules (summarized in TABLE 1) can be adopted, with A and B being propositions of the three-valued logic:

(1) If both A and B are true, their conjunction is true; if either A or B is false, their conjunction is false; in all other cases, the conjunction of A and B is undecided.
(2) If both A and B are false, their disjunction is false; if either A or B is true, their disjunction is true; in all other cases, their disjunction is undecided.

The two distributive rules are, as in bivalent logic,

$$A \cdot (B \cup C) \equiv A \cdot B \cup A \cdot C$$

and

$$A \cup B \cdot C \equiv (A \cup B) \cdot (A \cup C).$$

627

TABLE 1. Truth-Values Table

A	B	$A \cdot B$	$A \vee B$
T	T	T	T
T	U	U	T
T	F	F	T
U	T	U	T
U	U	U	U
U	F	F	U
F	T	F	T
F	U	F	U
F	F	F	F

It is clear from the table that the proof in equation 1, which is based on $(A \cup A')$ being a tautology, does not follow. A large amount of work in classical and "quantum" logic has been devoted to the attempt of understanding the "peculiar" aspects of quantum mechanics.[2] A three-valued logic preserves the fundamental structure of classical logic, while failure of the distributive rules represents a drastic departure from the laws of classical logic. Reichenbach shows that a three-valued logic, while preserving such fundamental rules, allows compatibility between the laws of quantum mechanics and the principle of separability, whereas a bivalent logic does not.[3]

REFERENCES

1. BIRKHOFF, G. & J. VON NEUMANN. 1936. Ann. Math. **37**: 823–843. (Reprinted in Hooker Ed., 1975.)
2. JAMMER, M. 1974. The Philosophy of Quantum Mechanics in Historical Perspective. Wiley. New York.
3. REICHENBACH, H. 1944. Philosophic Foundations of Quantum Mechanics, pp. 29–34. Univ. of California Press. Berkeley/Los Angeles.

Concluding Remarks

ABNER SHIMONY

Departments of Physics and Philosophy
Boston University
Boston, Massachusetts 02215

It is obviously an impossible task to summarize in a few minutes a conference at which over fifty talks were given and discussed and over twenty poster papers were presented. The best I can do is to offer a rough taxonomy of the presentations and comment selectively on each class. Two dichotomies define the taxonomy—theoretical versus experimental, and radical versus conservative.

Quite a few of the theoretical talks had a radical element in that they expressed doubts about the possibility of solving the measurement problem and other physical problems within the standard framework of quantum mechanics. Two talks deserve to be singled out from these because each proposed a quite specific alternative theory in order to solve one or more of the recalcitrant problems. Pearle proposed a variant of the time-dependent Schrödinger equation, with a random Hamiltonian, that could account for the occurrence of a definite measurement result in each individual instance and could recover the quantum mechanical statistics in an ensemble of instances. Noyes' was aimed at determining the quantum numbers and coupling constants of phenomenological particle theory without any danger of infinities. He did this by constructing quantum states on a discrete manifold, thus dispensing with the assumption of a continuous space-time. It is out of place here to attempt an assessment of these radical proposals, but several general remarks are in order. One is that courage is required to invest many years of effort in a line of research that the majority of experts regard with skepticism. Another is that an unorthodox proposal that is carefully formulated and clearly linked to experimental data has a value beyond its intrinsic merit: it can indicate the possibility of new types of explanation and can stimulate the imaginations of other scientists.

A number of the theoretical talks were conservative in the sense that they explored the consequences of previously formulated physical assumptions. Because the assumptions are commonly very condensed, and the boundary and initial conditions are often complicated, and normal human mathematical intuition is limited, the results of conservative theoretical investigations can sometimes be surprising. Probably, the most surprising result of this kind presented at the conference was Unruh's proof that from the standpoint of an accelerated frame of reference, the vacuum fluctuations of the electromagnetic field are indistinguishable from blackbody radiation at a temperature proportional to the acceleration. Conservative theoretical analysis, when carefully carried out, is, of course, essential for interpreting experiments. Noteworthy examples were the analyses by Hanggi and by Washburn and Webb of the effects of dissipation and temperature on tunneling in a Josephson junction, which thereby demonstrated that the observed decay of metastable states at sufficiently low temperatures was almost certainly a quantum mechanical effect. Sometimes conservative theorizing can be satisfying even when the results are not very surprising. The results of Wootters and

Scully on Wigner distributions for discrete systems are good examples because they round out our knowledge in an aesthetically pleasing way.

Another kind of theoretical analysis that I would classify as conservative is the unpacking of the assumption of Bell locality. To be sure, the hypothesis that quantum mechanics should be replaced by a local hidden variables theory is a radical one. However, it is not radical to reason conditionally and to determine with precision what are the consequences of a radical hypothesis, for unless this is done, one is not in a position to bring experimental results to bear upon the hypothesis. Good examples of this kind of theoretical analysis were Mermin's derivation of a Bell-type inequality holding when photons are detected with less than perfect efficiency, and Selleri's collection of inequalities resulting from locality conditions (even though the latter example is part of a program that envisages radical results in the long run).

Wheeler's talk was in a class by itself, for it may be classified as a radical conservative analysis. He was not attempting to find alternatives to quantum mechanics, and in this sense, his program is conservative. The radical element in his talk was the search for deeper principles from which quantum mechanics follows, rather than postulating a quantum mechanical framework as the starting point of physics. I recall that long ago Wheeler said (approximately) that quantum mechanics was the work of the first day of creation and the space-time framework was the work of the second day. His talk at this conference can be understood as an attempt to enter into the meditations that accompanied the work of the first day. His program is inspiring as a determined effort to extend the domain of rational explanation.

None of the experimental talks announced a radical result, but several expressed doubts that the conservative (i.e., quantum mechanical) results of earlier experiments were definitive, and they described ongoing experiments that might yield radical results. Franson described a 45-meter interferometer that he has constructed for which a local realist theory predicts no interference effects if there is a single-photon light source. This, then, permits a crucial experiment because quantum mechanics predicts interference effects in these circumstances. Vigier gave an argument that a causal interpretation of quantum mechanics is able to explain the violation of Bell's inequality observed by Aspect et al., but he stated that in an experiment under way in Italy, in which the detectors are far apart and the coincidence window is open for a very short time interval, the causal interpretation anticipates that the observed correlations will obey the inequality. Assessment of both of these experiments must be reserved for later conferences.

Most of the experimental talks presented conservative results that were in agreement with the predictions of quantum mechanics. Alley and Zajonc reported two independent executions of the delayed-choice experiment, with each finding quantum mechanical results for both of the choices of experimental arrangements. Grangier reported that single-photon impingement on a beam-splitter resulted in anticorrelation of photodetections on the two sides of the splitter, thus violating the lower limit on a classically predicted coincidence rate by 13 standard deviations. Rauch, Werner, and Zeilinger described a long series of neutron interferometer experiments that yielded results that were classically mysterious and quantum mechanically natural (such as the change of interference maxima into minima when there is a relative precession by 360° of the neutron in the two interfering beams). It must be emphasized that the results of any of these experiments might have been radical. The results were conservative, not because of the control of the experimenters, but because nature behaves according to quantum mechanical rules in a broad domain, even if we reserve judgment about the universal validity of these rules.

It should also be remarked that even results that are expected (modulo the assumption of quantum mechanics) are unexpectedly exhilarating when they actually materialize. At least I can attest to this subjective reaction. Perhaps one reason for the reaction is that many people retain a residue of skepticism about the literal truth of quantum mechanics in situations where it conflicts with common sense. Another reason for exhilaration is admiration of the skill of experimenters in exhibiting quantum mechanical effects that all too easily are masked and washed out by noise and impurities. Some of the effects that were presented are nothing short of spectacular: for example, Lichte's electron interferometry, in which potential distributions between single lattice planes of crystals show up, and Büttiker's exhibition of the Aharonov-Bohm effect in normal metals in spite of the inelastic scattering of the conduction electrons. Yet another explanation is provided by a wonderful remark by Eugene Wigner that was made to me when I first came to Princeton Graduate School and he was my adviser. He said that physics is concerned not only with grand generalizations that are philosophically significant, such as the atomicity of matter, but also with specific phenomena, and when one succeeds in understanding one of these phenomena, one has "an elevated feeling." It was an inspiring remark in 1955, and it remains inspiring today.

If experiments now being performed turn out to agree with the conservative results of the preponderance of experimental talks at this conference, then some problems in the foundations of quantum mechanics will appear to be even more formidable than at present. The more thoroughly and widely the quantum mechanical superposition principle is confirmed, the more difficult it is to solve the problem of the actualization of potentialities (known also as the problem of reduction of the wave packet and as the measurement problem). The actualization of one value of a physical variable from among the many that are present in a superposition as potentialities is a nonlinear step. The linearity both of quantum kinematics and quantum dynamics is an obstacle to the actualization of a potentiality, which is what Schrödinger dramatically illustrated with the cat paradox. Because the primary experimental evidence for the superposition principle is at the microscopic level, some of the physicists who have worried about this problem have suspected that there would be a breakdown of linearity at the macroscopic level. However, the preliminary results of the superconductor experiments discussed by Leggett, Chakravarty, and others strongly indicate that quantum mechanical principles hold in physical systems of macroscopic size. Where then does the nonlinearity requisite for the actualization of potentialities, and, indeed, for the occurrence of a definite outcome of a measurement, take place?

One possible answer is that nonlinearity is not exhibited until a mind enters an experimental situation, which finally does happen when the result is reported. This possible solution to the problem cannot be foreclosed, but it is radical in the extreme; furthermore, unless an advocate of this solution provides some of the details of the mind-matter interaction, it appears to be simply an evasion of the problem.

Less radical, and, nevertheless, far from current physical orthodoxy, is the hypothesis that nonlinearity is exhibited when the space-time field enters significantly into a physical situation. There has been little explicit discussion of this avenue of solution at the conference. However, in both of his talks, Wigner mentioned the great difficulty of treating localized states in relativistic quantum mechanics, and in some of his research, he has shown that quantum mechanics implies great difficulties in making sense of the space-time metric in the small. In other words, quantum mechanics may not peacefully coexist with special relativity, and it will coexist even less with general relativity. Some specific suggestions for the modification of both quantum mechanics and general relativity in order to achieve a coherent microscopic theory of space-time structure have been made, in very different ways, by Penrose and Károlyházy, and even though there has been no detailed presentation of their suggestions at this conference, it should be noted that some of the remarks in the discussions have pointed in their direction.

Over fifty discussions and several times that many comments in an interval of four days are very hard to absorb, and the time was much too short for resolving important disagreements by leisurely dialogue. (Galileo's *Dialogue Concerning the Two Chief World Systems* was brought to a conclusion in only three days, but only three interlocutors participated in the dialogue, and besides, it was stage-managed by Galileo.) What we can hope for here is that a good residue will remain after the conference ends and that the discussion will be continued by internal debates in the minds of the individual participants. We can also hope that the stimulus of the conference will generate new ideas and that we will leave here with our minds in excited states that will give rise to radiation.

My final remark concerns Daniel Greenberger, who was the real organizer of this conference, for doing more than the combined efforts of the four of us who are formally listed as co-organizers. His dedication, tenacity in overcoming obstacles, good humor, and good nature were little short of miraculous, and were responsible for the success of the conference.

Index of Contributors